DIVISION	CLASS	SUBCLASS	ORDER
Lichens			
Cyanophyta *(Blue-green Algae)*	Cyanophyceae		...cales ...iphonales ...rpales ...riales
Pyrrophyta	Dinophyceae *(Dinoflagellates)* Cryptophyceae *(Cryptomonads)*		
Chrysophyta	Chrysophyceae *(Golden Algae)* Bacillariophyceae *(Diatoms)*		Centrales Pennales
Phaeophyta *(Brown Algae)*	Phaeophyceae		Ectocarpales Sphacelariales Cutleriales Dictyotales Chordariales Desmarestiales Dictyosiphonales Laminariales Fucales
Rhodophyta *(Red Algae)*	Rhodophyceae	Bangiophycidae Florideophycidae	Porphyridiales Goniotrichales Bangiales Nemalionales Gelidiales Cryptonemiales Gigartinales Rhodymeniales Ceramiales
Euglenophyta *(Euglenids)*	Euglenophyceae		
Xanthophyta *(Xanthophytes)*	Xanthophyceae *(Yellow-green algae)* Chloromonadophyceae *(Chloromonads)*		
Chlorophyta *(Green Algae)*	Chlorophyceae Charophyceae		Volvocales Tetrasporales Chlorococcales Ulotrichales Schizogoniales Zygnematales Oedogoniales Cladophorales Siphonales Siphonocladales Dasycladales
Bryophyta	Hepaticae *(Liverworts)* Anthocerotae *(Hornworts)* Musci *(Mosses)*	Sphagnidae Andreaeidae Tetraphidae Polytrichidae Buxbaumiidae Bryidae	Calobryales Jungermanniales Metzgeriales Monocleales Sphaerocarpales Marchantiales Anthocerotales

(Algae)

(Bryophytes)

AN EVOLUTIONARY
SURVEY OF THE
PLANT KINGDOM

THE WADSWORTH
BOTANY SERIES

WILLIAM A. JENSEN AND LEROY G. KAVALJIAN,
SERIES EDITORS

PLANT BIOLOGY TODAY:
ADVANCES AND CHALLENGES
Jensen and Kavaljian, editors

AN EVOLUTIONARY SURVEY OF THE
PLANT KINGDOM
Scagel, Bandoni, Rouse, Schofield, Stein, and Taylor

FUNDAMENTALS OF BOTANY SERIES

Jensen: THE PLANT CELL

Cook: REPRODUCTION, HEREDITY, AND SEXUALITY

Doyle: NONVASCULAR PLANTS: FORM AND FUNCTION

Salisbury and Parke: VASCULAR PLANTS: FORM AND
FUNCTION

Billings: PLANTS AND THE ECOSYSTEM

Baker: PLANTS AND CIVILIZATION

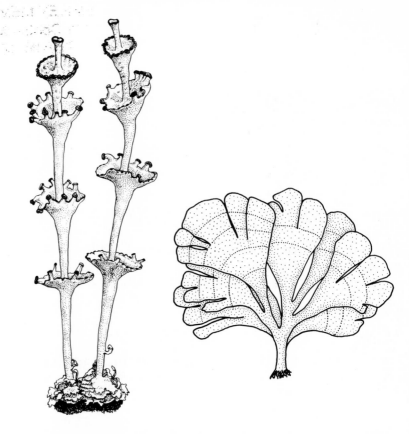

AN EVOLUTIONARY

SURVEY OF THE

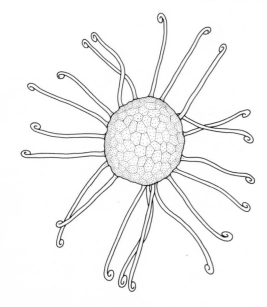

PLANT KINGDOM

ROBERT F. SCAGEL   ROBERT J. BANDONI

GLENN E. ROUSE   W. B. SCHOFIELD

JANET R. STEIN   T. M. C. TAYLOR

The University of British Columbia, Canada

WADSWORTH PUBLISHING COMPANY, INC.

Belmont, California

AN EVOLUTIONARY SURVEY OF THE PLANT KINGDOM, BY SCAGEL, BANDONI,
ROUSE, SCHOFIELD, STEIN, AND TAYLOR

L. C. CAT. CARD NO.: 65–14832
PRINTED IN THE UNITED STATES OF AMERICA

PREFACE

For several years we have collaborated in the presentation of a one-year course (two semesters) at the second-year university level, surveying the plant kingdom with emphasis on comparative morphology and evolution. The specialists in the teaching roster have included a mycologist, a phycologist, a bryologist, a paleo-botanist, and a higher plant taxonomist.

The stimulus for writing this text has come directly from our teaching experiences. We believe that the botanical student can gain much through contact with a number of instructors trained and experienced in the various highly specialized and diversified fields of botany. Similarly, we feel that a collaboration of specialists in one text may make a unique contribution to students of the plant kingdom at the more advanced second-year university level. We have been unable to find a balanced and modern text that satisfactorily covers each of the fields in our course at the level desired. For example, a text acceptable in phycology may be inadequate in fungi, bryophytes, or some other plant group. *An Evolutionary Survey of the Plant Kingdom* attempts to solve this problem.

This text is intended to lead the average student somewhat beyond what is expected of him at the second-year level and, at the same time, to provide him with additional reference material to stimulate further his interest and curiosity. The text assumes that the student has already had a first-year university course in botany or the equivalent, and that he has acquired an understanding of fundamental biological processes, such as mitosis and meiosis.

We have standardized our terminology throughout the text as far as is practical. We have also tried to maintain continuity in treatment so that the overall trends in phylogeny and evolution are not lost or interrupted. By the same token, we have attempted throughout to apply the findings of paleobotany directly to the living representatives in the various plant groups in order to gain perspective on these two complementary aspects of botanical science.

Individual contributions, which have been primarily in our respective fields of specialization, are as follows: bacteria, slime molds, and fungi (Robert J. Bandoni); lichens and bryophytes (W. B. Schofield); algae (Robert F. Scagel and Janet R. Stein); lower vascular plants and paleobotany (Glenn E. Rouse); and flowering plants (T. M. C. Taylor). However, since we have consolidated our efforts and consulted closely with each other in the interests of uniformity and continuity, it is impossible to define completely the limits of each person's contribution. In the processes of writing and editing this work we have come to know one another better and to understand and appreciate each other's disciplines and points of view to a greater extent.

The original drawings were prepared by P. Drukker Brammall, Frank A. Lang, and Ernani G. Meñez; their significant contribution to the text is deeply appreciated. The following figures were prepared by P. Drukker Brammall: 1–1; 3–6D, 3–8A; 4–34A, E, 4–35B, C, 4–36, 4–40A, D, 4–41A, 4–42A–C, 4–43A, 4–44, 4–46A, 4–68, 4–70A, B, D, 4–72, 4–75, 4–79A–C, 4–82A, 4–84, 4–85A; 5–2, 5–3, 5–8B, 5–7A, 5–11; 11–18; 16–4 to 16–7, 16–10 to 16–14, 16–16A, G, 16–17A, K, J, 16–18A–D, 16–19A, 16–20A–C, E, F, H, I, 16–21 to 16–23, 16–25, 16–27, 16–28, 16–29A, C, F–H; 27–1 to 27–11, 27–13, 27–15 to 27–36, 27–38. All drawings for Chapters 18 to 26 were executed by Frank A. Lang. All other drawings were prepared by Ernani G. Meñez.

We would also like to acknowledge the constructive criticisms provided by a number of people who read portions of the manuscript. We are especially indebted to Professors Paul D. Voth of the The University of Chicago, Warren H. Wagner, Jr. of the University of Michigan, Dominick J. Paolillo, Jr. of the University of Illinois, Shirley Sparling of California State Polytechnic College, C. J. Anastasiou, J. J. Stock, and Gilbert C. Hughes of The University of British Columbia, William A. Jensen of the University of California, and Leroy G. Kavaljian of Sacramento State College. Although their comments and criticisms contributed to our presentation, the authors take full responsibility for the final product.

We are indebted to individuals and publishers who loaned original illustrations and photographs and who gave permission to copy or redraw figures; these are acknowledged in the appropriate captions.

Finally, we want to acknowledge the assistance provided by the Department of Biology and Botany, The University of British Columbia.

CONTENTS

VASCULAR PLANTS

1 / INTRODUCTION

The plant kingdom is the most dominant and essential aspect of man's environment. Well over a quarter of a million species can be distinguished among living plants, and the fossil record reveals many additional species. This diverse array of plants can be studied from many aspects, depending on the special interest of the investigator. Those concerned primarily with the relationship of plants to environment would emphasize an ecological approach; others would emphasize a morphological, anatomical, physiological, or cytological approach, and so on through the range of fields of special interest into which the study of botany is usually divided. In this book, the concept of *organic evolution* is the theme linking together the representatives of the various **taxa.**

We start with the primitive divisions, the members of which are perhaps closest to their ancestral morphology, and proceed to the divisions that show the greatest amount of evolutionary change. Each division contains primitive and advanced members, and some trends may apparently lead to an evolutionary *cul-de-sac*—a dead end. There are also isolated groups, whose affinities with living and fossil plants are still obscure; these may always remain a matter of speculation. This situation has led to the classical, but now out-dated, picture of an evolutionary tree with a central trunk—the main line of evolutionary development—with many branches, large and small, arising from it. Most botanists agree that, in light of the evidence available, this is a very unsatisfactory

1

model, not only grossly oversimplified but inaccurate. We feel that the "family tree" is really best represented by a three-dimensional network of branches and twigs—a truly complicated picture. No wonder there is debate among botanists concerning relationships within most divisions!

There is no debate among biologists, however, that evolution has taken place and is still taking place in both plants and animals. There is also much agreement on the mechanisms involved; biologists recognize that while inherited changes may be brought about in many ways, the methods are essentially all variations on a limited number of themes. Charles Darwin recognized more than a century ago that variation was the biological basis for evolution. But he could not explain how variability arises in a population or how it is transmitted from generation to generation. His theory that evolution is an outcome of natural selection had no experimental support, but was a conclusion based on a large number of shrewd observations made in many parts of the world. The work of numerous other investigators, starting with Gregor Mendel, has made it possible for us to understand at least the broad outlines of the process.

In the present volume, space limits us to only a few basic considerations of the process of organic evolution. For details and summaries, consult the writings of Stebbins, Dobzhansky, Huxley, Ross, and others. The remainder of this chapter will be concerned with reviewing general biological topics and relating them to the broad question of evolution of plants.

ALTERNATION OF GENERATIONS

There is little doubt that the same general biological principles apply just as validly to evolution in the algae as in the flowering plants. Certain features are common to the life cycle of all organisms that reproduce sexually: (1) *syngamy,* in which two gametes fuse to form a **zygote,** and (2) *meiosis,* the special form of nuclear division in which four **haploid meiospores** are produced from each **diploid** spore mother cell. As a rule, syngamy and meiosis are inseparable; if one is present in a cycle, the other must be also. However, among the ferns there are interesting exceptions to this general rule. Certain ferns reproduce **apogamously,** and yet meiosis takes place. The chromosome number is doubled not by syngamy but by the failure of **cytokinesis** in the last mitotic division before the meiospore mother cells form. Therefore, the meiospore mother cells have two sets of **chromosomes** and so can undergo meiosis.

In the plant kingdom it is convenient to distinguish between the two generations that intervene between syngamy and meiosis, one normally diploid and the other haploid. The diploid generation is often spoken of as the *sporophyte* and the haploid as the *gametophyte.* These follow one another in the sexual life cycle and constitute *alternation of generations.* These generations are defined as follows: the sporophyte generation begins with the zygote, while the meiospore is the first cell of the gametophyte. The last cell, or the last **ontogenetic** stage of the sporophyte, is the meiospore mother cell, and the corresponding terminal stage of the gametophyte is the gamete. Relative sizes and photosynthetic nature of the sporophyte and gametophyte are details relevant to a particular kind of organism. Only when a *particular* organism is studied are we concerned about such matters as whether the gametophyte is large and the sporophyte small, or whether the gametophyte is dependent and the sporophyte independent.

The next step is to consider the biological implications and importance of the life cycle. When a phenomenon is widespread among living organisms of both the plant and animal kingdoms, it is most likely significant; otherwise it would not appear so frequently in unrelated groups of organisms. Therefore, one must look for the biological significance of sexual reproduction, since this is the obvious feature of the life cycle. The answer to this lies in genetics. It is generally accepted that chromosomes have individuality, so that one can refer to the first chromosome, the second chromosome, and so on. Each chromosome is composed of **genes** at a definite locus. As Mendel discovered, certain genes are dominant while others are recessive. When a cross is made between contrasting dominant and recessive characteristics, in the F_1 one gene *seems* to disappear—this is the recessive. Although this gene is not expressed, it is still present, and under certain circumstances it *can* be expressed. The circumstances are that it must be present in duplicate—in the **homozygous** condition. If two parents are homozygous—one for a dominant and the other for the corresponding recessive gene—the F_1 will be **heterozygous.** Homozygosity tends to produce uniformity. Theoretically, a population that is completely homozygous and exposed to a uniform environment would be completely uniform in all respects. But a population made up of heterozygotes will, in general, be a heterogeneous population, and thus variable.

At this point one should think of meiosis and what is involved in a meiotic division. Is it simply a device for halving the chromosome number, or has it a deeper biological significance? The meiotic division is the transition between the sporophyte and the gametophyte, and involves the division of a diploid nucleus. However, instead of thinking of the number of chromosomes in the sporophyte as being $2n$ in the ordinary algebraic sense, it should be regarded as being n pairs, which in fact it is. Each parent has contributed a set of n chromosomes, so that two sets of **homologous** chromosomes, known as **genomes,** are present. In the first anaphase of meiosis, chromosomes that make up pairs separate, so that whole chromosomes move to the poles in the first anaphase. In the second metaphase these chromosomes split, the two **chromatids** present in each chromosome separating and going to opposite poles. Since cell walls do not ordinarily develop until the end of the second telophase, a set of four haploid nuclei, each with a single genome, forms within the mother cell wall. Two pairs of genes on separate chromosomes may be represented by letters, with A and B being the dominants, and a and b the corresponding recessives. In the first phase of meiosis it is a matter of chance how the chromosomes of each pair will move. The chromosome with A may end up with $B,$ but there is an equal chance that it will end up with $b.$ This result is most important because it provides a mechanism for *segregation*—i.e., the breaking up of combinations of chromosomes and genes. This chance distribution makes it clear that the biological importance of meiosis is to provide a mechanism for segregating chromosomes, and consequently genes, in a random fashion. By contrast, the biological significance of syngamy is that it provides a mechanism for the *reassortment* of genes—the potential of bringing together genes in new or different combinations.

The importance of these conclusions can be illustrated by referring to a flower called the four-o'clock (*Mirabilis*), in which the gene for petal color produces red when one pair is homozygous and white when the other pair is homozygous. The heterozygote is pink. Selfing the heterozygote produces red, pink, and white flowers in the succeeding generation. Clearly, if there is no sexual reproduction in the life cycle of this organism, pink flowers will never appear. The pink flower has no special significance in the present connection except to illustrate that it can appear only as a consequence of meiosis followed by syngamy.

BIOLOGICAL IMPORTANCE OF SYNGAMY AND MEIOSIS

It can now be concluded that sexual reproduction (syngamy), followed by meiosis, provides a means of producing heterozygous populations—that is, populations made up of genetically dissimilar individuals. From a long-term biological point of view such populations have a much better chance of survival than those that are uniform. The reason that variability is biologically important should be quite apparent. Any environmental crisis, such as a severe frost, will reveal that in general all individuals of a species do not respond in exactly the same degree to the stress. Some individuals may be killed, but others will survive. If they had been genetically alike, all would have survived or all would have been eliminated. What is also important is that, as a result of the crisis, the proportion of advantageous genes is increased and that of the disadvantageous genes is decreased.

Table 1–1 shows for various numbers of gene pairs the number of kinds of spores, and subsequently of gametes, that theoretically can be produced as the result of meiosis, and the number of kinds of genotypes consequent on random mating in syngamy. If the original cross involves three pairs of genes, the number of kinds of gametes as the result of selfing of the F_1 will be eight and the number of kinds of genotypes that could result will be 27. Both these numbers increase exponentially, so that in man, with 46 chromosomes and thousands of genes, it is easy to see why no two individuals are alike unless they are identical twins.

TABLE 1–1

Number of gene pairs	2	3	6	n
Number of kinds of spores (and subsequent gametes)	4	8	64	2^n
Number of genotypes possible in F_2	9	27	729	3^n

A **heterogeneous** population is the raw material on which natural selection operates to produce new forms. However, if natural selection operates for a sufficiently long time the population will tend to become homogeneous again; unfit individuals (and their genes) will be eliminated from the population, and evolution should finally come to a stop. But there is no evidence that this happened—in fact quite the contrary. For example, the algae were present several hundred million years ago; the ferns and bryophytes had their origin 300,000,-000 years ago; and both are still with us, still apparently varying and hybridizing. The flowering plants, which first appear in the geological record over 100,000,000 years ago, are certainly still evolving.

The majority of animals are **unisexual**,
but plants for the most part are **bisexual.** This means that in plants there is an inherent possibility for self-fertilization, which is biologically undesirable since it tends to produce homozygous populations. So it is not surprising to find in plants that, through the operation of natural selection, there has been a very definite evolutionary trend away from self-fertilization. In other words, species in which the individuals are cross-fertilized have a genetic advantage over those that are self-fertilized. In the course of evolution of the plant kingdom, many ingenious devices (some of which will be discussed later in the text) have developed to ensure cross-fertilization.

MUTATIONS

In the course of time, even populations with prevalent cross-fertilization will tend to become more or less uniform, because neither syngamy nor meiosis can add anything new to the gene pool of a species. If evolution is to continue, new characteristics must be added to populations; these characteristics do appear from time to time and are due to **mutations.** Mutations are of several kinds. The simplest, and probably the most general, is the **gene** or **point mutation,** which involves an intrinsic change in a particular gene—a change recorded in the structure of the gene. This change is passed on to all succeeding replicates of the gene. The first mutation to be recognized in a wild colony of red-eyed *Drosophila* was a white-eyed individual. This new gene type was not produced as the result of segregation or of a new combination of genes; a distinctly new characteristic had been added to the gene pool of this colony. What is most important is that this characteristic could be inherited, and so transmitted to the progeny. There are now hundreds of mutations known in *Drosophila* as well as in many other animals and plants.

Point mutation is the basic type of mutation and, because this is the only way in which something new is actually added to the gene pool, it is probably the most important. It is particularly significant to members of plant groups (such as bacteria and blue-green algae) where sexual reproduction is infrequent or absent. However, other kinds of mutations are related to changes in chromosome structure due to such well-recognized genetic phenomena as **crossing-over, segmental interchange, inversions,** and **fragmentation.** These bring about changes in **linkage groups** resulting in new combinations of genes.

Another type of mutation, most common in plants, involves changes in the number of genomes present in the nuclei. Such mutants are referred to as **polyploids.** There are two basic kinds of polyploids—**autoploids** and **alloploids.** In autopolyploidy, a diploid individual with $2n$ chromosomes spontaneously produces diploid gametes due to some irregularity of meiosis. When two such diploid gametes fuse, the subsequent sporophyte will have $4n$ chromosomes—that is, each nucleus will have four genomes. In certain genera of plants, long polyploid series are known. For example, in the wheats, which have been studied in some detail, $n = 7$; and species are known with 14, 21, 28, 42, and 56 chromosomes. These are described as diploids, **triploids, tetraploids,** and so on.

A point to note is that in tetraploids, because $2n$ pairs of chromosomes are present, meiosis can usually take place quite normally. However, fertility is likely to be reduced somewhat, because in the first stage of meiosis three homologous chromosomes may go to one pole and only one to the other. If this happens, the chromosome imbalance may result in lack of vigor or even a lethal condition. Full fertility results only when the chromosomes actually divide into two *equal* sets—that is, with two complete genomes in each gamete. The gametes from a tetraploid will, of course, be diploid. They can often mate with the haploid gametes of the same species to produce a triploid zygote. There are wheats with 21 chromosomes—triploid wheats; also pentaploids, with five sets of genomes. Triploids are highly sterile because of the impossibility of dividing an odd number of genomes into two qualitatively equal parts at meiosis. Only by a remote chance will a viable gamete be produced, so for practical purposes triploids are regarded as sterile; the same holds true for all *odd* numbers of ploids (one that reproduces in a special way will be discussed in Chapter 27).

The second type of polyploid is the allopolyploid (or **amphipolyploid**), which results from an *interspecific* cross. Initially, the diploid hybrid will have $n + n^1$ chromosomes. It, too, is sterile because unless the two parental species happen to be closely related, genetically homologous chromosomes are not present in duplicate and so normal meiosis cannot take place. A number of interspecific hybrids are known.

Occasionally, quite spontaneously, such diploid hybrids will mutate to form an **allotetraploid,** which will have $2(n + n^1)$ chromosomes, or $(n + n^1)$ pairs. One of the classical examples is the case of *Primula kewensis,* which arose in cultivation. It is an interspecific hybrid between *P. floribunda* and *P. verticillata.* Each of the parents has 18 chromosomes, but the allotetraploid hybrid has 36. Such mutants are fertile, because each chromosome is now present in duplicate. However, these individuals are genetically isolated from their parents and, if they show sufficient morphological differences, can properly be regarded as a new species. In this way a new species can arise, literally overnight. As in *Primula kewensis,* no selection is involved; it is a matter of an interspecific cross in the first instance followed by doubling of the chromosome numbers to produce an allotetraploid. A number of naturally occurring species of flowering plants, thought to be allotetraploids, have been synthesized through appropriate crosses (*Spartina townsendii* = *S. alterniflora* × *S. maritima*).

Ownbey is probably the first botanist actually to see new allotetraploid species come into being in nature. He first observed sterile hybrids between three species of *Tragopogon.* Some years later, doubling of the genomes occurred, resulting in two completely fertile allotetraploids and a third that was partially sterile. Ownbey has designated the two fertile taxa as new species on the grounds that: "(1)

They are a natural group characterized by a combination of distinctive morphological features. (2) They are reproducing themselves under natural conditions. (3) Gene interchange between the amphiploids and the parental species is prevented by a genetic barrier (ploidy level). . . ." This is a striking example of the origin of a new species by a single mutation.

A third type of mutation is the **aneuploid,** which involves either the addition or the loss of a chromosome. The chromosome number in such instances is written as $2n + 1$ or $2n - 1$. In certain genera like *Carex, n* may have values of 6, 7, 8, 9, 10, 13, etc., depending on the species. Such a series is then an aneuploid series, in which one chromosome is present in triplicate (or unicate) in the sporophyte while all the others are in duplicate. The one present in triplicate is a **trisomic.** There can be only as many trisomics in a species as there are chromosomes in a genome; that is, if $n = 9$, there can be nine trisomics. These have been studied in detail in the genus *Datura* of the tobacco family (Solanaceae). An important point about trisomics is that again chromosome imbalance exists and greatly reduced fertility usually results.

It should be noted here that even where sexual reproduction is lacking, certain mutations do result in some, though more limited, genetic flexibility. Although the progeny are all of the same genotype, this may produce a population peculiarly well adapted to certain environmental conditions and so be very successful. Many weedy Compositae (e.g., dandelion) fall into this category.

THE TIME SCALE

In our consideration of evolution, attention has been drawn to the significance of mutations, variation, and natural selection. Another most important factor is *time;* all other factors require considerable periods of time for their fullest expression. Latest estimates place the age of the earth at 5,000,000,000 to 6,000,000,000 years; the first recorded fossils are about 2,000,000,000 years old. Between

the formation of the earth and the appearance of these early fossils, life evolved. Although the record of plants is meager until some 400,000,000 to 600,000,000 years ago, it can be safely assumed that prior to this time evolution must have been proceeding rapidly. In later geological epochs the fossil remains of several groups of plants provide some record of evolutionary developments. These remains are the clues available to **paleobotanists** to guide them in their reconstructions of the past.

It is extremely difficult for us, whose span of personal experience is limited to approximately 75 years, to comprehend time periods of several thousand million years. A useful concept is to think of the age of the earth (about 6,000,000,000 years) as represented by a calendar year, beginning on January 1. Prorating times, the first fossils would not be recorded until about September 1. Many of the algal groups and primitive animals would not appear until November 30; undoubted vascular plants not until December 7; and the first flowering plants not until about December 25!

If we could take a series of time-lapse photographs on a movie film of the various fossils from the different epochs, and project the films, we would see the over-all evolutionary picture unfolding before our eyes. This movie, of course, would allow us to see only the major evolutionary developments; we would likely not notice the imperceptible changes that result from minute mutations, interbreeding, and natural selection. However, from the evidence of modern genetical studies we know that such changes have been taking place for millenia, and we can confidently predict that the same influences have been the main contributors to evolution since life began.

It is easy to see that reconstructing and interpreting fossil plants is important for an understanding not only of evolution, but also of the origin and relationships of living plant groups. Where the fossil record is relatively well known, as in the vascular plants, the evolutionary history and relationships are best understood. By the same token, groups with inadequate records, such as the bryophytes, cannot be related with nearly the same satisfaction, and their assumed relationships are proportionately more doubtful. In such groups, it is obviously necessary to predict the probable course that evolution has taken, and to suggest relationships on the basis of the possession of similar morphological, anatomical, biochemical, or ecological characteristics.

ENVIRONMENTAL EFFECTS

We are aided in our predictions by an understanding of the evidence we have around us. We know that the phenotype of an individual is the result of the environment acting upon its genotype. The same genotype, exposed to different environmental conditions, may exhibit differing phenotypes correlated with the environmental differences. This is particularly conspicuous in some amphibious flowering plants. For example, in the pond weed *Potamogeton* the submerged leaves are thin, often linear, lack a cuticle, and possess no stomata. The emergent leaves, floating on the surface of the water, are thicker, usually elliptic, and possess stomata and a cuticle (Fig. 1–1A). The north temperate water crowfoot *Ranunculus aquatilis* (Fig. 1–1B) is an even more striking example. On this plant the submerged leaves are deeply dissected while the aerial leaves are merely lobed. Similar examples can be found in most plant groups. This phenotypic plasticity provides the plant with a wider range of environmental tolerance and assures it of more certain survival in a variable environment.

In a population consisting of a single species, there is often environmental selection for particular phenotypes. For example, in the common weed yarrow (*Achillea*) several phenotypic races have been noted. In mountainous California most yarrow plants are dwarfed, while those of the lowlands tend to be tall. Even when the plants originating from various topographic localities are grown in the same environment, each of the naturally selected phenotypes is maintained.

Environmental variation in both large and restricted geographic areas has led to the selection of plants whose morphology and other characteristics permit them to survive and reproduce. With a knowledge of the gross morphology of plants it is possible to generalize on climates. For example, a given area can be described as possessing a particular spectrum of life forms—a spectrum that results from the climate of the region. The life-form spectrum in arctic regions is quite different from that of a desert climate, since natural selection would sort out a different array of morphological types adapted to the environment in each area. Many plants are restricted morphologically to a seasonal period of luxuriance when conditions are favorable for the development of aerial parts; and if perennial, they must possess some means of surviving the unfavorable season. Many familiar spring wildflowers with a comparatively short vegetative season are perennials; they become dormant early in the summer.

The gross morphology of a plant, besides being determined by its genotype, is thus also affected by its environment. In turn, the environment acts as a basic selective factor for the spectrum of morphological types of a given region. The interaction of these factors, as well as others, has led to the evolution of the vegetational patterns of the world.

Similarly, the gross morphology of plants largely determines the role each will take in the development of a plant community. The first plants to occupy the area in a newly available site differ conspicuously from those that occupy it later. Obviously morphology is not the only factor involved, but morphology does give some indication of the physiological tolerances of many species.

Plants may be divided into groups according to their nutritional requirements. For example, most **autotrophic** plants need only inorganic substances and an energy source for growth. If the energy source is sunlight, the plants are called **photoautotrophs;** if the energy is derived from chemical reactions, the plants are called **chemoautotrophs.** Chemoautotrophs obtain energy through oxidation-reduction re-

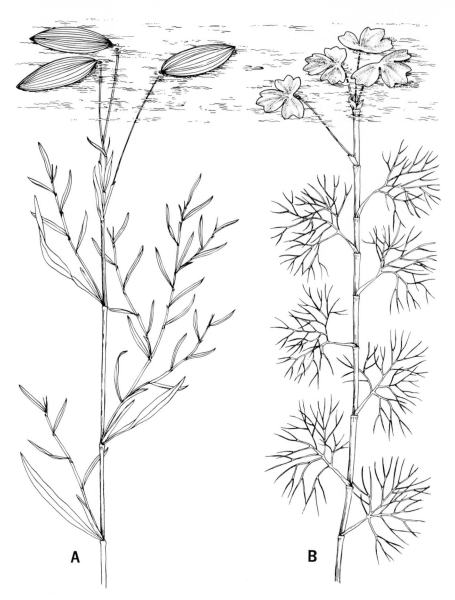

FIGURE 1–1   Differences in phenotypic response correlated with environmental differences, showing floating and immersed leaves. A, *Potamogeton grammineus,* ×0.5; B, *Ranunculus aquatilis,* ×0.5.

actions of various inorganic substances, such as hydrogen sulfide, ammonia, and hydrogen. Autotrophic plants assimilate carbon dioxide and, for the most part, obtain hydrogen from inorganic donors. However, a few photosynthetic bacteria may use organic acids as hydrogen donors.

In contrast to the autotrophs, **heterotrophic** plants must have exogenous supplies of one or more organic substances. These organic compounds serve as oxidizable substrates; they are both an energy and a carbon source. Some heterotrophic plants assimilate small amounts of carbon dioxide, but they must have additional carbon and organic compounds. These may be derived from dead plant or animal remains, in which case the organisms are called **saprophytes** or **saprobes. Parasitic hetero-**

trophs, on the other hand, obtain their requirements from living **hosts.** Some parasitic plants are **obligate parasites;** they must have a living host. Others, called **facultative parasites,** can exist either saprophytically or parasitically.

Most of the algae, bryophytes, and vascular plants are photoautotrophic. Although photoautotrophic, certain algae and bacteria are capable of existing on dissolved organic materials present in the surrounding environment. These may be considered as facultative heterotrophs, or **mixotrophs.** A few phototrophic algae are not completely independent of external supplies of organic substances; such **auxotrophs** are incapable of synthesizing certain substances necessary for growth. Although they belong primarily to autotrophic groups, a number of plants are either parasitic, semi-parasitic, or saprophytic, such as dodder, mistletoe, and Indian pipe, respectively.

None of the bacteria or fungi possesses chlorophylls of the types found in other plant groups. However, some bacteria possess somewhat similar pigments and do carry on photosynthesis; others are **chemotrophic.** Most bacterial species and all of the true fungi and myxomycetes are heterotrophic. Of these, only the myxomycetes are **phagotrophs**—i.e., ingest solid food particles. A few unicellular algal species are phagotrophic, although the characteristic is uncommon in species possessing chlorophyll.

Many interrelationships exist among organisms, and these are often important in their nutrition. There is a tendency to think of a single plant or animal body as an individual, but this is often true in only one sense. On close examination many such "individuals" are found to be aggregations of individuals of different species. For example, many algae, fungi, bacteria, and other organisms can be isolated from the inner portions or bark of a single tree. Some of these are parasites, or may become parasitic if the condition of the host permits. Others are saprophytes, living on dead portions of the plant. Still others form partnerships of a sort with the host plant. The term **symbiosis,** as originally applied by deBary, was used to cover any such relationship between dissimilar organisms. The term is now more commonly applied to what is best described as **reciprocal parasitism.** Examples of this in plants are the relationships between algae and fungi in lichens, and in **mycorrhizal** relationships where both partners benefit from the association. Those interested in a complete classification of symbiotic relationships should refer to the work of McDougal.

Nutrition and symbiosis might seem at first glance to be of little consequence in morphological studies. However, form and function go hand in hand, and the evolution of diverse groups of organisms is sometimes linked. One would not dispute the fact that leaves are morphologically well adapted for photosynthesis. Nor is there any doubt that certain morphological features of both plants and animals are directly correlated with symbiotic relationships. For example, the nectar of flowers appears to attract pollen-carrying insects. Predaceous fungi produce remarkable snares capable of capturing nematodes, in many instances being formed only when nematodes are present in the environment.

Other common examples of the correlation of structure with parasitic and symbiotic relationships include the following: **haustoria** of parasitic vascular plants and fungi; special pouches in fungus-culturing insects wherein the fungus inoculum is maintained; and the distinctive form of roots inhabited by mycorrhizal fungi, or by nitrogen-fixing bacteria.

THE EVOLUTIONARY APPROACH

The aim of certain botanical investigators is to try to determine **phylogenetic** relationships between organisms. Evolution undoubtedly holds the key to this understanding; thus, evidence that sheds light on evolutionary development will also shed light on phylogeny. For this reason fossil evidence, where available, has been included for each group of plants.

Almost certainly the bacteria, fungi, and algae were the earliest groups of plants to evolve. They have the oldest fossil record, and have members that appear closer to the presumed single-celled ancestral form of multicellular plants. Although the bryophytes have a meager fossil record, they are generally considered to have evolved at approximately the same time as vascular plants—that is, sometime during the Paleozoic Era. We know that vascular plants are recorded with certainty from the middle of the Paleozoic, but they may have had a beginning earlier in that era. Since they have the most complete fossil history of all plants, their evolution can accordingly be traced much more certainly. It is now generally held that the bryophytes and vascular plants evolved from green algae of the chlorophycean line, but the exact time and manner are still in question.

Since the evolutionary point of view provides a common thread for examining the development of the plant kingdom, the main theme of this book is evolution.

REFERENCES

Dobzhansky, T., *Genetics and the Origin of Species,* 2nd Ed. New York: Columbia University Press (1941).

Huxley, J. S., *Evolution: The Modern Synthesis.* New York: Harper & Row (1942).

McDougal, W. B., "The Classification of Symbiotic Phenomena." *Plant World,* 21: 250–256 (1918).

Ownbey, M., "Natural Hybridization and Amphiploidy in the Genus *Tragopogon.*" *Am. J. Bot.,* 37: 487–499 (1950).

Ross, H. H., *A Synthesis of Evolutionary Theory.* Englewood Cliffs, N. J.: Prentice-Hall, Inc. (1962).

Stebbins, G. L., Jr., *Variation and Evolution in Plants.* New York: Columbia University Press (1950).

2 / CLASSIFICATION

In science, as in other branches of learning, it is difficult to retain and recall a large number of unrelated facts. For this reason scientists have devised special methods of organizing information. Many of these methods have been refined into formal schemes or classifications. Botanists have adopted various systems of classification for plants. Some of these, based arbitrarily on a limited number of criteria, are termed *artificial classifications;* others, based on a large number of characteristics, are referred to as *natural classifications.* In some instances these may show evolutionary relationships, and are either **phenetic** or **phylogenetic.**

PHENETIC AND PHYLOGENETIC SYSTEMS

In both phylogenetic and phenetic systems of classification the biologist attempts to arrange plants or animals in a system proceeding from the simplest to the most complex organism, along lines that they appear to have followed in their evolution. Thus, in arriving at any grouping of species, biologists endeavor to select characteristics believed to have phylogenetic significance. The criteria vary greatly, depending on the particular group of plants and also on the level of classification. Phylogenetic systems include evidence from fossil ancestors, whereas phenetic systems are usually based only on information derived from extant plants (see Chapter 28).

11

In both systems, characteristics or criteria may be morphological, or anatomical if they concern cellular arrangement or the organization of cells of similar form and function in tissues. They may concern fundamental biochemical or physiological characteristics, such as the nature of the cell wall, food reserves, and pigments. They may deal with reproductive organs and the arrangement of parts or motile reproductive cells of these organs. Or they may concern cytological details, such as chromosome number or genetic characteristics. An essential feature of a useful criterion is that it must be reasonably constant.

Thus, in order to classify plants one must be able to observe and evaluate many different types of characteristics, usually in considerable detail. To arrive at a satisfactory arrangement, it may be necessary to examine the gross morphology of a plant and its anatomy; and to study it cytologically, genetically, biochemically, and ecologically.

THE NEED FOR PLANT IDENTIFICATION

In certain taxonomic aspects botany is mainly a descriptive field. Just as the physicist and chemist employ units such as ergs, degrees, electrons, and grams, the botanist has a fundamental unit—the **species.** However, in contrast to the exact units of the physicist and the chemist, species are not so readily defined, and few biologists define them in precisely the same way. This is mainly because species are not static. If we recognize that species are living evolutionary units, and that they are subject to genetic change, then it is apparent that they cannot remain static. They are dynamic populations subject to change and with fluctuations that sometimes produce overlapping in some essential features. This blurring of boundary lines often makes the determination of species somewhat arbitrary. Thus, as the concept of a species changes, so the system of classification must be modified. Changes become necessary

as more information is gained about species, and also because significant differences may appear in species themselves as a consequence of evolution.

In the more exact aspects of botany dealing with physiological and biochemical processes, conclusions must be related to particular species or genera. Thus, it is important that botanists learn how to identify them. For example, if certain fundamental processes are attributed to a given species, one must be sure that each time experimental work is performed, individuals of that same species are used. Ideally, one should be certain that the plants used are not only morphologically but also genetically similar. Indeed, physiological or experimental studies can be only as useful as the taxonomic foundation upon which they are based. Certain organisms are known to be very similar morphologically, but are quite different genetically and physiologically; again, other organisms are known to be very similar morphologically and physiologically, but to be genetically quite different. In other branches of biology, such as ecology and genetics, it is equally important to have a sound appreciation of the taxonomic aspects of the investigation.

LEVELS OF CLASSIFICATION

One must recognize that any system devised by man is subject to his interpretation of nature and natural processes as they are currently understood, and of past evolutionary history of plants as interpreted from the fossil record. It is for this reason that so many different systems of classification have been developed, particularly for the higher levels of classification. Botanists differ in their opinions and have evaluated the same evidence from living and fossil data with different degrees of emphasis on the criteria used to distinguish taxa.

The main categories generally used in plant classification are as follows:

Plant Kingdom
   Division
      Class
         Order
            Family
               Genus
                  Species

The system of classification with the names of the various groups adopted for this book is outlined on the front and back end papers of this volume.

NOMENCLATURE

The internationally accepted method for naming plants is based on a *binomial system of nomenclature*. Although not entirely original with him, our modern practice stems from the works of Linnaeus published in 1753. He proposed that genera be divided into species and that the name of each species consist of two words—the generic name followed by a specific epithet. The names and epithets were chosen largely from words with Greek or Latin roots, and are descriptive in many instances. An example of one of Linnaeus' binomials is *Pteridium aquilinum,* which literally translated is: Greek, *pteridos* (a kind of fern); Latin, *aquila* (eagle—a reference to the spreadeagle appearance of the vascular bundles in the petiole). Using this procedure, Linnaeus coined hundreds of binomials for plants and animals, many of which are still in use.

The major advantage of the Latin binomial is that it can be understood and applied by people anywhere in the world. Latin and Greek are ancient and well-established languages, and are sufficiently versatile to allow for an almost endless number of combinations for names. This is preferable to any system that employs local, provincial, or even national names. Such *common* names usually have little significance to people in other countries, or even in different parts of the same country, and are often confused with names applied to *different*

organisms elsewhere. A good example is found among various plants commonly called "cedar." This name is used, among others, for species of the conifer genera. *Chamaecyparis*—yellow cedar and yellow cypress, *Thuja*—western red cedar, *Cedrus*—cedar of Lebanon, *Libocedrus*—incense cedar, *Juniperus*—pencil cedar; and for the angiosperm genus *Cedrela*—cigar-box cedar.

The binomial is simply a name—a means of referring to a plant. It has no phylogenetic significance other than indicating the genus to which a species belongs. Thus, if a plant has been correctly identified and properly named, it will always bear the same binomial; and no other plant can bear that binomial.

To ensure stability, the International Association for Plant Taxonomy has been organized to establish principles and procedures for both classification (taxonomy) and nomenclature (naming). Many of the problems in nomenclature are exceedingly intricate, and the International Association publishes an *International Code of Botanical Nomenclature* every few years to assist botanists in maintaining uniformity in naming plants.

INTERRELATIONSHIPS AMONG LOWER PLANTS AND ANIMALS

Among the lower plants, several groups are closely related to lower groups of animals. For example, certain algae (as treated here) are often considered as protozoa by zoologists. Some of the fungus-like taxa are also often incorporated in the animal kingdom by zoologists. It will probably never be possible to assign many of these lower groups to either the plant or the animal kingdom to the complete satisfaction of both the botanist and the zoologist. However, there is little to be gained by arguing. If the principle of organic evolution is accepted, one should not be surprised at this close relationship. In fact one should expect it, since the earliest evolutionary forms were almost certainly not sharply differentiated from one another. It is really of little importance to be able to state whether some of these organisms are plants or animals. The important point is that some of them have both plant-like and animal-like characteristics. Therefore, with equal justification such organisms can be referred to as plants with animal-like affinities (and they can be regarded as plants), or as animals with plant-like affinities (and they can be regarded as animals). Groupings of organisms, distinct from both plant and animal kingdoms, called the Protista and Monera, have been proposed by some investigators to encompass this heterogenous group. Other biologists have decided to classify all groups of animals and plants as phyla, instead of classifying animals as phyla and plants as divisions. In principle, many biologists feel this is a more logical arrangement. But the *International Code of Botanical Nomenclature* clearly states that plants are to be classified in divisions; and since by usage division antedates phylum, there is perhaps more justification for classifying both animals and plants according to divisions rather than to phyla. Neither of these proposals has been universally accepted; and most biologists still classify plant groups as divisions and animal groups as phyla.

SEQUENCE OF PLANT DIVISIONS

In this text lichens (Chapter 5) are placed immediately after the fungi (Chapter 4), because most lichenologists now consider them to belong to the fungi. Although this curious association is referred to as a lichen, its gross morphology as well as its reproductive structures are strictly fungal in character. Following these chapters, the bacteria (Chapter 6) are discussed prior to the blue-green algae (Chapter 8) because of their possible affinities. Because the green algae (Chapter 15) are generally considered to be the progenitors of land plants and to constitute the main line of evolution leading to bryophytes and vascular plants, they are the last group of algae to be discussed.

REFERENCES

Bailey, L. H., *How Plants Get Their Names.* New York: The Macmillan Co. (1933).

Benson, L., *Plant Classification.* Boston: D. C. Heath & Co. (1957).

Bold, H. C., *Morphology of Plants.* New York: Harper & Row (1957).

Copeland, H. C., *The Classification of Lower Organisms.* Palo Alto, Calif.: Pacific Books (1956).

Cronquist, A., "The Divisions and Classes of Plants." *Bot. Rev.,* 26(4): 425–482 (1960).

Lawrence, G. H. M., *Taxonomy of Vascular Plants.* New York: The Macmillan Co. (1951).

Stebbins, G. L., Jr., *Variation and Evolution in Plants.* New York: Columbia University Press (1950).

NONVASCULAR PLANTS

3 / DIVISION

MYXOMYCOTA

Until relatively recent times, the *slime molds,* true fungi, and bacteria were placed together in a single division—the Fungi. Simplicity of structure, the absence of **chlorophyll,** and storage of food reserves in forms other than starch were the basis for this grouping. At the present time, these are generally treated as three separate divisions—the Myxomycota (slime molds), Eumycota, and Schizomycophyta. However, in some recent treatments the slime molds and true fungi are placed together in a single division, the Mycota. Because of differences in nuclear structure, cell-wall chemistry, and other characteristics, the bacteria are no longer considered to be closely related to the true fungi and slime molds. There is some uncertainty yet as to the relationship between the latter two groups.

The division Myxomycota includes organisms of two very distinct types: the class Myxomycetes, or true slime molds, and the cellular slime molds. Within the latter group are two classes— the Acrasiomycetes and Labyrinthulomycetes—which appear not to be closely related either to each other or to the true slime molds. All slime molds are characterized by naked **assimilative** stages. The assimilative body is multinucleate in the true slime molds and uninucleate in the cellular slime molds. In contrast to bacteria, the nuclei are enclosed within nuclear membranes and are like the nuclei in higher plants and animals. The Myxomycetes, Acrasiomycetes, and some Labyrinthulomycetes are capable of feeding

16

phagotrophically—i.e., by ingesting solid food particles. Except for these similarities and for some other superficial resemblances, the various slime-mold groups are quite distinctive in structure and reproduction. Because of this, each group is discussed separately.

CLASS MYXOMYCETES
(True Slime Molds)

About 450 species of true slime molds are known and most of these are universally distributed. They occur in moist dung, wood, soil, and decaying vegetation. All possess a naked, acellular assimilative stage called a **plasmodium.**

PLASMODIUM

The plasmodium is multinucleate and can move in an amoeboid fashion in many species. It ingests solid food particles in the same manner as an amoeba and also can absorb dissolved nutrients. Most species feed on bacteria and possibly other small organisms found in their environment. The plasmodium is a diploid structure of rather indefinite and sometimes changing form (Fig. 3–1). Most early descriptions of plasmodia are based on observations of those of a single order, the Physarales. Plasmodia of this group are often found on the wood surface or other materials, whereas those of many other myxomycetes remain concealed within such substrates. Recent studies have shown that the plasmodia of some species are much simpler than those of the Physarales.

Plasmodia of many myxomycetes are motile by means of a slow amoeboid movement. Migrating plasmodia typically are fan-shaped and are composed of a network of vein-like strands or tubules. Toward the base of the fan these tubules are large with few branches, but they become smaller and more frequently branched toward their tips. At the advancing margin, no vein-like organization is seen—i.e., a continuous layer of protoplasm is present. Each tubular strand of the plasmodium consists

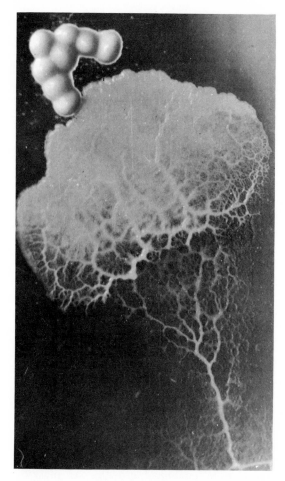

FIGURE 3–1   Small plasmodium of *Physarum* (plasmodium shown moving toward mass of yeast cells, upper left), ×3.

of a hyaline semisolid outer layer of protoplasm and a fluid inner portion. The entire strand consists of protoplasm, but the outer surface region is in a gel state while the inner portion is not. No cell wall is present. Within the tubules, the more fluid portion of the protoplasm undergoes rapid rhythmic streaming: it flows in one direction for a few seconds, slows to a stop, then reverses and flows in the opposite direction. The streaming portion of the protoplasm usually is granular in appearance due to the presence of **organelles** of the myxomycete, pigment granules, bacterial cells, and other materials ingested by the plasmodium.

A contractile protein, called myxomyosin, is present in the plasmodium and is possibly responsible for the streaming movements.

Plasmodia of relatively few species have been isolated and grown in pure culture. Only one species, *Physarum polycephalum,* has been grown in pure culture on a chemically defined medium. In culture, the plasmodium of *P. polycephalum* does not assume a fan shape as long as sufficient nutrient is available. It remains stationary and forms a thin, compact disc, which spreads over the surface of the culture medium.

Similar plasmodia are found in some groups of myxomycetes. That of *Echinostelium* is microscopic and amoeba-like; it lacks the vein-like organization and has only weak streaming movements. In *Stemonitis,* the plasmodium is larger than that of *Echinostelium,* but the protoplasm is nongranular and transparent. It seems to lack the gel-like outer layer of the tubules, except in the largest veins; the advancing fan consists of a network of very fine strands. The plasmodium of some species is colorless, but that of others may be yellow, violet, or reddish.

If conditions remain favorable, the plasmodium continues to take in food and other materials and enlarges. Under certain conditions where temperature and moisture are not favorable to continued growth, the plasmodium may be converted into a resting structure called a **sclerotium.** Sclerotia are hardened masses of irregular form consisting of many minute cell-like compartments. Sclerotia of some species have been reported to retain their viability for two or more years. Under favorable conditions, the sclerotium again becomes a plasmodium.

SPORULATION

Various environmental factors—including the effects of light, pH, moisture, exhaustion of food supply, etc.—have been thought to induce sporulation in myxomycetes. Perhaps the factors controlling this change vary from species to species or several of those mentioned may be involved in some species.

Before spore-bearing structures are produced, the plasmodium usually moves to an exposed position on the substrate. Some move up the stems or leaves of living or dead plants to positions more favorable to spore dispersal. There the plasmodia heap up into one or more masses, which slowly assume the form of mature spore-bearing structures, or **fructifications.** In one genus, *Ceratiomyxa,* **spores** are borne singly and externally on a white thread-like or columnar structure. In all others, the spores are formed endogenously—i.e., within the fructification. Several types of fructification are recognized. In one, called an **aethalium,** the entire plasmodium heaps up into one or more large pillow-shaped to rounded masses (Fig. 3–2A). Each of these becomes transformed into an outer sterile layer, the **peridium,** surrounding a mass of either spores alone or spores together with a **capillitium** (Fig. 3–2C). The capillitium is composed of thread-like strands, sometimes united to form a network, and interspersed with the spores. A second type of fructification, designated the **plasmodiocarp** (Fig. 3–2B), seems to develop directly from the major vein-like parts of the plasmodium. Plasmodiocarps are sessile and of variable form. Those of a single species are sometimes branched, ring-shaped, or simply elongate. In a third type, the **sporangium,** a plasmodium typically forms a large number of individual fructifications. Sporangia are smaller and more regular in shape than are many aethalia and plasmodiocarps and are stalked or sessile (Fig. 3–2C). A thin, shiny, membranous film, the **hypothallus,** is usually visible at the bases of myxomycete fructifications and is adherent to the substrate.

Some intergradation of the three types of fructifications is found. Both sporangia and plasmodiocarps are produced by some species. The sporangia of others form crowded masses in which the individuals are partially or completely fused.

Capillitia are not found in sporangia of all species, although sterile structures of some sort are usually present. Some capillitia are accompanied by a central columnar structure, the **columella** (Fig. 3–2C), which may be only a continuation of the **stipe** (stalk) into the spore-bearing portion of the sporangium.

A

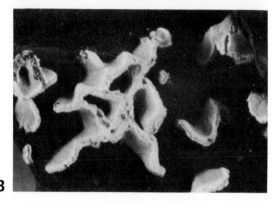

B

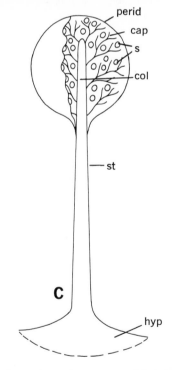

C

FIGURE 3–2   A, aethalium of *Fuligo septica*, ×0.5. B, plasmodiocarps of *Physarum bivalve*, ×5. C, sporangium. *perid,* peridium; *cap,* capillitium; *s,* spores; *col,* columella; *st,* stipe or stalk; *hyp,* hypothallus.

Meiosis occurs during spore formation within the developing fructification. Uninucleate portions of protoplasm become surrounded by walls and mature into spores. At this time, the threads of the capillitium also are formed. In some species, the capillitium appears to develop through deposition of materials into or upon the surfaces of **vacuoles.** A tubular network of invaginations, developing from the peridium inward, also may be involved. In some of the Stemonitales, neither vacuoles nor invaginations are formed. Here the developing capillitial threads appear to blend gradually into the protoplasm. **Chitin** and **cellulose** have been reported in the capillitium of myxomycetes, but more studies are needed before these reports can be accepted.

When the sporangium is mature, the spores are unattached, but are enmeshed in the capillitial network. Mature sporangia open in one of several ways. In some myxomycetes, the peridium is a very delicate structure that disappears as soon as the sporangium is mature. In others, the peridium splits either irregularly or along definite lines, exposing the spores. Following this, the capillitium may expand, forming a more open network. The capillitium of some species is **hygroscopic,** expanding and contracting with changes in humidity.

The mature spore is spherical or nearly so and has a wall reported to contain cellulose. In many species this wall is covered by a characteristic pattern of warts, spines, or ridges (Fig. 3–3A). Myxomycete spores are very resistant, and some have been induced to germinate after more than 60 years of storage. Spore germination is often enhanced if the spore wall is first wetted with dilute solutions of bile salts. However, spores of some species germinate in as little as 15 minutes if simply placed in distilled water, liberating one to eight naked cells of one of two types: (1) **swarm cells** or **swarmers** if flagellated; and (2) **myxamoebae** if lacking **flagella.** Myxamoebae may develop flagella after a time; conversely, swarmers may lose the flagella and become myxamoebae. Thus, the two types of naked cells are essentially similar, except for the presence or absence of flagella.

SWARM CELLS AND MYXAMOEBAE

The swarm cell (Fig. 3–3B) is an anteriorly uniflagellate or sometimes biflagellate cell capable of both amoeboid and swimming movements. It is typically pear-shaped, although this is altered during amoeboid movement. A false flagellum is also visible at times; this is a narrow strand of protoplasm that forms near the base of the flagellum and projects out from the cell margin. It migrates toward the posterior region and is finally withdrawn.

Under unfavorable conditions, myxamoebae and swarm cells often encyst. The **cysts** possess a distinct wall and are more resistant than the naked cells that produce them. When conditions again become favorable, the cyst germinates to form a new myxamoeba or swarm cell.

Swarm cells and myxamoebae feed on bacteria and other food substances and the myxamoebae may undergo **fission.** In some species, these cells fuse in pairs soon after their release from the germinating spore. In others, fusion may be delayed for some time. The swarm cells of some myxomycetes fuse only after they have lost their flagella and become amoeboid. However, in all cases studied these cells eventually function as **gametes,** whether flagellated or amoeboid.

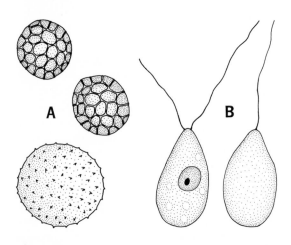

FIGURE 3–3   A, spores of myxomycetes, ×1,750. B, uniflagellate and biflagellate swarm cells of *Fuligo septica,* ×2,500.

From the first, the zygote is either amoeboid or flagellated, depending on the condition of the gametes at the time of fusion. If flagellated, the flagella are soon lost and the zygote becomes amoeboid. The zygote nucleus divides mitotically and a new plasmodium develops. Mitotic divisions of nuclei within the plasmodium occur at regular intervals, all of those within a plasmodium dividing at about the same time—i.e., synchronously. Occasionally the size of a plasmodium is increased through fusion with other plasmodia; zygotes also can fuse this way to form small plasmodia. In these cases, only cytoplasmic fusion occurs. A plasmodium may also break apart or fragment, producing two or more plasmodia.

The life history of *Physarum polycephalum,* a typical myxomycete, is shown in Fig. 3–4.

THE SIX ORDERS OF MYXOMYCETES

ORDER CERATIOMYXALES.   This contains a single family and genus—*Ceratiomyxa. Ceratiomyxa fruticulosa,* the most common species, produces an extensive hypothallus, which is white and thread-like and bears numerous spores exogenously on individual stalks (Fig. 3–5A–C). The individual spores of this group may be directly comparable to sporangia of other myxomycetes. Spores of *Ceratiomyxa* release eight swarmspores upon germination, whereas those of other myxomycetes release only one to four.

ORDER LICEALES.   In this order fructifications lack a true capillitium and have no limy materials. Some contain a few irregular thread-like remnants of the plasmodium, called **pseudocapillitia.** The spores in this order are mostly pale—yellow, olivaceous, etc.

Neither a capillitium nor a pseudocapillitium is present in sporangia of *Dictydium* and *Cribraria* (Fig. 3–6A–C). These have a peridium composed of a network of delicate strands. Spores gradually sift out through the meshes of this network.

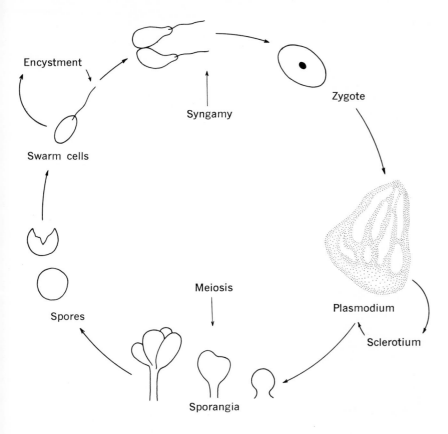

Encystment

Syngamy

Zygote

Swarm cells

Meiosis

Plasmodium

Spores

Sclerotium

Sporangia

FIGURE 3–4   Life history of *Physarum polycephalum.*

Tubifera ferruginosa (Fig. 3–6D) produces compact clusters of sporangia, in which the individuals are almost completely fused with one another. This mass resembles an aethalium and is referred to as a **pseudoaethalium.** The aethalia of *Lycogala epidendrum* (Fig. 3–6E) are similar in appearance and function to puff balls of basidiomycetes. At maturity, an irregular opening develops in the peridium at the top of the aethalium. The force of raindrops striking the peridium produces a bellows-like action, and spores are blown out through the opening.

ORDER TRICHIALES.   Among the more brightly colored myxomycete fructifications are those of the Trichiales. The spores are usually yellowish or rosy. Most members of the order produce sporangia or plasmodiocarps with well-developed capillitia. In some genera—e.g.,

Trichia and *Hemitrichia* (Fig. 3–7A–C)—the capillitium is marked by regular spiral bands. That of *Arcyria* (Fig. 3–7D–F) has prominent cogs or spines on the threads.

In many species of Trichiales, the upper part of the peridium falls away when the sporangium is mature. The capillitium remains attached to the goblet-shaped lower portion of the peridium. Capillitia of some of the Trichiales expand considerably after the peridium has ruptured.

ORDER ECHINOSTELIALES.   Only one genus, *Echinostelium,* is placed in this order. The species are characterized by microscopic plasmodia that exhibit no vein-like pattern and are amoeboid in appearance; streaming movements are weak and irregular. At maturity, each plasmodium produces a single sporangium. The sporangiate fructification lacks a

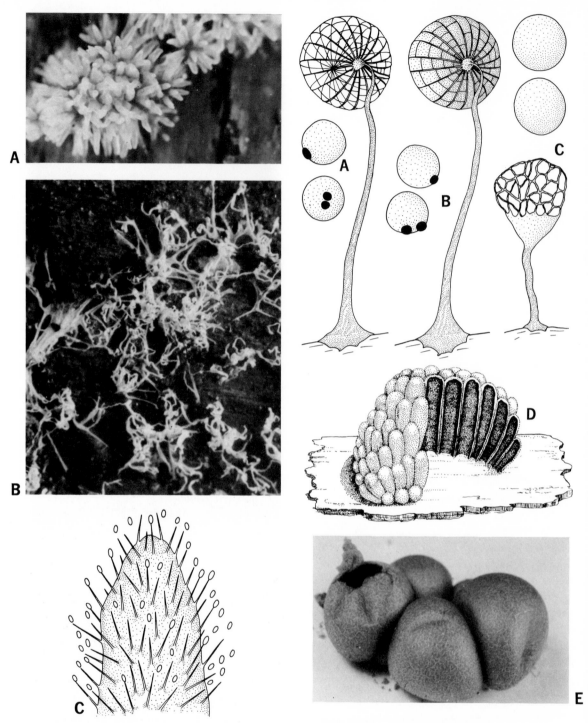

FIGURE 3–5 *Ceratiomyxa fruticulosa*. A, early stage in sporulation process, ×12.5; B, mature stage of slightly different form, ×12.5. C, habit sketch of single branch, showing attachment of spores, ×1,330.

FIGURE 3–6   A, B, sporangia (×30) and spores (×2,800) of *Dictydium cancellatum*. C, sporangium (×22) and spores (×2,200) of *Cribraria*. D, habit sketch showing section through pseudo-aethalium of *Tubifera ferruginosa*, ×5. E, aethalia of *Lycogala epidendrum*, ×6.

peridium and may lack a capillitium. The spores are light colored and have irregularly thickened walls.

ORDER STEMONITALES. *Stemonitis* and most related forms produce dark-brown to violet-brown spores. The sporangium is columellate and the capillitium arises as branches from this structure. A peridium is absent in mature sporangia of *Stemonitis* and *Comatrichia* (Fig. 3–8A, B), but persists and is beautifully iridescent in *Lamproderma* (Fig. 3–8C) and *Diachea*. No lime is present in the peridium or capillitium, but a thick layer is found on the stipe of *Diachea*.

ORDER PHYSARALES. Largest order of slime molds is the Physarales. Its representatives have dark spores, as in the Stemonitales, but have limy peridium or capillitium or both. In *Physarum* (Fig. 3–9A–C, 2B), the peridium is often of two distinct layers—one membranous and the other limy. The capillitium of *Physarum* has very fine hyaline threads connecting small lime knots; that of *Badhamia* (Fig. 3–9D) has minute limy tubules. In most of the forms included here, the limy material is amorphous, but in *Didymium* and related genera it is crystalline.

Fructifications of all types—e.g., sporangia, aethalia, and plasmodiocarps—are found in Physarales. *Fuligo septica* (Fig. 3–2A), a common species, produces aethalia sometimes reaching 20 cm in diameter.

CLASS ACRASIOMYCETES

This class includes a single order—the Acrasiales. In recent years this small but interesting group has become the subject of intensive study. The Acrasiales are distinguished from true slime molds by a unicellular amoeboid assimilative stage, as well as by other characteristics. The life cycle is similar in some respects to that of the Myxobacteriales. The Acrasiales are common in certain types of soils, on dung, and in other habitats where bacteria are abundant. Most are cultured readily in the laboratory only when grown with bacteria.

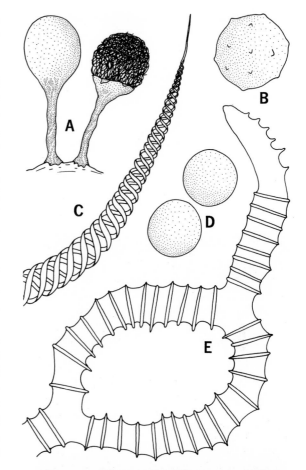

FIGURE 3–7   A–C, *Hemitrichia*. A, sporangia, ×22.5; B, spore, ×1,800; C, portion of a single capillitial strand, ×1,800. D–F, *Arcyria*. D, spores, ×1,800; E, portion of capillitial strand, ×1,800; F, sporangia, ×12.

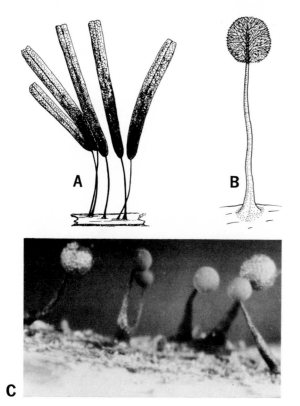

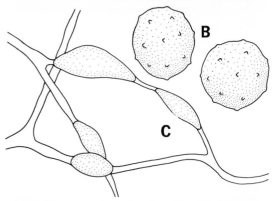

FIGURE 3–8   Sporangia of Stemonitaceae. A, *Stemonitis,* ×8; B, *Comatricha,* ×13; C, *Lamproderma,* ×15.

FIGURE 3–9   A–C, *Physarum.* A, sporangia of *Physarum leucopus,* ×30; B, spores, ×1,800; C, capillitium, ×875. D, sporangium of *Badhamia utricularis,* ×25.

The assimilative units, called myxamoebae or simply amoebae, are indistinguishable in appearance from amoebae classified in the Protozoa. They move in similar fashion and feed phagotrophically on bacterial cells. Under certain conditions, many of these myxamoebae come together and produce a communal structure, the **pseudoplasmodium.** The pseudoplasmodium migrates as a unit in some species, eventually forming a fruiting body.

The life history of *Dictyostelium discoideum,* the most intensively studied acrasiomycete, is described here and outlined in Fig. 3–10. The uninucleate amoebae of this species move over the substrate, feeding on bacterial cells and reproducing by fission. During this time, each amoeba acts independently of all others. The assimilative stage may go on indefinitely if environmental conditions are favorable and there is an adequate supply of food. Depletion of the food supply, humidity, increasing concentration of amoebae, and other factors affect the duration of this stage.

An interphase period, lasting from four to eight hours, occurs between the active assimilative phase and the beginning of **aggregation,** the next stage of development. During the interphase, the amoebae stop feeding and undergo a number of changes: decrease in size, disappearance of food vacuoles, and appearance of certain granules in the cytoplasm. When aggregation commences, the amoebae move together, forming branched stream-like groups. The amoebae converge on a central collection point or aggregation center (Fig. 3–11A), forming a single heap.

Movement of the cells toward the aggregation center is a chemotactic response to substances called acrasins. The acrasins are secreted by amoebae of all acrasiomycetes, the exact chemical composition varying from species to species. The acrasins that have been identified are steroids, and it is interesting to note that the chemotactic response can be induced with urine from a pregnant woman This undoubtedly is due to the presence of steroid hormones—e.g., progesterone, estradiole, etc.—in the urine.

The rounded mass of amoebae at the aggregation center soon assumes a definite elongate form—the pseudoplasmodium (Fig. 3–11B). The cartridge-shaped pseudoplasmodium of *D. discoideum* migrates away from the place of aggregation. Although the pseudoplasmodium appears to be a multicellular unit, it is actually composed of many myxamoebae. If the pseudoplasmodium is placed in a drop of water and shaken, the myxamoebae separate and resume individual activity.

Migration may last for several hours after the pseudoplasmodium has formed. During the slow, gliding movement of migration, a slimy sheath is deposited behind the moving structure. The anterior portion of the pseudoplasmodium is light and heat sensitive; it responds positively to both factors and controls the direction of migration. The pseudoplasmodium may glide with its long axis parallel to the substratum, with the body flexed and only a portion lying on the substratum, or standing erect on the posterior tip. It has been demonstrated through amputation experiments that

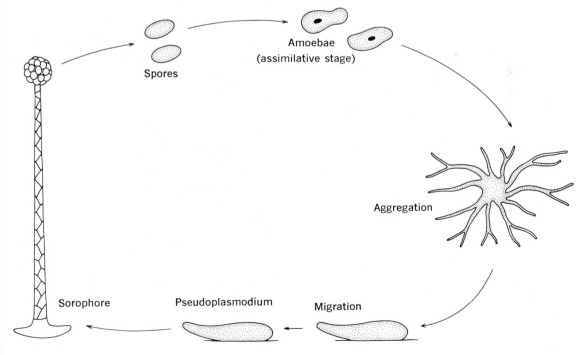

Spores

Amoebae
(assimilative stage)

Aggregation

Sorophore Pseudoplasmodium Migration

FIGURE 3–10   Life History of *Dictyostelium discoideum.*

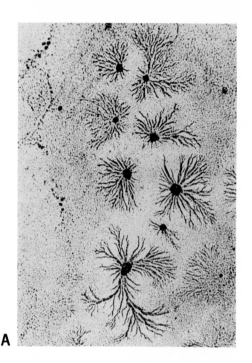

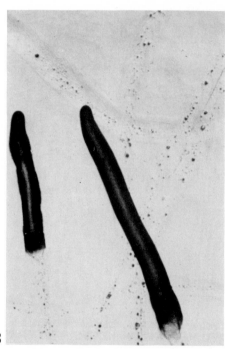

A

B

FIGURE 3–11 *Dictyostelium discoideum.* A, aggregation, ×5. B, migrating pseudoplasmodium, ×50. (Photographs by K. B. Raper, courtesy J. T. Bonner from *The Cellular Slime Molds,* permission of Princeton University Press, copyright © 1959.)

cells in various regions of this structure will eventually form specific portions of the fruiting body. If any cells of the pseudoplasmodium are excised, the fruiting body will be abnormal in form, and the abnormality is consistent for the portion of the pseudoplasmodium removed.

The length of the migration period varies with environmental conditions, especially humidity. It may last up to 10 to 20 days if the pseudoplasmodium is kept in a very moist environment. If cultures are exposed to drying conditions, the next stage in the life cycle is soon initiated. The length of the migration period directly affects the form of the fruiting body in several species of *Dictyostelium:* the longer the migration period, the greater is the stalk length of the fruiting structure.

Following migration, the pseudoplasmodium of *D. discoideum* stops gliding, contracts somewhat in length, and becomes erect (Fig. 3–12). Within the pseudoplasmodium, a cellulose cylinder forms and becomes the stalk of the fructification. Cells inside the cylinder secrete walls about themselves. As the stalk lengthens, the remainder of the pseudoplasmodium migrates upward around the outside of the stalk. At the tip of the completed stalk, or **sorophore,** the remaining cells produce a globose mass. Each of the amoebae in this mass secretes a wall about itself, producing a cystlike structure called a spore. The spherical mass of spores is called a **sorus,** and this together with the sorophore constitutes the fruiting body or **sorocarp** (Fig. 3–13). The spores are not comparable to those of the Myxomycetes, each being formed by a single amoeboid cell rather than through division of a large protoplast. On germination, each spore releases a single myxamoeba. Thus, spore production here does not give the potential increase in numbers of individuals that it does in the Myxomycetes.

Sexual reproduction through fusion of amoebae has been reported in this group. This has been disclaimed by some workers, although available genetic evidence supports the idea that sexual reproduction does occur. Both haploid and diploid strains of *D. discoideum* are known. Furthermore, genetic recombination has been observed following haploidization of a diploid strain.

CLASS LABYRINTHULOMYCETES

Included in the class Labyrinthulomycetes is one order, the Labyrinthulales, with approximately a dozen species in two genera. All are aquatic, and both fresh-water and marine species are known. None of the species has been sufficiently studied to provide a complete life history. There is also disagreement concerning some structural aspects of the group.

The assimilative state in *Labyrinthula* consists of naked uninucleate cells. Each of these spindle or oval-shaped cells secretes a slimy filament from either end (Fig. 3–14A,

FIGURE 3–12   Culmination of migration, and development of sorocarp of *Dictyostelium discoideum*, ×40. (Photograph courtesy J. T. Bonner from *The Cellular Slime Molds*, by permission of Princeton University Press, copyright © 1959.)

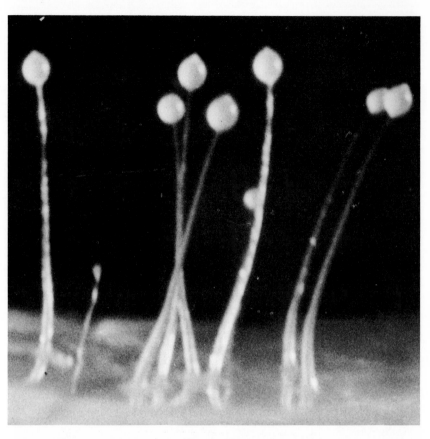

FIGURE 3–13   Mature sorus and sorophore of *Dictyostelium discoideum,* ×40. (Photograph courtesy J. T. Bonner from *The Cellular Slime Molds,* by permission of Princeton University Press, copyright © 1959.)

B), and the filaments of adjacent cells become fused into a network. The cells glide over this network, secreting new filaments at the edge of it. The network of filaments with the gliding cells is referred to as a net plasmodium. It bears little resemblance to either the true plasmodium of the Myxomycetes or to the pseudoplasmodium of the Acrasiales.

The cells may divide mitotically to form two or four cells. In *Labyrinthula macrocystis,* the spindle-shaped cells have been observed to heap up and form a membrane-covered sorus. Development within the sorus has not been studied, but it is known that the spore-like structures eventually are released. Each of these spores releases a single spindle-shaped cell at the time of germination. Biflagellate zoospores have been reported in one species of *Labyrinthula* and multinucleate structures in

another. The latter possibly represents some type of true plasmodium.

Two genera of Labyrinthulales are now recognized: *Labyrinthula* and *Labyrinthoriza.* In *Labyrinthula,* the filamentous network is nonliving and the cells are nonphagotrophic. All species of this genus are marine; *L. macrocystis* causes a serious disease of eel grass. *Labyrinthoriza* is a fresh-water genus with a living network of "tracks," and the cells can ingest food phagotrophically. If the differences attributed to the two genera are correct, it is doubtful that they are closely related.

RELATIONSHIPS OF THE MYXOMYCOTA

MYXOMYCETES.   Relationships of this

group have long been debated. The great German mycologist deBary considered them to be unrelated to the true fungi and placed them

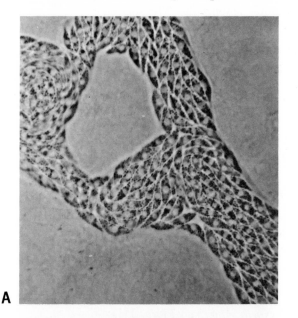

A

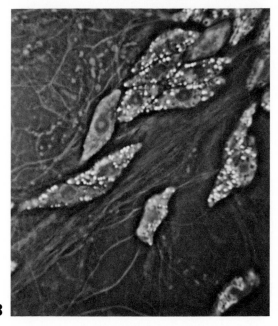

B

FIGURE 3–14   *Labyrinthula vitellina.* A, plasmodium-like mass of cells, ×300. B, cells and tracks, ×1,100. (Phase contrast photographs courtesy S. W. Watson, from "*Labyrinthula minuta* sp. nov." by S. W. Watson and K. B. Raper, *Journal of General Microbiology,* Vol. 17, 1957, with permission of Cambridge University Press.)

in a group—the Mycetozoa—in the Protozoa. Although many mycologists have accepted this, others—including G. W. Martin, one of today's leading authorities—have considered myxomycetes to be related to true fungi. All myxomycetes were classed in various fungal orders without question before their animal-like assimilative state was known. A glance at the synonymy of some species will show names in genera as diverse as *Mucor* and *Lycoperdon,* which occur in the Eumycota.

The amoeboid plasmodium certainly has some animal characteristics—e.g., lack of rigid walls, phagotrophic feeding, and amoeboid movement. The reproductive structures resemble nothing in the Protozoa, but are similar to those of some fungi. Also, not all true fungi possess rigid walls. A few phycomycetes lack walls during part or all of the assimilative stage, and some are capable of amoeboid movement (see Chapter 4). The rapid streaming of cytoplasm within the plasmodial network is duplicated in many true fungi with **coenocytic hyphae.** Although knowledge of the myxomycetes is insufficient to place the group with certainty, they may be included with the fungi as justifiably as with the protozoa.

ACRASIOMYCETES.   The Acrasiales were first grouped with the myxomycetes before the true nature of their pseudoplasmodium was understood. It was once thought that this structure was a true plasmodium, formed through the union of myxamoebae. The myxamoeba stage strongly suggests a relationship to the amoeboid protozoa. As now depicted, their life histories bear a remarkable resemblance to those of the Myxobacteriales; but obviously the Acrasiales bear no close relationship with the latter forms, and the similarity must be attributed to convergent evolution.

LABYRINTHULOMYCETES.   The Labyrinthulales are so poorly known that little can be said concerning their possible relationships. They appear to form a group distinct from both the Acrasiales and from the true slime molds. However, further study may reveal evidence linking them to one of these groups.

GENERAL REFERENCES

Alexopolous, C. J., "Gross Morphology of the Plasmodium and Its Possible Significance in the Relationships among the Myxomycetes." *Mycologia,* 52: 1–20 (1960).

Alexopolous, C. J., "The Myxomycetes, II." *Bot. Rev.,* 29: 1–78 (1963).

Daniel, J. W., Kelly, J., and Rusch, H. P., "Hematin Requiring Plasmodial Myxomycetes." *J. Bact.,* 84: 1104–1110 (1962).

Guttes, E., Guttes, S., and Rusch, H. P., "Morphological Observations on Growth and Development of *Physarum polycephalum* Grown in Pure Culture." *Devel. Biol.,* 3: 588–614 (1961).

Hagelstein, R., *The Mycetozoa of North America, Based upon the Specimens in the New York Botanical Garden.* Mineola, N. Y.: Published by the author (1944).

Koevenig, J. L., "Studies on the Life Cycle of *Physarum gyrosum* and Other Myxomycetes." *Mycologia,* 56: 170–184 (1964).

Lister, A., *A Monograph of the Mycetozoa,* 3rd Ed. (Revised by G. Lister). London: Trustees of the British Museum (1925).

Martin, G. W., "The Myxomycetes." *Bot. Rev.,* 6: 356–388 (1940).

Martin, G. W., "Fungi, Myxomycetes." *North American Flora,* 1(i): 1–151, with bibliography, pp. 153–178, by H. W. Rickett and index, pp. 179–190, by G. M. Miller (1949).

Ross, I. K., "Syngamy and Plasmodium Formation in the Myxogastres." *Am. J. Bot.,* 44: 843–850 (1957).

Ross, I. K., "Pure Cultures of Some Myxomycetes." *Bull. Torrey Bot. Club,* 91: 23–31 (1964).

Wilson, C. L., and Ross, I. K., "Meiosis in the Myxomycetes." *Am. J. Bot.,* 42: 743–749 (1957).

REFERENCES ON ACRASIOMYCETES AND LABYRINTHULOMYCETES

Bonner, J. R., *The Cellular Slime Molds.* Princeton, N. J.: Princeton University Press (1959).

Chadefaud, M., in Chadefaud, M., and Emberger, L., *Traité de Botanique Systématique.* Vol. I. Paris: Masson et Cie (1960).

Raper, K. B., "Isolation, Cultivation, and Conservation of Simple Slime Molds." *Quart. Rev. Biol.,* 26: 169–190 (1951).

Watson, S. W., and Raper, K. B., "*Labyrinthula minuta* sp. nov." *J. Gen. Microbiol.,* 17: 368–377 (1957).

Young, E. L., "Studies on *Labyrinthula.* The Etiologic Agent of the Wasting Disease of Eel Grass." *Am. J. Bot.,* 30: 586–593 (1943).

4/DIVISION

EUMYCOTA

The *true fungi,* or Eumycota, differ from slime molds in a number of important respects. Some true fungi have unicellular, uninucleate assimilative stages, but most have a filamentous organization. In either case, there is a rigid cell wall in most species; a few of the Eumycota do, however, lack rigid walls during the early stages of development or for much of their life cycle. The thallus in true fungi can only absorb dissolved nutrients; it cannot ingest food phagotrophically as the plasmodium does. As in the bacteria, fungi produce exoenzymes capable of digesting various materials in the surrounding environment. The breakdown products can then be absorbed by the fungi.

All of the Eumycota are heterotrophic; most are saprobes, although some species are parasites of man, other animals, or plants. Many of the nonpathogenic species are cosmopolitan in distribution, while others are restricted to the temperate or tropical zones. They occur on plant and animal remains of all types and in most environments. Symbiotic associations with plants or animals are not uncommon in this group.

The true fungi have been estimated to number above 200,000 species, and at the present time 1,000 to 2,000 new species are described annually. Although more than 9,000 genera have been described, only half this number are considered valid. The group is sufficiently large and heterogeneous to present formidable problems in classification. No completely acceptable classification system is currently available for the entire group.

31

CLASS PHYCOMYCETES

The class Phycomycetes includes those fungi thought to be the most primitive in the Eumycota. They are relatively simple in structure and many have **flagellated** reproductive stages. The phycomycetes occur in both aquatic and terrestrial habitats, either as parasites or as saprobes. Some parasitize small animals, fungi, algae, or other plants; others form symbiotic associations with plants or animals. Most are saprobes and grow upon dead plant or animal remains.

The simplest phycomycetous thallus is globose or ovoid and is uninuculeate. It may lack a rigid wall during early stages of development, although one is present at maturity. The entire protoplast of such a thallus is eventually converted into one or more reproductive cells. Fungi with this type of development are said to be **holocarpic.** If the thallus has distinct assimilative (somatic) and reproductive portions, it is termed **eucarpic.** In those producing filaments—i.e., **hyphae—septa** are typically lacking. False septa, growing from the periphery inward and not completely separating portions of the hyphae, occur in some species; in these, reproductive structures are always separated from the remainder of the thallus by complete septa. The rigid walls of phycomycetous fungi contain either chitin or cellulose or, in some species, both of these substances.

Some simple eucarpic forms consist of a globose portion, the cyst, plus a few **enucleate** root-like filaments called **rhizoids;** the latter anchor the thallus and absorb materials from the host or substrate. Some of the highly developed parasites of vascular plants produce absorptive structures, called **haustoria,** which penetrate cells of the host.

ASEXUAL REPRODUCTION

Asexual reproduction in most phycomycetes is by means of **sporangiospores.** Sporangiospores are called **planospores** if motile, **aplanospores** if nonmotile. The planospores are naked, uninucleate in most instances, and do not enlarge and undergo fission as do the myxamoebae of myxomycetes; aplanospores contain one or more nuclei and possess rigid walls. During formation of sporangiospores, progressive cleavage of the sporangial protoplast occurs, and the bits of protoplast become spores.

Planospores, frequently called **zoospores,** are important in determining the relationships of fungus groups. Those species producing motile spores are thought to be the most primitive of fungi. Separation of this group into various taxa is based upon flagella number, type, and position on the zoospore. Although fungal zoospores usually swim by flagellar movement, most are also capable of amoeboid movement.

If the zoospore has a single flagellum, it is inserted either anteriorly or posteriorly (Fig. 4–1A, B); in biflagellate zoospores (Fig. 4–1C, D), the flagella are anterior or lateral. Flagella of fungi are of two types: in the **tinsel** type, lateral hair-like processes, called "flimmers" or **mastigonemes,** form two rows along the flagellum (Fig. 4–1B); in the second type, called a **whiplash** flagellum (Fig. 4–1A), mastigonemes are lacking and the flagellum resembles an old-fashioned buggy whip. Biflagellate fungal cells have one tinsel type flagellum and one whiplash flagellum.

Flagella of fungi studied by electron microscopy consist of 11 strands (Fig. 4–1E), arranged in the nine-plus-two pattern characteristic of motile cells of all organisms other than bacteria. At the base of the flagellum there is a small "basal granule" or **blepharoplast** (Fig. 4–1B), which is double in zoospores of some uniflagellate fungi. This has been interpreted as indicating that uniflagellate forms arose from biflagellate ancestors through the loss of one flagellum. The blepharoplast is connected to the nucleus by a thread-like structure, the **rhizoplast,** or it may be connected to a body closely associated with the nucleus. Various other structures have been found in fungal zoospores and probably are important in determining relationships within the group.

Aplanospores possess one or more nuclei and are surrounded by rigid walls. They are dispersed by insects, water, or wind. In addition

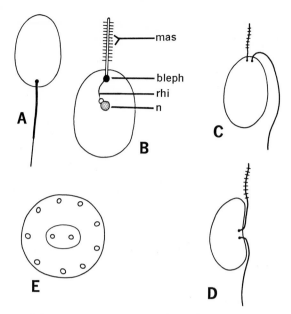

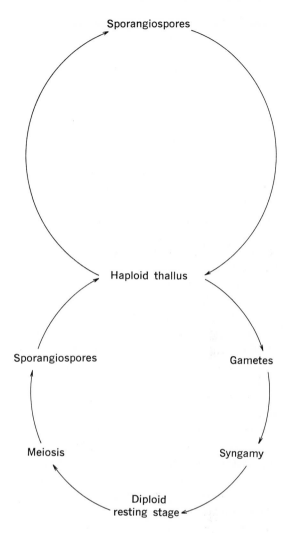

FIGURE 4–1   Motile cells of fungi. A, uniflagellate with posterior whiplash flagellum; B, uniflagellate with anterior tinsel-type flagellum (*mas,* mastigonemes; *bleph,* blepharoplast; *rhi,* rhizoplast; *n,* nucleus); C, D, anterior and lateral insertion of flagella in biflagellate cells; E, transverse section through flagellum showing 9 + 2 arrangement of strands.

to sporangiospores, or in place of them, some of the higher phycomycetes reproduce by means of other types of asexual spores.

SEXUAL REPRODUCTION

In many primitive phycomycetes, sexual reproduction is by fusion of motile **isogametes.** Motile gametes, or **planogametes,** are similar in form and structure to zoospores of the same species. **Anisogamy,** in which the fusing planogametes differ only in size, is known in the genus *Allomyces.* Oogamy—or fusion of a small motile sperm with a large nonmotile egg (**aplanogamete**)—is known only in the order Monoblepharidales, but sexual reproduction in the Oomycetidae is similar. Here, nuclei in the **antheridium** function as gametes and are carried to the "eggs" by means of fertilization tubes that develop after contact of the male and female **gametangia.** Sexual reproduction occurs in some phycomycetes through the fu-

FIGURE 4–2   Life history typical of many phycomycetes.

sion of whole protoplasts—i.e., by **conjugation,** or **gametangial copulation.** In most conjugating forms, the gametangia are not distinguishable as male and female but are of similar form and often the same size. The gametangia are unicellular in all of these types of sexual reproduction.

Life histories of these simple fungi vary considerably among species. A few have an alternation of relatively equal—i.e., **isomorphic**—generations, but in most this is not the case. Perhaps the commonest life-cycle type is that in which the greater portion is haploid, the resting spore or sporangium being the only diploid cell (Fig. 4–2). Asexual reproduction may be the predominant means of maintenance and dispersal of a species. This is the only known type of reproduction in many species.

SUBCLASS CHYTRIDIOMYCETIDAE

ORDER CHYTRIDIALES. In structure, the Chytridiales, or chytrids, are among the simplest fungi. They parasitize various small organisms or live as saprobes on cellulose, chitin, or other substrates. All are thought to have chitin as a wall constituent, although cellulose has also been reported in some.

Asexual reproduction of chytrids is by means of planospores. Sexual reproduction, which has been observed in a small number of species and is varied in these, is by fusion of motile isogametes in some, in others by copulation of gametangia. The zygote develops into a thick-walled resting spore or sporangium, within which meiosis occurs. Haploid zoospores are released upon germination of this resting structure.

The chytrid zoospore moves by means of a posterior whiplash flagellum. Its protoplast is roughly globose, although this shape changes during amoeboid movement. Zoospores of some species have a conspicuous oil globule adjacent to the nucleus; in others, there is a nuclear cap composed of ribonucleic acid. The nuclear cap is a crescent-shaped body lying adjacent to the nucleus and partially encircling it. The zoospore, motile for a time, eventually settles on a suitable substrate where it encysts and develops in one of several ways (the examples discussed indicate some of these).

Species of *Olpidium* (Fig. 4–3) parasitize many types of plants and animals. The encysted zoospores of this genus produce a minute infection tube that penetrates the host cell wall; the protoplast then passes through this tube into the host cell, where it absorbs nutrient from the host, enlarges, and secretes a wall. Absorption of materials apparently occurs over the entire surface of the protoplast. At maturity, the globose or elongate thallus is

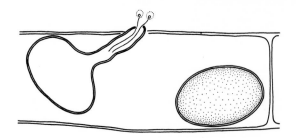

FIGURE 4–3   *Olpidium endogenum.* Two thalli in cell of filamentous green alga (*Spirogyra*), ×1,075. Cell on left has produced discharge tube through which planospores are escaping.

transformed into a zoosporangium. A discharge tube develops and penetrates the host cell wall. The zoospores then escape the infected cell through a pore at the tip of the tube.

Thick-walled resting spores, characteristic of a number of species of *Olpidium,* are assumed to result from isogamy, although syngamy has been observed in only a few species. In those where syngamy is known, cells indistinguishable from zoospores function as gametes. Following syngamy, the motile zygote, called a **planozygote,** infects a host cell, as with the zoospores. However, in this instance a thick-walled resting sporangium develops, from which haploid zoospores are eventually released.

Synchytrium and *Micromyces* are similar to *Olpidium* in many respects. *Synchytrium* parasitizes various vascular plants, whereas *Micromyces* is found in algal cells. Thalli of both are holocarpic and endobiotic—i.e., entirely within the host cells. Infection by *Synchytrium* results in considerable enlargement of the host cell (Fig. 4–4A, B). At maturity, the uninucleate protoplast is bounded by a slightly thickened wall. Upon germinating, its protoplast is extruded and a number of mitotic divisions of the nucleus follow; the protoplast divides into several multinucleate segments (Fig. 4–4C, D), each of which functions as a sporangium or gametangium. Zoospores are produced during the growing season of the host, but late in the season the motile cells function as gametes. Zoospores swim about and then reinfect the host plant.

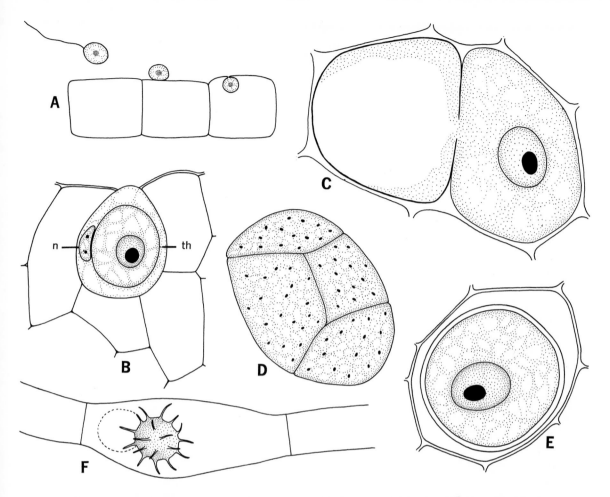

FIGURE 4–4   A–E, *Synchytrium*. A, infection of host epidermal cell by zoospore; B, enlarged thallus of *Synchytrium* in cell of host (*th,* thallus of *Synchytrium; n,* nucleus of host cell), ×1,000; C, extrusion of protoplast prior to formation of sporangia, ×1,000; D, division of protoplast nucleus and cytoplasm (each multinucleate segment functions as a sporangium), ×1,100; E, thick-walled resting sporangium, ×1,100. F, thin-walled sporangium of *Micromyces,* the protoplast of which has been extruded, ×875.

Gametes of *Synchytrium* are indistinguishable from the zoospores in form and in production. Environmental conditions apparently determine whether the cells function as spores or as gametes. Following syngamy, the planozygote infects a host cell. The diploid thallus resembles the haploid thallus in form, but the host's reaction to it is different. In the presence of the diploid thallus, host cells surrounding the infected one are stimulated to divide to a greater extent. Because of this, the diploid *Synchytrium* cell becomes rather deeply embedded in the host, where it forms a thick-walled resting sporangium (Fig. 4–4E) that is the overwintering stage.

Micromyces infections in algal cells cause some enlargement but no noticeable increase in cell division (Fig. 4–4F). The thallus of *Micromyces* is spiny.

Species of *Chytridium* (Fig. 4–5) parasitize fresh-water and marine algae, pollen grains, protozoa, or other fungi; or they live as saprobes on these substrates. The encysted zoospore produces a penetration tube through the wall of the host, as in *Olpidium*. However, the protoplast remains within the cyst. A branching rhizoidal system develops at the tip of the penetration tube, or, in some species, the tube simply elongates and branches are not produced. The rhizoidal system is thought to function in absorption, whereas the cyst enlarges and eventually functions as a sporangium. The discharge pore in this genus is covered by a minute lid, or **operculum** which is dehiscent at maturity of the zoospores, allowing their escape. Sexual reproduction has been reported in a single species of *Chytridium,* although resting spores have been observed in many.

All of the chytrids previously discussed have only one center of development. Some chytrids produce a more extensive thallus with several sporangia, as in species of *Cladochytrium.* They form an extensive system of rhizoids embedded in dead plant materials in water (Fig. 4–6). Spindle-shaped swellings, often once-septate, are produced here and there in the rhizoidal system. Both thin-walled sporangia and thick-walled resting sporangia are formed. Sexual reproduction is as yet unknown in the genus.

ORDER BLASTOCLADIALES. Members of the Blastocladiales have uniflagellate zoospores resembling those of the Chytridiales. These fungi produce thick-walled resting sporangia, the walls of which are pitted and mostly brown or brownish. Where studied, the brownish pigments have been found to belong to the melanin group. In contrast to the Chytridiales, resting spores in this order are not the immediate products of syngamy.

Some Blastocladiales produce simple thalli as in the chytrids, but others are **mycelial** forms. Most possess rigid chitinous walls. However, species of the genus *Coelomomyces* parasitize mosquito larvae and produce a **dichotomously** branched thallus, which lacks a cell wall and has been compared to the myxomycete plasmodium. Thick-walled resting sporangia of the type characteristic of the order are formed at maturity.

Sexual reproduction in the Blastocladiales is by fusion of motile iso- or anisogametes. The most intensively studied species in this

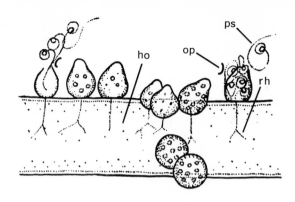

FIGURE 4–5   *Chytridium sphaerocarpum* growing on hypha of *Achlya,* ×1,000. *ps,* planospore; *op,* operculum; *rh,* rhizoid; *ho,* host hypha. (After Sparrow from *Journal Linnean Society* (Botany), 50, p. 446, 1936, and with permission of University of Michigan Press.)

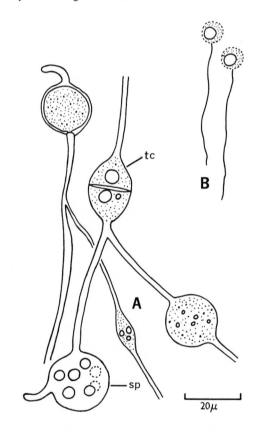

FIGURE   4–6   *Cladochytrium   aurantiacum,* ×800. A, portions of two thalli bearing sporangia (*sp*) and turbinate cells (*tc*). B, zoospores. (After Richards with permission of *Transactions of British Mycological Society.*)

order are those of the genus *Allomyces*. Some of these have life histories involving an alternation of isomorphic generations, a type of life cycle not common in fungi.

The thallus of *Allomyces arbuscula* (Fig. 4–7) is filamentous with a series of rhizoids at its base, the young hyphae being dichotomously branched. On mature diploid thalli two types of sporangia are formed: thin-walled sporangia and thick-walled resting sporangia. The thin-walled sporangia produce zoospores that are released through one or more exit **papillae;** these zoospores are diploid and give rise to new sporangium-bearing thalli. Meiosis takes place within the thick-walled resting sporangia; upon

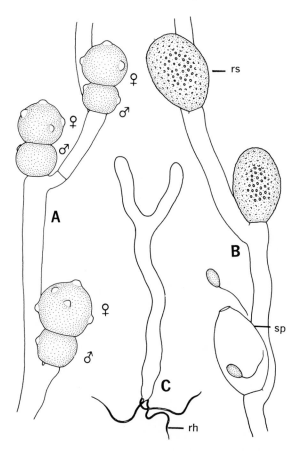

A

B

C

— rs

— sp

— rh

FIGURE 4–7   *Allomyces arbuscula.* A, portion of a haploid thallus bearing gametangia, ×475. B, portion of a diploid thallus bearing resting sporangia (*rs*) and a thin-walled sporangium (*sp*), ×475. C, young thallus showing rhizoids (*rh*) and dichotomous branching typical of both haploid and diploid thalli, ×960.

germinating, these release zoospores that develop into haploid gamete-bearing thalli. The latter resemble the diploid thallus in all gross characteristics, but they produce male and female gametangia.

The resting sporangia of *Allomyces* require a period of maturation following their formation. They are more resistant to drying and high temperatures than are thin-walled sporangia, gametangia, or mycelium. This fact is made use of in obtaining cultures of the haploid gamete-bearing thalli in those species that have an alternation of isomorphic generations. If cultures containing the resting sporangia are dried at 30°–40° C for 24 hours, only the resistant sporangia survive. Cultures containing only the haploid, gamete-bearing thalli will develop if these are then placed on a suitable medium. Undoubtedly the resistant structures are important in the survival of *Allomyces* in nature. Most of the species of this genus inhabit soil or water of warmer regions, especially in the tropics.

In *A. arbuscula,* the orange male gametangium is borne just below the slightly larger and colorless female gametangium. Both male and female gametangia release their planogametes through one or more exit papillae. The gametes are anisogamous, the "female" being somewhat larger but morphologically similar to the "male." They copulate in pairs, forming a biflagellate planozygote that swims for a time and then germinates to produce a new diploid, spore-bearing thallus. The female gametes produce a hormone called sirenin that attracts male gametes. The chemical nature of this substance has not yet been determined.

In the related genera *Blastocladia* and *Blastocladiella,* production of resting sporangia can be induced in culture. If cultures of one species of *Blastocladia* are grown in an atmosphere high in carbon dioxide (99.5 per cent), resting sporangia develop. None occur under ordinary culture conditions, although they are formed together with thin-walled sporangia in nature. Addition of bicarbonate to cultures of *Blastocladiella* induces production of resting sporangia almost to the exclusion of thin-walled sporangia.

SUBCLASS HYPHOCHYTRIDIOMYCETIDAE

ORDER HYPHOCHYTRIALES. These are simple forms, parallel in structure to the Chytridiales. Like the Chytridiales, they produce uniflagellate zoospores, but the flagellum is anterior (Fig. 4–1B). Furthermore, it is a tinsel flagellum rather than the whiplash type found in all chytrids.

Early development from zoospores may be similar to the Chytridiales. Both chitin and cellulose have been found in walls of some species. Zoospores mature either in the sporangium or after discharge of the sporangial protoplast. Resting spores have been noted in a number of the hyphochytridiomycetes, but their origin is known only in *Anisolpidium ectocarpi.* Syngamy in this species is dependent upon the infection of a single host cell by two planospores. As in *Olpidium,* the planospores encyst on the surface of the host and produce a small infection tube. Following this, the protoplast of the cyst is discharged into the host cell through the tube. If two such protoplasts come together, they fuse, forming a zygote. A thick-walled resting spore, developing from the zygote, germinates by the production of a discharge tube, through which anteriorly uniflagellate planospores are released.

SUBCLASS OOMYCETIDAE

ORDER SAPROLEGNIALES. Although "water molds" is often used to designate certain members of this order, this term is misleading, since many other fungi grow in aquatic habitats. Furthermore, many of the saprolegniaceous fungi can be isolated as readily from certain soils as from water.

The zoospores of this group are biflagellate (Fig. 4–1C, D). The flagella are equal or unequal in length; one is a tinsel type, the other a whiplash. The zoospores produced in the sporangium are **primary zoospores** and their flagella are anterior. If the primary spores are released from the sporangium, they swim about for a time and then encyst. Each cyst formed in this way later releases a laterally biflagellate zoospore called a **secondary zoospore.** The primary zoospore is more or less pyriform; the secondary spore is commonly reniform. The secondary zoospores are much more durable and vigorous swimmers than are the primary. Secondary spores often encyst one or more times, but when these cysts germinate they give rise to the same type of zoospore (i.e., secondary). The tinsel flagellum is directed anteriorly and the whiplash flagellum trails in both spore types.

In the Saprolegniales, a series of simple forms parallels those in the Hyphochytriales and Chytridiales. Only the more advanced members (Saprolegniaceae) of the order are discussed here.

Saprolegnia (Fig. 4–8A–D) and its relatives occur in fresh water and in soil. Most are saprobes, although a few species are weak parasites of aquatic animals and their eggs, or of roots of higher plants. They possess an extensive coenocytic mycelium, the walls of which contain cellulose. Reproductive structures and injured portions of hyphae are cut off by complete septa. Sporangia are produced abundantly and are typically elongate and of about the same diameter as the hyphae on which they are found. Cleavage of the multinucleate sporangial protoplast is followed by development of primary zoospores. In *Saprolegnia,* these spores are released through a terminal pore in the sporangial wall and they swim about for a time. Then they settle down and encyst, later germinating to produce secondary zoospores. In *Achlya* (Fig. 4–8E), primary zoospores are released from the sporangium but encyst just outside the pore. *Dictyuchus* (Fig. 4–8F) derives its name from the netted appearance of its sporangia. This appearance results from the encystment of primary zoospores within the sporangium. Each encysted spore produces a short germ tube through which a secondary zoospore is released. In these genera, the secondary spores swim about for a time, then settle down and encyst again. A new filamentous thallus is developed upon germination of the encysted spore.

The saprolegniaceous fungi produce distinguishable male and female gametangia (Fig. 4–9A–C) but no motile gametes. Female gametangia, called **oogonia,** are borne on short lateral branches of the main hyphae. The oogonia are globose and contain the "eggs" or **oospheres.** Male filaments may arise from the same hyphae or thallus, or from different thalli. At maturity, one or more antheridia lie in contact with the oogonium. From each anther-idium a simple or branched **fertilization tube** develops and grows to an oosphere. Nuclei are transferred from the antheridium to the oospheres and bring about fertilization. Following fertilization, each zygote develops into a thick-walled resting spore called an **oospore.** This type of sexual reproduction is referred to as **gametangial contact.**

In certain species of *Achlya*—e.g., *A. bisexualis* and *A. ambisexualis*—antheridia and oogonia usually are borne on separate thalli. Such thalli will not produce sexual structures if they are grown separately, but they do so when grown together in compatible pairs. J. R. Raper has studied reproduction in these species and has noted that a series of distinguishable stages can be observed in the reproductive process. These are: (1) production of antheridial filaments on the male thallus; (2) production of oogonial initials on the female thallus; (3) growth of antheridial filaments toward the oogonial initials and delimitation of the antheridia after contact of initials; (4)

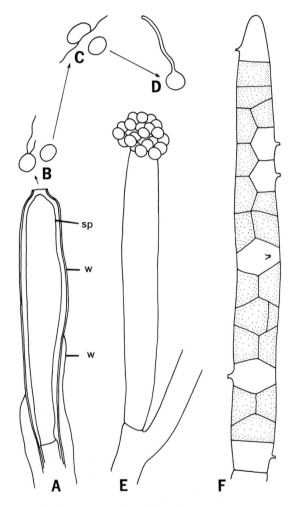

FIGURE 4–8   A-D, *Saprolegnia.* A, sporangium (*sp*) ensheathed by walls (*w*) of previously formed sporangia, ×415; B, primary planospore and cyst, ×415; C, secondary planospore and cyst, ×415; D, germination of encysted secondary planospore, ×415. E, sporangium of *Achlya* with apical cluster of encysted primary spores, ×415. F, sporangium of *Dictyuchus* containing encysted primary spores, ×860 (a few of the encysted cells have released secondary planospores).

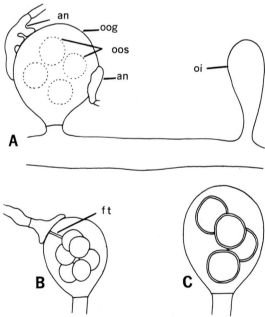

FIGURE 4–9   Sexual reproduction in *Saprolegnia.* A, oogonium (*oog*) and two antheridia (*an*), (*oos,* oospheres), ×535; an oogonial initial (*oi*) is present at the right. B, mature oogonium with fertilization tube (*ft*) extending from the antheridium to one oosphere, ×535. C, oogonium containing oospores, ×535.

TABLE 4–1

THE EFFECTS OF HORMONES PRODUCED BY THALLI OF *ACHLYA*

HORMONE	PRODUCED BY:	ACTION
A, A²	♀ ♂ Thallus	Initiation of antheridial filaments on thallus
A¹, A³	♂ Thallus	A¹ augments the action of A and A²; A³ tends to suppress this action
B	♂ Thallus (after stimulation by A's)	Development of oogonial initials on ♀ thallus
C	Oogonial initials	Regulates directional growth of antheridial filaments; delimitation of antheridium after contact
D	Antheridia	Delimitation of oogonium and differentiation of oospheres

delimitation of the oogonium and differentiation of oospheres; and (5) production of fertilization tubes and migration of antheridial nuclei through these to the oospheres.

Raper performed a series of experiments demonstrating that this regular sequence is controlled by a number of hormones. These are produced by the two thalli or by the antheridial and oogonial initials. The designation of the hormones, the place of production, and their action are indicated in Table 4–1. The process is shown diagrammatically in Figure 4–10. Further studies have demonstrated that development of sexual structures is regulated in a similar manner in species bearing both antheridia and oogonia on the same thallus.

The oospore undergoes a long resting period; the factors responsible for inducing germination are unknown. A short filament is produced upon germination of the oospore, and a typical sporangium is formed at the tip of this filament. Meiosis was long thought to occur at the time of oospore germination. However, recent studies indicate that meiosis occurs in the gametangia in this order and in the Peronosporales.

ORDER PERONOSPORALES. The sexual reproduction found in the Saprolegniaceae is also characteristic of fungi in the order Peronosporales. In the latter group, only one

oosphere is formed in each oogonium, but the process is otherwise the same. The simpler members of this order produce zoosporangia that differ little from those of the Saprolegniaceae. However, sporangia of the more advanced species included in the Albuginaceae and Peronosporaceae are quite different. All species in these two families are obligate parasites of vascular plants. Their hyphae are intercellular, producing special absorptive branches or haustoria, which penetrate the cells of the host (Fig. 4–11A).

Asexual reproduction in the Peronosporaceae and Albuginaceae is by means of sporangia borne on special branches, the **sporangiophores.** The sporangium, deciduous at maturity, is transported by wind. The sporangia of most genera may form either zoospores or a hypha upon germinating, but some forms have lost the ability to produce motile cells.

The sporangiophore is of determinate growth and relatively regular in form. Genera of the Peronosporaceae are distinguished on the basis of these structures. *Albugo* (Fig. 4–11B–E), the only genus in the Albuginaceae, produces sporangia in chains.

Many economically important plant **pathogens** are found in the Peronosporales. One of the most destructive of these is *Phytophthora infestans* (Pythiaceae) (Fig. 4–11F), which causes late blight in potato; this species caused

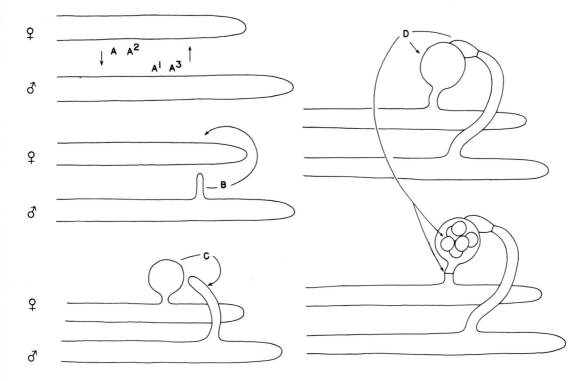

FIGURE 4–10   Sequence showing regulation of development in *Achlya*. Starting at left, interaction of hormones A and A^2, produced by female thallus, and A^1 and A^3, produced by male thallus, initiates development of antheridial filament. Production of hormone B by male filament initiates development of oogonial initial. Hormone C, produced by oogonial initial, controls directional growth of antheridial filament and delimitation of antheridium. Hormone D, produced by antheridium, controls delimitation of oogonium and development of oospheres.

the complete destruction of potato crops in Ireland and other areas resulting in the Irish famine of 1845. Another species, *Plasmopara viticola* (Fig. 4–11G), causes a serious disease of the grape.

SUBCLASS ZYGOMYCETIDAE

The remaining Phycomycetes are characterized by production of **zygospores** formed by gametangial copulation, a process involving fusion of gametangia. Unlike those of the Saprolegniales, the two fusing gametangia are typically identical in form and often in size. Asexual reproduction occurs by either sporangiospores (aplanospores) or by **conidia**—the term applied to many types of asexual spores (but not sporangiospores). A conidium is essentially a separable portion of a hypha or of a special branch, the **conidiophore.** Sporangia of

the Zygomycetidae are borne on sporangiophores. No flagellated cells of any type are produced in this subclass.

Most species form an extensive mycelium, but some symbiotic and parasitic species have thalli consisting of a single hyphal filament. The hyphae are coenocytic in most zygomycetes and the cell walls contain chitin.

The saprobic zygomycetes are common on decaying materials, in soil, dung, and other habitats. A few are obligate parasites of related zygomycetes or of small animals such as protozoa and insects, or of vascular plants. Species sometimes placed in a separate subclass, the Trichomycetidae, are found in the digestive tract of arthropods.

ORDER MUCORALES.   Most of the Mucorales are saprobes abundant in soil, dung, decay-

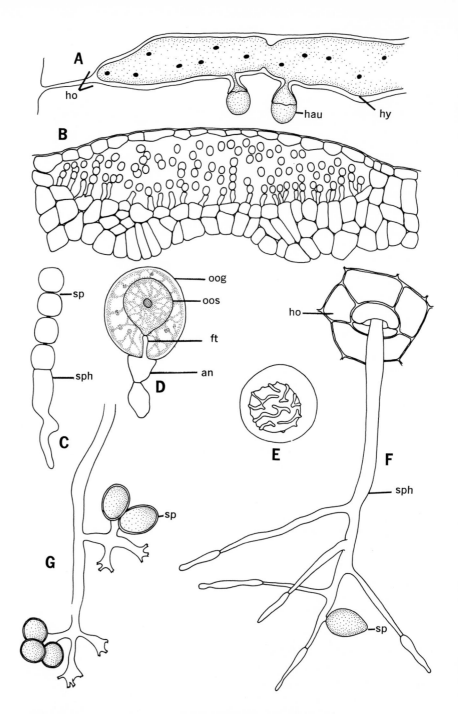

FIGURE 4–11   A, haustoria of downy mildew (*hau,* haustorium; *hy,* intercellular hypha; *ho,* host cells), ×1,080. B–E, *Albugo candida.* B, section through infected leaf, showing cluster of sporangiophores and sporangia under epidermis, ×215; C, enlarged sporangiophore (*sph*) bearing chain of sporangia (*sp*), ×500; D, sexual reproduction, ×500 (*oog,* oogonium; *oos,* oosphere; *an,* antheridium; *ft,* fertilization tube); E, mature oospore, ×500. F, sporangiophore of *Phytophthora infestans,* ×590 (*sph,* sporangiophore; *sp,* sporangium; *ho,* host epidermis). G, sporangiophore and sporangia of *Plasmopara viticola,* ×585.

ing plant and animal materials, etc. Certain species can grow at temperatures near or below freezing and are often found on stored meat. Others are weak parasites of stored fruits and vegetables. Some species parasitize green plants, animals, or even other mucoraceous fungi, and several have been reported to cause fatal infections in humans.

In this group, the mycelium usually consists of both aerial and submerged hyphae. The hyphae are typically coenocytic, but reproductive structures are cut off by crosswalls. Crosswalls are regularly present in some species, and the cells of most such forms are multinucleate.

Sporangia containing numerous spores are found in the species considered most primitive. More advanced species have one- to few-spored sporangia or **sporangiola.**

The terms **heterothallism** and **homothallism** were first used by the geneticist Blakeslee in his work with the Mucoraceae. There are two morphologically indistinguishable types of thalli in each heterothallic species. These thalli, designated as + and −, reproduce only by asexual means when grown separately. However, if two such thalli are grown together, they produce gametangia on aerial branches. The + and − gametangia copulate, forming a large multinucleate cell, the **coenozygote,** that is transformed into a thick-walled resting spore or **zygospore.** Sexual reproduction in the homothallic species occurs in a similar manner, but the copulating gametangia are produced on branches of a single thallus. Thus, in homothallic forms, all thalli are of a single type with respect to sexual reproduction.

The fusing gametangia of both heterothallic and homothallic species are alike in form and size in most instances. However, in some, such as *Zygorrhynchus,* the gametangia are unequal.

The species of *Mucor* are common on dung, in soil, and in other habitats. They produce an extensive coenocytic mycelium, much of which is submerged in the substratum. Short segments of the hyphae sometimes become delimited by crosswalls and may be transformed into **chlamydospores** (Fig. 4–12A).

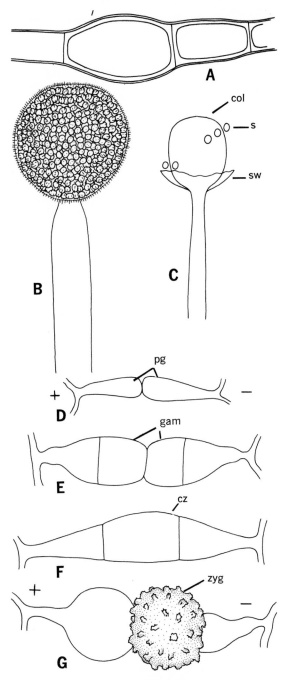

FIGURE 4–12   A, chlamydospores in hypha of *Mucor,* ×2,250. B–G, *Mucor mucedo.* B, portion of sporangiophore bearing mature sporangium, ×835; C, sporangium after escape of spores, ×900 (*col,* columella; *s,* spore; *sw,* collar-like remnant of sporangial wall); D–G, sexual reproduction between + and − thalli, ×205 (*pg,* progametangia; *gam,* gametangia; *cz,* coenozygote; *zyg,* zygospore).

These are thick-walled, nondeciduous spores, which can be either **intercalary** or terminal in position. They are more resistant to adverse conditions than are the unaltered hyphal strands, and they can germinate to form a new mycelium. Both the chlamydospores and the unaltered hyphae often contain numerous large oil droplets.

Sporangiophores generally grow toward light; in other words, they exhibit positive **phototropism.** At the apex of the sporangiophore, a sporangium forms and becomes separated from the sporangiophore by a bulbous septum, the **columella.** Within the multinucleate sporangium, the protoplast divides into numerous one- to few-nucleate segments. A wall is formed around each segment, transforming it into a sporangiospore.

When the sporangium is mature, the spores are released in one of two ways. In most species of *Mucor,* such as *M. mucedo* (Fig. 4–12B–G), the sporangial wall deliquesces and the spores are then surrounded by a slimy drop of liquid. These spores are carried away by rain water or by insects. In other species of *Mucor,* the sporangial wall, which is fragile and dry at maturity, cracks and falls away, exposing the dry spores to air currents.

The genus *Mucor* contains both homothallic and heterothallic species; *Mucor mucedo* is heterothallic. As hyphae of + and − strains approach one another, branches called **zygophores** are formed (Fig. 4–12D–G). These secrete volatile substances (hormones) which apparently control directional growth of the zygophores toward one another. The tips of the zygophore branches contact end to end and are called **progametangia.** A wall is then formed in each progametangium, separating a cell at its tip. This cell, called the gametangium, soon becomes confluent with its mate and the resulting single multinucleate cell is called a coenozygote. Within it, pairs of + and − nuclei fuse (**karyogamy**) and, within a week, undergo reduction-division. A thick dark wall is formed around the coenozygote, transforming it into a resting spore or zygospore. Germination of the zygospore typically results in formation of a short sporangiophore and spo-

rangium containing haploid sporangiospores.

Conjugation in *Mucor genevensis,* a homothallic species, occurs in much the same way (Fig. 4–13A, B). However, the conjugating branches in this species arise from a single thallus.

Rhizopus stolonifer (Fig. 4–14A, B), commonly called black bread mold, is similar to species of *Mucor* in most respects. It produces aerial hyphae that function like the stolons of strawberries. These, too, are called **stolons** and grow from place to place over the substrate. At points of contact with the substrate, root-like rhizoidal systems are formed. These rhizoids provide anchorage and above them clusters of sporangiophores and sporangia are formed. This species frequently attacks stored fruits, especially the more succulent ones such as strawberries and peaches.

Sexual reproduction in the heterothallic *Rhizopus stolonifer* is similar to that described for *Mucor hiemalis.* However, in this instance meiosis does not occur during the early development of the zygospore, but at the time of its germination. This may occur several months after the zygospore has formed. In one species of *Phycomyces,* both nuclear fission and meiosis are delayed until just before germination of the zygospore.

In various heterothallic mucoraceous fungi, the young sporangia produced by germinating zygospores may contain either + or − nuclei, or both. These are incorporated into

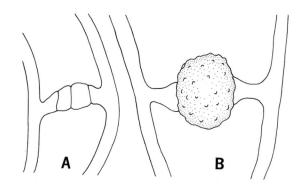

FIGURE 4–13 A, B *Mucor genevensis;* zygospore formation, ×335 (conjugating gametangia of this species arise from different hyphae of same thallus).

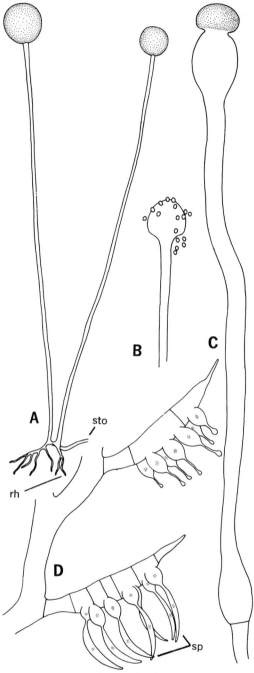

sporangiospores that can give rise to the two types of mycelia.

The species of *Pilobolus* (Fig. 4–14C), in the family Pilobolaceae, grow on dung of herbivores. Their sporangia have thick cutinous walls, and the entire sporangium is forcibly shot from the sporangiophore at maturity. The sporangium adheres to objects such as stems or leaves of green plants, where it may be eaten by an herbivore and pass through the animal's digestive tract. The spores germinate following excretion.

Coemansia (Fig. 4–14D) and its relatives (Kickxellaceae) are characterized by production of one-spored sporangia—i.e., sporangiola. Certain forms, such as *Blakeslea trispora* (Choanephoraceae), produce sporangia intermediate between those of *Coemansia* and those of the Mucoraceae. These contain only a few spores. Some biologists think that conidia may have evolved through reduction of sporangia to single-spored structures. However, those with a single spore still retain the sporangial wall.

Although asexual reproductive structures of the Mucorales seem extremely varied, sexual reproduction is more uniform. In some forms, such as *Zygorrhynchus* (Fig. 4–15A, B), the conjugating progametangia are of unequal size. The zygospore of others develops in a cell formed to one side of the two gametangia; in others, a sterile mantle of hyphae is produced around the conjugating filaments.

OTHER ZYGOMCETES. Many of the remaining zygomycetes are associated in some way with animals. Species of *Entomophthora* (Order Entomophthorales), for example, are insect parasites. *E. muscae* (Fig. 4–16) infects the common housefly, growing within the body and assimilating all of the proteinaceous material there. Conidiophores then grow out between segments of the host's exoskeleton and the conidia are shot from the conidiophores at maturity. The infected flies are often found adhering to windows or walls and are surrounded by a whitish halo of spores.

Zoopage and *Endocochlus* (order Zoo-

FIGURE 4–14   A, sporangiophores and sporangia of *Rhizopus stolonifer*, ×60 (*rh*, rhizoids; *sto*, stolon); B, sporangiophore and columella after rupture of sporangial wall, ×160. C, mature sporangium and sporangiophore of *Pilobolus*, ×130. D, portion of sporangiophore of *Coemansia* with two sporangium-bearing branches, ×1,575 (the lowermost branch bears a number of one-spored sporangia, *sp*).

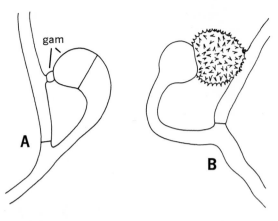

FIGURE 4–15   Conjugation in *Zygorrhynchus moelleri*, a homothallic species. A, early stage, ×520; note unequal size of gametangia (*gam*) and origin of these from single branch. B, mature zygospore, ×520.

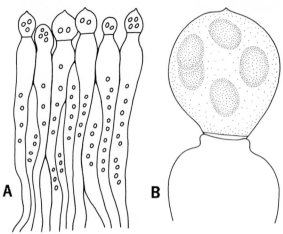

FIGURE 4–16   *Entomophthora muscae*. A, cluster of conidiophores bearing conidia, ×625. B, apex of conidiophore with single conidium, ×3,000.

pagales) capture protozoa and other small animals and are obligate parasites of these organisms. Asexual reproduction is by means of conidia and either these or the hyphae are provided with adhesive surfaces. Amoebae contacting these surfaces adhere firmly and are penetrated by absorptive hyphae.

RELATIONSHIPS OF THE PHYCOMYCETES

The class Phycomycetes is sometimes divided into several classes, including Chytridiomycetes, Hyphochytridiomycetes, Oomycetes, or Dimastigomycetes. Division in this manner results partly from emphasis on flagellar structure and arrangement in those forms with motile cells. Each of the groups producing flagellated cells is thus placed in a separate class; their similarities are attributed to convergent evolution. One might carry this concept to its logical conclusion, treating each group as a separate division. However, it is possible that the forms with uniflagellate motile cells have evolved from biflagellate ancestors. Until more factual information is available concerning the structure of the motile cells and other features of these fungi, division of the class Phycomycetes into several classes (or divisions) is viewed by some as premature and possibly arbitrary.

One view, prevalent in the past and still held by some, is that the Phycomycetes evolved from algal ancestors. The basis for this concept lies in the similarity in form and in reproduction found in certain species of the two groups. For example, thalli of both *Saprolegnia* and *Vaucheria* (a yellow-green alga; see Chapter 13) are coenocytic and tubular; the sexual reproductive structures are also similar. Some think that these similarities are superficial and of little consequence, but recent studies have shown additional similarities in the ultrastructure of these organisms. However, with the possible exception of the biflagellate forms, the evidence now available does not indicate a close relationship between most phycomycetes and filamentous algae. Many mycologists feel that the phycomycetes arose from protozoalike ancestors. Amoeboid organisms reproducing by flagellated cells, the chrysomonads (see Chapter 10), and others have been suggested as the ancestral types from which the phycomycetes evolved.

CLASS ASCOMYCETES

The "sac" fungi or ascomycetes are a large and extremely varied group with sexual stages involving **ascus** and **ascospore** formation. The ascus, which may or may not be preceded by recognizable male and female structures, is the site of both karyogamy and meiosis. Ascospores develop following meiosis or, more commonly, after a mitotic division following meiosis. Asci are produced in complex structures called **ascocarps** or "fruiting bodies" in the more advanced ascomycetes.

Both filamentous and unicellular ascomycetes are known. They are most numerous in terrestrial habitats, but some occur in various aquatic environments. The terrestrial species grow on many substrates including wood, keratinic materials such as feathers, horn, and hair, or on dung, soil, and foods. A few are parasites of plants and animals, including man.

The simpler ascomycetes, including yeasts and related forms, are placed in the subclass Hemiascomycetidae. Many of these are unicellular, and their asci are not borne in ascocarps. The Euascomycetidae have filamentous thalli and all produce ascocarps.

SUBCLASS HEMIASCOMYCETIDAE

A few hemiascomycetes are parasitic, but most are saprobes. They are abundant in water and soil, on fruits, and in exudates from injured plants.

ORDER ASCOIDEALES. This order contains a few species found in plant exudates or on plants. *Ascoidea rubescens* grows in the "slime flux" oozing from wounds of trees and other woody plants. It produces a coarse mycelium that is septate and has multinucleate cells. The tips of some hyphae produce large conidia (Fig. 4–17A); on others the terminal cell becomes an ascus (Fig. 4–17B). Numerous derby-shaped ascospores develop and are released through rupture of the ascal apex. Growth of the hypha resumes and a new ascus is formed within the ruptured wall of the first. Because of this proliferative process, the bases of asci may be surrounded by the remnants of several old asci. Proliferation of this type is also found in zoosporangia of the water mold *Saprolegnia*. This and other characteristics

have led some to consider *Ascoidea* as a phycomycete and to refer to the asci as sporangia. Complete details of the life cycle in *Ascoidea* are not known.

Dipodascus uninucleatus (Fig. 4–17C–E) is a related form in which the life cycle has been elucidated. Here the hyphae are divided into uninucleate segments. Two adjacent cells of a hypha fuse and karyogamy

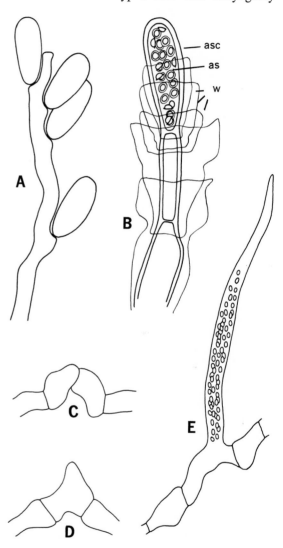

FIGURE 4–17   A, B, *Ascoidea rubescens*. A, conidia, ×865; B, ascus containing ascospores, ×575 (*asc*, ascus; *as*, ascospores; *w*, ensheathing walls of previously formed asci). C–E, *Dipodascus uninucleatus*. C, D, conjugation; C, ×2,080. D, ×1,500. E, mature ascus containing ascospores, ×1,500.

occurs. The cell expands into an elongate ascus within which meiosis is followed by a number of mitotic divisions. The numerous nuclei become incorporated into ascospores, which are later released through the ascus tip. The ascospores germinate by germ tubes.

ORDER ENDOMYCETALES. Filamentous and unicellular forms are included in this order. All the filamentous species have asci with eight or fewer ascospores; thus, they can be distinguished readily from the Ascoideales. However, the validity of such an arbitrary separation is questionable.

Within the Saccharomycetaceae are the simplest ascomycetes, the yeasts. These do not normally produce hyphae, although short filaments are formed under certain culture conditions. Because the production of hyphae is apparently a vestigial trait in yeasts, they are thought to have descended from filamentous ancestors. The cell walls of yeasts are composed of mannans, proteins, and other substances.

Since Pasteur discovered in the last century that yeasts and other microorganisms are responsible for fermentation, this group has been the subject of intensive study. A number of species, including *Saccharomyces cerevisiae* and *S. ellipsoideus,* can live anaerobically. They cannot completely respire sugars under these conditions, but convert them to ethyl alcohol and carbon dioxide. Beverage alcohol and, to a certain extent, industrial alcohol is produced in this way.

Saccharomyces cerevisiae, commonly called baker's yeast or brewer's yeast, might be considered one of the most important of domesticated organisms. In addition to alcohol, vitamin D, ephedrine, enzymes, and other substances are obtained from this species. A great deal of effort has gone into development or isolation of strains most suitable for each industrial process.

Asexual reproduction in *Saccharomyces cerevisiae,* as in most yeasts, is by **budding** (Fig. 4–18A). In this process, a small protuberance forms, expands, and usually separates from the mother cell. The nucleus under-

goes division during bud formation, and one daughter nucleus migrates into the developing bud. The nature of the nuclear division is still uncertain; the nuclear membrane apparently persists through the dividing process and individual chromosomes are not visible.

Saccharomyces cerevisiae is heterothallic, the two mating strains being referred to as α and a (or $+$ and $-$) types. Fusion of two haploid cells (**plasmogamy**) is soon followed by karyogamy. But budding of the diploid cell occurs and may continue indefinitely. Under certain conditions, a single diploid cell can function as an ascus. Meiosis occurs and four ascospores develop (Fig. 4–18B). There is no special dehiscence mechanism; the spores eventually are released through breakdown of the ascus wall. Buds are again produced when the ascospores germinate.

The haploid and diploid budding stages found in *Saccharomyces cerevisiae* are not present in all other yeasts. For example, in

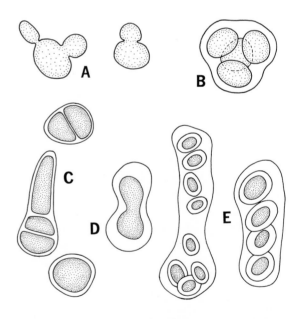

FIGURE 4–18   A, B, *Saccharomyces cerevisiae.* A, budding cells, ×3,500; B, mature ascus and ascospores, ×5,250. C–E, *Schizosaccharomyces octosporus.* C, vegetative cells, two of which are divided by crosswalls, ×2,300; D, young zygote formed through conjugation of two cells, ×2,300; E, mature asci and ascospores, ×2,300.

Saccharomycodes ludwigii conjugation occurs upon germination of the ascospores while they are still within the ascus; they then give rise to diploid buds. The life cycle of this species is thus diploid, except for the ascospore stage. Cells of *Schizosaccharomyces octosporus* (Fig. 4–18C–E) conjugate immediately before ascus formation and the diploid stage is limited to the zygote. The latter species reproduces asexually by fission of cells rather than by budding.

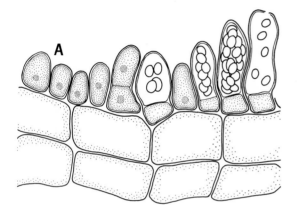

FIGURE 4–19 *Taphrina deformans.* A, section through infected peach leaf showing asci in various stages of development, ×895; B, peach leaves infected by *Taphrina deformans*, ×0.66 (note characteristic curling and distortion of leaf).

ORDER TAPHRINALES. This order includes a single genus, *Taphrina,* the species of which are parasites of vascular plants. *T. deformans,* causing peach leaf curl, is one of the common species (Fig. 4–19A, B). The hyphae of *T. deformans* penetrate between cells of the host leaves, twigs, and other parts. Their presence typically induces abnormal growth of host tissues. The hyphae bear asci at the surface of the portion of the host affected. In *Taphrina,* budding of the ascospores often takes place while they are still within the ascus. Apparently this is the normal means of ascospore germination in most species, and budding colonies can be maintained indefinitely in culture. Conjugation occurs by formation of short tubes, although fusion may not be followed immediately by karyogamy. The mycelium formed is septate, each cell containing a pair of sexually compatible nuclei. This **dikaryotic** condition is maintained until asci are produced. Karyogamy and meiosis occur within the ascus.

SUBCLASS EUASCOMYCETIDAE

The Euascomycetidae and many Basidiomycetes produce complex sporulating structures called **sporocarps.** In the Phycomycetes, union of two gametes or gamete nuclei is soon followed by the formation of a single diploid thallus or resting spore. However, in the Euascomycetidae and the Basidiomycetes, the equivalent of syngamy is divided into two phases. The first of these, called plasmogamy, results when the protoplasts of two cells fuse. This is followed by pairing but not fusion of compatible nuclei. The paired nuclei divide mitotically and hyphae with numerous binucleate cells are produced. This dikaryotic stage is of limited duration in the Euascomycetidae, occurring only at the time of ascocarp formation. In most Basidiomycetes, the dikaryotic mycelium may persist indefinitely. In both groups, many of the nuclear pairs eventually undergo karyogamy, or nuclear fusion. This constitutes the second phase of syngamy.

ASSIMILATIVE STAGE. All Euascomycetes have well-developed, filamentous assimilative stages. Their hyphae are regularly septate and chitin is present in all groups studied. Septa develop from the periphery inward but do not become complete. A small central pore remains and the cytoplasm is thus continuous from cell to cell (Fig. 4–20). Each cell contains from one to several nuclei; nuclei are sometimes carried from cell to cell, apparently by cytoplasmic streaming. The mycelium of most euascomycetes is embedded in the substratum, and only the reproductive structures are visible.

HETEROKARYOSIS AND PARASEXUALITY. If a hypha develops from a uninucleate spore, the nuclei present are all of the same genetic type; such a hypha or mycelium is **homokaryotic.** In contrast to this, two or more genetically distinct nuclei are present within **heterokaryotic** hyphae. Heterokaryosis is common in the higher fungi (ascomycetes and basidiomycetes), and can arise in several ways: (1) through fusion of hyphae of two distinct mycelia; following hyphal fusion, a nucleus may migrate from one thallus to another, increasing mitotically in the new mycelium; (2) through mutation in a homokaryotic mycelium.

Nuclear fusion or karyogamy occasionally takes place within heterokaryotic mycelia. This may involve either genetically identical nuclei or unlike nuclei. The diploid nuclei thus formed multiply side by side with haploid nuclei in the hyphae. During divisions of the diploid nuclei, recombination and segregation can occur through mitotic crossing-over. New nuclear types are produced in this way, and they too multiply in the mycelium. Haploidization of the diploid nuclei can also occur. If this takes place after mitotic crossing-over, new types of haploid nuclei are formed. The net result is a recombination of hereditary properties, as in sexual reproduction. However, there is no regular sequence of such events in time; all of these processes may be occurring in the mycelium at any given time. Furthermore (and unlike sexual reproduction) the processes do

FIGURE 4–20   Diagram of section through euascomycetous septum showing central pore.

not occur in specific parts of the thallus. Any of the nuclear types found in such thalli may be incorporated into conidia and released from the parent thallus. Mycelia developing from such conidia may differ genotypically from the parental types.

The terms **parasexuality** or the **parasexual cycle** are applied to the group of processes just described (heterokaryosis, karyogamy, recombination, and segregation through mitotic crossing-over, and haploidization). The parasexual cycle was originally discovered in *Emericella* (*Aspergillus*) *nidulans* by Pontecorvo and Roper. It has since been found in a number of unrelated forms and is thought to be common in the higher fungi.

The benefits of both heterokaryosis and parasexuality are striking. The first renders the mycelium a functional diploid (or polyploid), since all nuclei exert their influence in the developing hyphae. The number of genetically distinct nuclei that can be present is very large, for fusion of somatic (assimilative) hyphae is common in many fungi. The results of parasexuality are similar to those of sexual reproduction. However, parasexual processes can occur at any time in the developing mycelium, whereas sexual reproduction often occurs only under exacting conditions of nutrition and environment. It is also noteworthy that the parasexual cycle has been found in fungi having no known sexual stage (Deuteromycetes).

ASEXUAL REPRODUCTION. Asexual reproduction of the euascomycetes is commonly by conidia. These are essentially separable portions of the hyphae or of special branches, the conidiophores, and are produced in various ways (Fig. 4–21A, B). The conidiophores of some euascomycetes are formed within flask-shaped structures (Fig. 4–21C) called **pycnidia** or in discoid structures called **acervuli** (Fig. 4–21D).

Conidial stages constitute a repeating or reinfecting stage in many parasitic ascomycetes—e.g., *Venturia inaequalis* and species of Sclerotiniaceae. Conidia are produced in large numbers during the growing season of the host and infect new host plants. The sexual stage in many such species matures in the spring and initiates infection.

The asexual stages are also those most commonly encountered in many saprobic species. The production of an abundance of asexual spores and the possibility of parasexual activity preceding their formation is undoubtedly important in evolution and survival in these fungi.

SEXUAL REPRODUCTION. The number of euascomycetes in which sexual reproduction has been thoroughly studied is relatively small. In those studied, both male and female reproductive structures (or structures so designated) are generally present on a single thallus

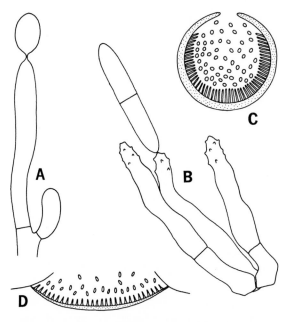

FIGURE 4–21 Asexual reproduction in the Euascomycetidae. A, B, conidiophores and conidia; A, ×1,500; B, ×2,750. C, D, diagrams of pycnidium (C) and acervulus (D) containing numerous conidiophores and conidia.

(Fig. 4–22A). The thallus may be able to reproduce sexually by itself; such a species is best designated as hermaphroditic and self-fertile, although some have inaccurately referred to this condition as "homothallism." Alternatively, cross-fertilization with a similar thallus may be required; such a species is best described as hermaphroditic and self-sterile, although some have inaccurately referred to this condition as "heterothallism."

The gametangia in some species are practically identical and are hypha-like in form. However, the female gametangium or **ascogonium** is more often somewhat larger than the antheridium (Fig. 4–22A). A tubular appendage, the **trichogyne,** is often present on the ascogonium. Other structures perform the function of the antheridium in some species. Antheridia have not been found or have been reported to be nonfunctional in others.

Plasmogamy in species with ascogonia and antheridia is typically through fusion of the trichogyne with the antheridium (Fig. 4–22B). Following this, nuclear transfer from the antheridium occurs through the trichogyne to the ascogonium. In some species, a single nucleus is transferred; in others, a number of nuclei are involved. Compatible pairs of nuclei become closely associated within the ascogonia, but karyogamy does not take place. The pairs of compatible nuclei, or dikaryons, may undergo a series of mitotic divisions. These are termed **conjugate divisions,** the two members of a pair dividing simultaneously. Hyphae develop from the surface of the ascogonium, and nuclear pairs move into these (Fig. 4–22C). The hyphae, called **ascogenous hyphae,** continue to elongate, and crosswalls are soon deposited within them. Cells near the ascogonium may be multinucleate, but those further along the ascogenous hyphae are dikaryotic.

In some species lacking antheridia, either **spermagonia** (small flask-shaped structures containing many **spermatiophores**) or single spermatiophores are produced; the spermatiophores bear minute spore-like bodies, the **spermatia,** which are dispersed by insects, water, or air currents. When a spermatium comes in contact with the trichogyne, plas-

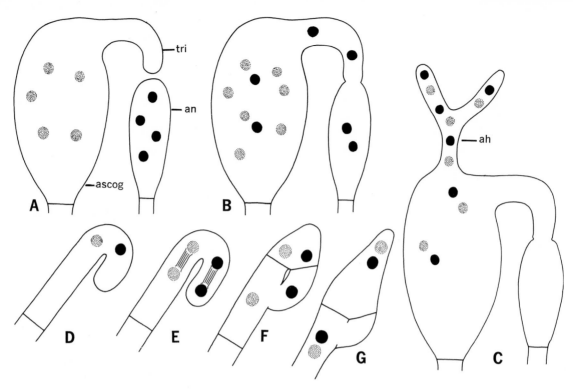

FIGURE 4–22   A–C, sexual structures and plasmogamy. A, ascogonium (*ascog*) with trichogyne (*tri*) and antheridium (*an*); B, nuclei migrating from antheridium through trichogyne to ascogonium; C, pairs of nuclei, or dikaryons, moving into developing ascogenous hypha (*ah*). D–G, crozier formation. D, hook; E, nuclear division; F, crosswall formation; G, continued growth of hypha from tip (penultimate cell) of crozier.

mogamy occurs and the spermatium nucleus migrates into the ascogonium. Spermatization, as this is designated, is followed by development similar to that where antheridia are present. Nuclear transfer in some heterothallic and homothallic species occurs through fusion of assimilative hyphae; this is referred to as **somatogamy.**

As new cells are formed at the tips of ascogenous hyphae, a process called **crozier formation** often takes place (Fig. 4–22D–G). The tip cell of a hypha grows back upon itself, forming a broad crook. The two nuclei migrate to the curve of this crozier and divide mitotically. When division is completed, two daughter nuclei lie in the curve, a third near the tip of the hypha, and the fourth toward the base of the cell. Two septa are then deposited, one cutting off the tip or ultimate cell and a second forming a **penultimate** cell. Two of the

cells thus produced, the ultimate and basal cells, are uninucleate; the penultimate cell is binucleate. The basal and ultimate cells then fuse, forming another binucleate cell. If growth resumes, it does so from the penultimate cell, and crozier formation occurs each time a new cell is formed. The two nuclei in each cell of an ascogenous hypha are presumed to have been derived one each from nuclei originally present in the antheridium and ascogonium respectively. Eventually, terminal cells of ascogenous hyphae function as ascus mother cells, developing into asci (Fig. 4–23A–E).

THE ASCUS.   Within ascus mother cells, the two haploid nuclei unite, the ascus mother cell enlarges, and meiosis occurs. Mitotic division follows meiosis in most ascomycetes and results in an eight-nucleate ascus. Cell walls then form, each encircling a nucleus and a bit

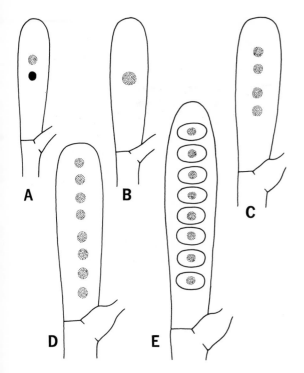

FIGURE 4–23   Ascus development. A, dikaryotic ascus mother cell; B, karyogamy; C, D, meiotic and mitotic divisions resulting in eight-nucleate ascus; E, mature ascus, the individual nuclei surrounded by walls to form ascospores.

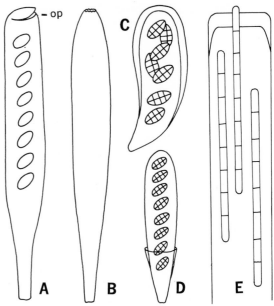

FIGURE 4–24   Ascus types. A, operculate ascus (*op,* operculum); B, inoperculate ascus with irregular opening; C, bitunicate ascus before rupture of outer wall; D, bitunicate ascus with inner wall protruding through ruptured outer wall; E, ascus with apical pore through which spores are shot singly.

of the surrounding cytoplasm. The cells thus formed are ascospores.

The characteristics of asci are considered basic in determining relationships within this very large group of fungi (Fig. 4–24A–D). In the majority of Euascomycetidae, the asci appear to have a single wall and are called **unitunicate;** in others, the ascus wall is double, or **bitunicate.** Ascospores are released differently among unitunicate types. Some asci open by means of a small preformed lid or operculum at the time of spore discharge. In contrast to these **operculate** forms, asci of **inoperculate** species open by an irregular rupture of the ascus end wall. Still others have asci in which there is a minute canal through the ascus tip; spores in these species are shot individually through this pore (Fig. 4–24E).

ASCOCARP   DEVELOPMENT.   Ascocarp

(sporocarp)   development   typically   commences about the time of plasmogamy. The ascocarp is produced by hyphae, which grow up from those bearing the antheridia and ascogonia. Thus, the ascocarp proper is composed of haploid hyphae, as are all sterile structures within the ascocarp. The ascogenous hyphae are the only dikaryotic filaments present. Ascocarp initials in some species are present before plasmogamy takes place; however, their development into ascocarps can take place only after plasmogamy.

The most common types of ascocarps (Fig. 4–25A–D) are: (1) **cleistothecia,** in which the asci are completely enclosed; (2) **perithecia,** in which the asci are enclosed except for a single small opening or **ostiole;** (3) **apothecia,** with asci completely exposed at maturity; and (4) variously shaped **ascostromata.** The relative positions of ascogonia and antheridia within these ascocarp types also are indicated in Fig. 4–25A–D.

Ascocarps are produced through synchronized growth and development of a number of individual strands of hyphae. Thus, the resulting structure is not composed of tissues comparable to those of most other higher organisms. If the hyphal filaments remain more or less identifiable in mature ascocarps, the structure is said to be **prosenchymatous** (Fig. 4–26A). However, if individual cells of the hyphae become rounded and closely packed into a tissue-like mass, the ascocarp is said to be **pseudoparenchymatous** (Fig. 4–26B).

Cleistothecia have either prosenchymatous or pseudoparenchymatous walls. Within the cleistothecium, ascogenous hyphae (and asci) are commonly scattered at varying levels. Most cleistothecia reach no more than 1 mm in diameter, although larger forms are known. Typically perithecia are pseudoparenchymatous and about the same size as cleistothecia; they possess an apical pore, the ostiole, through which spores are released. Ascogenous hyphae and asci are more or less restricted to the basal portion of the perithecium. Sterile hyphae, called **paraphyses,** frequently protrude up among the asci, and similar structures, called **periphyses,** line the ostiolar canal.

The apothecium has asci arranged in a continuous layer, the **hymenium,** which is completely exposed at maturity. Apothecia are commonly **discoid** or **cupulate** and are **stipitate** in some species. In some stipitate apothecia, the fertile portion is neither cupulate nor discoid and is referred to as a **pileus.**

A **stroma** is a variously shaped mass of fungus cells, or of these together with substrate materials. Typically it is pseudoparenchymatous and may be rather dense. An ascostroma is a stroma in which ascus-containing chambers develop. These chambers or **locules,** which appear after stromatic development, are wall-less cavities.

Some ascomycetes may have perithecia or apothecia embedded in, or superficial on, stromata. Others produce their ascocarps on stroma-like structures called sclerotia, which are of regular form and function in most cases as overwintering structures. There is little

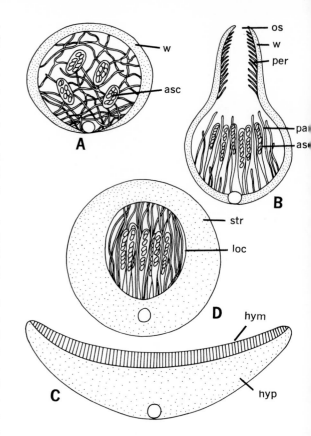

FIGURE 4–25   Common types of ascocarps. A, cleistothecium (*w,* wall; *asc,* ascus); B, perithecium (*os,* ostiole; *w,* wall; *per,* periphyses; *par,* paraphyses; *asc,* ascus); C, apothecium (*hym,* hymenium; *hyp,* hypothecium); D, ascostroma (*str,* stroma; *loc,* locule). Note: clear circles in each structure indicate approximate positions of ascogonia and antheridia.

difficulty in distinguishing the ascostromatal from perithecial forms because perithecia have distinct walls, even when embedded within a stroma. The locule does not have these and, in most instances, is further distinguished by having bitunicate asci.

LIFE HISTORY.   Although there is a large amount of variation in structure and form in the euascomycetes, the life histories of these fungi often follow a similar pattern (Fig. 4–27). Conidia are produced by most species, but a few (e.g., *Sordaria fimicola*) reproduce only by sexual means. Those producing conidia do not have an obligate alternation of

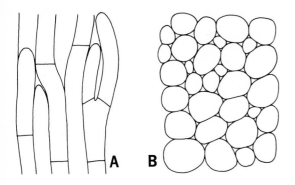

FIGURE 4–26   Cell arrangement. A, prosenchyma; B, pseudoparenchyma.

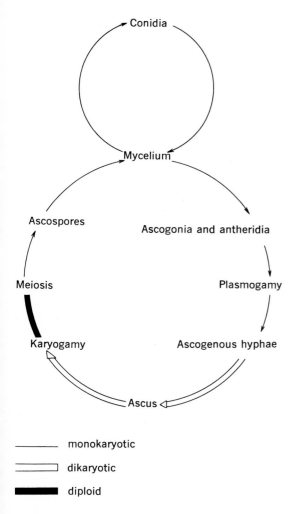

FIGURE 4–27   Typical euascomycetous life cycle.

sexual and asexual phases. Instead, the two types of reproduction may occur simultaneously on a single thallus or, more commonly, conidia are formed on a young thallus, which later produces ascocarps.

The subclass Euascomycetidae constitutes the largest group of true fungi. It includes about 15 commonly recognized orders and 1,800 accepted genera. The group as a whole is poorly known, with no widely accepted system of classification. We shall divide the group into four series—the Plectomycetes, Pyrenomycetes, Loculoascomycetes, and Discomycetes. These are characterized by ascocarps of the cleistothecial, perithecial, ascostromatal, and apothecial types, respectively. The names have no official taxonomic status as used here, but are useful in designating general groups of ascomycetes.

Plectomycetes

ORDER EUROTIALES.   The simplest plectomycetes have cleistothecia of loosely interwoven hyphae. *Arthroderma* (Fig. 4–28) and other members of the Gymnoascaceae have ascocarps of this type. The asci dissolve when the ascocarp matures, and the ascospores then sift out between the loose meshes of the cleistothecial wall. These fungi are frequently found on keratinic materials, such as hooves, horn, and hair. Some species are thought to be responsible for certain fungal diseases of man.

The related Eurotiaceae includes a number of the most intensively studied species of fungi. They are of considerable economic importance because they are both beneficial and detrimental. Some produce organic acids, antibiotics, and other substances of great value. Others are responsible for deterioration or destruction of a variety of materials, including stored foods, leather goods, and fine lenses. A few are implicated in human disease.

The **imperfect stage,** or conidial state, of these fungi is most often found. The conidiophores of *Talaromyces* and *Carpenteles* are of the *Penicillium* type (Fig. 4–29A). They derive their name from the Latin *penicillum,*

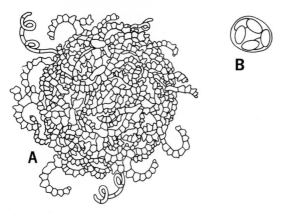

FIGURE 4–28 *Arthroderma curreyi*. A, habit sketch of cleistothecium, ×605; B, ascus and asco-spores, ×2,750.

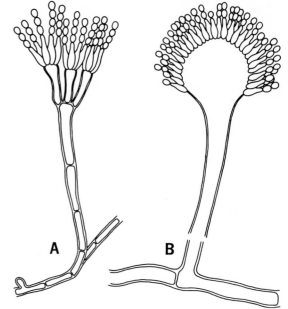

FIGURE 4–29 Conidiophores and conidia of eurotiaceous fungi. A, *Penicillium*, ×1,250; B, *Aspergillus*, ×1,000.

meaning a small brush. Conidiophores of *Eurotium* and *Emericella* are of the *Aspergillus* type (Fig. 4–29B), so-named because of their resemblance to an aspergillum. Numerous minute conidia, dispersed by air currents, are formed on the conidiophores of these fungi. The masses of conidia impart the greenish or bluish colors characteristic of colonies of many of the species.

Ascogonia and antheridia are produced on separate hyphal branches of a single mycelium in *Talaromyces vermiculatus* (Fig. 4–30A–D). Although plasmogamy occurs, it has been reported that the antheridial nucleus is not transferred to the ascogonium. The ascocarp is derived from hyphae that grow up around the sexual structures. These produce a spherical cleistothecium, the walls of which are composed of interwoven hyphae. Ascogenous hyphae bear numerous scattered asci within the cleistothecium and the asci **deliquesce** at maturity of the ascospores. The ascospores are eventually released by irregular dehiscence of the brittle cleistothecial walls.

The ascocarps of *Eurotium* (Fig. 4–30E) develop as in *Talaromyces*. However, the cleistothecial walls are pseudoparenchymatous and are a single cell layer thick.

Within the Eurotiaceae, there is a rather consistent correlation between the type of conidial stage and the ascocarp type. However, this is not the case with all ascomycetes. It is not uncommon in other groups to find that conidial stages are unlike in two or more closely related species. Furthermore, similar conidial stages may be found in widely separated genera.

Pyrenomycetes

ORDER ERYSIPHALES. These "powdery mildews" are obligate parasites that infect many flowering plants. For the most part, these fungi cause little visible damage to the host plant. However, some species (*Uncinula necator* on grape, *Podosphaera leucotricha* on apple and pear) are extremely destructive if conditions are favorable for their development and spread. Their mycelium develops on the surfaces of leaves, twigs, and fruits of the host. Haustorial branches (Fig. 4–31A) typically penetrate only the host epidermis or the layer immediately below it.

Masses of whitish conidia (Fig. 4–31B) impart a powdery appearance to host surfaces infected by erysiphaceous fungi. These conidia, which are borne in chains on simple erect conidiophores, are wind-dispersed and bring about further infection of the host species.

The ascocarps of powdery mildews have pseudoparenchymatous walls that bear a series of radiating appendages (Fig. 4–32A–D). The appendages of *Erysiphe* and *Phyllactinia* are hypha-like; those of the latter genus have bulbous bases. The appendage tips are hooked or coiled in *Uncinula,* and dichotomously branched in *Microsphaera* and *Podosphaera.* There is a single ascus (Fig. 4–32E) in ascocarps of *Sphaerotheca* and *Podosphaera;* several asci are present in those of *Microsphaera, Uncinula,* and others. The ascocarps reach maturity late in the growing season of the host, or during cooler periods following. They swell and burst during wet periods of the following spring. The scattered asci then burst, freeing the ascospores that infect developing host plants.

Although no ostiole is present in ascocarps of this group, the structure and development suggest a relationship to the Pyrenomycetes rather than to the Plectomycetes.

ORDER XYLARIALES. Members of this order produce ostiolate perithecia with dark-colored pseudoparenchymatous walls. The perithecia occur either on the surface of the substrate or partially embedded in it in *Neurospora* and

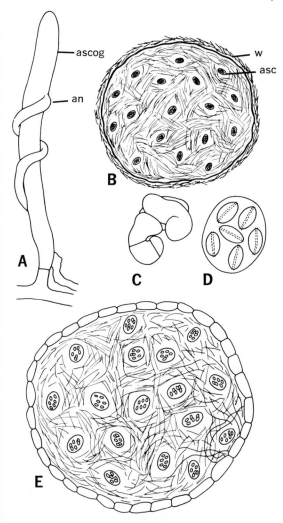

FIGURE 4–30   A–D, *Talaromyces vermiculatus.* A, ascogonium and antheridium, ×2,000 (*ascog,* ascogonium; *an,* antheridium); B, semi-diagrammatic drawing of section through cleistothecium, ×1,000 (*w,* wall; *asc,* ascus); C, portion of ascogenous hypha with developing croziers, ×2,665; D, ascus and ascospores, ×3,000. E, section through cleistothecium of *Eurotium* showing pseudoparenchymatous wall layer, ×1,220.

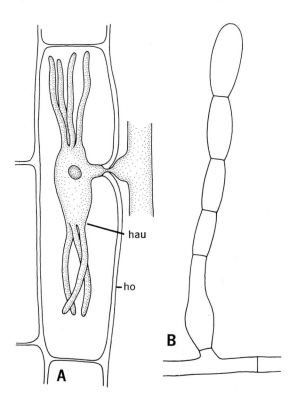

FIGURE 4–31   *Erysiphe graminis.* A, haustorium in epidermal cell of host, ×1,500 (*hau,* haustorium; *ho,* host); B, aerial conidiophore and chain of developing conidia, ×1,000.

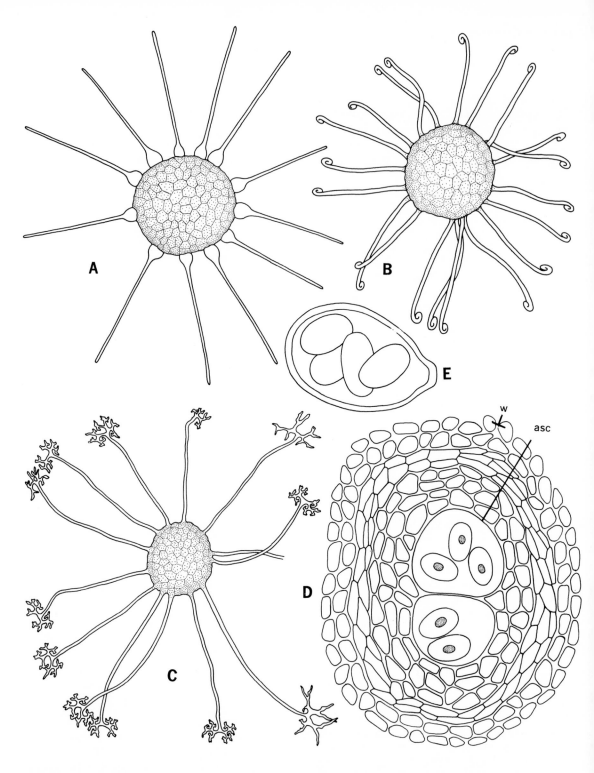

FIGURE 4–32   Erysiphales. A–C, habit sketches of ascocarps. A, *Phyllactinia*, ×125; B, *Uncinula*, ×400; C, *Microsphaera*, ×200. D, E, *Erysiphe graminis*. D, cross section through cleistothecium, ×940 (*w*, pseudoparenchymatous wall; *asc*, ascus). E, mature ascus, ×200.

Sordaria. Other genera, such as *Hypoxylon* and *Xylaria,* produce well-developed stromata, within which the perithecia are formed.

Sordaria fimicola (Fig. 4–33) occurs on the dung of various animals. This species reproduces only by means of ascospores; no asexual spores are formed. Ascogonia have been observed by several investigators, but there are conflicting reports concerning the presence of antheridia. The asci are arranged in a basal cluster in the perithecium. Paraphyses are present in the early stages of perithecial development, but they deliquesce before maturity of the asci. At maturity, a single ascus elongates until its apex extends a short distance through the ostiole. The ascospores are shot from the ascus; the ascus then collapses and retracts back into the perithecium, where another ascus repeats the process. Both the ascus tip and the neck of the perithecium show a positive phototropic response.

S. fimicola is a "homothallic" species, producing fertile cultures from single spores. However, hyphal fusions will occur between two strains with a subsequent transfer of nuclei from one mycelium to the other. Ascospores of both parental types or strains may later appear in a single ascus. Thus, both cross-fertilization and self-fertilization can occur in this species.

Neurospora, a genus closely related to *Sordaria,* has been utilized for many genetic studies. Much of our knowledge concerning the biochemical aspects of genetics has been derived from studies of *Neurospora crassa* and *N. sitophila,* which are hermaphroditic self-sterile forms. Ascogonia with trichogynes and perithecial initials are produced on each thallus. The male elements are small conidiophores (or spermatiophores), which produce numerous minute conidia. Although these conidia can function as spermatizing agents if transferred to the trichogyne, they also are capable of germinating to form a new mycelium. Larger macroconidia are found on each thallus; these too can function either as spermatizing agents or germinate to produce a new mycelium.

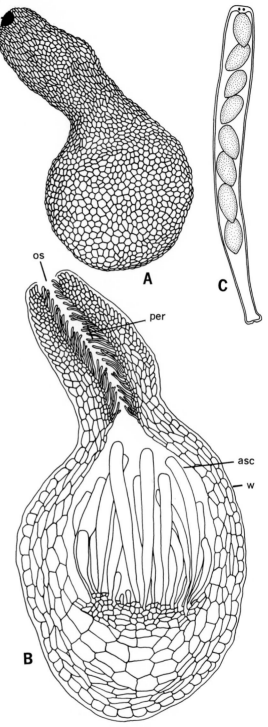

FIGURE 4–33 *Sordaria fimicola.* A, habit sketch of perithecium, ×190; B, section through mature perithecium, ×575 (*os,* ostiole; *asc,* ascus; *per,* periphyses; *w,* perithecial wall); C, mature ascus with ascospores, ×560.

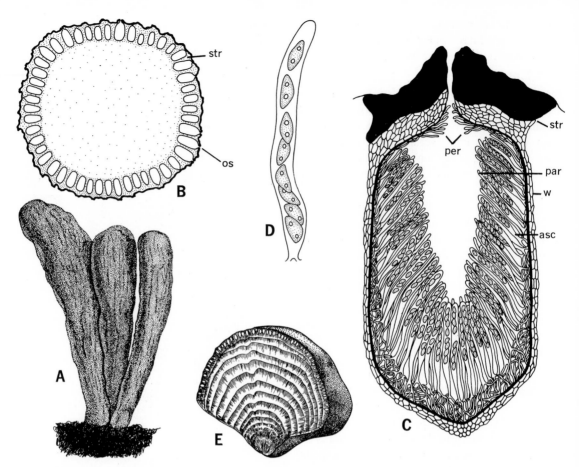

FIGURE 4–34   A–D, *Xylaria*. A, habit sketch of stromata, ×1; B, cross section through stroma (*str*) showing embedded perithecia, ×4; C, section through single perithecium, × 150 (*w,* perithecial wall; *per,* periphyses; *par,* paraphysis; *asc,* ascus; *os,* ostiole; *str,* stroma); D, mature ascus and ascospores, ×600. E, section through stroma of *Daldinia concentrica,* ×1; note concentric zones in stroma and the single line of perithecia near surface.

Perithecia of *Neurospora* are similar to those of *Sordaria*. The former genus derives its name from the nerve-like ridged pattern of the ascospore wall. *N. sitophila,* or red bread mold, is sometimes a nuisance in bakeries; once established, it is difficult to eradicate, because of the numerous small conidia.

In the species of *Xylaria* perithecia are embedded in erect stromata (Fig. 4–34A–D). A conidial stage, which is formed on the surfaces of young stromata in this group, consists of a velvety, often brightly colored, layer of conidiophores and conidia. Perithecia develop later within the same stroma.

The genus *Daldinia* has stromata composed of concentric layers (Fig. 4–34E) and is capable of storing large amounts of water. If a stroma is removed from the substrate and brought into the laboratory, sporulation continues for many days; apparently this is at the expense of water stored in the stroma.

ORDER HYPOCREALES. *Claviceps purpurea* (Fig. 4–35A–F), commonly called ergot, is a parasite on rye and other grasses. It infects the ovaries of these plants, producing large numbers of conidia. The conidia are exuded in a sticky liquid, or "honey dew," which is apparently attractive to insects. Conidia carried by insects or splashed by water spread the infection to adjacent plants.

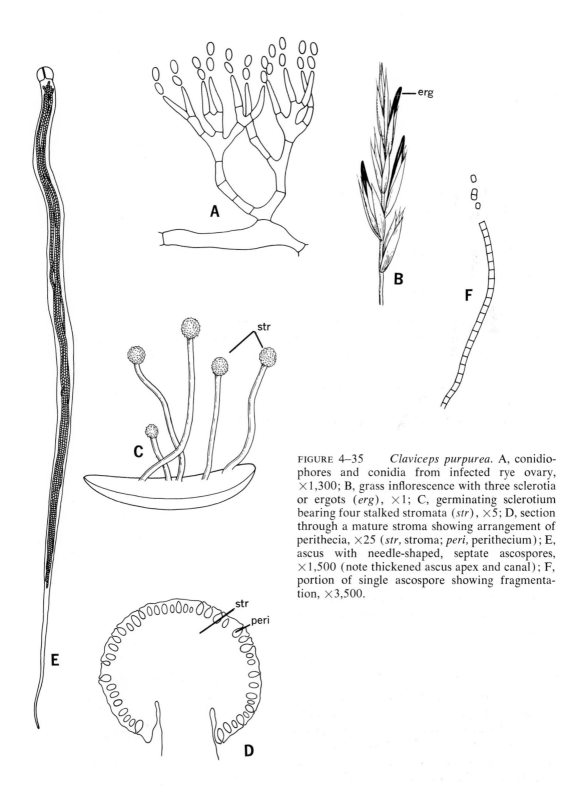

FIGURE 4–35 *Claviceps purpurea*. A, conidiophores and conidia from infected rye ovary, ×1,300; B, grass inflorescence with three sclerotia or ergots (*erg*), ×1; C, germinating sclerotium bearing four stalked stromata (*str*), ×5; D, section through a mature stroma showing arrangement of perithecia, ×25 (*str,* stroma; *peri,* perithecium); E, ascus with needle-shaped, septate ascospores, ×1,500 (note thickened ascus apex and canal); F, portion of single ascospore showing fragmentation, ×3,500.

The hyphae within the host continue to grow, forming a hard purplish sclerotium. At maturity, the sclerotium has the form of a grain produced by a healthy ovary, but it is somewhat larger. The sclerotia or "ergots" fall to the ground and function there as overwintering or resting structures. They retain their viability for several years, eventually germinating by the formation of one or more stalked stromata. Perithecia are formed within the swollen apices of these stromata. The asci of *Claviceps* and other Clavicepitales are narrow and cylindrical with a minute canal through the thickened apex (Fig. 4–35E). The threadlike ascospores are released while susceptible hosts are in flower.

Ergot is important because of losses it causes in rye crops, because of poisoning resulting from ingestion of sclerotia, and because it is the source of several valuable drugs. "St. Anthony's Fire," a serious type of intoxication caused by ergot, was once relatively common in humans. It usually resulted from eating rye flour contaminated by ergot and was often fatal. Cattle eating infected grain are also poisoned. Several important substances are now extracted from ergots; the most valuable of these is used in the control of hemorrhage during childbirth. Another, lysergic acid (LSD), offers some promise in the study and treatment of mental disease; if taken in minute amounts, this highly toxic chemical induces a temporary state of insanity.

Species of *Cordyceps* (Fig. 4–36) produce stalked stromata similar in structure to those of *Claviceps*. The brightly colored stromata, which reach a height of more than one foot in some species, arise from mummified bodies of insects or spiders, or from ascocarps of other fungi.

Loculoascomycetes

Stromata of the Loculoascomycetes are pseudoparenchymatous. In *Pleospora* (Fig. 4–37A–D) in the order Pleosporales, species of which are found on dead herbaceous stems of many types, the stroma is small and one-chambered. Gametangia form within the stroma and locules develop around or adjacent to these. The asci are conspicuously bitunicate and contain brownish multiseptate ascospores; the spores are released through an ostiole-like opening that forms in the stroma. Conidial stages are known for some species of *Pleospora* and are of the *Alternaria* or *Stemphylium* type (Fig. 4–37E, F).

Venturia inaequalis (Fig. 4–37G, H) in the order Pleosporales, which causes apple scab, is similar to *Pleospora* in most respects. Here the conidial stage is produced on a thin subcuticular stroma on the leaves and fruits of the host. Hyphae eventually penetrate into the deeper tissues where they form the ascogenous stage. This stage matures through the fall and spring, releasing ascospores early in the growing season of the host.

The stromata of *Dibotryon* (Dothidales) are much more extensive than those of *Pleospora* and *Venturia*. As in some of the Xylariales, the young stromata are covered by a velvety layer of conidiophores and conidia. *D. morbosum* (Fig. 4–38A–C) is responsible for the disease called black knot, occurring on branches of cherry. In this species, small protrusions, each of which contains a single locule, develop on surfaces of the stromata.

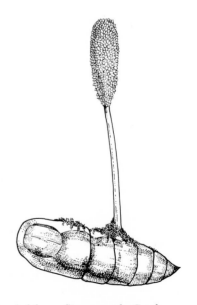

FIGURE 4–36   Stroma of *Cordyceps* arising from infected insect pupa, ×2.5.

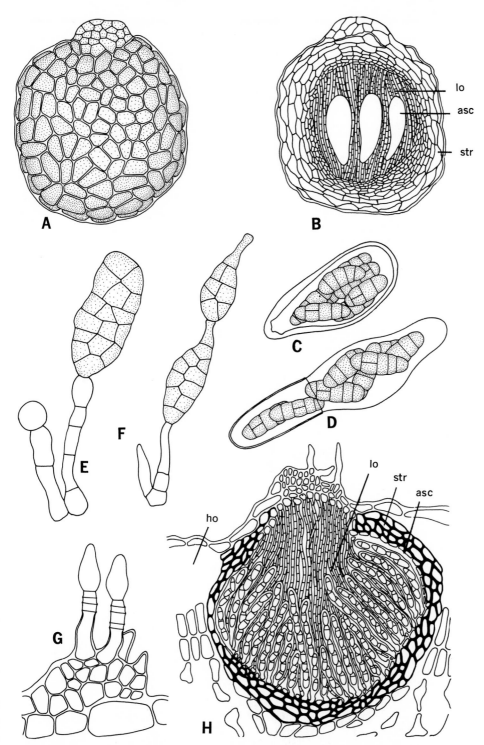

FIGURE 4–37   A–D, *Pleospora*. A, habit of ascostroma, ×250; B, semidiagrammatic drawing of section through ascostroma, ×250 (*lo,* locule; *asc,* ascus;
str, stroma); C, bitunicate ascus and ascospores, ×400; D, ascus after rupture of
outer wall layer, ×400. E, F, conidial stages (E, *Stemphyllium* type, ×825; F,
Alternaria type, ×800). G, H, *Venturia inaequalis*. G, conidiophores and conidia, ×825; H, section through host leaf and ascostroma (*ho,* host; *lo,* locule;
str, stroma; *asc,* ascus), ×500.

Discomycetes

ORDER HELOTIALES. The Helotiales, or inoperculate discomycetes, are mainly saprobic and grow on dead plant parts. However, some species are parasites of green plants and others grow on soil.

The minute discoid apothecia of *Pseudopeziza* (Fig. 4–39) are embedded in leaves of alfalfa. The apothecia consist of only a thin **hypothecial layer** (sterile layer below the hymenium) together with a hymenium. Conidia in this species are produced in a discoid subepidermal structure, the acervulus.

The majority of Helotiales produce somewhat larger apothecia. Those of *Helotium citrinum* (Fig. 4–40A–C), a common temperate species, are stipitate and have a disc reaching 2 to 3 mm in diameter. Sterile portions of the apothecium in this species and closely related genera are more or less prosenchymatous. Those of *Mollisia* (Fig. 4–40D–F) and *Pseudopeziza* are pseudoparenchymatous. The fertile portion, or hymenium, is composed of asci and of paraphyses.

Conidial stages of only a few inoperculate discomycetes are known. However, in one important group of parasites, the Sclerotiniaceae, conidia are produced abundantly on the host; these are borne in chains on surfaces of the infected plant parts. Species of *Monilinia* are responsible for "brown rot" of various stone fruits. Fruits infected with *Monilinia fructicola* (Fig. 4–41A–C) first rot and then are gradually transformed into shriveled "mummies," which function as sclerotia and give rise

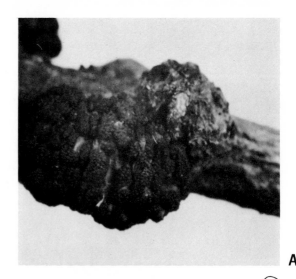

A

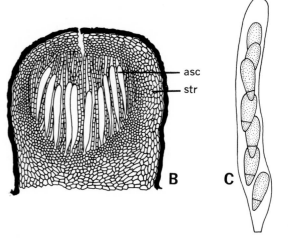

asc
str

B   C

FIGURE 4–38   *Dibotryon morbosum.* A, portion of an infected branch of *Prunus*, ×3; B, section through small portion of ascostroma, ×170 (*str,* stroma; *asc,* ascus); C, mature ascus and ascospores, ×875.

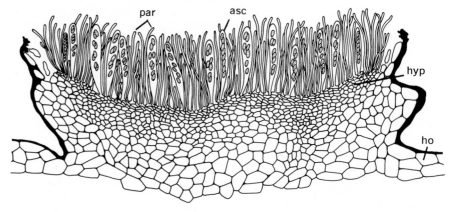

par   asc

hyp

ho

FIGURE 4–39   *Pseudopeziza medicaginis;* section through apothecium and host leaf (*ho,* host; *par,* paraphysis; *asc,* ascus; *hyp,* hypothecium), ×360.

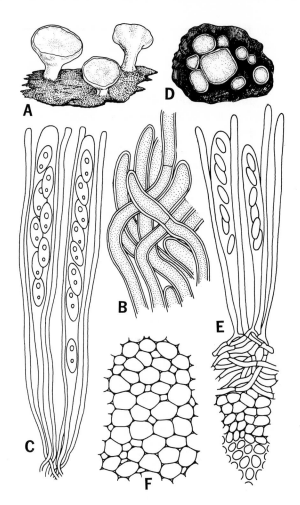

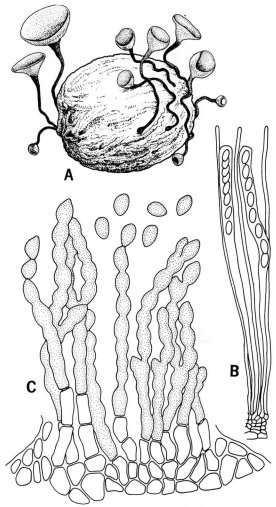

FIGURE 4–40   A–C, *Helotium citrinum*. A, habit sketch of stalked apothecia, ×5; B, prosenchyma from outer portion of hypothecium, ×1,640; C, portion of hymenium showing asci and paraphyses, ×1,330. D–F, *Mollisia cinerea*. D, habit of sessile apothecia, ×5; E, asci and paraphyses, ×1,640; F, pseudoparenchyma from hypothecial layer, ×500.

FIGURE 4–41   *Monilinia fructicola*. A, mummified plum on which a number of apothecia have developed, ×1. B, asci and paraphyses, ×750. C, cluster of conidiophores arising from the surface of infected fruit, ×415.

to stalked apothecia upon germinating. Species of *Sclerotinia* produce definite sclerotia of regular form.

In *Leotia* and related genera, the apothecia are stipitate and pileate. The pileus in *Leotia* (Fig. 4–42A) is more or less discoid, but that of *Mitrula* is globose or oval (Fig. 4–42B). *Geoglossum* species (Fig. 4–42C–D), sometimes called "earth tongues," have a club-shaped pileus merging into the stipe.

ORDER PEZIZALES.   Operculate discomycetes have apothecia similar to those of the Helotiales; however, in many instances they reach a much greater size. Many Pezizales are primarily inhabitants of soil and dung; only a few are found on dead plant parts. Some species, such as *Pyronema omphalodes*, occur only on burned-over soils.

The larger apotheciate forms, such as *Peziza* and *Aleuria* (Fig. 4–43A–D), produce cupulate apothecia sometimes reaching 15 to 18 cm in diameter. In apothecia of the opercu-

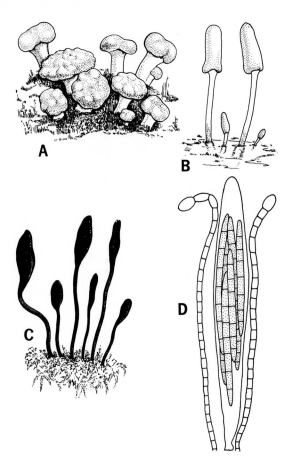

FIGURE 4–42   A–C, habit sketches. *A, Leotia lubrica,* ×1; B, *Mitrula phalloides,* ×1; C, *Geoglossum glabrum,* ×0.5. D, asci and paraphyses of *G. glabrum,* ×460.

late discomycetes, asci are arranged in a hymenium, as in the inoperculate Helotiales. The ascus tips bend toward the light and ascospores are fired from the ascus. If an undisturbed apothecium is suddenly touched or blown upon, a cloud of spores may be released with an audible hiss.

A series of transitional forms connects the cupulate members of this group with the pileate species (Fig. 4–44, 45). In *Helvella elastica* the pileus is obviously somewhat discoid, although folded and saddle-shaped. In *Verpa bohemica* the ridged pileus is bell-shaped and folded down over the stem. In *Morchella* the hymenium lines large pits on the pileus. In contrast to *Verpa,* the stipe of *Morchella* is attached to the base of the pileus. *Morchella*

and related genera are highly prized by mushroom hunters; one species, *Gyromitra esculenta* (Fig. 4–45), is sometimes poisonous and may cause fatal illness.

ORDER TUBERALES.   Operculate discomycetes form a continuous series leading to the Tuberales or truffles. Truffles are hypogeous ascomycetes—i.e., their ascocarps mature below the soil surface. They are the most esteemed of edible fungi. In Europe, pigs or dogs are trained to hunt the buried ascocarps, a feat made possible by the distinctive odors of these fungi. The ascocarps (Fig. 4–46) are closed and their ascospores remain within the asci; dispersal is probably accomplished entirely through animals.

RELATIONSHIPS OF THE ASCOMYCETES

The Euascomycetidae are thought by some to have evolved from floridean algal ancestors (see Chapter 12). This evolutionary scheme is based mainly upon similarities in structure and reproduction of the two groups. The simpler Hemiascomycetidae are considered in this scheme to have developed through simplification or regression of euascomycetous forms.

In a second commonly accepted theory, the ascomycetes are derived from phycomycetous (Zygomycetidae) ancestors. In this scheme certain filamentous hemiascomycetes are considered as most primitive and the euascomycetes are derived from them. The yeasts are treated as reduced forms as in that scheme deriving the ascomycetes from the red algae.

The ascomycetes are thought to be closely related to the remaining class, the Basidiomycetes. Points of similarity between the two groups are the dikaryon, croziers, and clamp connections; and early development of asci and basidia.

CLASS BASIDIOMYCETES

The basidiomycetes are characterized by the production of **basidia** and **basidiospores.** As with the euascomycetous ascus, basidia are

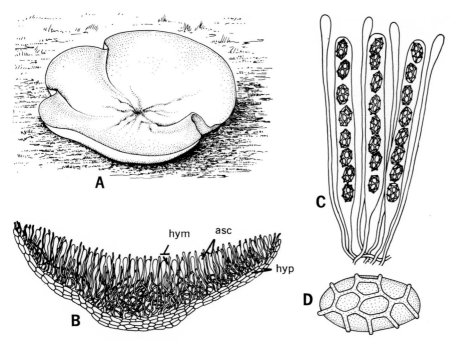

FIGURE 4–43   *Aleuria aurantia.* A, habit sketch of apothecium, ×1; B, diagram of section through apothecium (*hym,* hymenium; *asc,* asci; *hyp,* hypothecium); C, asci and paraphyses, ×325; D, single ascospore showing reticulate pattern of ridges on spore wall, ×1,250.

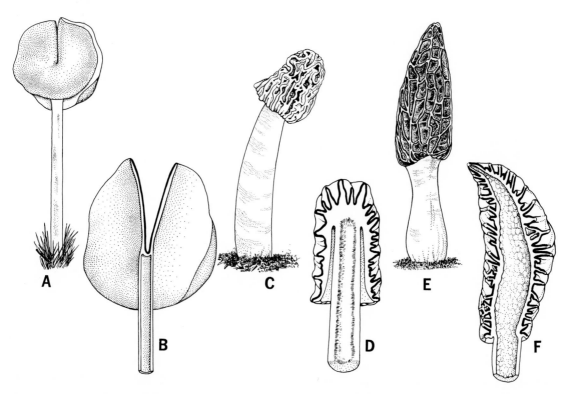

FIGURE 4–44   Habit and sectional views of ascocarps. A, B, *Helvella elastica,* ×0.5; C, D, *Verpa bohemica,* ×0.5; E, F, *Morchella angusticeps,* ×0.5. (Heavy lines in sections of ascocarps indicate extent of hymenium.)

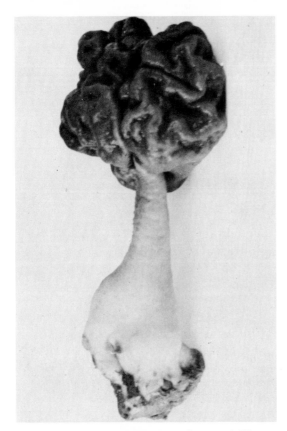

FIGURE 4–45   *Gyromitra esculenta,* ×0.75.

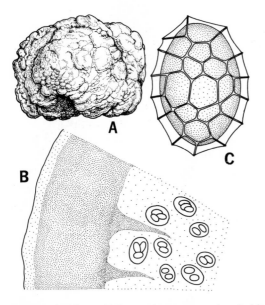

FIGURE 4–46   *Tuber giganteum.* A, habit sketch of ascocarp, ×1; B, section through a portion of ascocarp showing sterile outer layers and scattered asci, ×140; C, single ascospore, ×1,210.

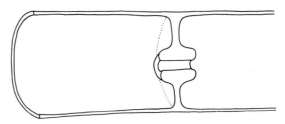

FIGURE 4–47   Diagram of section through basidiomycetous septum.

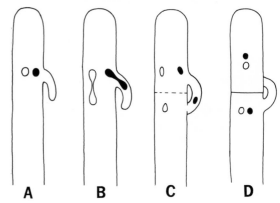

FIGURE 4–48   A–D, formation of clamp connections (compare with crozier formation, Fig. 4–22, D–G).

borne on dikaryotic hyphae and are the cells in which karyogamy and meiosis occur. The basidiospores are formed exogenously and are shot from the basidium in many basidiomycetes. No recognizable gametangia are formed in most groups of basidiomycetous fungi.

ASSIMILATIVE STAGE

Germination of basidiospores gives rise to a primary or **monokaryotic** mycelium in most heterothallic species. This mycelium consists of regularly septate hyphae with uninucleate cells. Dikaryotization is accomplished either through **somatogamy**—i.e., fusions between two compatible monokaryotic hyphae—or by spermatization. Following plasmogamy, nuclei are transferred and the dikaryotic hyphae are produced. This dikaryotic, or secondary mycelium is the main assimilative stage in most basidiomycetes; in some soil- and wood-inhabiting forms this stage is indefinitely long. The dikaryotic mycelium of homothallic species arises from a single basidiospore. Chitin is present in walls of most groups studied. The perforated septa of some basidiomycetous hyphae (Fig. 4–47) are more complex than those of ascomycetes.

CLAMP CONNECTIONS

Many dikaryotic basidiomycetous hyphae produce structures—called **clamp connections** (Fig. 4–48A–D)—that differ only in minor respects from the croziers of ascomycetes. The formation of a clamp connection involves a portion of the hypha immediately behind the growing tip. A small lateral branch forms on the terminal hyphal cell and curves back toward the base of the hypha. At this time, the two nuclei present in the cell divide. Two of the four daughter nuclei resulting are located above the short branch, a third is in the branch, and the fourth is below it. The branch grows back to, and fuses with, the hypha that produced it. Two septa are then formed and the end result, as in crozier formation, is the production of two dikaryotic cells.

ASEXUAL REPRODUCTION

Where known, asexual reproduction is by means of conidia. Several distinct types of conidia are formed in the life cycles of some primitive basidiomycetes. In many of the more advanced forms, no conidial stages are known. Thus, asexual reproduction appears to play a less prominent role in dispersal of basidiomycetes than in the ascomycetes. Conidia in some species are formed on both the monokaryotic and dikaryotic mycelia; in others they are found on only one of the two. Where known, the methods of conidial formation are essentially the same as in the Euascomycetidae. One noteworthy exception is that many of those produced on dikaryotic hyphae are themselves binucleate. Conidia borne on the monokaryotic mycelia may function as spermatizing cells.

SEXUAL REPRODUCTION

Plasmogamy, following somatogamy or spermatization, can be considered the initial step in sexual reproduction of heterothallic species. The final steps do not occur until basidia are formed. Thus, there is a unique situation in which plasmogamy and karyogamy are separated from one another by a prolonged dikaryotic assimilative stage.

Gametangium-like structures are found in only a few of the more primitive basidiomycetes, such as the rusts. Spermagonia containing spermatia and special receptive hyphae are formed by the monokaryotic mycelia of such basidiomycetes. Only two mating classes, designated $+$ and $-$, are known, and dikaryotization requires spermatization of one class by spermatia of the other.

Most of the remaining heterothallic basidiomycetes do not produce spermatia or receptive hyphae; dikaryotization is accomplished through somatogamy. Compatibility systems here are more complex than those found in other fungi. In **bipolar** species, a series of factors, the A factors, determine compatibility. These are such that, if a sexually reproducing thallus is to be established, the fusing mycelia must be of two different types, for example, $A \times a$, $A \times a_1$, etc. Mycelia arising from basidiospores of a single **basidiocarp** are commonly of two classes, as A and a or A and a_1. However, those from other basidiocarps can represent completely different mating classes, as a_2, a_3, etc.

In tetrapolar heterothallism, two sets of factors, the A's and B's, are involved. If a sexually reproducing thallus is to be established, somatogamy must occur between mycelia differing in both sets of factors—for example, $AB \times ab$. The number of mating classes is somewhat greater than in bipolar forms, since four types typically arise from spores of a single basidiocarp. Obviously these mating types, numbering in the hundreds in both bipolar and tetrapolar species, cannot be designated as sexes!

BASIDIOCARPS

A number of the simpler parasitic basidiomycetes produce no basidiocarps. Their basidia are formed on the host surfaces, either directly from dikaryotic cells or from thick-walled resting spores. However, in the majority of basidiomycetes some type of basidiocarp is produced.

The establishment of a basidiomycetous dikaryotic mycelium is not immediately or directly associated with sporocarp formation. The dikaryotic phase may grow indefinitely, producing either annual crops of basidiocarps or perennial basidiocarps. Once the mycelium has become sufficiently developed, production of basidiocarps is controlled by certain external environmental factors, such as temperature, moisture, and light.

Basidiocarps are extremely varied in form; however, all share a few characteristics in addition to the presence of basidia. For example, the entire sporocarp is composed of dikaryotic hyphae. Basidia are borne on or in the basidiocarp, either irregularly or in a definite hymenial layer. The main functions of the basidiocarp are to protect developing basidia and basidiospores and to aid in dispersal of these spores.

BASIDIA

The cytological events occuring in the developing basidium (Fig. 4–49A–D) are also similar to those in the young ascus. However, meiosis is not usually followed by mitosis and, consequently, four basidiospores are produced on the basidia of most species. The spores of the majority of basidiomycetes are borne on minute spicules, or **sterigmata.** One haploid nucleus and a portion of the basidial protoplast are transferred through the sterigma into the expanding spore. Mature basidiospores of many basidiomycetes are violently **abstricted**— i.e., shot from the basidium—but this is not characteristic of all groups. The basidia bear fewer than four spores in some species and more than four in others.

The abstriction mechanism has not yet been explained satisfactorily. Abstricted basidiospores typically are bilaterally symmetrical and are borne on the sterigma at a slight angle (Fig. 4–50A–C). Just before spore discharge, a bubble-like protrusion develops on a small point located on the spore to one side of the sterigma attachment. The abstriction force is sufficient to carry the spore a distance of ten to 20 times the spore length. Gravity and air currents then complete dispersal.

CLASSIFICATION

The class Basidiomycetes is divided into two subclasses, the Heterobasidiomycetidae and the Homobasidiomycetidae. These are separated from one another on the basis of basidial structure, basidiospore germination, and other features. Basidia of the Heterobasidiomycetidae are either septate or deeply divided, and they frequently arise from thick-walled resting spores. Basidia of the homobasidiomycetes are relatively uniform, non-septate, and more or less club-shaped. Basidiospores of most homobasidiomycetous species form a germ tube or hypha upon germinating; those of many heterobasidiomycetes produce conidia of one or more types.

SUBCLASS HETEROBASIDIOMYCETIDAE

Three orders—the Tremellales, Uredinales, and Ustilaginales—are recognized in the Heterobasidiomycetidae. These extremely varied and variable groups are considered by most mycologists to be more primitive than the Homobasidiomycetidae. Although morphologically simpler than the homobasidiomycetes in many instances, their life cycles may be more complex.

Species in the Tremellales produce definite basidiocarps and are predominantly saprobes. One family, the Septobasidiaceae, contains only scale-insect parasites, and some species in other families parasitize green plants or other fungi. The Ustilaginales and Uredinales are parasites of vascular plants. They do not produce basidiocarps, but form spores in small groups (sori) below epidermal layers of their hosts.

ORDER TREMELLALES. Species in this order frequently are referred to as "jelly" fungi, a name derived from the gelatinous basidiocarp texture· found in many species. Germination of the basidiospores may be by germ tube, by budding, by conidial formation, or by repetition. Yeast-like colonies are produced where budding of the basidiospores occurs. Conidial formation occurs either directly on the basidiospore or on conidiophores that develop from it. The spores produced by repetitive germination are sometimes called secondary basidiospores; they are produced and abstricted from sterigmata that develop on the basidiospore.

A dikaryon is established by fusion of compatible hyphae or possibly by fusion of conidia with hyphae. The dikaryotic mycelium of many species produces clamp connections.

The families included in the Tremellales are separated on the basis of basidial structure. Only three of these are discussed here. Basidia in the Tremellaceae (Fig. 4–51A–D) are roughly globose and are cruciately septate following karyogamy and meiosis. The three septa are formed between nuclei during meiosis. A single septum is formed following the first division, separating the two daughter nuclei from one another. Two secondary septa are deposited at right angles to the first after completion of meiosis. A tubular extension then develops from each cell and is tipped by a sterigma and basidiospore. The contents of the

basidium are transferred to the basidiospores and the latter are shot from their sterigmata. The empty basidium then collapses.

Basidiocarps in this family range from irregular, poorly developed structures to some as complex as those of the homobasidiomycetes. In species of *Tremella* (Fig. 4–52A, B) the basidiocarps are cushion-shaped to irregularly lobed. Most of the exposed surface is covered by a hymenium consisting almost entirely of basidia. However, the hymenial zone

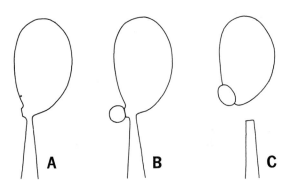

FIGURE 4–50   A–C, basidiospore abstriction.

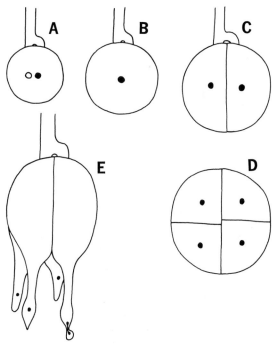

FIGURE 4–51   Development of cruciate-septate basidium.

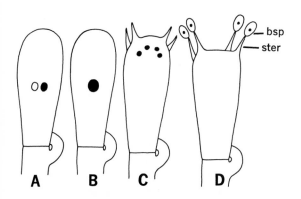

FIGURE 4–49   Basidial development. A, dikaryotic cell; B, karyogamy; C, meiosis; D, mature basidium with exogenous basidiospores (*bsp*) borne on sterigmata (*ster*).

in the young sporocarps of some species is covered by a layer of dikaryotic conidiophores and conidia. In the more highly developed species of *Exidia*, basidiocarps are more regular in form. On their morphologically superior surface (i.e., that opposite the point of attachment) they have a unilateral hymenium, which consists of both basidia and sterile paraphysis-like structures (Fig. 4–53A, B). In *Tremella*, spores shot from the basidia often fall back on the hymenium. This occurs less commonly in *Exidia*, where the hymenium is mostly directed downward. Some genera, such as *Sebacina* and *Exidiopsis*, produce **effused** basidiocarps that are spread over the lower surfaces of logs and branches. In the more delicate effused forms, the structure iş made up primarily of a hymenial layer.

In the genus *Aporpium*, the basidiocarp is poroid; the hymenium lines the surfaces of the pores. *Phlogiotis* (Fig. 4–53C) basidiocarps are pileate and stipitate, and the hymenium is restricted to the undersurface of the funnel-shaped pileus. In these genera, basidiocarp development has reached a level comparable to that in many homobasidiomycetous species.

The Dacrymycetaceae possess basidia that are nonseptate but are deeply divided; they are sometimes referred to as "tuning fork" basidia because of their shape (Fig. 4–54C). The young basidium, or **probasidium,** is club-shaped. Following meiosis, two sterigma-tipped extensions are formed, each bearing a single basidiospore. Two of the four nuclei pass into the basidiospores; the remaining two degenerate within the basidium. Mature basidiospores of most dacrymycetaceous fungi are septate. Upon germinating, minute conidia or germ tubes arise from the basidiospores.

To a certain extent, basidiocarp form, in this family, parallels that in the Tremellaceae. The basidiocarp form in the genus *Dacrymyces* is similar to that of *Tremella*. *Dacrymyces deliquescens* (Fig. 4–54A–E) produces asexual and sexual sporocarps side by side, or the asexual spores may be formed within the young basidiocarps. The basidiocarps are cushion-shaped and have a continuous surface

A

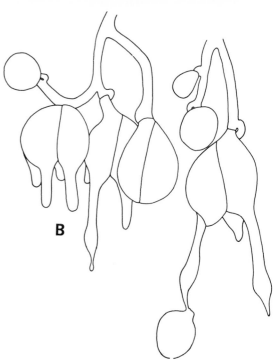

B

FIGURE 4–52   *Tremella aurantia*. A, young basidiocarp, ×2; B, portion of hymenium showing basidia in various stages of development, ×1,200.

hymenium. The asexual sporocarps are of the same form, but pinkish rather than yellow as in the basidium-bearing structures. The dikaryotic conidia, referred to as **arthrospores,** are predominantly two-celled and develop by separation of hyphae into fragments (Fig. 4–54E).

The basidia of *Calocera* are borne on simple or branched horn-shaped basidiocarps.

In the genus *Guepiniopsis* (Fig. 4–54F) basidiocarp form is similar to that of some discomycetes.

In the Auriculariaceae and related families, the basidium typically has a cylindrical four-celled sporogenous portion. As in the Tremellaceae, septa are deposited during meiotic division of the fusion nucleus. Sterigma-tipped extensions are formed by the four cells and each bears a single basidiospore. Conidiophores and conidia are formed in the hymenia of some species.

The basidiocarps of most auriculariaceous genera, such as *Helicogloea* and *Helicobasidium,* are effused and form thin adherent sheets on the undersurfaces of decaying wood. Those of *Auricularia* (Fig. 4–55A–D) are more complex, ear-like in form, and attached by the margin to the substrate. The sporocarps of *Auricularia* and *Helicogloea* are gelatinous in texture; those of *Helicobasidium* are felt-like.

Near their base, the basidia of *Helicogloea* have a lateral saccate structure within which karyogamy occurs (Fig. 4–55E, F). The basidia of *Helicobasidium* (Fig. 4–55G, H) are helically coiled and those of *Auricularia* are cylindrical (Fig. 4–55B, C).

ORDER UREDINALES. No basidiocarps are produced in the rusts, although as many as five different kinds of spores are formed by a single species. The rusts are all obligate parasites, and their spores are produced subepidermally or subcortically on the host. The hyphae are mainly intercellular with haustoria, and clamp connections have been reported on dikaryotic hyphae of some species. If a particular rust requires two different hosts to complete its life cycle, it is **heteroecious; autoecious** forms require a single host. As seen in Table 4–2, the two hosts of a heteroecious species are always from very different groups of vascular plants. The life cycle of *Puccinia graminis* (Fig. 4–56) is typical of that of a number of heteroecious rusts. Basidiospores are released early in the spring and infect leaves of the common barberry, *Berberis vulgaris*. Spermagonia are formed on the upper surfaces of the

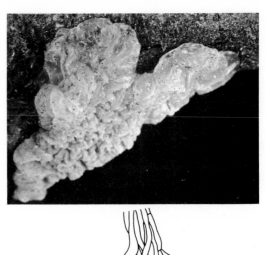

A

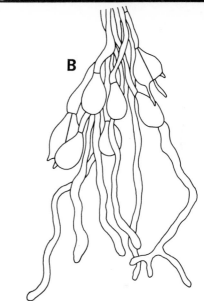

B

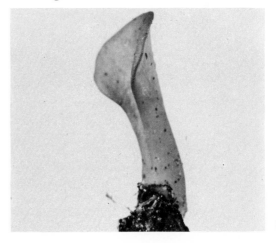

C

FIGURE 4–53   A, B, *Exidia candida*. A, habit of basidiocarp, ×1.5; B, hymenium with basidia and paraphysis-like sterile elements, ×850. C, *Phlogiotis helvelloides,* ×1.

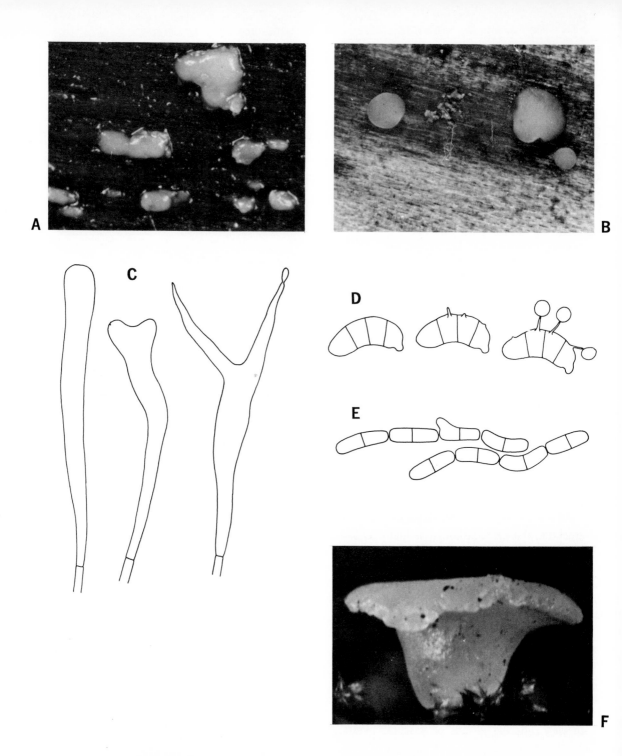

FIGURE 4–54   A–F, *Dacrymyces deliquescens.* A, conidial fructifications, ×7; B, basidiocarps, ×5; C, basidia, ×2,000; D, basidiospores, two of which have germinated by formation of conidia, ×2,000; E, conidia (from A), ×1,450. F, basidiocarp of *Geupiniopsis alpinus,* ×3.

A

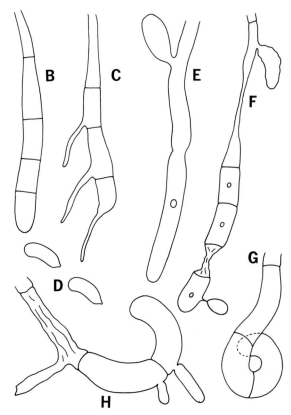

FIGURE 4–55   A–D, *Auricularia auricula.* A, habit view of upper surface of basidiocarp, ×2; B, C, basidia, ×1,000; D, basidiospores, ×1,000. E, F, young and mature basidia of *Helicogloea lagerheimi,* ×750. G, H, young and mature basidia of *Helicobasidium corticioides,* ×750.

leaves (Fig. 4–57A). They are perithecium-like in shape and contain many small spermatia

that are exuded together with a sugary liquid, or "honey dew." Craigie discovered that if insects were kept from visiting infected leaves, only spermagonia and aecial primordia developed. He demonstrated that spermagonia in this species were of two types or sexual phases, usually designated as + and –. The + spermatia must be transferred to receptive hyphae of – spermagonia, or vice versa, in order for aecial primordia to complete their development. It is assumed that a nucleus transferred from a spermatium to the receptive hypha brings about dikaryotization of the aecial initial. The **aecia** are formed mainly on the lower surfaces of the leaves and produce dikaryotic **aeciospores** (Fig. 4–57B), which infect wheat and closely related small grains, where they produce the uredial stage (Fig. 4–57C). **Uredospores** of *P. graminis* are repeating spores, spreading the infection to other wheat plants. In late summer, **telia** are produced (Fig. 4–57D); these contain stalked, two-celled, dikaryotic **teliospores.** Teliospores of this and most rust species are not dispersal agents; they remain attached to the grass plant and are the resistant or overwintering stage. Soon after they have formed, karyogamy occurs within their dikaryotic cells. In the spring, they germinate *in situ,* producing basidia and basidiospores (Fig. 4–58). Meiosis occurs during germination.

Puccinia malvacearum infects various malvaceous hosts and has a greatly reduced life history. This species produces teliospores similar to those of *P. graminis,* but these germinate immediately and the basidiospores infect new host plants. Only those teliospores formed late in the growing season function as resting spores. They germinate and initiate infection the following spring. The dikaryotic mycelium is thought to develop following somatogamy between two adjacent monokaryotic mycelia.

Cronartium ribicola, called white pine blister rust, has a life cycle similar to that of *Puccinia graminis.* However, there are some noteworthy differences in morphology between the two. In *C. ribicola* the spermatia are pro-

TABLE 4–2

SOME HETEROECIOUS RUSTS AND THEIR HOSTS

RUST	HOSTS	
	SPERMAGONIA AND AECIA	UREDIA AND TELIA
Gymnosporangium clavariiforme	Rosaceae (*Pyrus, Amelanchier*)	Cupressaceae (*Juniperus*)
Melampsora abietis-canadensis	Pinaceae (*Abies*)	Salicaceae (*Populus*)
Pucciniastrum epilobii	Pinaceae (*Abies*)	Onagraceae (*Epilobium, Clarkia,* etc.)
Tranzschelia discolor	Ranunculaceae (*Ranunculus, Anemone,* etc.)	Rosaceae (*Prunus*)
Uredinopsis longimucronata	Pinaceae (*Abies*)	Polypodiaceae (*Athyrium, Dryopteris,* etc.)
Uromyces lineolatus	Umbelliferae (*Cicuta, Sium,* etc.)	Cyperaceae (*Scirpus*)

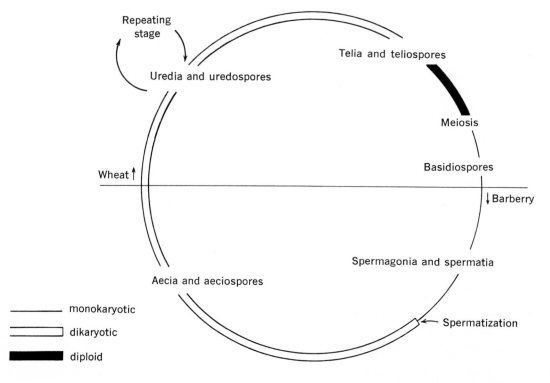

FIGURE 4–56   Life history of *Puccinia graminis*.

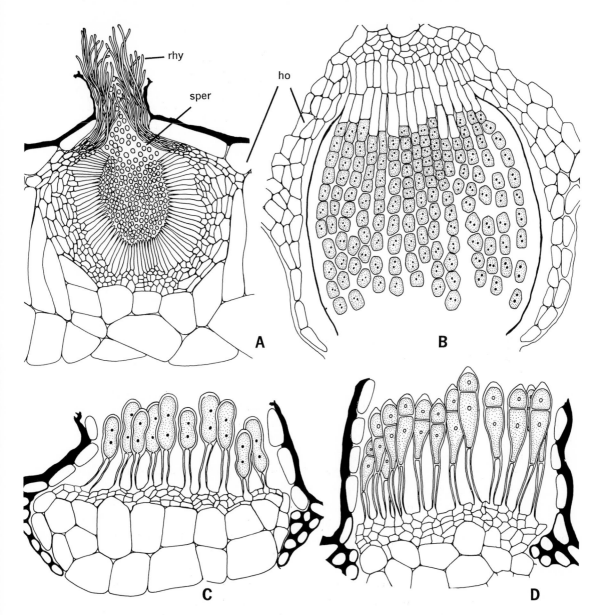

FIGURE 4–57 *Puccinia graminis*. A, section through spermagonium and host leaf, ×550; B, aecium and aeciospores, ×450; C, uredium and uredospores, ×575; D, telium and teliospores, ×420. *ho,* host; *rhy,* receptive hyphae; *sper,* spermatia.

duced on spermatiophores forming a palisade-like layer below the host periderm. These spermatia are exuded together with a nectar-like secretion following rupture of the periderm. Aecia are formed the following year in the area previously occupied by spermatial sori. The aecium is orange to yellow and is covered by a membranous layer, the peridium. These large blister-like structures are the

source of the name "blister" rust. When the aecial peridium ruptures, the powdery mass of spores is exposed.

The aeciospores infect species of currants (*Ribes*) or gooseberries (*Grossularia*), where the uredial stage is formed a week or more later. Uredospores function as repeating spores, infecting other currant or gooseberry plants. Telia develop later in the summer on

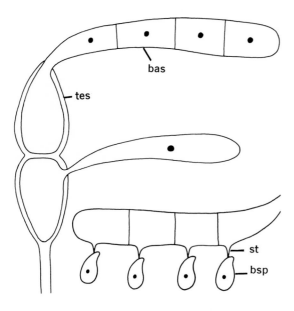

FIGURE 4–58 Basidial development in *Puccinia* (*tes,* teliospore; *bas,* basidium; *bsp,* basidiospore; *st,* sterigma).

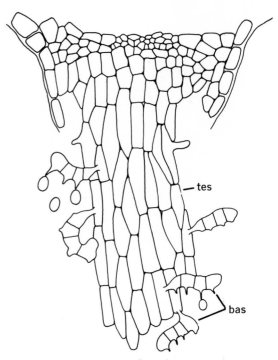

FIGURE 4–59 Section through telial horn of *Cronartium ribicola,* ×465. Note united thin-walled teliospores (*tes*), some of which have germinated and produced basidia (*bas*).

the leaves bearing uredia, where the teliospores are borne in a column. The teliospores are thin-walled, rectangular, and fused to one another; they germinate immediately and the basidiospores infect white pines (Fig. 4–59).

The examples discussed here give only a slight indication of the variation in spore and sorus form found in the rusts. Some of the conspicuous differences in teliospore form are illustrated in Fig. 4–60.

ORDER USTILAGINALES. Smuts, like rusts, are all parasites of vascular plants. However, the smuts can be grown in culture, and a few species have been induced to complete their life cycles in this way. All known species require a single host for completion of development. Most have a single binucleate spore stage, but some species produce conidia on the mono- or dikaryotic mycelia.

The resting spore, or teliospore, is thought to be homologous to that of the rusts. It is usually one-celled, at first dikaryotic, and typically thick-walled. Teliospores of some species form compound masses called spore balls. Upon germinating, the teliospore gives

rise to one or more cylindrical basidia (Fig. 4–61A, B), which are transversely septate in the Ustilaginaceae and resemble the basidia of the rusts. At maturity each cell gives rise to one or more basidiospores. The basidiospores are budded from the sides of the basidium, rather than being abstricted as in the rusts. In the Tilletiaceae the basidia are cylindrical and aseptate, or have but a single transverse septum (Fig. 4–62). Spores in this group are needle-shaped and are borne at the basidial tip. Each is shot from the basidium at maturity, but the abstriction mechanism appears to differ from that in other basidiomycetes.

The bud-like basidiospores of *Ustilago* may multiply through budding (Fig. 4–61C) and, in culture, yeast-like colonies are produced. Conjugation tubes are formed if compatible cells are adjacent to one another (Fig. 4–61D). Conjugation of *Tilletia* sporidia often occurs while the spores are maturing on the basidia. A dikaryotic phase follows conju-

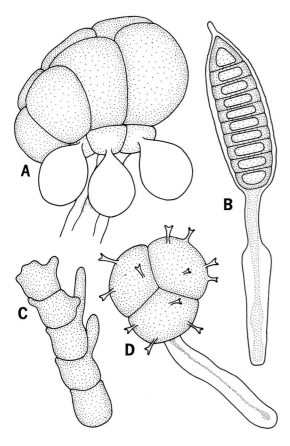

FIGURE 4–60 Teliospores of rusts. A, *Ravenelia,* ×860; B, *Phragmidium,* ×605; C, *Kuehneola,* ×640; D, *Nyssopsora,* ×885.

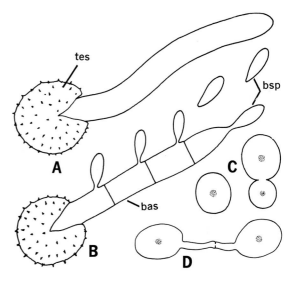

FIGURE 4–61 *Ustilago.* A, germinating teliospore, ×2,600; B, mature basidium with basidiospores (*tes,* teliospore; *bas,* basidium; *bsp,* basidiospore); C, cells produced by budding of basidiospores; D, conjugation.

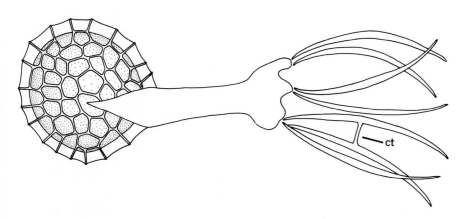

FIGURE 4–62 Teliospore and mature basidium of *Tilletia.* Note conjugation tube (*ct*) between two basidiospores.

gation, although this may be of limited duration in cultures. In nature these fungi apparently conjugate on or in the host plant, and a stable dikaryotic mycelium is maintained. Infection by a monokaryotic mycelium is of limited extent in most species.

Dikaryotic mycelium within host plants is intracellular in early stages, and later becomes intercellular. Hausoria are often present in the latter instance, and an abundance of clamp connections can also be present. The mycelium commonly develops within meristematic tissues of the host and keeps pace with the development of the meristem. Older portions of the hyphae—i.e., those in the matured portion of the host—die. In the meristematic zones or in infected ovaries or other portions of the hosts, masses of teliospores (sori) are formed. The hyphae in the sorus consists of numerous short dikaryotic cells (Fig. 4–63). These become swollen and a new wall is formed around the protoplast of each cell. The old cell wall gelatinizes, eventually disappearing. The so-called sorus is not surrounded by a peridium-like layer of fungal hyphae, but is often more or less enclosed in host tissues. The dry, dusty masses of teliospores are exposed at maturity through disintegration of host parts. Teliospores can be either single or in spore balls in both the Ustilaginaceae and the Tilletiaceae. The spore wall is distinctively marked in many species. Teliospores of Urocystis species (Fig. 4–64A) are provided with a layer of sterile jacket cells.

In the genus Entyloma, teliospores develop singly within the host leaf or other tissues (Fig. 4–64B). The teliospores are scattered within host parts rather than in masses, and they do not escape from the host tissue but germinate in situ. When this occurs, the elongate basidium extends through the old host tissue and basidiospores are formed externally.

Smuts may infect the host plant in several ways. The teliospores of some species adhere to seeds of the host, infecting the seedling at the time of germination. In others, flowers or meristems of the host are infected by sporidia or conidia. Perhaps the most highly developed in this respect are certain species of Ustilago. For example, in U. tritici, infection of the developing embryo may occur at the time of flowering. An infection tube grows into the meristematic zone of the embryo and remains dormant there until the seed germinates. Smut spores of some species, such as U. maydis, may retain their viability and infectiveness in the smut masses for five to ten years. However, in some smuts the viability period of free smut spores in the soil is less than 60 days. If the teliospores germinate in compost heaps or soil rich in organic matter, the basidiospores will continue to bud. Large amounts of inoculum may be built up in this way.

The smuts parasitize a number of economically important plants, especially cereals. Since they commonly infect the inflorescences or fruits, the yield and quality of such crops are greatly affected. Species of Ustilago and Tilletia are responsible for losses amounting to many millions of bushels of grain each year. For example, in some seasons, U. maydis (Fig. 4–65) is the most destructive of corn parasites. The reduction in yield caused by this species sometimes exceeds one fourth of the total loss caused by all corn diseases.

SUBCLASS
HOMOBASIDIOMYCETIDAE

Most of the large conspicuous fungi that one encounters, such as mushrooms, puffballs, and bracket fungi, are members of the homobasidiomycetes. They are characterized by nonseptate, club-shaped, or cylindrical basidia. Their basidiospores germinate by germ-tube formation. Basidiocarps are produced by most and are highly developed in many species. The homobasidiomycetes are mainly saprobes, existing in soil, compost, dung, or dead wood. Their activity in decay of such materials is a beneficial and vital process; however, it also leads to considerable financial loss through the decay of standing and sawn timber. A few species parasitize green plants and many form mycorrhizal associations with such plants. Some species also live in close association with animals; for example, Termitomyces, a genus of gill fungi, inhabits termite nests.

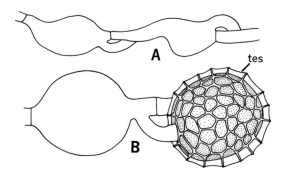

FIGURE 4–63   Development of teliospores in *Ustilago commelina*. A, early development showing hyphal cells with clamp connections at septa, ×2,000; B, later stage with one mature teliospore (*tes*), ×2,000.

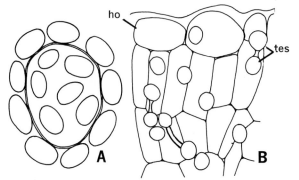

FIGURE 4–64   A, single teliospore of *Urocystis cepulae* with sterile cells surrounding fertile cell, ×2,500. B, section through host leaf showing scattered teliospores of *Entyloma*, ×500 (*tes*, teliospore; *ho*, host tissue).

LIFE HISTORIES. The life histories of homobasidiomycetous fungi are relatively simple. The life history illustrated in Fig. 4–66 is typical of most heterothallic species, which comprise the majority (about 90 per cent) of those where sexuality has been investigated. About one third of the heterothallic species are bipolar and the remaining species tetrapolar.

Dikaryotization can result through somatogamy between two monokaryotic mycelia or by fusion of spores and mycelia. Transfer of nuclei may also occur from a dikaryotic to a monokaryotic mycelium, resulting in dikaryotization of the latter. The dikaryotic mycelium is the main assimilative stage in most homo-

FIGURE 4–65   *Ustilago maydis;* infected kernels on upper portion of ear have ruptured, releasing powdery spores, ×0.75.

basidiomycetes. Its growth in some soil- and wood-inhabiting species may continue for hundreds of years. The "fairy rings" characteristic of many mushroom species are produced on perennial mycelia of this type. Mycelial growth in such forms radiates out from the initial starting point and, as the diameter increases, older portions toward the center of the mycelial

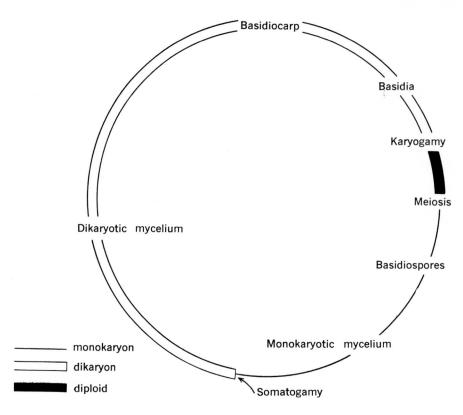

Basidiocarp

Basidia

Karyogamy

Meiosis

Basidiospores

Dikaryotic mycelium

Monokaryotic mycelium

———— monokaryon

[=====] dikaryon

■■■■ diploid

Somatogamy

FIGURE 4–66   Typical homobasidiomycetous life cycle.

mass die. The period of continuous growth (i.e., the age) of such a mycelium can be calculated by determining the annual increase and total diameter of the ring. This has been estimated at more than 500 years in some instances.

Wood-decaying species inhabiting the heartwood of living trees are also known to grow for centuries. The basidiocarps of some, such as *Fomes,* are also perennial; those of *F. igniarius* have been reported to reach ages of 80 years or more.

CLASSIFICATION.   The Exobasidiales, a small order of plant parasites, do not form basidiocarps. The basidia of *Exobasidium,* the only genus in this order, are scattered over the surfaces of infected host parts. The remaining homobasidiomycetes can be conveniently grouped into two series, the Hymenomycetes and the Gasteromycetes. Basidia in hymeno-

mycetous types are formed in a definite hymenial layer, and this is exposed before maturity of the basidiospores. The spores are violently abstricted and are wind-dispersed. Gasteromycetous basidiocarps are closed, although they may open after the basidiospores mature. The basidia are arranged in definite hymenial layers in some gasteromycetes and are irregularly arranged in others. Basidiospore dispersal is accomplished through a variety of mechanisms. The basidiospores are not abstricted, but either break free or are freed through dissolution of the basidia.

Neither the Hymenomycetes nor the Gasteromycetes are considered here as natural groups. There is now very good evidence for a polyphyletic derivation of a number of gasteromycetes from different hymenomycetous ancestors. The latter group, too, does not now appear to be as closely knit as was once thought.

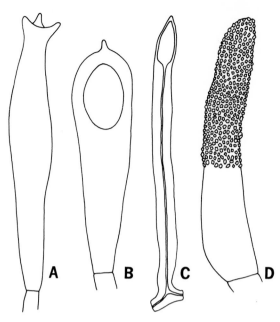

FIGURE 4–67   A–D, cystidia characteristic of hymenia of various Homobasidiomycetidae. A, ×800; B, ×2,250; C, ×1,660; D, ×2,080.

Hymenomycetes

Basidiospore abstriction, coupled with wind dissemination, is a highly effective means of dispersal. Once this became established during the evolution of basidiomycetous fungi, further development probably occurred along two lines: (1) toward increasing surface area of the hymenium; (2) changes in basidiocarp form leading to even greater efficiency in spore dispersal. These should not be viewed as being mutually exclusive. That is, the two trends probably occurred together in some groups, alone in others. As a result, the extant species reveal much evidence of convergent evolution. The older classification systems are based upon similarities in gross structure, especially hymenial configuration. But, because of parallelism in evolution, such classification systems must now be viewed as artificial.

HYMENIUM. Although the hymenia of homobasidiomycetes appear upon casual examination to be rather uniform microscopi-

cally, they are relatively variable from species to species. The most significant differences are in the basidia themselves, which are the best indicators of relationships in many instances. In addition to the basidia, sterile elements are produced in the hymenia of many hymenomycetes. Perhaps the most common of these sterile structures are those referred to as **cystidia** (Fig. 4–67). Cystidia are varied in structure, being typically hyaline, somewhat larger than the basidia and protruding beyond them. They can be thick- or thin-walled and are sometimes encrusted with crystalline materials. The function of the sterile elements, if any, is not known in most instances. Cystidia of some lamellate species—for example, *Coprinus atramentarius*—maintain separation of hymenial surfaces of adjacent lamellae. It has been suggested that other sterile structures protect the delicate hymenium against damage by snails and slugs.

HYMENIAL CONFIGURATION.   The hymenium in the simpler hymenomycetes is borne on even supporting layers, and it is either unilateral or **amphigenous**—i.e., formed over the entire surface of the basidiocarp. The development of shallow pits or of tooth-like projections in the supporting layers serves to increase the hymenial area. In some forms, increased surface area has resulted through branching and greater size of the hymenium-supporting structures. The greatest hymenial area in proportion to basidiocarp size is found in those species having poroid or lamellate hymenial configurations (Fig. 4–68C, D). The so-called pores are actually minute tubular chambers extending for some distance into the basidiocarp. The chamber surfaces are entirely covered by the hymenium. The supporting portion—i.e., that between adjacent hymenia—is the **trama;** in lamellate species, the inner portion of the gills also is referred to as the trama (Fig. 4–79D). The hymenium and trama are borne on the lower surface of a cap or pileus in the more complex hymenomycetes. The sterile inner part, or "flesh," of the pileus is referred to as the **context** (Fig. 4–79B).

THE BASIDIOCARP. Variation in basidiocarps may be found in gross form, in texture, and in microscopic structure. The simplest basidiocarps form a flattened canal layer, often of indeterminate growth. These basidiocarps are said to be effused (Fig. 4–68A) and usually occur on the lower surfaces or sides of the substratum.

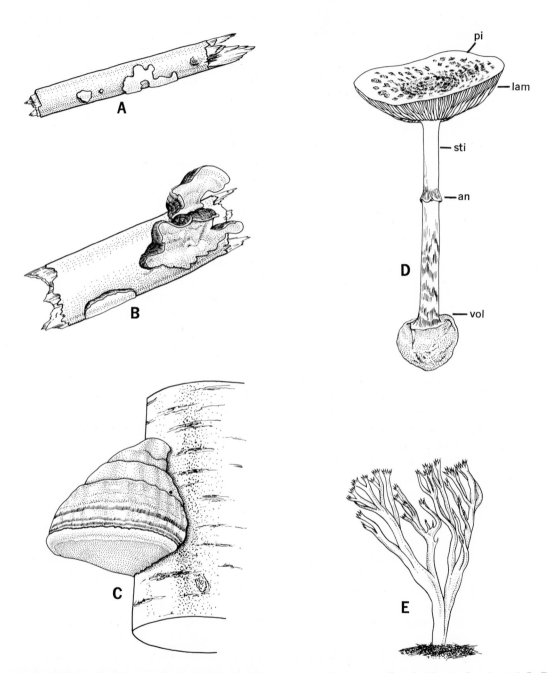

FIGURE 4–68   Basidiocarp form, habit sketches. A, resupinate or effused (*Peniophora*), ×1.5; B, effused-reflexed (*Stereum*), ×1; C, pileate, the pileus sessile and laterally attached to substrate (*Fomes*), ×0.5; D, pileate, stipitate basidiocarp of *Amanita*, ×0.5 (*pi*, pileus; *lam*, lamellae; *sti*, stipe; *an*, annulus; *vol*, volva); E, coralloid basidiocarp (*Clavulina*), ×1.

Most species of *Peniophora* have effused basidiocarps. However, in other species, and in the related genus *Stereum,* the basidiocarp is often **effused-reflexed** (Fig. 4–68B). This has both a resupinate part attached to the substrate and a reflexed shelf-like portion. The pileus is sessile and laterally attached in some forms (such as bracket or shelf fungi, Fig. 4–68C), whereas others are provided with a distinct stalk or stipe (Fig. 4–68D). Hymenia of the basidiocarp types just mentioned are unilateral or restricted to the lower (inferior) surfaces. In *Clavaria* and its relatives, with more or less amphigenous hymenia, the basidiocarps are simple and club-shaped, or branched in a coralloid fashion (Fig. 4–68E).

Wetting of the hymenial surfaces interrupts spore dispersal in basidiomycetes with abstricted spores. In erect coralloid types and certain others, the hymenium is directly exposed to falling rain. In these, spores can be abstricted, but they do not fall free if the hymenium is wet. The hymenial surfaces are protected from rain in shelving and pileate basidiocarps.

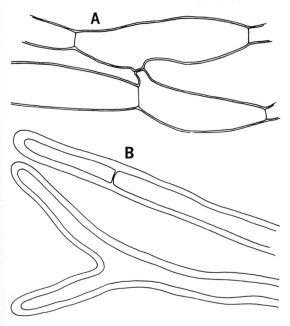

FIGURE 4–69   A, inflated, thin-walled hyphae typical of fleshy basidiocarps, ×1,400; B, thick-walled hyphae from leathery basidiocarp, ×350.

Basidiocarp form is not directly correlated with hymenial configuration. Thus, effused or resupinate species can have the hymenia covering smooth surfaces, teeth, or pores. Shelf-like basidiocarps and the pileate forms also have different types of hymenial configuration.

Texture of the basidiocarp is a rather nebulous characteristic varying with age and with moisture content in a single individual. However, in part it is a direct reflection of microscopic anatomy of the basidiocarp. Fleshy mushrooms and other hymenomycetes are composed of thin-walled, frequently inflated hyphae (Fig. 4–69A). The leathery and woody basidiocarps are composed to a large degree of thick-walled hyphae (Fig. 4–69B).

ORDER POLYPORALES.   This order includes a large number of species of extremely diverse form. In the Clavariaceae, the basidiocarps are erect and simple or branched. Most occur on soil, but some species grow on living or dead plants. The species of *Typhula* (Fig. 4–70A), some of which parasitize vascular plants, produce sclerotia similar to those of certain ascomycetes. Although they are very small, basidiocarps arising from these sclerotia are similar in form to the "cat tails" of *Typha.* The hymenium covers only the slightly enlarged portion of the structure. The species of *Clavariadelphus* (Fig. 4–70B) grow in the soil, producing basidiocarps with few or no branches. The hymenium is amphigenous, covering the surface of the branches. In *Clavulina* (Fig. 4–68E), *Clavicorona,* and other genera, the basidiocarps are often much-branched. Basidia of *Clavulina* (Fig. 4–70C) are secondarily septate, becoming so after the basidiospores have been released. Most clavariaceous fungi are soft-fleshy in texture and some of the species are edible.

The family Thelephoraceae includes those species in which the hymenium is unilateral and is borne on smooth surfaces. Some of the distinctive types of basidia found in this group are shown in Fig. 4–71A–E. The simplest basidiocarps are of the effused type and consist of little more than a hymenium (in

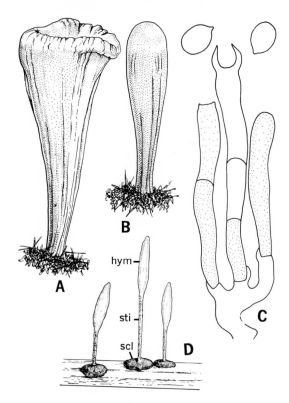

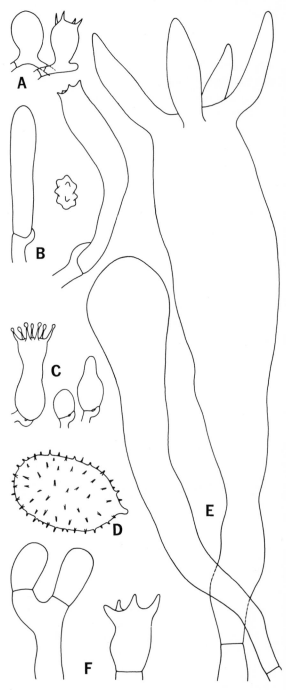

FIGURE 4–70   Clavariaceae. A, B, young and
mature basidiocarps of *Clavariadelphus truncatus*
(A, B, ×0.5); C, basidia and basidiospores of
Clavulina, ×1,260 (note secondary septa above
basal clamp connections); D, *Typhula*, ×5 (*scl*,
sclerotium; *sti*, stipe; *hym*, hymenium).

Xenasma, Galzinia, and other genera). The
more substantial resupinate or effused-reflexed
basidiocarps of *Peniophora* and *Stereum* consist of several sterile layers in addition to the
hymenium. The minute discoid sporocarps of
Solenia (Fig. 4–72A) are apothecium-like in
form and are macroscopically indistinguishable
from those of some ascomycetes. Most soil-
inhabiting thelphoraceous forms, such as
Thelephora, and *Sparassis,* have large
basidiocarps that are either funnel-shaped or
much-branched. In *Thelephora* (Fig. 4–71B,
72B) the basidiospores are brown and spiny;
those of *Sparassis* are hyaline and smooth.
Sparassis (Fig. 4–73), once included in the
Clavariaceae, produces the largest basidiocarps in the family Thelephoraceae. These
basidiocarps consist of numerous flattened
lobes arising from a single central axis.

FIGURE 4–71   Basidia and basidiospores of
thelephoraceous fungi. A, *Xenasma;* B, *Thelephora;* C, *Trechispora;* D, E, basidiospore and two
basidia of *Aleurodiscus;* F, basidia of *Pellicularia*
(all figures ×1,310; note range in size of basidiospores shown in B and D).

Basidiocarps of some of the Hydnaceae resemble those of the Clavariaceae. For example, those of *Hericium* (Fig. 4–74A) are large, much-branched, fleshy structures. The ultimate branches are spine-like and pendant, and bear the hymenium. In other genera the hymenium is also borne on tooth-like projections. Except for the toothed hymenium, resupinate hydnaceous fungi, such as *Odontia* and *Radulum,* are similar to **resupinate** species of the Thelephoraceae. The sporocarps of *Stec-cherinum ochraceum* are effused-reflexed, resembling those of *Stereum* and of some polypores. Those of *Hydnum* (Fig. 4–74B) and *Auriscalpium* are pileate and stipitate (Fig. 4–75).

The family Polyporaceae includes a number of the more important wood-decaying fungi. In this family the hymenia line tubular chambers. Resupinate basidiocarps are produced by the many species of *Poria* (Fig. 4–76A). The poroid surfaces are labyrinthuliform in *Daedalea* and lamellate in species of *Lenzites* (Fig. 4–76B, C). The texture in *Polyporus* (Fig. 4–76D) is fleshy to rather tough, the sporocarps being pileate and often stipitate. Perennial basidiocarps of *Fomes* (Fig. 4–68C, 77) are woody to punky in texture. The name *Fomes* is derived from the Latin term for "tinder," and the context of some species was once used in tinder boxes. *Fomes* (or *Laricifomes*) *officinalis* has basidiocarps that are chalky in color and texture; the extremely bitter context was once used medicinally.

Cantharellus (Fig. 4–78), previously included in the Agaricaceae, is now placed in a separate family, Cantharellaceae, in the Polyporales. The pileate basidiocarps have a hymenial configuration similar to that of the gill

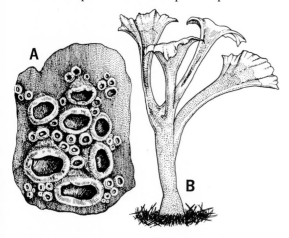

FIGURE 4–72   Habit sketches. A, *Solenia,* ×15; B, *Thelephora,* ×1.

FIGURE 4–73   *Sparassis radicatus,* ×0.5. (Photograph courtesy Provincial Museum, Victoria, B. C.)

FIGURE 4–74   A, *Hericeum,* ×0.5; B, *Hydnum,* ×0.5. (Photographs courtesy Provincial Museum, Victoria, B. C.)

FIGURE 4–75   *Auriscalpium,* ×1 (basidiocarp growing on partially buried cone of *Pseudotsuga*).

fungi. The **lamellae,** or gills, are shallow, blunt-edged, and branch frequently.

ORDER AGARICALES.   This includes all of the true gill fungi and one group of pore fungi. Most are fleshy or tough-fleshy and **putrescent**—i.e., they decay rapidly. Unlike those of many Polyporales, basidiocarps in the majority of Agaricales do not revive after having dried.

In the family Boletaceae, the hymenium is poroid; and in the remaining families it is lamellate. The lamellae or pores are often covered by a membranous layer, the **partial veil,** in the "button" state of development (Fig. 4–79B). This membrane, extending from the margin of the pileus to the stipe, ruptures as the cap expands, and its remnants remain attached to the stipe or to the cap margin. If it remains on the stipe, it is called an **annulus.** Basidiocarps of some lamellate genera have another membrane, the **universal veil,** extending upward from the base of the stipe. This also ruptures as the button expands,

leaving a cup-like fragment or **volva** (Fig. 4–68D) on the lower portion of the stipe. In addition, fragments of the universal veil frequently remain as warty patches on the pileus surface.

Basidiospore characteristics, cystidia, and other microscopic features, together with gross characteristics of the basidiocarp, aid in delimiting genera within the order. For example, the basidiospore color may be white, pink, ochre, purple-brown, or black. Basidiospores of some genera are marked by reticulations or warts. Cystidia are frequently present in the hymenium, and they may occur on gill edges and on surfaces of the pileus and stipe.

Development of basidiocarps of the common market mushroom, *Agaricus bisporus,* is shown in Fig. 4–79A–C. Basidiospores in this genus are purple-brown at maturity. Remnants of the partial veil form a conspicuous annulus in this mushroom. The species of *Amanita* are white-spored and have both an annulus and a volva (Fig. 4–68D). *Amanita phalloides* and related species, the "death angels" or "destroying angels," are the most poisonous of fleshy fungi. The white-spored *Russula* and *Lactarius* have large spherical cells making up much of the flesh of their basidiocarps. Their basidiospores have ridged **amyloid** (i.e., staining blue-black in iodine) reticulations.

Pilei of some genera, such as *Pleurotus* (Fig. 4–80) and *Crepidotus,* are laterally attached to the substratum. These pilei may have a short stipe or none. The stipe in *Paxillus* is often excentrically attached to the pileus.

Perhaps the most complex basidiocarps in this group are those of some *Coprinus* species (Fig. 4–81A, B). Here the basidia mature in waves, starting at the lower edge of the gill and working upward. Following discharge of the first basidiospores along the lower part of the lamella, autodigestion occurs. Another group of basidiospores is then released from higher up and autodigestion proceeds. In this way, the entire gill is eventually digested and forms an inky mass.

Gasteromycetes

The Gasteromycetes include puffballs, stinkhorns, and other groups, in which the

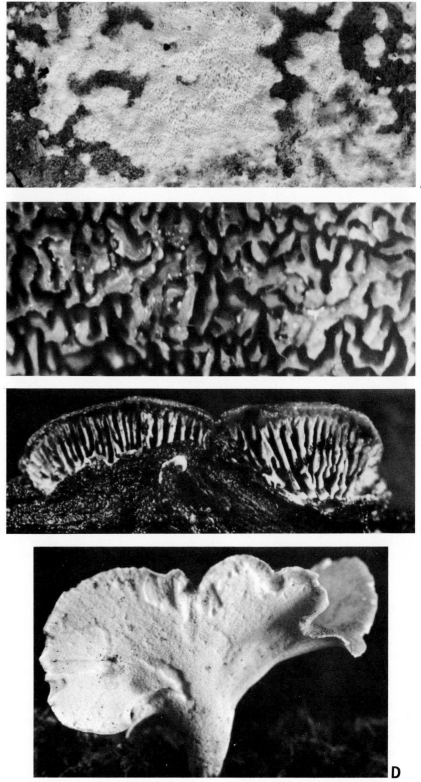

FIGURE 4–76   Polyporaceae. A, resupinate basidiocarps of *Poria*, ×2; B, labyrinthuliform hymenial surface of *Daedalea*, ×3; C, lamellate hymenial surface of *Lenzites*, ×1; D, pileate and stipitate basidiocarp of *Polyporus*, ×0.8

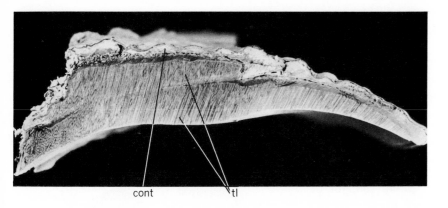

cont   tl

FIGURE 4–77 Vertical section through basidiocarp of *Fomes applanatus,* ×1 (*cont,* context; *tl,* tube layers).

FIGURE 4–78 *Cantharellus subalbidus* (note shallow, branching, and anastomosing gills), ×0.75. (Photograph courtesy Provincial Museum, Victoria, B. C.)

basidia mature in closed basidiocarps. The basidia occur in scattered patches in some forms and in definite hymenial layers in others. The basidiospores may be sessile—i.e., borne directly on the basidium—or they are sterigmate. The sterigmata often remain attached to the basidiospores following their release from the basidia.

In contrast to the Hymenomycetes, spore dispersal is brought about in a number of different ways: by wind, by water, and by insects or other animals. The basidiocarps of some species are **hypogeous**—i.e., they develop below the soil surface. Others are hypogeous only in early stages of development or are **epigeous** from the start. Some species occur only on wood. Although none is known to be parasitic, mycorrhizal associations are probably not uncommon among the Gasteromycetes.

ORDER HYMENOGASTRALES. Many members of this order seem intermediate between hymenomycetous forms and other groups of Gasteromycetes. Although they remain closed, the basidiocarps can have lamellae similar to those of the Agaricaceae. In some of these, the mature pilei expand, exposing the spore-bearing layers. However, the spores are not abstricted.

ORDER LYCOPERDALES. Basidiocarps in this order are completely closed and, for the most part, hypogeous. *Lycoperdon perlatum* (Fig. 4–82A–D), a widely distributed species, frequently grows in lawns and gardens. The basidiocarps are pear-shaped and consist of an outer wall, the **peridium,** and a soft fleshy inner mass, the **gleba.** Basidia are borne in small cavities within the gleba. When the basidia are mature, the gleba undergoes autodigestion, after which only the basidiospores and a mass of thread-like capillitial strands remain in the peridium. The basidiocarp dries out rapidly, the peridial layers becoming papery and flexible. A pore, or ostiole, develops at the apex of the basidiocarp and spores are puffed out through this. Any force applied against the flexible peridium, such as by raindrops or animals, results in a bellows-like action.

The genera *Bovista* and *Calvatia* (Fig. 4–83A, B) are closely related to *Lycoperdon.* No ostiole is present in these, but the mature peridium cracks irregularly. Basidiocarps of *Bovista* and some species of *Calvatia* are weakly attached to the soil at maturity. They are easily blown free by winds and are tumbled along, scattering the basidiospores. The tangled capillitium prevents rapid loss of the spores. *C. gigantea* produces huge basidiocarps; it has been estimated that the largest of these contain approximately 160,000,000,000 spores.

ORDER PHALLALES. Stinkhorns are so called because the digestion of the gleba leaves a foul-smelling, slimy mass. This attracts insects, which effect spore dispersal.

In most instances, early stages in development of the basidiocarps are below the soil surface. In the genus *Phallus* (Fig. 4–84A),

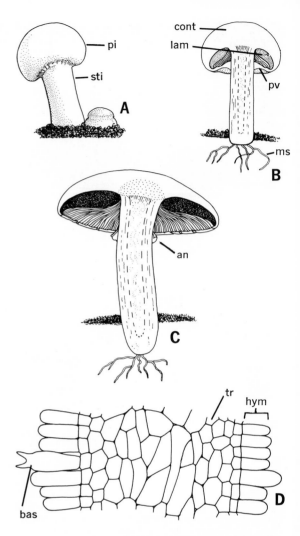

FIGURE 4–79   *Agaricus bisporus.* A–C, basidiocarp development. A, habit sketch of young basidiocarps, ×0.5 (*pi,* pileus; *sti,* stipe); B, vertical section through immature basidiocarp, ×0.5 (*cont,* context; *lam,* lamellae; *pv,* partial veil; *ms,* mycelial strands); C, vertical section through mature basidiocarp, ×0.5 (*an,* annulus). D, section through small portion of lamellae, ×1,000 (*tr,* trama; *hym,* hymenium; *bas,* basidium).

the buttons are egg-like in appearance and have a tough but flexible peridium. Immediately under the peridium is a thick layer of gelatinous material which functions in water storage. The gleba is borne in a stipitate, cap-like pileus or receptacle. At maturity, the stipe elongates and ruptures the peridial layers. The slimy glebal mass then lies exposed on the

FIGURE 4–80   *Pleurotus ostreatus.* Habit of laterally attached pilei, ×0.5.

upper surface of the pileus. Species of *Mutinus* (Fig. 4–84B) are similar in form, but the pileus is practically continuous with the stipe. A third genus found in temperate zones is *Dictyophora.* Here a lacy skirt-like structure is present just below the receptacle. Bright colors, especially red, are not uncommon in the Phallales and possibly aid in attracting insects. When mature, some of the Phallales are almost flower-like in form.

ORDER NIDULARIALES.   Basidiocarps in this order are formed on wood or on the soil. The basidia are in hymenial layers lining cavities of the gleba. Each fertile region becomes surrounded by firm wall layers; at maturity, these are hard lenticular bodies, the **peridioles,** within which the basidiospores are produced. In *Nidularia,* the peridium is of uniform thickness and ruptures irregularly. In other genera,

such as *Nidula* and *Crucibulum* (Fig. 4–85A–C), the lower portion of the peridium is rigid and relatively thick. The basidiocarps are funnel-shaped to more or less cupulate and contain from few to many peridioles. The upper cover-like portion of the peridium breaks free, exposing the peridioles. Dispersal of the latter occurs through splashing by raindrops, and the peridioles may be carried to distances of more than a meter by this action.

RELATIONSHIPS OF THE
BASIDIOMYCETES

It is unlikely that the intricate basidiospore discharge mechanism found in many basidiomycetes is polyphyletic in origin. Thus, those with this mechanism—including both the Heterobasidiomycetidae and the Homobasidio-

A

B

FIGURE 4–81   *Coprinus*. A, mature basidiocarps before autodigestion has occurred, ×1; B, later stage showing caps expanded and after occurrence of some autodigestion, ×1.

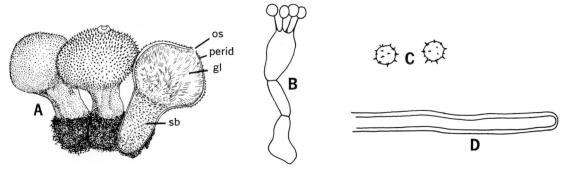

FIGURE 4–82   *Lycoperdon perlatum*. A, habit sketch of basidiocarps, one of which (at right) has been sectioned vertically (*os,* ostiole; *perid,* peridium; *gl,* gleba; *sb,* sterile base), ×1; B, C, mature basidium and basidiospores, B, ×1,025; C, ×2,200; D, portion of capillitial strand, ×2,200.

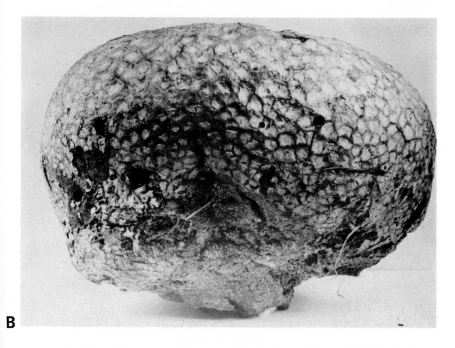

FIGURE 4–83   Mature basidiocarps (A, *Bovista pila,* ×0.75; B, *Calvatia gigantea,* ×0.25).

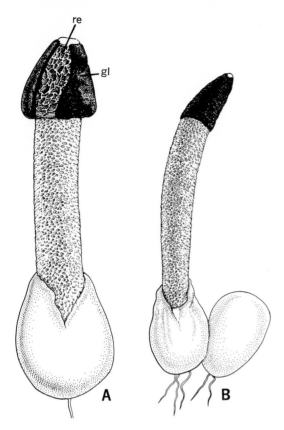

FIGURE 4–84   A, habit sketch of *Phallus impudicus;* portion of the gleba (*gl*) has been removed to show the pitted nature of the receptacle (*re*), ×1. B, *Mutinus caninus,* ×1.

mycetidae—are thought to have descended from the same ancestral forms. Those species lacking the spore abstriction mechanism—for example, the gasteromycetous fungi—are undoubtedly derived from those with it. Apparently the loss is associated with the development of closed basidiocarps.

The heterobasidiomycetes are now commonly accepted as the most primitive of fungi in this class, for the following reasons: (1) the low level of basidiocarp development; and (2) variability in microscopic structure, both within individual species and in the group as a whole. Assuming that this is correct, it is then relatively easy to find several possible transitions leading to homobasidiomycetous forms. It is probable that the "holobasidium"—i.e., that of the Homobasidiomycetidae—is not of monophyletic origin as once believed. Transitional forms are found leading from both the cruciate septate and the transversely septate basidia to holobasidium types.

If the Heterobasidiomycetidae are assumed to be the primitive forms, the problem of their origin remains; here the greatest diversity of opinion is found. Two suggested pathways are: (1) from floridean (red algal) ancestors, either through ascomycetous forms

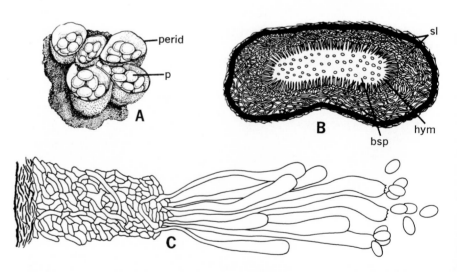

FIGURE 4–85   *Crucibulum laeve.* A, basidiocarps, ×3 (*perid,* peridium; *p,* peridioles); B, semidiagrammatic sketch of section through peridiole (*sl,* sterile layers; *hym,* hymenium; *bsp,* basidiospores), ×65; C, portion of hymenium enlarged to show basidiospores and basidia, ×1,290.

or directly to the rust fungi; and (2) directly from ascomycetes. The suggestion of relationship with red algae is based on similarities in the life cycles of these forms and those of rusts or ascomycetes. However, the evidence on hand would appear to favor ascomycetous ancestry of the basidiomycetes. The presence of a dikaryotic stage, the suspected homology of asci and basidia, and of clamps and croziers, all favor this concept. Both hemi- and euascomycetous ancestry have been suggested. The hemiascomycetes or their ancestors would seem to offer the more favorable possibilities; their asci are not highly specialized and, in some instances, their development is similar to that of some heterobasidiomycetes.

FORM CLASS FUNGI
IMPERFECTI
(Deuteromycetes)

In many species of fungi only asexual reproductive structures are known. The relationships of these are obvious in a few cases, but are not in the great majority. Thus, in part, the Fungi Imperfecti (also known as Deuteromycetes) is a receptacle for incompletely known species of uncertain relationships. It was once thought that, as these fungi were studied, all would eventually be placed in the natural classes. However, it now appears probable that some species have lost the ability to reproduce sexually. Therefore, it seems unlikely at this time that the form class Fungi Imperfecti will be eliminated in the near future.

Many fungi have names based on both the sexual and asexual stages. For example, the name *Tubercularia vulgaris* is often applied to the conidial stage of *Nectria cinnabarina* (Euascomycetidae). Such use of two binomials for the same organism is usually the result of an incomplete knowledge of the fungal life history. The name first associated with the sexual stage is the accepted one. Most of this duplication of names results from discovery and naming of the asexual stage, then finding the **perfect**

stage at a later date.

The group Fungi Imperfecti is separated somewhat arbitrarily into orders, families, and genera. Because of this, these taxa are called **form orders, form families,** and **form genera.** There are many known instances where similar asexual stages are produced by two or more fungi of only distant relationship. But the asexual stages of two closely related species, as determined by the sexual stage, may be quite distinct. Thus, the form taxa in the Fungi Imperfecti must be treated only as assemblages, not as natural groups.

Four form orders, based on the types of spore-bearing structures, are recognized. These are the Sphaeropsidales, Melanconiales, Moniliales, and Mycelia Sterilia. The latter includes fungi in which no spores are produced.

The form genera in each group are separated at the present time according to a scheme suggested by Saccardo—a scheme based on the shape, color, and septation of the spores. Although admittedly arbitrary, this scheme has allowed classification and identification of species. Other classification systems have been suggested for the group—the most noteworthy being that of Hughes, which emphasizes the method of formation of the conidia rather than the conidia themselves. Unrelated fungi occupying the same ecological niche often produce spores of similar form. Such fungi can be readily distinguished from one another if the method of spore formation is studied. Thus, basing the classification system on the method of conidium formation, rather than on conidial characteristics, should eventually lead to a more natural arrangement of the group.

FORM ORDER SPHAEROPSIDALES. In the Sphaeropsidales, conidia are borne in pycnidia or pycnidium-like structures. Many of these fungi are important parasites of crop plants; these include species of *Phoma, Septoria, Phomopsis* (Fig. 4–86A–D), and others. *Phoma* species produce hyaline one-celled spores that are ellipsoid or oval. The spores of *Septoria* are hyaline and their length greatly exceeds their

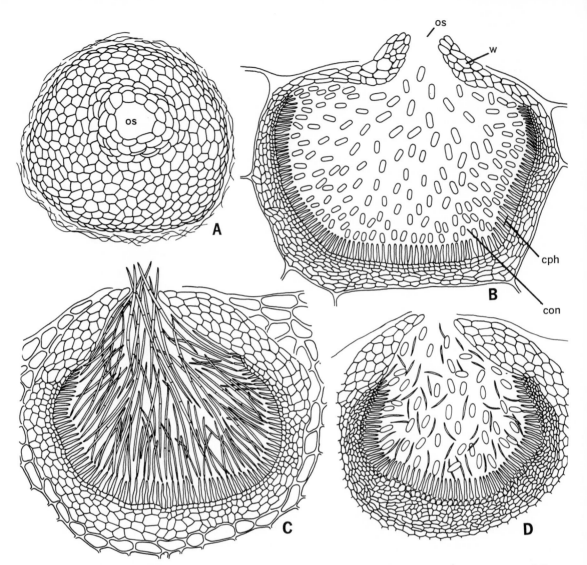

FIGURE 4–86   A, B, *Phoma*. A, habit sketch of pycnidium, ×1,050; B, section through pycnidium, ×1,230 (*os*, ostiole; *w*, pycnidial wall; *cph*, conidiophores; *con*, conidia). C, D, sections through pycnidia (C, *Septoria*, ×1,250; D, *Phomopsis*, containing two types of conidia, ×1,285).

thickness. Two types of conidia are found in pycnidia of *Phomopsis*.

FORM ORDER MELANCONIALES.   Conidia of the Melanconiales are borne in acervuli, which are saucer-shaped and usually produced subepidermally on plants. Many of the species are parasites, causing a type of plant disease called anthracnose. Among the more important genera are *Colletotrichum* and *Pestalotia* (Fig. 4–87A, B). Stiff bristle-like hairs (setae) are formed around acervuli of *Colletotrichum* spe-

cies. Their hyaline ellipsoid spores are embedded in a viscous substance. The spores of *Pestalotia* are dark colored, septate, and provided with hyaline appendages.

FORM ORDER MONILIALES.   Fungi placed in this form order produce neither pycnidia nor acervuli. In some genera, only budding cells are formed. These asporogenous yeasts are usually grouped in a form family, the Pseudo-saccharomycetaceae. The "mirror yeasts," or Sporobolomycetaceae produce both buds and

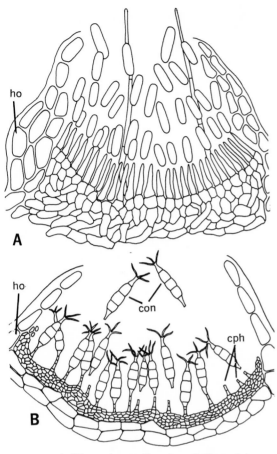

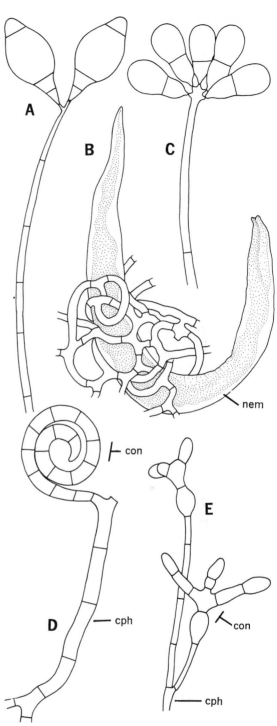

FIGURE 4-87   Acervuli. A, *Colletotrichum*, ×1,200; B, *Pestalotia*, ×550. *ho,* host tissue; *cph,* conidiophores; *con,* conidia.

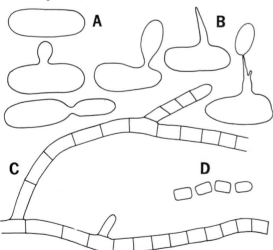

FIGURE 4-88   A, B, *Sporobolomyces roseus.* A, cells, three of which are budding, ×2,900; B, reproduction by ballistospore formation, ×2,900. C, D, *Geotrichum.* C, septate hyphal branches before fragmentation has occurred, ×3,000; D, after fragmentation, ×3,000.

FIGURE 4-89   A, B, *Dactylaria.* A, apex of conidiophore with two conidia, ×845; B, network of adhesive loops with entrapped nematode (*nem*), ×90. C, portion of conidiophore of *Arthrobotrys* with terminal group of conidia, ×1,000. D, conidium (*con*) and conidiophore (*cph*) of *Helicoma,* ×1,570. E, conidiophore of *Clavariopsis* bearing two conidia, ×1,115.

ballistospores. Ballistospores are formed and abstricted like basidiospores, but they are not formed on basidia. Because of the ballistospores, a mirror image of a colony is produced on the lid of inverted cultures of these fungi. *Sporobolomyces roseus,* one of the commonest species, is shown in Fig. 4–88A, B.

Some of the hyphal Moniliales reproduce through fragmentation of the hyphae. Species of *Geotrichum* (Fig. 4–88C, D) are common laboratory contaminants forming "arthrospores" in this manner. Most of the Moniliales bear their spores on definite conidiophores. *Dactylaria* species (Fig. 4–89A, B), common on compost and dung, are of this type. A number of species in this genus are interesting because of the nematode-trapping snares produced on their hyphae. *Arthrobotrys* (Fig. 4–89C) and other genera have similar snares or adhesive structures that capture small animals. Once captured, the bodies of such animals are penetrated by special absorptive hyphae and are utilized as nutrient by the fungus. Many of these fungi, which can live entirely as saprobes, are readily grown in culture. Some species no longer produce snares when grown for a time in pure culture; but, snare production may be induced if nematodes are added to such cultures.

Perhaps the most striking conidia are those of certain aquatic Fungi Imperfecti. Here the spore form is apparently correlated with the habitat type and presumably is important in dispersal. In one group, as illustrated by the genus *Helicoma* (Fig. 4–89D), the spores are helically coiled; in another, the spores are four-armed or tetraradiate, as in *Clavariopsis* (Fig. 4–89E).

GENERAL REFERENCES ON EUMYCOTA

Ainsworth, G. C., *Dictionary of the Fungi.* Kew: Commonwealth Mycological Institute (1961).

Alexopoulas, C. J., *Introductory Mycology,* 2nd Ed. New York: John Wiley & Sons, Inc. (1962).

Bessey, E. A., *Morphology and Taxonomy of Fungi.* Philadelphia: The Blakiston Co. (1950).

Chadefaud, M., in Chadefaud, M., and Emberger, L., *Traité de Botanique Systématique.* Vol. I. Paris: Masson et Cie (1960).

Cochrane, V. W., *Physiology of Fungi.* New York: John Wiley & Sons, Inc. (1958).

Gaumann, E. A., *The Fungi.* (Trans. by F. L. Wynd). New York: Hafner Publishing Co. (1952).

Gray, W. D., *The Relation of Fungi to Human Affairs.* New York: Holt, Rinehart & Winston, Inc. (1959).

Hawker, L. E., *The Physiology of Reproduction in Fungi.* Cambridge: Cambridge University Press (Cambridge Monogr. in Exp. Biol., 1957).

Hawker, L. E., Linton, A. H., Folkes, B. F., and Carlile, M. J., *An Introduction to the Biology of Micro-organisms.* London: Edward Arnold (Publishers) Ltd. (1960).

Ingold, C. T., *Dispersal in Fungi.* Oxford: Clarendon Press (1953).

Ingold, C. T., *The Biology of Fungi*. London: Hutchinson Educational Ltd. (1961).

Johnson, T. W., Jr., and Sparrow, F. K., Jr., *Fungi in Oceans and Estuaries*. New York: Hafner Publishing Co. (1961).

Martin, G. W., "Key to the Families of Fungi." In Ainsworth, G. C., *Dictionary of the Fungi*. Pp. 497–517. Kew, Surrey: Commonwealth Mycological Institute (1961).

Raper, J. R., "Sexual Versatility and Evolutionary Processes in Fungi." *Mycologia*, 51: 107–124 (1959).

Raper, J. R., "The Control of Sex in Fungi." *Am. J. Bot.*, 47: 794–808 (1960).

Snell, W. H., and Dick, E. A., *A Glossary of Mycology*. Cambridge, Mass.: Harvard University Press (1957).

REFERENCES ON PHYCOMYCETES

Blakeslee, A. F., "Sexual Reproduction in the Mucorinae." *Proc. Am. Acad. Arts Sci.*, 40: 205–319 (1904).

Cantino, E. C., "Physiology and Phylogeny in the Water Molds—A Reevaluation." *Quart. Rev. Biol.*, 30: 138–149 (1955).

Cantino, E. C., "The Relation between Biochemical and Morphological Differentiation in Non-filamentous Fungi." *11th Symposium, Soc. Gen. Microbiol.* Cambridge: Cambridge University Press (1961).

Coker, W. C., *The Saprolegniaceae with Notes on Other Water Molds*. Chapel Hill: University of North Carolina Press (1923).

Emerson, R., "The Biology of the Water Molds." In *Aspects of Synthesis and Order of Growth*. Princeton, N. J.: Princeton University Press (1955).

Fitzpatrick, H. M., *The Lower Fungi. Phycomycetes*. New York: McGraw-Hill Book Co., Inc. (1930).

Hawker, L. E., and Abbott, P. M., "Fine Structure of Young Vegetative Hyphae of *Pythium debaryanum*." *J. Gen. Microbiol.*, 31: 491–494 (1963).

Hesseltine, C. W., "Genera of Mucorales with Notes on Their Synonymy." *Mycologia*, 47: 344–563 (1955).

Koch, W. J., "Studies of the Motile Cells of Chytrids, I: Electron Microscope Observations of the Flagellum, Blepharoplast, and Rhizoplast." *Am. J. Bot.*, 43: 811–819 (1956).

Koch, W. J., "Studies of the Motile Cells of Chytrids, II: Internal Structure of the Body Observed with Light Microscopy." *Am. J. Bot.*, 45: 59–72 (1958).

Lovett, J. S., and Cantino, E. C., "The Relation between Biochemical and Morphological Differentiation in *Blastocladiella emersonii,* I and II." *Am. J. Bot.,* 47: 499–504; 550–560 (1960).

Sansome, E., "Meiosis in *Pythium debaryanum* Hesse and Its Significance in the Life History of the Biflagellatae." *Trans. Brit. Mycol. Soc.,* 46: 63–72 (1963).

Sparrow, F. K., "Interrelationships and Phylogeny of the Aquatic Phycomycetes." *Mycologia,* 50: 797–813 (1958).

Sparrow, F. K., *Aquatic Phycomycetes.* Ann Arbor: University of Michigan Press (1960).

Waterhouse, G. M., "The Zoospore." *Trans. Brit. Mycol. Soc.,* 45: 1–20 (1962).

Zycha, H., *Mucorineae. Kryptogamenflora der Mark Bradenburg.* Vol. 6a. Leipzig: Gebrüder Borntraeger (1935).

REFERENCES ON ASCOMYCETES

Benjamin, C. R., "Ascocarps of *Aspergillum* and *Penicillium.*" *Mycologia,* 47: 669–687 (1955).

Benjamin, R. K., "A New Genus of the Gymnoascaceae with a Review of the Other Genera." *El Aliso,* 3: 301–328 (1956).

Cook, A. H. (Ed.), *The Chemistry and Biology of Yeasts.* New York: Academic Press, Inc. (1958).

Dennis, R. W. G., *British Cup Fungi and Their Allies.* London: The Ray Society (1960).

Gilkey, H. M., "Tuberales." *North American Flora,* II, 1: 1–36 (1954).

Guilliermond, A., "Sexuality, Developmental Cycle, and Phylogeny of Yeasts." *Bot. Rev.,* 6: 1–24 (1940).

Lindegren, C. C., *The Yeast Cell, Its Genetics and Cytology.* St. Louis: Educational Publishers, Inc. (1949).

Lodder, J., and Kreger-van Rig, N. J. W., *The Yeasts.* Amsterdam: North Holland Publishing Co. (1952).

Luttrell, E. S., "Taxonomy of the Pyrenomycetes." *Univ. Missouri Stud.,* 24(3), Columbia (1951).

Luttrell, E. S., "The Ascostromatic Ascomycetes." *Mycologia,* 47: 511–532 (1955).

Miller, J. H., "A Revision of the Classification of the Ascomycetes with Special Emphasis on the Pyrenomycetes." *Mycologia,* 41: 99–127 (1949).

Moore, R. T., and McAlear, J. H., "Fine Structure of the Mycota." *Am. J. Bot.,* 49: 86–94 (1962).

Munk, A., "Danish Pyrenomycetes." *Dansk. Bot. Arkiv.,* 17: 1–491 (1957).

Nannfeldt, J. A., "Studien Über die Morphologie und Systematik der Nicht Lichenisierten Inoperculaten Discomyceten." *Nova Acta Reg. Soc. Sci. Upsal.,* Ser. IV, 8(2): 1–368 (1932).

Nickerson, W. J., "Symposium on Biochemical Bases of Morphogenesis in Fungi." *Bact. Rev.,* 27(3): 293–304 (1963).

Pontecorvo, G., "The Parasexual Cycle in Fungi." *Ann. Rev. Microbiol.,* 10: 393–400 (1956).

Pontecorvo, G., and Roper, J. A., "Genetic Analysis without Sexual Reproduction by Means of Polyploidy in *Aspergillus nidulans.*" *J. Gen. Microbiol.,* 6: vii (1952).

Seaver, F. J., *The North American Cup-Fungi (Operculates).* New York: Published by the Author (1928).

Seaver, F. J., *The North American Cup-Fungi (Inoperculates).* New York: Published by the Author (1951).

REFERENCES ON BASIDIOMYCETES

Arthur, J. C., *Manual of the Rusts of the United States and Canada.* Lafayette, Ind.: Purdue Research Foundation (1934).

Bracker, C. E., Jr., and Butler, E. E., "The Ultrastructure and Development of Septa in Hyphae of *Rhizoctonia solani.*" *Mycologia,* 55: 627–632 (1963).

Brodie, J. H., "The Splash-cup Dispersal Mechanism in Plants." *Can. J. Bot.,* 29: 224–234 (1951).

Coker, W. C., and Couch, J. N., *The Gasteromycetes of the Eastern United States and Canada.* Chapel Hill: University of North Carolina Press (1928).

Corner, E. J. H., *A Monograph of Clavaria and Allied Genera.* London: Oxford University Press (1950).

Craigie, J. H., "Discovery of the Function of the Pycnia of the Rust Fungi." *Nature* (London), 120: 765–767 (1927).

Cummins, G. B., *Illustrated Genera of Rust Fungi.* Minneapolis: Burgess Publishing Co. (1959).

Cunningham, G. H., *The Gasteromycetes of Australia and New Zealand.* Dunedin, New Zealand: Published by the Author (1944).

Eriksson, J., "Studies in the Heterobasidiomycetes and Homobasidiomycetes—Aphyllophorales of Muddus National Park." *Symbol. Bot. Upsal.,* 16 (1958).

Fergus, C. L., *Illustrated Genera of Wood Decay Fungi.* Minneapolis: Burgess Publishing Co. (1960).

Fischer, G. W., and Holton, C. S., *Biology and Control of Smut Fungi.* New York: Ronald Press Co. (1957).

Martin, G. W., "Revision of the North Central Tremellales." *Univ. Iowa Stud. Nat. Hist.,* 19: 1–122 (1952).

Ramsbottom, J., *Mushrooms and Toadstools.* London: Collins (1953).

Rogers, D. P., "The Basidium." *Univ. Iowa Stud. Nat. Hist.,* 16: 160–183 (1934).

Savile, D. B. O., "Cellular Mechanics, Taxonomy and Evolution in the Uredinales and Ustilaginales." *Mycologia,* 46:735–761 (1954).

Seaver, F. J., *The North American Cup-Fungi (Inoperculates).* New York: Published by the Author (1951).

Takemaru, T., "Genetical Studies on Fungi, X: The Mating System in Hymenomycetes and Its Genetical Mechanism." *Biol. J. Okayama Univ.,* 7: 133–211 (1961).

Talbot, P. H. B., "Micro-morphology of the Lower Hymenomycetes." *Bothalia,* 6: 249–299 (1954).

REFERENCES ON FUNGI IMPERFECTI

Barnett, H. L., *Illustrated Genera of Imperfect Fungi,* 2nd Ed. Minneapolis: Burgess Publishing Co. (1960).

Duddington, C. L., "Fungi That Attack Microscopic Animals." *Bot. Rev.,* 21: 377–439 (1955).

Hughes, S. J., "Conidiophores, Conidia, and Classification." *Can. J. Bot.,* 31: 577–659 (1953).

Pramer, D., "Nematode-trapping Fungi." *Science,* 144: 382–388 (1964).

Saccardo, P. A., *Sylloge Fungorum Omnium Hucusque Cognitorum.* Vol. 14. Pavia: Published by the Author (1899).

Tubaki, K., "Studies on the Japanese Hyphomycetes, V: Leaf and Stem Group with a Discussion of the Classification of Hyphomycetes and Their Perfect Stages." *J. Hattori Bot. Lab.,* 20: 142–244 (1958).

Tubaki, K., "Taxonomic Study of the Hyphomycetes." *Ann. Rept. Inst. Fermentation,* Osaka, 1961–1962. No. 1. (1963).

5 / LICHENS

Although *lichens* are often treated as a separate plant division, most lichenologists now consider them part of the fungi. More than 17,000 species of lichens have been described and more than 2,000 of these are known from North America. Lichen fungi differ little from other parasitic fungi, except that the lichen fungal hyphae and algal cells are so mutually dependent that the resulting association behaves as a single plant. This association, or lichen, reproduces itself as an association rather than as an alga or a fungus. Indeed, in most instances the **mycobiont,** or fungal partner, cannot reproduce itself or live independently in nature. But the algal partner is able to survive either as an algal component of a lichen or as an independent organism. Under pure culture conditions in the laboratory a large number of **phycobionts** (algal partners) have reproduced sexually and have thrived better than in the lichen association. No cultured mycobiont has been induced to reproduce sexually, and only in rare cases have asexual reproductive structures been produced. Many lichens may represent the perfect stage of deuteromycetes.

In the lichen thallus the cells of the phycobiont are often distorted. It is difficult or impossible to determine the component algal species, unless it is cultured separately. The mycobiont, on the other hand, is generally a species restricted to a lichenized existence. Thus, lichen taxonomy is essentially fungal taxonomy, since the mycobiont usually gives the lichen its gross morphology.

More important, the sexual reproductive structures are strictly fungal.

Most lichens contain a single species of alga, although in some instances two or even three species are represented. The same species of alga may also be found in several different lichens. In most lichens the phycobiont is a green alga (Division Chlorophyta)—most commonly the green alga *Trebouxia*. The blue-green algae (Division Cyanophyta) are also represented in many lichens. In some instances *Nostoc* forms the bulk of the lichen thallus; in others, as in the lichen *Ephebe,* the thallus is composed predominantly of *Stigonema*.

The mycobiont is generally an ascomycete; but a few tropical basidiomycetes, some deuteromycetes, and reportedly a single phycomycete lead a lichenized existence. Bacteria are present as contaminants in lichens, but it has never been satisfactorily demonstrated that they are an essential component of the lichen.

The lichen thallus may be unstratified or stratified (Fig. 5–1). In the unstratified type, the algal cells are scattered throughout, a condition called **homoiomerous.** Because of its lack of organization, this type is regarded as more primitive than the **heteromerous** (stratified) thallus, in which the algal cells are restricted mainly to a specific layer.

The growth form of the lichen thallus is constant for a given species, and is highly important in the classification of lichens. Several common growth forms are readily recognizable: **sorediate, crustose, foliose, squamulose, fruticose,** and **gelatinous.**

The sorediate thallus is very primitive (Fig. 5–2D), and in many instances sexual reproductive structures are unknown. Because of its homoiomerous organization and lack of any distinctive morphology, a sorediate lichen sim-

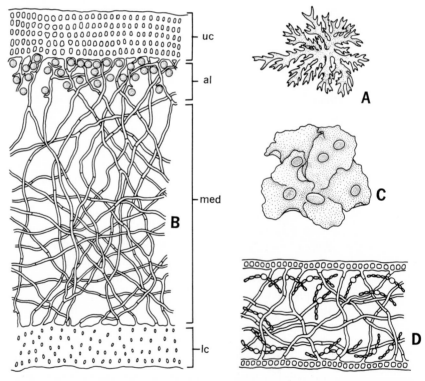

FIGURE 5–1   Foliose lichens, showing thallus structure. A, *Parmelia perlata,* habit, ×0.5; B, *P. perlata,* cross section showing heteromerous thallus with upper cortex (*uc*), algal layer (*al*), medulla (*med*), lower cortex (*lc*), ×450; C, *Leptogium tremelloides,* habit, ×0.5; D, *L. tremelloides,* cross section of thallus showing homoiomerous thallus, ×220. (B, D, after Schneider.)

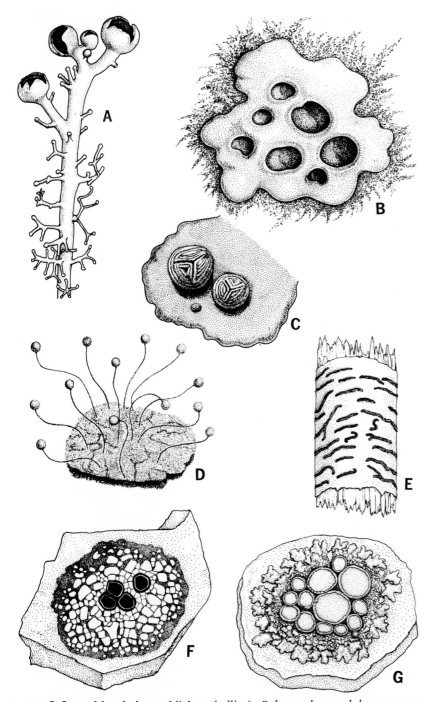

FIGURE 5–2   Morphology of lichen thalli. A, *Sphaerophorus globosus;* upper portion of fruticose thallus with thalloid receptacles containing apothecia, ×5. B, *Solorina saccata,* showing apothecia depressed in foliose thallus, ×2. C, *Umbilicaria polyphylla,* showing gyrate apothecia on foliose thallus, ×10. D, *Coniocybe furfuracea,* sorediate thallus with stipitate apothecia, ×10. E, *Graphis scripta,* hypophloedal crustose thallus with lirelline apothecia, ×2.5. F, *Rhizocarpon geographicum,* crustose thallus with apothecia, ×2.5. G, *Caloplaca elegans,* foliose thallus with apothecia, ×3.

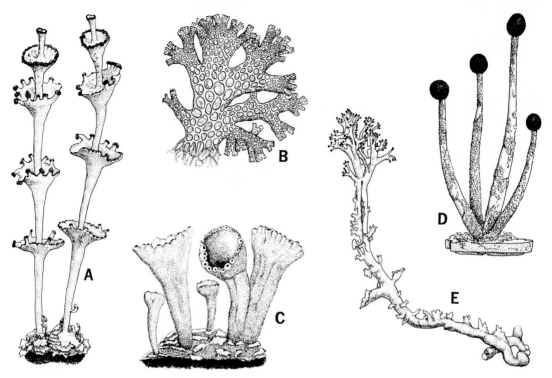

FIGURE 5–3   Fruticose podetia of lichens. A, *Cladonia verticellata*, ×2; B, *C. retipora*, ×2.5; C, *C. deformis*, ×2; D, *Pilophoron cereolus*, ×35; E, *Cladonia furcata*, ×1.5.

ply forms a powdery layer over the substrate and is therefore exceedingly puzzling to identify when sexual reproductive structures are absent. Many of these lichens are included in the genus *Lepraria*.

A crustose thallus may be homoiomerous or heteromerous (Fig. 5–2 E, F). In heteromerous crustose forms, the lichen is a thin crust closely adherent to the substrate. The hyphae in the upper portion of the crust form an upper cortex. These hyphae are usually tightly compacted and highly gelatinized; they may be colored or nearly translucent. The cells of the algal layer, which underlies the cortex, are surrounded by a loose network of hyphae. Below the algal layer is a **medulla** of varying thickness composed of loosely arranged hyphae. The lowermost hyphae act as rhizoidal hyphae, attaching the thallus to the substratum. In some crustose forms occurring on a relatively soft substrate (e.g., bark), much of the thallus penetrates the outer layers of the substrate. Thus, substrate cells and those of the lichen thallus are intermingled. This does not imply either saprophytism or parasitism; the substrate is simply texturally suitable for the lichen, which apparently derives little or no nutrient from it. In homoiomerous crustose lichens stratification is essentially absent, although a thin upper cortex may be differentiated.

The foliose thallus strongly resembles the crustose thallus (Fig. 5–1, 2B, C, G, 9A). It, too, possesses an upper cortex, an algal layer, and a medulla. However, in crustose forms the thallus cannot be removed intact from the substrate; it is essentially "painted" to the substrate. In foliose forms, the thallus can be carefully peeled from the substrate—partly because of the greater thickness of the foliose thallus, and also from its looser attachment to the substrate. In some foliose lichens the thallus may be attached by a single bundle of hyphae, forming a central cord; the rest of the thallus expands over this single point of attachment. In others the thallus is attached by a number of bundles of hyphae **(rhizines).** Depending upon

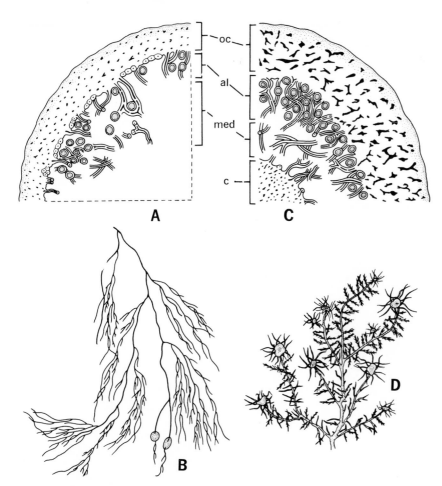

FIGURE 5–4   Fruticose thalli of lichens. A, *Alectoria,* cross section of thallus showing outer cortex (*oc*), algal layer (*al*), medulla (*med*), central strand (*c*), ×165; B, *Alectoria,* habit, ×1; C, *Usnea,* cross section of thallus showing anatomy, ×165; D, *Usnea,* habit, ×1. (A, C, after des Abbayes with permission of Paul Lechevalier.)

the species, the foliose thallus may possess a lower cortex of densely packed hyphae beneath the medulla. The lower cortex is either colored or colorless and varies considerably in texture.

The squamulose thallus is structurally similar to the foliose type (Fig. 5–3A, C). However, the squamulose thallus is made up of many small lobes, which may be loosely attached to each other; in some species of *Cladonia,* these lobes (or **squamules**) form colonies, in which each squamule is free of its neighbor. In others, as in some species of *Lecidea,* the squamules form a rough lobulate thallus, in which the lobes may be all intimately interconnected.

The fruticose thallus is shrub-like, with cylindrical or flattened branches (Fig. 5–2A, 4). Branching is either simple or very complex. The thallus may be stiffly erect or pendulous, some pendulous forms being more than 20 feet long (e.g., *Usnea longissima*). Most fruticose thalli are heteromerous, but stratification differs somewhat from the previously described types. The thallus is hollow or solid in cross section. The outer cortex is thick or, less commonly, rather thin. The algal layer is generally thinner than in foliose or crustose thalli. The medulla often fills the center of the thallus, but it may simply form a layer that encloses the algal layer, leaving the center hollow (e.g., *Alectoria*). In some fruticose forms the medulla is in two layers: the outer layer of loosely packed hyphae, the inner a strand of closely packed thick-walled hyphae (Fig. 5–4).

The gelatinous thallus is essentially homoiomerous with a blue-green alga dominating the structure (Fig. 5–5); the fungus is scarcely apparent. Most gelatinous lichens are black or blackish. The name is derived from the texture of the moist lichen.

Geosiphon pyriforme has been described as the only lichenized phycomycete. It is obviously different from any other lichen, particularly in its morphology (Fig. 5–6). The plant is ephemeral, appearing only in the autumn (September to December) on clay soils of central Europe. In *Geosiphon* bulbous structures, rich in food reserves, are produced. Some of these incorporate *Nostoc* strands, and growth of the *Nostoc* colony causes enlargement of the *Geosiphon* cell into a pear-shaped vesicle. Since the fungus is colorless, the lichen resembles a *Nostoc* colony. Close examination shows that hyphae attach the pear-shaped vesicles to the soil. There is some debate whether or not *Geosiphon* is a lichen; it has been treated both as an alga and as a fungus.

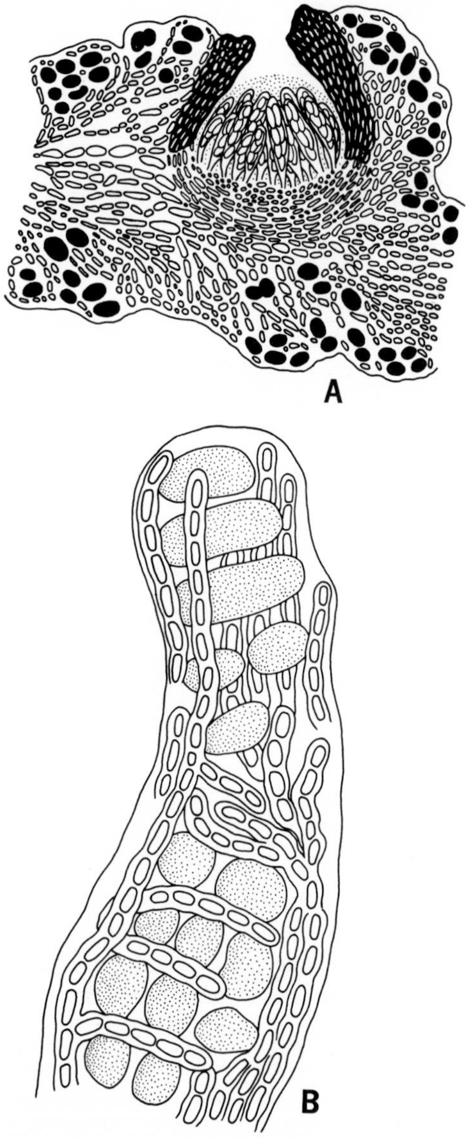

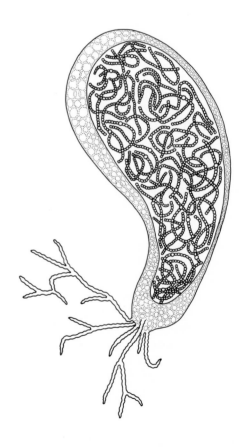

FIGURE 5–5   Gelatinous thallus of *Ephebe lanata,* showing anatomy. A, section through apothecium, ×310; B, tip of branch, ×1,000. (After Galløe with permission of Ejnar Munksgaard.)

FIGURE 5–6   Detail of a presumed phycomycetous lichen, *Geosiphon pyriforme,* ×75.

STRUCTURE OF THE THALLUS

Some lichens (e.g., *Parmelia saxatilis*) bear coral-like outgrowths on the thallus. These consist of rigid protuberances of upper cortex, plus algal and medullary layers of the thallus, and are termed **isidia** (Fig. 5–7). Isidia readily break from the thallus and probably act as vegetative propagules.

In many lichens the upper or outer cortex ruptures and algal cells surrounded by fungal hyphae from the medulla erupt as loose dusty masses on the surface of the thallus (Fig. 5–8). These dusty masses, termed **soredia,** are probably important in the reproduction of the lichen. Many species of *Cladonia* are coated with a yellow-green dust of soredia (Fig. 5–3C).

Some lichens—for example, *Peltigera aphthosa*—have wart-like protuberances on the upper cortex. These are termed **cephalodia** and consist of an epiphytic lichen growing on the surface of the *Peltigera* thallus (Fig. 5–9). Cephalodia may be either internal or external. It is uncertain how internal cephalodia originate, but they are constantly present in some lichens, such as *Solorina crocea*. The algal cells of the cephalodia differ from those of the host lichen. In most cases the cephalodia contain blue-green algae while the host contains a green alga. External cephalodia are produced by windblown soredia landing on the "host" thallus. Their rhizoidal hyphae penetrate the host, and then grow and differentiate to form the epiphytic cephalodia. Soredia will not form cephalodia unless they land on the host to which they are specific.

The lichen *Sticta* has cup-shaped depressions of nongelatinized hyphae that form openings through the lower cortex called **cyphellae** (Fig. 5–10A); these have no known function, but they may be significant in aerating the thallus. **Pseudocyphellae,** pores found in the upper or lower cortex of some lichens (Fig. 5–10B), are generally smaller than the cyphellae and form small white dots. Soredia are sometimes erupted through pseudocyphellae, but never through cyphellae.

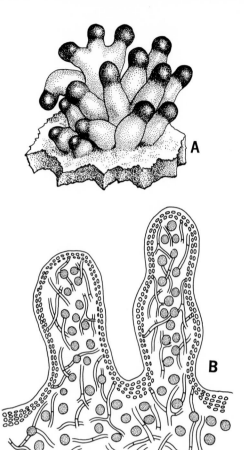

FIGURE 5–7   Isidia of *Lobaria pulmonaria*. A, isidia from upper surface of thallus, ×50; B, diagrammatic longitudinal section through isidia, ×200.

REPRODUCTIVE STRUCTURES AND REPRODUCTION

In the tropical American basidiomycetous lichen *Cora pavonia,* the foliose thallus resembles a small thin bracket fungus and, like the latter, grows on trees and shrubs (Fig. 5–11). The thallus stands out perpendicular to the branch on which it grows. When wet, it is blue-green; when dry, it is greyish-white. As in most bracket basidiomycetes, the hymenial surface is on the lower surface of the thallus and bears basidia.

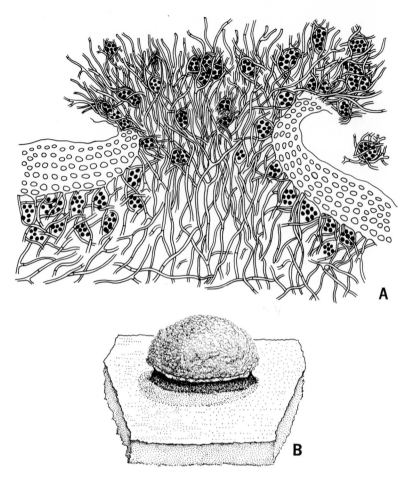

FIGURE 5–8   A mass of soredia of *Lobaria verrucosa*. A, cross section through thallus showing bursting mass of soredia, ×140; B, external view of sorediate mass on upper cortex of thallus, ×30.

The ascomycetous lichens bear sexual ascocarps termed apothecia and perithecia (Fig. 5–12). The apothecium is an open concave or convex disc; it is borne on the surface of the thallus, depressed within it, or raised high on a stalk. Several apothecia are generally produced on each thallus (Fig. 5–1C, 2, 3, 4B, D, 9A). The apothecium is small, seldom exceeding 1 cm in diameter and generally less than 5 mm in diameter. In *Pilophoron,* a crustose lichen, the apothecium is borne on a stiff, erect stalk—the **podetium** (Fig. 5–3D). In *Cladonia,* the primary (first-formed) thallus gives rise to a secondary thallus of fruticose podetia (Fig. 5–3A–C, E), which usually bear many apothecia.

In many lichen apothecia, in contrast to those of most ascomycetous fungi, spore-bearing capacity is retained over a period of several years. Lichens growing in fairly deep shade bear fewer apothecia than the same species of lichen in a more intensely illuminated habitat.

The anatomy of a common type of apothecium is shown in Fig. 5–12A. The **epithecium** may be brightly colored and is frequently different in color from the rest of the thallus. Asci and paraphyses vary in shape, size, and morphology, depending on the lichen species. The asci may contain one, two, four, six, eight, or more spores—the number generally constant for a given species. The asci are inoperculate.

Spores are released by bursting of the ascal wall when the thallus is moist; when the thallus becomes desiccated, spore discharge ceases. As in most discomycetous ascomycetes, the spores are shot from the asci.

The ascospores are morphologically characteristic of the lichen species. They vary in size from a length of 2 microns to 400 microns, the largest being visible to the naked eye, but most species have spores 10 microns to 30 microns long. Spores are simple or septate with trans-

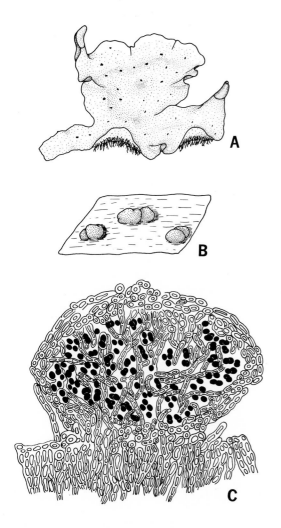

verse and longitudinal walls. Some ascospores have a very thick median septum, making the spore appear to be two-celled; these are termed **polarilocular** spores. Lichen spores are opaque or hyaline and often brightly colored. Ascospores are probably significant in lichen reproduction, but lichenologists have not satisfactorily demonstrated this. The germinating spore must contact the appropriate phycobiont, and the spores are generally slow to germinate.

Perithecia are urn-shaped and are partially or entirely immersed in the medulla of the thallus or substrate in which the lichen grows (Fig. 5–12B). They open through the upper cortex by an ostiole. In the perithecium the hypothecium is sharply delimited from the medulla and is often carbonized. In lichens, perithecia are less common than apothecia.

A number of asexual spores are also produced by lichens. Some lichens have pycnidia (Fig. 5–12A), superficially resembling perithecia, but containing simple or branched hyphae that form asexual spores (conidia). Conidia are also produced in various parts of some lichens, but are often not restricted to a special organ-like portion. Conidia vary in size and shape and their function is uncertain.

There is still much doubt concerning the nature of lichen reproduction. In the majority of genera the lichens appear to reproduce by simple fragmentation. When dry, most lichen thalli are exceedingly brittle; fragments are easily broken off and carried to a new locality to produce a new thallus. This method is probably significant in all but the crustose forms, in which there is often no means of fragmentation. In many crustose forms, asexual reproductive bodies, such as soredia and isidia, are also lacking. Most crustose lichens produce an abundance of ascospores; and since many are widely distributed, it is generally assumed that the ascospore is the means of dispersal. No one has ever succeeded in following the development of the lichen thallus from the spore.

When released, the ascospore in some lichens carries with it some cells of the phycobiont. Thus, the very unlikely chance encounter with the phycobiont partner is avoided. However, in most lichens the fungal

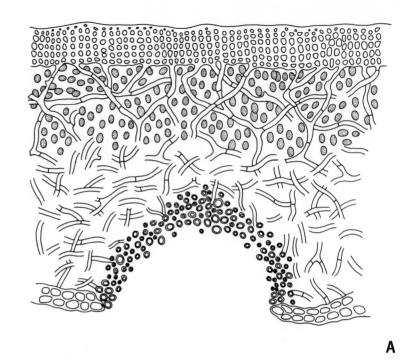

A

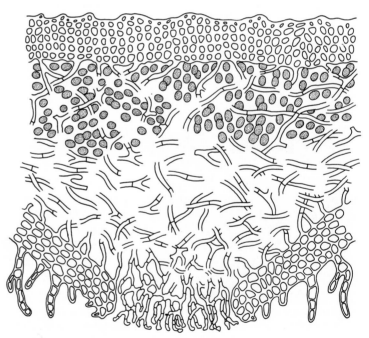

B

FIGURE 5–10   Cyphella and pseudocyphella. A, cyphella of *Sticta sylvatica*, ×325; B, pseudocyphella of *Sticta* sp., ×325 (Modified after Schneider.)

FIGURE 5–11   Habit sketch of a basidiomycetous lichen, *Cora pavonia,* ×1.

Growth of most lichens is very slow. In some crustose forms there is an annual increase in radius of from 0.1 to 10 mm. In some fruticose forms annual growth varies from 2 to 4 cm. Crustose thalli grow at the margins only; in most crustose lichens the center ultimately erodes while the margin continues to grow. In foliose types, growth is similar. In fruticose types, growth is apical and intercalary. In fruticose podetia of some species of *Cladonia,* each period of growth is marked by a new series of branches; thus, it is possible to estimate the approximate age of a *Cladonia* thallus by counting the number of branch series. However, in some species of *Cladonia* the lower portion of the podetia slowly disintegrates while the younger portions are flourishing; this decay is generally very slow.

By determining the average radial growth of a crustose thallus, and by measuring the diameter of the thallus, it is possible to calculate the approximate age of the lichen. Some crustose lichens have been estimated to be over 4,000 years old and are regarded as the oldest living organisms. In most lichens, however, growth rate is too erratic to determine the age with any degree of accuracy.

spore is released independent of the phycobiont.

The general pattern of formation of a lichen thallus, beginning with the ascospore, is speculated to be as follows:

1. The ascospore is released, carried by wind or water, and lands in a suitable environment. Suitable conditions vary considerably in terms of light intensity, humidity, and temperature.

2. The ascospore germinates, producing a mass of hyphae. If no suitable algal partner is encountered, presumably the hyphae die. If a suitable alga is encountered, it is surrounded by the hyphae and lives within the new lichen. At this stage the lichen would resemble a soredium. If unsuitable algae are encountered, they may be surrounded by hyphae and destroyed. In many instances the germination of the spore is exceedingly slow. In some genera it has been impossible to germinate spores; in many, too, the phycobiont partner is never found in nature leading a nonlichenized existence.

3. The thallus expands and differentiates.

PHYSIOLOGY

In contrast with most fungi, most lichens are tolerant of extreme illumination and nearly complete desiccation. When wetted, the desiccated lichen simply absorbs water passively like a blotter. The dry thallus can absorb three to 35 times its own weight in water. Water loss is by simple evaporation and is rapid, so that little may be retained for growth and metabolism of the lichen.

The basic organic material, on which the lichen fungus depends, is produced by the phycobiont. Part of this is utilized by the phycobiont and part by the mycobiont, but the balance is so delicate that both can survive. If the balance is upset, one or both partners die. For example, if a light-intolerant lichen is moved to a brightly illuminated area, and moisture is abundant, the phycobiont greatly increases while the mycobiont dies. Thus, the lichen partnership is dissolved. The mycobiont perishes while the phycobiont continues its existence as a free-living alga.

Minerals enter the thallus with rainwater and dew absorbed by the thallus. In crustose forms some dissolved minerals may be obtained from the substrate. The thallus has no means of eliminating minerals; thus, if minerals are ac-

cumulated in toxic quantities, the thallus dies.

The metabolic products of the phycobiont are rapidly absorbed by the lichen thallus and are very slowly assimilated. Consequently, a reservoir of basic nutrients is built up in the lichen thallus under favorable conditions. This reserve may be drawn upon later by either mycobiont or phycobiont. The thallus contains many metabolic products, some of which are useful in determination of lichen species. The fungal cell walls in most lichens are largely of

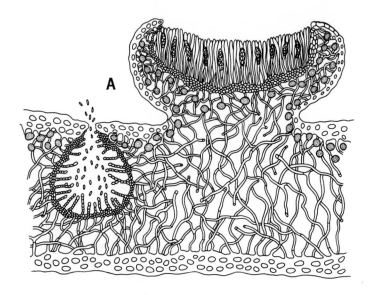

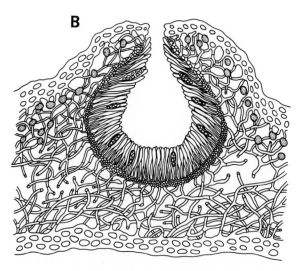

FIGURE 5–12   Apothecia, pycnidia, and perithecia of lichens. A, apothecium of *Lecanora* (right), and pycnidium (left), ×30; B, perithecium of unidentified lichen, ×30. (After Nienburg with permission of Gebrüder Borntraeger.)

lichen starch, **lichenin,** which is iodine negative. Chitin is present in many lichens. Both of these substances are absent in the phycobiont. Some of the organic products of the lichen (forming from 2 to 5 per cent of the dry weight of the lichen thallus) are insoluble in water; these accumulate as crystals on the hyphal surfaces. Many of these substances—among them, the **lichenic acids**—appear to be peculiar to lichens, but some have been found in non-lichenized fungi.

The presence or absence of a particular lichenic acid is useful in distinguishing between some lichen species. However, in certain lichen species there are several races, identified by their component lichenic acids. Some authors would accord each of these races a specific rank. Identification of a particular lichenic acid is relatively simple. A fragment of the lichen is crushed and treated with a solvent (or solvents). The acid recrystallizes and can be identified on the basis of the crystal morphology characteristic for each lichenic acid. Another method used in lichenic acid determination is the application of various reagents, which produce characteristic color reactions and denote the presence or absence of a given lichen substance.

SYNTHESIS

Given proper nutrient media, the phycobiont and mycobiont can be cultured independently of each other. In most cases the cultured phycobiont thrives and reproduces sexually, but it seldom does this in its lichenized state. The cultured mycobiont produces a number of the same lichenic acids that it produces in its lichenized state. In rare cases, it forms asexual spores. No cultured mycobiont has been demonstrated to produce sexual spores in the absence of the phycobiont.

Attempts to isolate the phycobiont and mycobiont, culture them independently, and then resynthesize the lichen, have met with varying success. In rare cases a thallus anatomically similar to that of the original lichen has been produced. All reports of completely resynthesizing a lichen, until it produced sexual reproductive spores, are open to question. In resynthesizing the lichen from its original component partners, apparently growth conditions must not highly favor either partner. In such cases the potential partners will dissociate and live independently. The lichen association is one in which balanced growth is necessary. Conditions that favor rapid growth of the alga are intolerable to the lichen fungus, while those that favor rapid growth of the fungus are intolerable to the alga. For the lichen association to be maintained, growth conditions must be poor for both partners; thus, growth is invariably slow.

USES

The lichen *Letharia vulpina* is said to have been used in Scandinavia to poison wolves, but most lichens are nonpoisonous and may be used as food in an emergency. Rock tripe (*Umbilicaria*), for example, was used by early Arctic explorers to reduce the incidence of scurvy. In some Scandinavian countries a number of lichens are used in preparation of soups or other foods. It is generally necessary to treat the lichen to remove bitter ingredients before it is used as food. The food value, though very low, is higher than in a number of popular breakfast foods!

A number of animals utilize lichens as food. Reindeer and caribou are well-known lichen grazers, but evidently they resort to lichens only if nothing better is available. Some lichens are harvested as supplemental winter fodder for domesticated reindeer. The extensive lichen pastures in the birch forests of Scandinavia and the lichen woodlands in subarctic Canada are important feeding areas for reindeer and caribou. A number of invertebrates also feed on lichens.

Lichens have long been used as a source of natural dyestuffs. Litmus, so useful in elementary chemistry, was first obtained from lichens. The dyes used in dyeing the wool for Harris tweeds of Scotland are derived from native lichens.

A number of lichens have been important in the perfume industry, not only for their own pleasant scents but also because they possess various essential oils.

Lichens have been used for medicinal purposes. The lung lichen *Lobaria,* for example, was used to treat lung diseases. A number of lichens possess antibiotic substances, which are used in a limited way to produce commercial preparations for treatment of external wounds and burns.

Lichens are natural indicators of industrial pollution of the air. Since they cannot excrete the substances they absorb from the air, lichens accumulate quantities of industrial waste material. When this accumulation reaches a toxic level, the lichen dies. Some lichens are slightly more tolerant of industrial waste than others. The presence of tree bark lichens is a good indication that excessive industrial waste is not entering the atmosphere. One can estimate the degree of air pollution in industrial areas by sampling the lichen population at varying distances from the source of air pollution.

HARMFUL EFFECTS OF LICHENS

Since the hyphae penetrate into the cambial area and retard growth, lichens may damage very young trees, but they are probably harmless in old trees with thick bark. Lichens frequently overgrow and kill mosses. Some crustose lichens have been noted to etch stained glass cathedral windows, which they occasionally colonize.

LICHENS AND PLANT SUCCESSION

A few workers consider lichens important in the breakdown of rock. Certainly crustose lichens are pioneers on newly exposed rock surfaces, but they grow and break the rock down chemically very slowly. Thus, lichens cannot be considered significant in initiating plant succession. The reindeer lichen (*Cla-*

donia) appears to require organic material as a basic substrate, although the initial colony will expand and form a porous mat over inorganic material. Since such mats dry rapidly, they provide a poor substrate for other plants that might otherwise colonize the lichen surface.

DISTRIBUTION

Lichens will grow on well-illuminated areas on most substrates. They are best known from rocks and trees, or as mat formers on soil. Most lichen species are quite specific in their substrate requirements. Thus, some will grow only on substrates poor in calcium; others will grow only on substrates rich in calcium. Still others appear to grow on any stable substrate that is not overgrown by another organism.

Lichens are widely distributed. They are found on rocks in deserts as well as rocks at extreme altitudes and latitudes, where they do not compete for space with other organisms. Indeed, lichens form the most conspicuous living terrestrial cover in Antarctica. However, in the high Arctic, lichens are less conspicuous than bryophytes and vascular plants. Rockall, an otherwise barren granite rock isolated in the Atlantic approximately 300 miles west of Scotland, is colonized by the crustose lichen *Verrucaria microspora*.

A number of lichens are found most frequently near human habitation (e.g., *Xanthoria parietina*); others (e.g., *Caloplaca elegans*) are found on rocks frequently visited by carnivorous birds. A few lichens are found only near the sea—for example, *Verrucaria maura* forms a distinct black band just above high tide line along the rocky coasts of much of the Northern Hemisphere.

FOSSIL LICHENS

Lichens are poorly represented as fossils; consequently, it is impossible to rely on fossils for information concerning their antiquity. Some fossil lichens are embedded in Miocene amber; among these are recognizable remains of a number of modern genera. Modern species names have been assigned to most of them, but the fragmentary nature of the fossils leads one to treat such determinations with doubt. In recent peat and tufa deposits, remains of modern lichen genera have also been found.

REFERENCES

des Abbayes, H., "Traité de Lichénologie." *Encycl. Biol.,* 41. Paris: Lechevalier (1951).

Ahmadjian, V., "Lichens." In Lewin, R. A., *Physiology and Biochemistry of Algae.* New York: Academic Press, Inc. (1962).

Ahmadjian, V., "The Fungi of Lichens." *Sci. Am.,* 208: 122–132 (1963).

Beschel, R. E., *Dating Rock Surfaces by Lichen Growth and Its Application to Glaciology and Physiography (Lichenometry).* In Raasch, G. O. (Ed.), *Geology of the Arctic.* Vol. 2. Toronto: University of Toronto Press (1961).

Brightman, F. H., "Neglected Plants—Lichens." *New Biol.,* 29: 75–94. Middlesex: Penguin Books Ltd. (1959).

Fink, B., *The Lichen Flora of the United States.* Ann Arbor: University of Michigan Press (1935).

Hale, M. E. *Lichen Handbook: A Guide to the Lichens of Eastern North America.* Washington, D. C.: Smithsonian Institution (1961).

Lamb, I. M., "The Remarkable Lichens." *Nat. Hist.,* 67: 86–93 (1958).

Lamb, I. M., "Lichens." *Sci. Am.,* 201: 144–159 (1959).

Llano, G. A., "Lichens, Their Biological and Economic Significance." *Bot. Rev.,* 10: 1–65 (1944).

Llano, G. A., "Economic Uses of Lichens." *Ann. Rept. Smithsonian Inst.* (1950): 385–422 (1951).

Nearing, G. G., *The Lichen Book.* Ridgewood, N. J.: Published by the Author (1939).

Smith, A. L., *Lichens.* Cambridge: Cambridge University Press (1921).

Smith, D. C., "The Biology of Lichen Thalli." *Biol. Rev.,* 37: 537–570 (1962).

Smith, D. C., "Experimental Studies in Lichen Physiology." *Symposium Soc. Gen. Microbiol.,* 13: 31–50 (1963).

Weber, W. A., "Environmental Modifications and the Taxonomy of the Crustose Lichens." *Svensk. Bot. Tidsskr.,* 56(2): 293–333 (1962).

6 / DIVISION

SCHIZOMYCOPHYTA

The *bacteria* were for many years treated as a single class—the Schizomycetes. Some thought that this class was closely allied with the true fungi; others considered the group to be more closely related to the blue-green algae (Cyanophyta). The supposed relationship to the fungi was based on a common lack of features found in other plant groups. For example, most bacteria and all of the fungi lack chlorophyll, they produce little or no starch, and their cell walls are most often composed of materials other than cellulose. The features thought to relate the Cyanophyta and bacteria are concerned with the simplicity of structure and reproduction found in the two groups. As in the blue-green algae, most bacteria are either unicellular or poorly developed colonial forms, in which reproduction is mainly by fission.

Studies in biochemistry and in ultrastructure now have shown that the Schizomycophyta and the Cyanophyta are similar and that the two divisions are not closely related to other plant groups. Cells of both lack membrane-enclosed organelles of the types found in all other organisms. They possess no plastids, mitochondria, or nuclear membranes. Thus, the available evidence would seem to exclude the possibility of a close relationship between the true fungi and the bacteria, but not between the latter group and the blue-green algae.

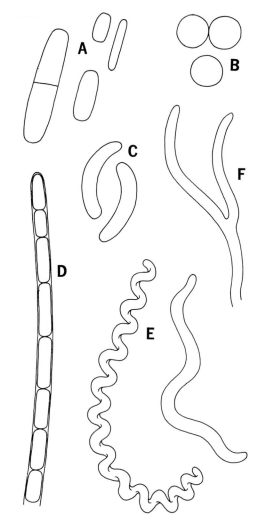

FIGURE 6–1   Bacterial form. A, bacillus; B, coccus; C, vibrio; D, filamentous; E, spirillum; F, coenocytic filament.

DISTRIBUTION

Bacteria live in a variety of habitats. Most species are saprobic heterotrophs and obtain organic nutrients from the surrounding environment. Such bacteria are abundant in soil, water, sewage, and in many foods; they are responsible for much of the process of decay. The parasitic heterotrophs obtain their nutrients from living organisms of many kinds. Bacteria produce exoenzymes, which break down proteins, polysaccharides, and other complex molecules; some of the breakdown products are then utilized as food.

The autotrophic bacteria are inhabitants mainly of water and mud. They may require only carbon dioxide, sunlight, and inorganic nutrients if photosynthetic. However, the photosynthetic purple nonsulfur bacteria may utilize an organic source of hydrogen. The chemosynthetic species obtain energy through a number of oxidation-reduction reactions and usually require only carbon dioxide as a carbon source. They are abundant in those habitats having a supply of the necessary oxidizable substrates. Thus, the sulfur bacteria, which oxidize hydrogen sulfide, are found in water containing large amounts of decaying material. In this habitat, the required hydrogen sulfide is released through protein decay by various microorganisms. Bacterial photosynthesis occurs only under anaerobic conditions, molecular oxygen being neither liberated nor consumed in the process. Because of this, and because of the absorption range of their photosynthetic pigments (circa 4,000–9,000 Å), bacteria can carry on photosynthesis where other plants cannot.

STRUCTURE

As a group, bacteria have few conspicuous morphological features. This is especially true of the unicellular forms constituting the majority of the group. Perhaps the most conspicuous features visible with light microscopy are cell shape and size. The commonly encountered forms (Fig. 6–1) are spheres and straight or curved rods. Spherical bacterial cells are called **cocci** and the straight rod-shaped bacteria are designated as **bacilli.** Helically curved bacteria are called **spirils,** or sometimes **spirilla,** and very short curved rods are termed **vibrios.** Cell shape is a relatively constant feature in most bacterial species. However, cell shape may alter somewhat with aging of the culture or under unusual culture conditions.

Cells of *Rhizobium leguminosarum,* growing in legume root nodules, vary from typical bacillus to X-, Y-, or club-shaped (Fig. 6–2);

they are referred to as bacterioids. In the Beggiatoales and other groups, the cells are organized into long filaments (Fig. 6–1D). Filaments are also produced by the Actinomycetales, although these are aseptate (Fig. 6–1F). They

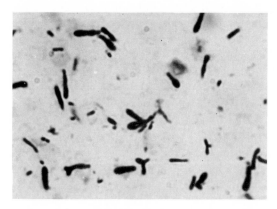

FIGURE 6–2   Bacterioids of *Rhizobium leguminosarum,* ×1,300.

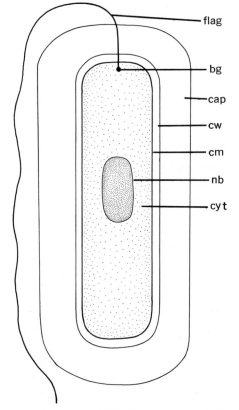

FIGURE 6–3   Bacterial structure (*flag,* flagellum; *bg,* basal granule; *cap,* capsule; *cw,* cell wall; *cm,* cell cytoplasmic membrane; *cyt,* cytoplasm; *nb,* nuclear body).

resemble the filaments, or hyphae, of true fungi but are of smaller diameter.

Bacillus type cells of some species may measure less than 0.5 microns in diameter and 1 micron long; the longest bacteria are about 500 microns long. In most species having cells of bacillus type, the size range is 1 to 5 microns in length and 0.5 to 1 micron in diameter. Cocci usually attain a diameter of 0.5 to 1 micron.

Structures common to many bacterial species are shown in the composite diagram in Fig. 6–3 of a bacilliform cell. In most bacteria, a rigid cell wall surrounds the protoplast. The wall, less than 100 millimicrons thick, may be composed of one or more layers. When viewed under very high magnification (i.e., with the electron microscope), walls of many bacterial species appear homogeneous. In others, the wall has a geometric pattern ascribed to the packed macromolecular structure. A single species, *Bacillus megaterium,* has a wall in which the pattern may be attributed to the presence of **microfibrils.** In contrast to this, the walls of most algae and true fungi are composed of distinct microfibrils visible with the electron microscope.

Pure preparations of bacterial cell walls can be obtained for chemical analysis. The cells are first crushed or broken apart in one of several ways. Fractions of the cell—i.e., cell walls and protoplasts—are then separated from one another through differential centrifugation. Analysis of such preparations has shown that heteropolymers, called **mucopeptides** (or mucocomplexes), are substances that give the wall its rigidity. The mucopeptides are composed of amino-acid and amino-sugar molecules. One of the amino sugars, muramic acid, is ubiquitous in, and possibly unique to, the cell walls of bacteria. Diaminopimelic acid, an amino acid found in the mucopeptide of some bacterial species, is known as a wall constituent only in bacteria and blue-green algae. In addition to the mucopeptides, other polymers, proteins, polysaccharides, and lipids are present in the walls of some bacteria.

The most noteworthy variations in wall chemistry of different bacterial groups are those between the Gram-positive and Gram-negative species. The Gram stain, originally devised to stain bacterial cells in animal tissues, has long been used as an aid in bacterial identification. In this staining procedure, bacterial smears are fixed by heating, stained with crystal violet, and then mordanted with an iodine solution. The smear is next treated with an organic solvent (commonly ethyl alcohol). Gram-positive bacteria retain the mordant-stain complex; the organic solvent quickly removes all stain from the cells of Gram-negative bacteria.

Walls of the Gram-positive bacteria contain relatively large amounts of mucopeptide and, in some instances, other polymers called teichoic acids. Those of the Gram-negative bacteria are more complex, consisting of several distinct layers, the innermost of which is mucopeptide. Here the wall contains large amounts of lipid material, proteins, and polysaccharides. In the Gram stain procedure, the organic solvent removes the lipid materials from the wall; the iodine-stain complex is then leached out by the solvent. The thicker mucopeptide layer of Gram-positive bacteria is thought to form a barrier to the removal of the stain.

The effectiveness of penicillin as an antibiotic is in part related to its interference with incorporation of muramic acid into mucopeptides. As might be expected from this fact and from the wall composition, penicillin is very effective against most Gram-positive bacterial species, but not usually against Gram-negative species. Further, since mucocomplexes are not known in animal cells, relative nontoxicity of penicillin to such cells is thus explained.

A slime layer of varying thickness may be present immediately outside the cell wall. If this layer is of relatively constant thickness and is sharply defined, it is called a **capsule** (Fig. 6–4A, B). In some species, the slime layer is either very thin and inconspicuous or it is composed of relatively soft material lost in the surrounding medium. Two of the more spectacular slime producers of the latter type are *Leuconostoc mesenteroides* and *Acetobacter xylinum*. *L. mesenteroides* is common in solutions containing sugars and may cause difficulties in sugar refineries. It converts simple sugars to dextran, a type of polysaccharide. Dextrans are more viscous than sugar solutions and they can impede or stop the flow of the solutions through refinery pipes. This slime is now of some importance medicinally, for it can be used as a substitute for blood plasma. The slime of *A. xylinum* consists of minute fibers of pure cellulose, a substance rarely found in bacteria.

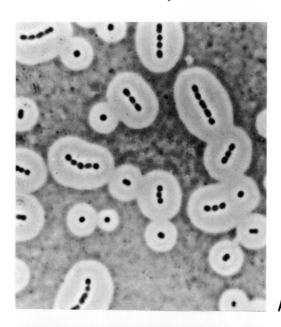

A

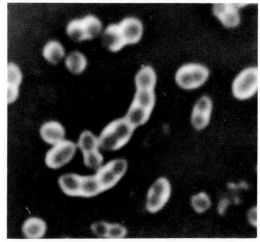

B

FIGURE 6–4   Photomicrographs showing bacterial capsules. A, wet mount of an encapsulated bacterium in India ink (scale line shown is 10 microns); B, *Diplococcus pneumoniae*, ×3,500. (B, photograph courtesy E. Juni, after Taylor and Juni with permission of *Journal of Bacteriology*.)

The slimes and capsules of most bacteria are composed of other polysaccharides or polysaccharide complexes with proteins, mucins, etc.

The presence of a capsule is correlated with pathogenicity in some bacterial species. For example, virulent cells of *Diplococcus pneumoniae* and *Bacillus anthracis* are normally encapsulated. They produce smooth glistening colonies in culture and are designated as S-forms. In cultures of S-forms, one may find occasional colonies of roughened appearance—R-forms, with cells that lack capsules. The R-forms are less capable of producing disease, although they may regain this property through transformation or mutation (see p. 130).

The presence or absence of a capsule (S- and R-forms), and other capsule variations such as mucoid forms, are genetically controlled in *Diplococcus pneumoniae* and *Bacillus anthracis*. Environmental and nutritional factors also may affect capsule formation in these and other species of bacteria. Among such factors are the types of carbohydrate, phosphorus, and nitrogen compounds supplied in the medium, and the carbon dioxide concentration. The addition of blood serum to the culture medium will stimulate capsule production in some species; the age of the culture is an important factor with other species.

THE PROTOPLAST

As in cells of other organisms, a cytoplasmic membrane surrounds the protoplast. This membrane is composed of proteins and lipids, and it functions in control of movement of materials into and out of the cell. It also has been stated that the membrane may function in cell respiration, a suggestion based on the presence of a number of respiratory enzymes in the membrane.

The cytoplasm near the periphery of the protoplast, called **ectoplasm,** stains more strongly than does the inner portion of the cell. No vacuoles are present in the bacterial cell, and the protoplast usually has a very homogeneous appearance. Several types of granules

may be seen if the bacteria are stained, the most common of which are of **volutin** (metachromatic bodies) and of **glycogen.** Starch-like materials found in some species of *Clostridium* are not common in other bacteria. Fat bodies or globules are not infrequent and may be relatively large. In some species the fat globules remain clear in stained cells, giving the cell a banded appearance. **Mitochondria** of the type found in other organisms are not present in bacterial cells (Fig. 6–5). Possibly some of the smaller granules in the cytoplasm correspond functionally to mitochondria.

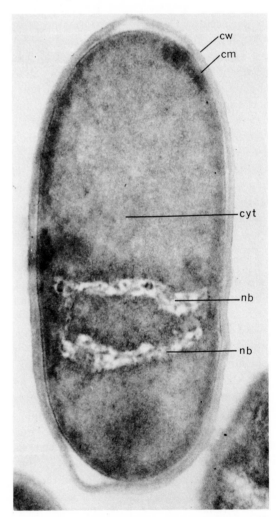

FIGURE 6–5   Electron micrograph of a thin section through a bacterial cell (*cw,* cell wall; *cm,* cell membrane; *cyt,* cytoplasm; *nb,* nuclear body), ×50,000. (After Chapman with permission of *Journal of Bacteriology.*)

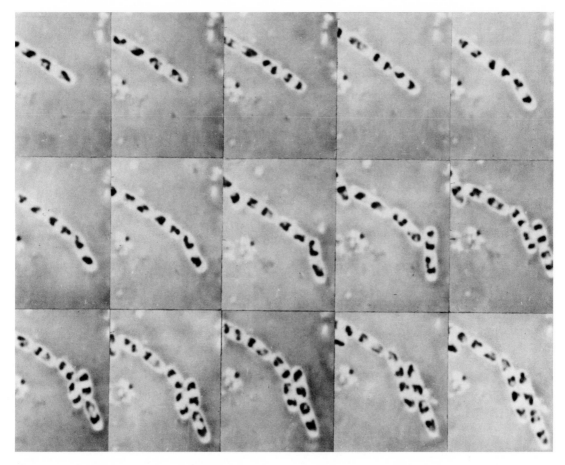

FIGURE 6–6   Nuclear division and growth in single group of living cells of *Escherichia coli*. Sequence of phase contrast photographs taken over period of 78 minutes, ×1,800. (Photographs courtesy D. J. Mason, from Mason and Powelson with permission of *Journal of Bacteriology*.)

THE NUCLEAR BODY

Nuclear structure in the bacteria has been the subject of much controversy. Until relatively recently it was widely believed that the bacterial cell either lacked a nucleus or contained a "diffuse nucleus." Some bacteriologists felt that the whole bacterial cell was comparable to the nucleus in other organisms. The cytological techniques used, such as fixation by heat, and use of nuclear stains other than those specific to **DNA,** were responsible for some of the confusion. It is now known that bacterial cells have one or more **nuclear bodies** (Fig. 6–6). Although most cells have only one, several may be present when nuclear division occurs at a more rapid rate than cellular division.

Nuclear bodies of bacteria are somewhat simpler in structure than are the nuclei of other organisms. They lack nuclear membranes, nucleoli, and the chromosome organization found in nuclei. Their shape is rather variable in stained preparations, appearing globoid, dumbbell-shaped, or helical in form. Those usually seen are globoid or oval; the dumbbell shape is characteristic of dividing nuclear bodies, and helical forms occur in the endospores of some species.

Recent studies of the nuclear body, using electron microscopy and carefully lysed preparations, demonstrate that it is composed of a continuous strand of DNA. This strand is embedded in a matrix that appears to be distinct from the cytoplasm of the cell.

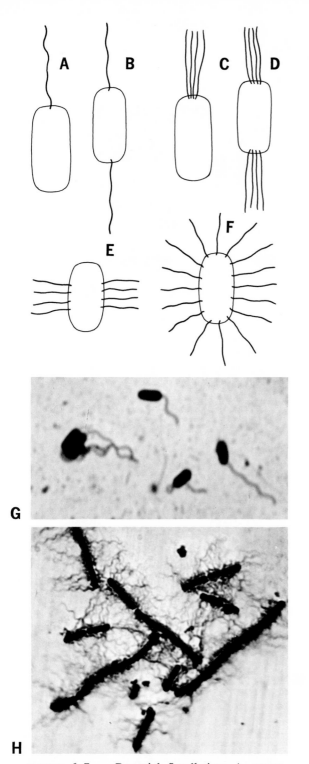

Although true chromosomes (i.e., of the type found in higher organisms) are not known in the bacteria, the continuous strand of DNA can be considered as an analogous structure; it bears the hereditary units, or genes, and therefore is functionally similar to a chromosome. As with nuclei of other organisms, division of the bacterial nuclear body must in some way ensure equal distribution of genetic material between daughter cells.

FLAGELLA

Many bacterial species exhibit either swimming or gliding types of movement. In most of the swimming types, motility is dependent on the action of flagella (Fig. 6–7A–H). Flagella may occur singly or in tufts and are variously placed on the cells. In some cases there is a single flagellum at one end of the cell (**monotrichous** species); in others flagella are at both poles of the cell (**amphitrichous** species). A polar tuft, at one or both ends of the cell, is present in the **lophotrichous** species, and **peritrichous** forms have flagella over the entire surface.

The end of each flagellum is embedded in the cytoplasm where it is terminated by a small granule. This granule probably corresponds in function to the basal granule or blepharoplast of other organisms. The flagellum itself is simpler in structure than that in other flagellated cells and usually consists of a single strand, instead of the nine-plus-two arrangement common to other groups. The strand is about 12 millimicrons in diameter, the length varying with the species. Because of the small diameter, bacterial flagella can be seen by light microscopy only after mordanting and staining, which greatly increases the apparent diameter and renders the structure opaque.

In one order, the Spirochaetales, flagella are not present, although motility is of the swimming type. Motility is thought to depend upon flexing of the entire cell. Gliding movements are found in the Beggiatoales and Myxobacteriales (and Cyanophyta, see Chapter 8), but there is as yet no satisfactory explanation for the mechanics involved.

FIGURE 6–7   Bacterial flagellation. A, monotrichous; B, amphitrichous; C, D, lophotrichous; E, F, peritrichous. G, monotrichous bacteria, ×2,-400; H, peritrichous bacteria, ×5,800.

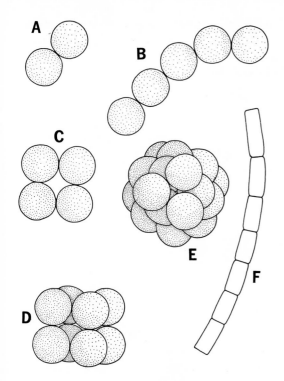

FIGURE 6–8   Cell aggregates. A, pairs or diplococci; B, chains (streptococci); C, plate or tetrad; D, packet; E, clustered (staphylococcus); F, chain of rod-shaped cells.

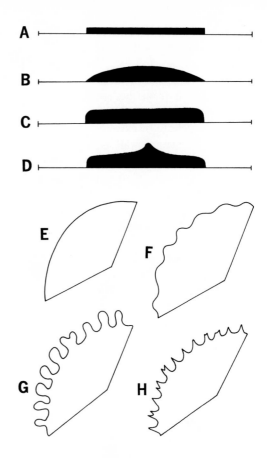

FIGURE 6–9   Colony form. A–D, profiles. A, flat; B, convex; C, raised; D, umbonate. E–H, margins. E, entire; F, undulate; G, lobate; H, erose.

COLONIES

Cocci frequently produce loose aggregations of cells, which may correspond to colonies in some algal groups. These aggregates are relatively constant in form and are characteristic for a given species (Fig. 6–8A–F). When division of cocci occurs consistently on a single plane, the cells may adhere in pairs or in chains. Such pairs (diplococci) are found in the genus *Diplococcus,* and chains (streptococci) are characteristic of the genus *Streptococcus.* In other cocci, division in two or three opposing planes results in the formation of tetrads and packets of cells. The genus *Staphylococcus* is characterized by grape-like clusters of cells, with division on many different planes. Cell division occurs only in the transverse plane in rod-shaped cells. Thus, short chains or filaments are characteristic of some bacillus types of bacteria.

The appearance of masses or colonies of bacterial cells on solid culture media is of some value in characterization of schizomycetous taxa. Some of the variations found in the colony are illustrated in Figure 6–9. The color of the colony and the nature of any pigments produced varies from species to species. In some, the pigments are water soluble and diffuse out into the culture medium. In others, they are water insoluble and remain within the cells.

ENDOSPORES AND CYSTS

Many bacilli produce **endospores** or, less commonly, **cysts.** The endospore is a thick-walled resistant structure formed within the parent cell wall. The first observable stage in endospore formation is the appearance in the cytoplasm of a clear area, the **forespore.** This primordium soon is surrounded by a refractile wall, separating it from the remainder of the cytoplasm (Fig. 6–10A–E). Water content of the spore is thought to be extremely low and the chemistry of the spore wall is very different from that of the vegetative cell. Eventually the remnants of the parent cell disintegrate, freeing the endospore.

A series of cytological changes has been reported to precede endospore formation in some bacteria. The cells contain two nuclear bodies prior to the appearance of the forespore. These bodies are thought to fuse, forming a single rod-shaped structure that then separates into several smaller parts. One of these portions moves into the area to be occupied by the forespore; it is then cut off from the remainder of the cell by a delicate crosswall. The crosswall can be seen only through use of thin sections and electron microscopy.

Endospores can be spherical, ellipsoid, or oval; they occupy a terminal, subterminal, or central position within the parent cell wall, depending on the species. In many species of *Clostridium,* endospores are broader than the vegetative cells, whereas in the genus *Bacillus* they are of lesser diameter.

The endospore is extremely resistant to heat, chemicals, desiccation, and other unfavorable conditions. In some species, they have been reported to withstand boiling for several hours and to withstand the action of chemicals that rapidly kill vegetative cells. They may retain their viability for more than 50 years.

It is sometimes stated that endospores are produced as a response to unfavorable environmental conditions; however, experimental evidence for this is lacking. The conditions leading to their formation seem to vary among the species; in some species they are formed regularly under what appear to be ideal conditions for growth. The nature of the culture medium and various environmental factors have been found to influence endospore production.

When an endospore germinates (Fig. 6–11), it gives rise to a single vegetative cell.

Thus, no increase or decrease in numbers of individuals is associated with endospore formation.

Cysts are formed by cells in the genus *Azotobacter* and in the Myxobacteriales. In cyst formation, the entire bacterial cell rounds up and becomes surrounded by a thick wall. As with endospores, these resistant structures eventually give rise to a single vegetative cell.

ASEXUAL REPRODUCTION

Reproduction in most bacteria is by simple binary fission (Fig. 6–12A–D). First, the nuclear body divides; then a wall develops from the periphery inward, dividing the protoplast. This transverse wall (crosswall) splits as the two newly formed cells separate. A delicate membranous septum is formed prior to the appearance of the transverse wall in some species. However, it is not yet known whether this occurs in all bacteria. In cell division, the inward development of crosswalls does not always proceed to completion—i.e., a small pore remains at the center of the crosswall in some filamentous forms.

Under ideal conditions, cell division can occur in some species as frequently as once every 20 minutes. The increase in numbers of individuals under these conditions could theoretically result in immense masses of bacterial cells. Fortunately, various natural factors prevent such an increase in bacterial cells. In nature, competition with other microorganisms, depletion of nutrient supplies, accumulation of respiratory by-products, and changes in moisture and temperature help to regulate bacterial growth rates.

In addition to fission, or in the place of it, reproduction can occur through budding (Hyphomicrobiales, Actinomycetales) or by means of sporangiospores, conidia, and fragmentation (Actinomycetales). The sporangiospores of actinomycetes are flagellated planospores. Motile reproductive cells are produced by *Rhizobium* (Eubacteriales) and by some of the Chlamydobacteriales. These methods of reproduction are

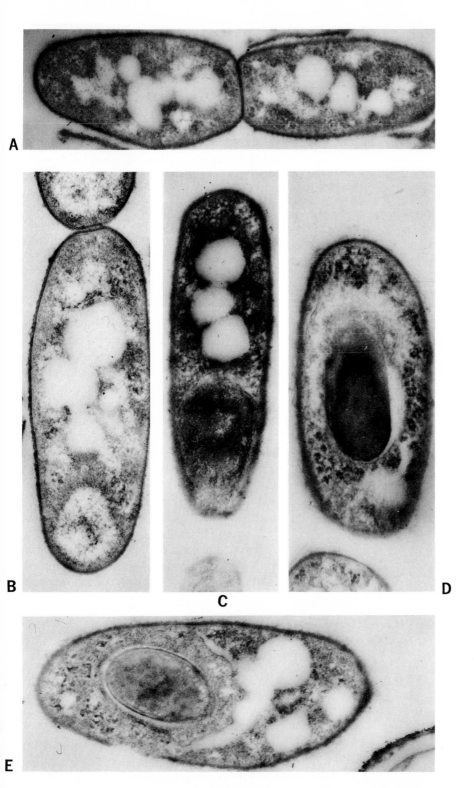

FIGURE 6–10   A–E, endospore formation in *Bacillus cereus;* A, ×29,000;
B–E, ×38,600. (After Chapman with permission of *Journal of Bacteriology.*)

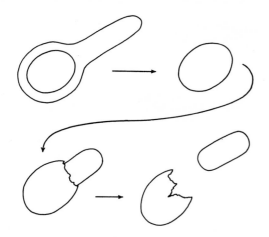

FIGURE 6–11   Endospore germination following release from the parent cell.

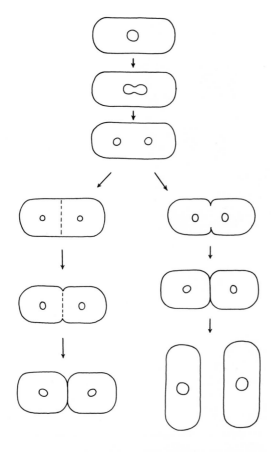

FIGURE 6–12   Binary fission. Top, division of nuclear body; below, left, division involving deposition of delicate septum (dotted line); right, possible alternative division involving constriction only.

discussed under the orders for which they are characteristic.

SEXUAL REPRODUCTION

Sexual reproduction as found in other plant groups is not known to occur in the Schizomycophyta. However, several types of phenomena occur that give end results similar to sexual reproduction; these involve a unidirectional transfer of genetic material, rather than syngamy and meiosis. The term **meromixis** has been suggested for these phenomena, three of which are described here.

CONJUGATION

Conjugation can take place between donor and recipient cells of *Escherichia coli*. By analogy, these haploid cells can be considered comparable to male and female respectively. During conjugation, a slender bridge is formed between donor and recipient cells (Fig. 6–13), through which genetic material moves. It can be shown that the amount transferred depends upon the length of time the bridge is maintained. Typically, only a portion of the donor's genetic material is transferred to the recipient. Following conjugation, the recipient cell possesses duplicate genes for a number of characteristics. The recipient may be considered as a partial diploid cell, but generations arising from it are completely haploid and frequently exhibit characteristics of both the donor and the recipient strains.

TRANSFORMATION

In **transformation** (Fig. 6–14), deoxyribonucleic acid (DNA) from donor cells initiates heritable changes in recipient cells. The DNA, released from dead bacterial cells, is genetically effective in very small amounts. In the laboratory, pure DNA extracts are used in transformation experiments. Transformation typically involves only one trait, although several may be acquired independently in this way.

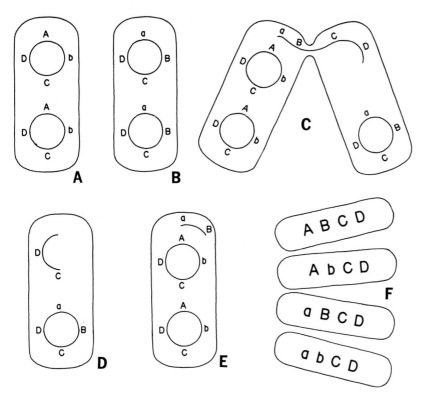

FIGURE 6–13   Bacterial conjugation. A, B, recipient and donor cells, each with two nuclear bodies; C, transfer of genetic material from donor to recipient; D, E, cells after conjugation; F, possible types of descendants from recipient cell E.

TRANSDUCTION

Transduction (Fig. 6–15) involves bacterial viruses called **bacteriophages** or simply "phages." Phage particles infecting a donor may carry away some of the genetic substance; this can be transferred to a second cell, or recipient, infected by the same phage particle. Simultaneous transfer of several characteristics has been reported to occur in this manner, but a single characteristic is involved in most instances. The changes brought about in transduction are passed on to descendants of the recipient cell.

CLASSIFICATION AND IDENTIFICATION

Because of the simplicity of bacterial structure it is necessary to use nonmorphological features to identify and classify. Parasitic species can be identified in part by their serological reactions, by the identity of the host, and in some instances by symptoms produced. Among both parasitic and saprophytic species, the ability to utilize specific substrates and any special requirements such as vitamins or amino acids, can be of value in identification. The end products of respiration (e.g., gases, acid) help to characterize some species; temperature, pH, and oxygen requirements also are important; and the Gram stain and similar staining procedures aid in bacteria identification. These nonmorphological characteristics serve in the identification of bacterial species, but there is uncertainty concerning their value in determining relationships within the group.

The classification system used here is taken from that in Bergey's *Manual of Determinative Bacteriology*. It includes most bacteria in a single class, the Schizomycetes, divided into ten orders. A second class, the Microtatobiotes, is designated for the orders Rickettsiales, Mycoplasmatales, and Virales.

ORDER EUBACTERIALES. The Eubacteriales and the Pseudomonadales are often referred to as the "true bacteria" or eubacteria. In some classification systems, these two orders are combined into a single order, the Eubacteriales, which includes the majority of economically important bacteria, such as the pathogenic species, those used in industrial processes, and the nitrogen-fixing bacteria. Most of the introductory discussion concerning structure and reproduction in bacteria is based on studies in these groups. Thus, the following discussion will be concerned primarily with activities of certain species.

In Bergey's classification, the Eubacteriales and Pseudomonadales are retained as separate orders. The eubacteria are cocci or bacilli, the motile cells having peritrichous flagella. The pseudomonads are mostly vibrios, spirilla, or bacilli, the motile forms generally having polar flagella. Most species in both groups are heterotrophic, but a few pseudomonads are autotrophic. Several staining reactions also aid in distinguishing between the Pseudomonadales and Eubacteriales.

Many eubacteria are abundant in soil, water, sewage, decaying plant and animal material, foods, and the atmosphere. Others exist as parasites in the bodies of animals or plants. This group is of considerable economic importance, because of both beneficial and detrimental activities.

Species capable of fixing free (atmospheric) nitrogen are found in several families of the Eubacteriales. The more important species are in the genera *Azotobacter, Rhizobium,* and *Clostridium.* The species of *Azotobacter* and *Clostridium* are free-living organisms common in the soil. *Azotobacter* species have relatively large cells (Fig. 6–16A) that are more or less rod-shaped, often occur in pairs or chains, and are varied in shape. In *Azotobacter, Rhizobium,* and in some other eubacteria, such variation occurs regularly in

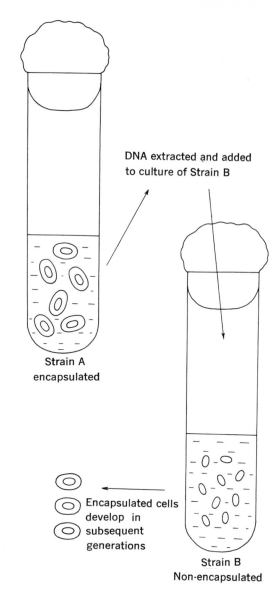

FIGURE 6–14   Bacterial transformation.

the life cycle. *Azotobacter* cells have been reported to bud in some instances. They do not form endospores, but produce cysts with greatly thickened walls. The azotobacters live in well-aerated neutral soils, obtaining carbohydrates from the surrounding environment and using atmospheric nitrogen as a nitrogen source. The species of *Clostridium* also are soil inhabitants and almost all are saprophytes. The nitrogen-fixing clostridia—for example, *C. pasteurianum*—may live in poorly drained, acidic

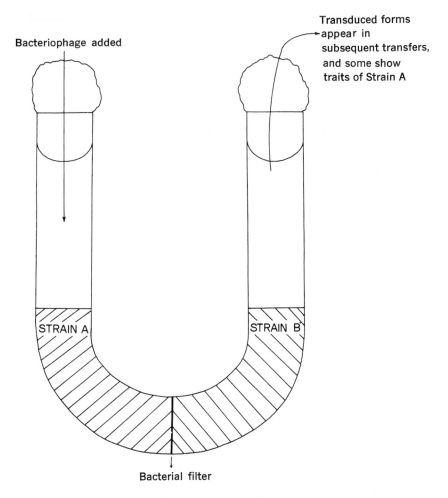

Bacteriophage added

Transduced forms appear in subsequent transfers, and some show traits of Strain A

STRAIN A

STRAIN B

Bacterial filter

FIGURE 6–15   Apparatus used in demonstrating transduction (the bacterial filter prevents mixing of strains A and B, but allows free passage of the bacteriophage).

soils of bogs, and most of the species are obligate **anaerobes.** They produce endospores that are of a larger diameter than the parent cell. *C. botulinum* and *C. tetani,* causing botulism and tetanus, respectively, produce powerful toxins. *C. acetobutylicum* has long been used commercially in the production of butyl alcohol.

The strains of *Rhizobium* (Fig. 6–2) are important symbiotic nitrogen-fixing bacteria found in root nodules of legumes. Although only one species is recognized (*Rhizobium leguminosarum*), many different strains are found in the roots of various legumes. Cell shape in *Rhizobium* is especially variable when the bacteria grow in the root nodules. In addition to the bacterioids found there, motile reproductive cells (swarmers) have been observed in this species. *Rhizobium* does not utilize atmospheric nitrogen when grown in culture. Therefore, it is believed that nitrogen-fixation is a joint enterprise requiring both the legume and the bacterial cells.

Rhizobia live in the soil and infect the root hairs of developing plants. Following entrance into the root hair, an infection thread is formed through the root-hair cell. Eventually the characteristic nodule is produced and within this many bacterial cells are found. Healthy root nodules contain a hemoglobin pigment and are pink. When grown alone, neither the plant nor the bacterium synthesizes hemoglobin—a substance that may be important in the nitrogen-fixing process. It is now common agricultural practice to dust seeds of legumes with appropriate strains of *R. leguminosarum* at planting time. This assures immediate infection of the root by the best strain of *Rhizobium* for the particular legume. In some instances, roots become infected by strains that fix little or no nitrogen; these strains can be considered parasites.

Probably the most important bacterial activity in the soil and elsewhere is in decay. This process, while detrimental in some instances, is absolutely essential in nature. Through decay, elements incorporated into plant and animal bodies are eventually released and can again serve in the growth of others.

A large flora of bacteria, including many eubacteria, inhabits the intestine of animals. Some of these bacteria are potential pathogens; others are essential to the well-being of their host. For example, cellulose eaten by ruminants is digested by bacteria and protozoa; the ruminant then derives much of its food through digestion of the multiplying microbial populations. Thus, from the microflora the ruminant obtains most of the essential amino acids and vitamins; other mammals must obtain these from an external source. Man also plays host to beneficial and detrimental species of bacteria. For example, some bacteria are essential to the proper functioning of the digestive tract; others are pathogenic—e.g., *Salmonella typhi,* which often spreads through fecal contamination of water supplies and causes typhoid fever. *Escherichia coli,* normally a nonpathogenic species inhabiting the intestine of man, is used as an indicator in testing water supplies for recent fecal contamination. Cells of this species will be present in much greater numbers than are pathogens such as *S. typhi* if fecal contamination has occurred.

Some Eubacteriales are important in food processing and in food spoilage. Manufactured food products, such as butter, cheeses, and yogurt, sauerkraut, pickles, and cocoa, are examples of foods in which processing involves bacteria. In cheeses, bacteria break down pro-

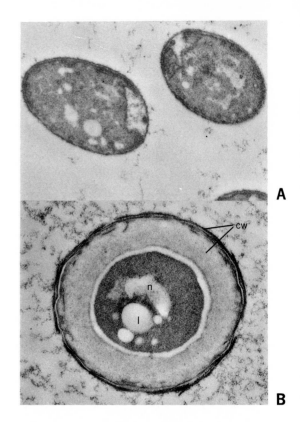

FIGURE 6–16   Vegetative cells (A) and thin section of cyst (B) of *Azotobacter.* cw, wall layers; *n,* nuclear material; *l,* lipid globule; A, ×24,500; B, ×27,500. (After Scolofsky and Wyss with permission of *Journal of Bacteriology.*)

teins and other substances, some of the breakdown products being responsible for the characteristic flavors. The important genera of bacteria concerned are *Lactobacillus, Streptococcus*, and *Leuconostoc*. These and other eubacteria common in dung and in soil are usually present in milk; they may cause souring or other types of spoilage of fresh milk. Species of *Clostridium* and *Staphylococcus* are often responsible for food poisoning; the clostridia are especially noteworthy since their poisoning is often fatal. Some diseases, such as undulant fever and salmonellosis (gastroenteritis), are regularly transmitted in meat, eggs, and dairy products.

ORDER PSEUDOMONADALES.   Most of the Pseudomonadales are found in fresh-water or marine habitats. Almost all of the autotrophic bacteria and many heterotrophic species are included in this order.

Members of the Pseudomonadales are similar to the Eubacteriales in both structure and reproduction. Motile pseudomonads, except *Selenomonas,* have either a single polar flagellum or tufts of polar flagella. In *Selenomonas* the cells are curved and have a tuft of flagella centrally located on the concave side. Reproduction is by binary fission in this order.

Photosynthetic pseudomonads are separated into three families: the Thiorhodaceae or purple sulfur bacteria, Athiorhodaceae or purple nonsulfur bacteria, and the Chlorobacteriaceae or green sulfur bacteria. The purple bacteria contain a photosynthetic pigment called **bacteriochlorophyll** and in the green sulfur bacteria two **chlorobium chlorophylls** are found; all of these pigments, while related chemically to chlorophylls of other plant groups, have their absorption maxima in the near-infrared portion of the spectrum. This enables the phototrophic bacteria to carry on photosynthesis in the absence of visible light. As with the true chlorophylls, carotenoid pigments are associated with the bacterial chlorophylls. Plastids are lacking in bacteria, but the photosynthetic pigments are localized in simpler structures called **chromatophores** (Fig. 6–17). In addition to the pigments, chromatophores contain the enzymes and electron carriers that function in photochemical reactions.

Although the bacterial photosynthetic pigments are chemically related to those of higher plants, the photosynthetic process differs in a number of respects. Carbon dioxide is utilized, but oxygen is not released in bacterial photosynthesis. The photosynthetic bacterial species are found mainly in anaerobic habitats. In the purple sulfur bacteria, reduced sulfur compounds—often hydrogen sulfide—serve as hydrogen donors; free sulfur results and accumulates in the form of refractile granules within the cells. Green sulfur bacteria carry on a similar process, but the sulfur is deposited externally. The purple nonsulfur bacteria are versatile organisms living either anaerobically in light or aerobically in the dark. In photosynthesis, they can make use of various hydrogen donors, such as organic compounds and molecular hydrogen; or they oxidize these same substances in the dark to obtain energy for synthesis.

The chemosynthetic Pseudomonadales oxidize such compounds as ammonia, nitrites, methane, carbon monoxide, sulfur, and sulfur compounds. Included here are the nitrifying bacteria, which oxidize ammonia to nitrites, and nitrites to nitrates (*Nitrosomonas* and *Nitrobacter*). Energy obtained in these oxidation reactions functions in the generation of high-energy phosphate bonds and in the reduction of carbon dioxide. In contrast to photosynthetic forms, chemosynthetic pseudomonads are predominantly aerobic. Atmospheric oxygen serves as the final hydrogen acceptor in most instances.

Morphologically, one of the more unusual groups of Pseudomonadales is the Caulobacteriaceae. In this family, the cells usually are attached to the substrate by means of a stalk, which is provided with a basal holdfast (Fig. 6–18A). In the genus *Caulobacter,* the cells are vibrio-like—i.e., with curved rods—and have a protoplasmic stalk attached at one end. In *Gallionella* (Fig. 6–18B, C), the cell is reniform or biconcave with a laterally attached, spirally twisted stalk containing ferric hydroxide. The stalk of *Gallionella* is nonliving.

Cells of the Spirillaceae are of the spirillum or vibrio types. They are polarly flagellated in *Spirillum* (Fig. 6–19A–C), but some vibrios have a lateral tuft of flagella. These bacteria are primarily aquatic forms, although several species (including *Vibrio comma,* the cause of cholera) are pathogenic to man or animals.

ORDER CHLAMYDOBACTERIALES. Cells of the Chlamydobacteriales, or "sheathed bacteria," are similar in structure to those of the Eubacteriales. However, many cells are enclosed in a cylindrical sheath, forming a long filament. Within the sheath, the rod-shaped or coccoid cells reproduce by fission. Ferric hydroxide or manganese hydroxide is frequently deposited in the sheath, giving it a yellow-brown color. In *Crenothrix,* cells are coccoid and are

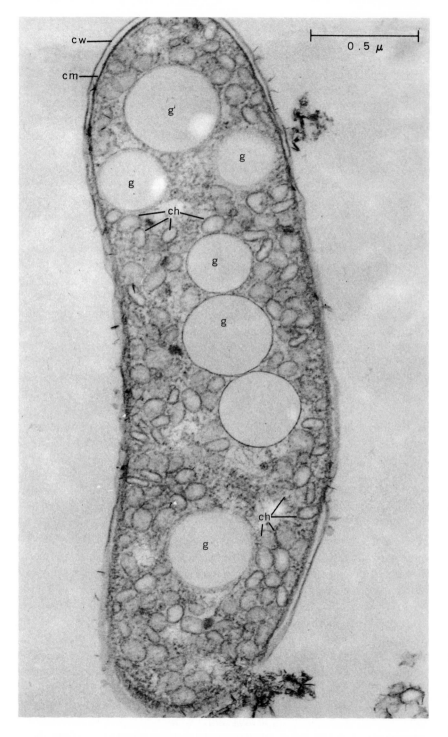

FIGURE 6–17   *Rhodospirillum rubrum*. Electron micrograph of an ultrathin section showing chromatophores. *cw*, cell wall; *cm*, cytoplasmic membrane; *ch*, chromatophore; *g*, granule. (From Boatman, reprinted by permission of the Rockefeller Institute Press, from *Journal of Cell Biology*, 1964, Vol. 20(2), p. 303, fig. 7.)

A

B

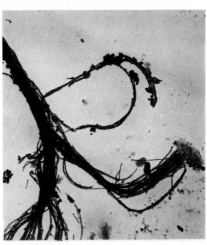

C

FIGURE 6–18   A, *Caulobacter vibrioides*. Rosette of stalked cells, ×37,500. B, C, electron micrographs of *Gallionella ferruginea*. B, stalk secreted by several cells, two of which are visible at the stalk tip, ×75,000; C, branched stalk, each branch terminated by a single ghost-like cell, ×65,000. Note that each stalk is composed of a number of separate strands. (A, photograph courtesy E. A. Grula; B, C, photographs courtesy R. S. Wolfe, after Vatter and Wolfe with permission of *Journal of Bacteriology*.)

B

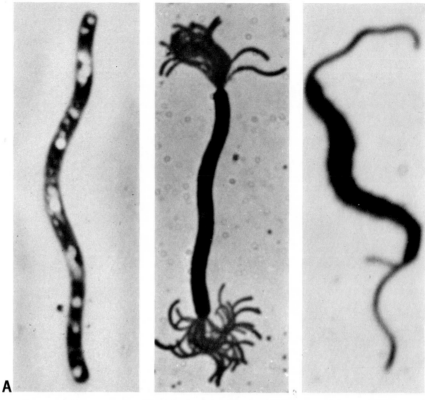

A   **C**

FIGURE 6–19   A, B, *Spirillum serpens*. A, darkfield photograph of living cell,
flagella not visible, ×2,500; B, with flagellar stain, ×4,400. C, *S. beijerinckii*,
×6,000. (After Williams and Rittenberg with permission of *International Bulletin of Bacteriological Nomenclature and Taxonomy*.)

arranged in several series within a funnel-
shaped sheath; in *Sphaerotillus* (Fig. 6–20A,
B) bacilliform cells form a single series within a
cylindrical sheath.

Flagellated cells (swarmers) are released
from the open end of the sheath in *Sphaerotillus*. The swarmers swim about and eventually
settle down to produce new filaments. A
swarmer may settle on an established filament
—in which case the new filament that develops
appears to be a branch of the older one. The
term **false-branching** refers to this situation, or
to that where branch-like projections of the
filament arise by slippage of cells within the
sheath. Cells of *Crenothrix* often float away
from the open end of the funnel-shaped sheath
and give rise to new filaments. Filaments also
can be produced by fragmentation in these
genera.

The Chlamydobacteriales are aquatic organisms, some of which are responsible for the
deposition of "bog iron ore." *Sphaerotillus* is
found in water rich in organic matter, such as
sewage, and is often used as an indicator of
pollution.

ORDER BEGGIATOALES.   The aquatic species included here might be designated as colorless blue-green algae. *Beggiatoa* (Fig. 6–21)
and *Thiothrix,* the best-known genera, appear
nearly identical to the filamentous blue-green
alga *Oscillatoria. Beggiatoa* and *Thiothrix* are
chemoautotrophs that oxidize sulfides to sulfur
and, as in the purple sulfur bacteria, free sulfur
granules accumulate within the cells. Because
of the refractile sulfur granules, masses of the
filaments appear whitish.

Filaments of *Beggiatoa* are free floating
and capable of gliding and flexing movements.
The cells are not flagellated and motility cannot

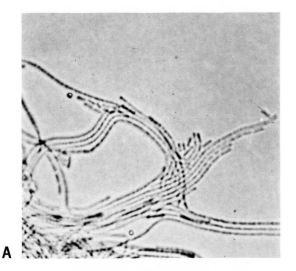

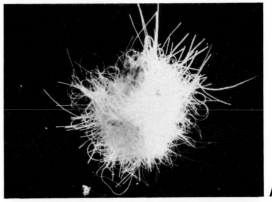

A

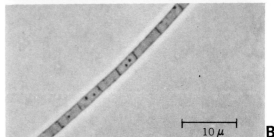

B

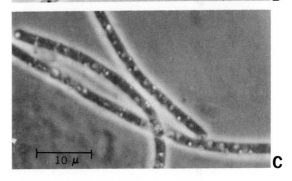

C

FIGURE 6–21   *Beggiatoa alba.* A, colony of filaments in water, photographed by reflected light, ×18. B, C, detail of filaments, dark phase-contrast. Crosswalls visible in dying filament (B); sulfur granules present in filaments (C) that have been exposed to atmosphere containing hydrogen sulfide. (Photographs courtesy R. S. Wolfe, from Faust and Wolfe with permission of *Journal of Bacteriology.*)

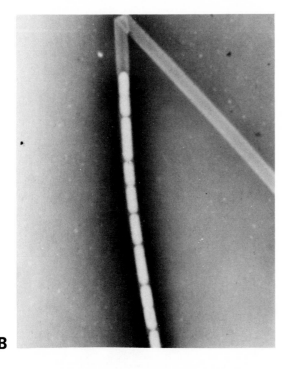

FIGURE 6–20   *Sphaerotillus natans.* A, mass of filaments in colony, ×650; B, single filament enlarged to show detail, ×2,500. (Photographs courtesy J. L. Stokes with permission of *Journal of Bacteriology.*)

be attributed to any mechanism known in other groups of bacteria. The same types of movement, however, are found in the blue-green alga *Oscillatoria* (see Chapter 8). Filaments of *Thiothrix,* which are nonmotile and attached to the substrate, are gregarious, occurring in rosette-like clusters.

In the Beggiatoales, reproduction of cells is by fission, although new colonies may be produced by fragmentation. Short pieces of the filament consisting of a few cells are often liberated. These are comparable to certain reproductive structures of many blue-green algae.

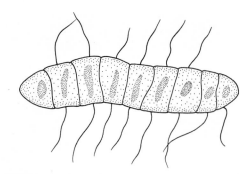

FIGURE 6–22   Habit sketch of *Caryophanon* filament, ×4,500.

ORDER CARYOPHANALES. The Caryophanales is a small group of uncertain relationships. Filaments up to 40 microns long and 4 microns wide are produced in *Caryophanon* (Fig. 6–22). These produce segments consisting of ten to 30 cells. The segments are released and are motile through the action of numerous flagella. Cells within a filament reproduce by fission. Nuclear bodies in these organisms are clearly distinguishable in unstained living cells.

Caryophanon frequently occurs in large numbers in cow dung. Related forms can be found in water rich in organic matter and in the intestinal tracts of animals.

ORDER SPIROCHAETALES. In the Spirochaetales the cells are long, slender, helically coiled, and motile. They have delicate walls and are very flexible. These spirilla may reach 0.5 mm long, but are small in diameter. The cell is surrounded by a thin wall, outside of which a bundle of fine filaments is spirally wound. This bundle of filaments is firmly anchored in the cytoplasm at either end of the cell. The filaments have a chemical composition similar to the flagella of other bacteria and are contractile. The flexing action of the cell and motility are apparently caused by contraction of these filaments.

Two families are recognized—the Treponemataceae and the Spirochaetaceae. Cells of the former are under 20 microns long; those of the latter group range from 30 to 500 microns. The Treponemataceae are mainly parasites, causing syphillis (*Treponema pallidum*—Fig. 6–23) and yaws (*T. pertenue*) in man, and

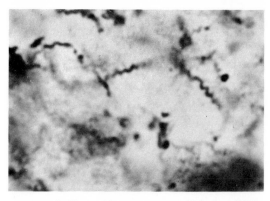

FIGURE 6–23   *Treponema pallidum.* Silver-impregnated cells within section of human liver tissue, ×5,000.

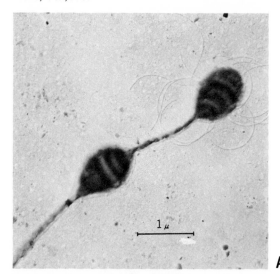

A

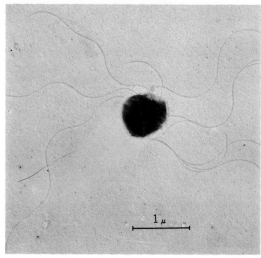

B

FIGURE 6–24   *Rhodomicrobium vanniellii.* A, cells attached to stalks; B, single flagellated cell. (After Douglas and Wolfe with permission of *Journal of Bacteriology*.)

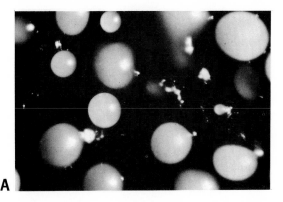

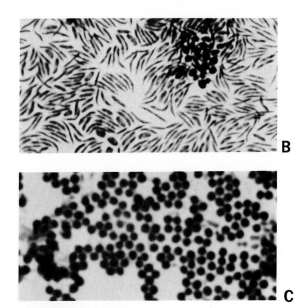

FIGURE 6–25 A, B, *Myxococcus fulvus*. A, mature fruiting bodies, ×30; B, stained cells, some of which are forming microcysts, ×1,100. C, *Myxococcus* sp., stained mature microcysts from smeared fruiting body, ×1,500. (Photographs by N. A. Woods, after Henrici and Ordal with permission of D. C. Heath and Company.)

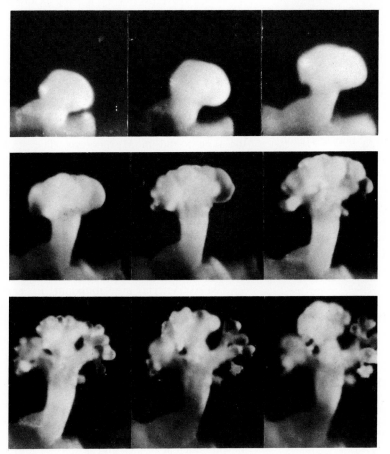

FIGURE 6–25D Successive stages in fruiting body development of *Chondromyces*, ×15. (Photograph courtesy J. T. Bonner, from *Morphogenesis* by J. T. Bonner by permission of Princeton University Press, copyright 1952.)

various diseases of mammals and birds. One member of this group, *Leptospira,* can be obtained in scrapings from apparently healthy teeth and gums. Species of *Borrelia* cause relapsing fever, and one (*B. vincenti*) is associated with trench mouth. Most Spirochaetaceae inhabit stagnant water, sewage, and similar habitats, although a few parasitize shellfish.

ORDER HYPHOMICROBIALES. The Hyphomicrobiales, or budding bacteria, are unique in both structure and reproduction. The elliptical or oval cells of *Hyphomicrobium* have a single polar flagellum. After a motile period, these cells settle down and become attached to the substrate. A fine filament then develops from the end of the cell opposite the point of attachment. At the tip of this filament a bud-like outgrowth, the daughter cell, is produced. This daughter cell may then break away and swim to a new location, where it attaches to the substrate and produces a new filament. Successive "buds" are produced at the tip of the filament. Buds of *Rhodomicrobium* (Fig. 6–24) remain attached to the filament tip where they form new filaments terminated by buds. Crosswalls develop in the filament midway between each pair of cells. The resulting colony or network of cells is held together by the filaments; some daughter cells are flagellated and can swim away, as in *Hyphomicrobium.* The manner in which growth occurs suggests that the filaments of both genera are actually tubular in structure. *Rhodomicrobium* is photo-autotrophic and possibly related to the purple non-sulfur bacteria; *Hyphomicrobium* is saprophytic.

ORDER MYXOBACTERIALES. The Myxobacteriales are referred to as the slime bacteria. Their cells are rod-shaped with either rounded or pointed ends and they have thin walls. No flagella are present, but the organisms are capable of either individual or mass gliding movements. The cells glide on secreted slimy materials, which also tend to hold the cells together. Reproduction is by fission.

The most remarkable feature of the slime bacteria is their production of communal "fruiting bodies." Some of these, visible to the

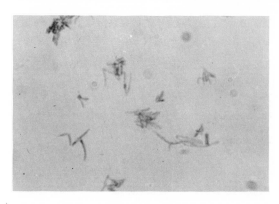

FIGURE 6–26 Photomicrograph of young culture of *Mycobacterium tuberculosum,* ×1,000. Note branching of filaments.

unaided eye, may be brightly colored. In the formation of fruiting bodies, many cells migrate together, producing a heaped mass. In *Myxococcus* (Fig. 6–25A–C) the cells in such a cushion-shaped heap are converted into cyst-like bodies, and no further development occurs. In the more complex genus *Chondromyces* (Fig. 6–25D), the massed cells produce a small, branched, shrub-like structure. Each branch is tipped by a large macrocyst; within this are numerous small cysts (microcysts) of the type found in *Myxococcus.* The stalk is composed of hardened slime and nonencysted cells. Upon germinating, each microcyst gives rise to a single vegetative cell. Not all of the species included in the Myxobacteriales form complex fruiting bodies and cysts. Cells of *Sporocytophaga* encyst but do not produce fruiting bodies; those of *Cytophaga* produce neither cysts nor fruiting bodies.

Myxobacteria are abundant in certain types of soils, in dung or rotting vegetation, and in marine habitats. Some are capable of killing and digesting cells of other bacteria and fungi found in such habitats; others are active in decomposition of cellulose.

ORDER ACTINOMYCETALES. The major distinguishing feature of the actinomycetes is their production of **coenocytic** (i.e., with numerous nuclear bodies and no crosswalls) filaments or hyphae similar to those found in many true fungi. These hyphae are smaller in diameter than in true fungi, usually not exceeding 1.5

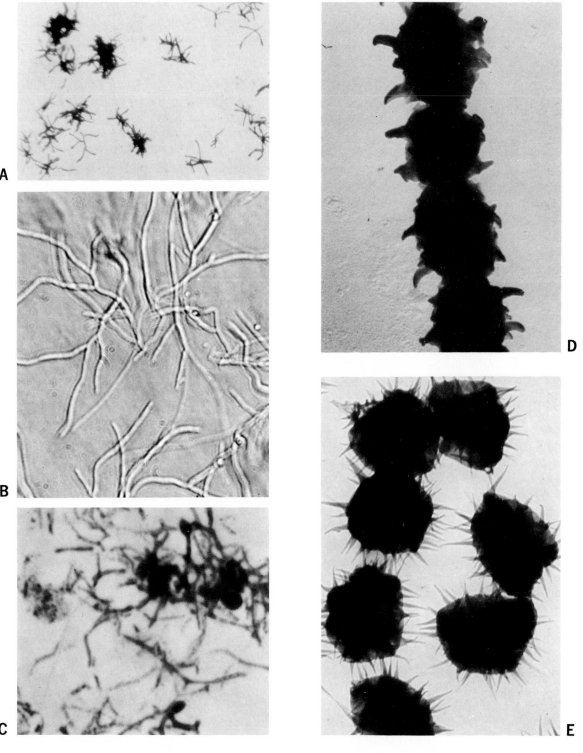

FIGURE 6–27   A, B, *Actinomyces,* ×750. C, *Nocardia* filaments from young culture, ×1,200. D, E, *Streptomyces.* D, electron micrographs of spores in chains, ×40,000; E, single spores, ×55,000. (A, B, photographs courtesy A. Howell, from Howell, Murphy, Paul, and Stephan with permission of *Journal of Bacteriology;* C, photograph courtesy M. Fore; D, E, photographs courtesy H. D. Tresner, from Tresner, Davis, and Backus with permission of *Journal of Bacteriology.*)

microns. Reproduction is through fragmentation, budding, fission, conidia, or by motile sporangiospores.

Four families are placed in this order—the Mycobacteriaceae, Actinomycetaceae, Streptomycetaceae, and Actinoplanaceae. The Mycobacteriaceae are sometimes included with the Eubacteriales, but in most respects seem closely related to the Actinomycetales. In *Mycobacterium* (Fig. 6–26), only a rudimentary mycelium develops, and it soon undergoes fragmentation into rod-shaped or branched segments. The segments can reproduce by fission and also are capable of starting a new mycelium. Strains of *Mycobacterium tuberculosis,* a ubiquitous species, cause tuberculosis in man, animals, and birds; *M. leprae* causes leprosy.

The mycelium of the Actinomycetaceae is more extensive than that of the Mycobacteriaceae, although it does break up in a similar manner. The fragments reproduce by binary fission in *Actinomyces* and *Nocardia* (Fig. 6–27A–C). In addition, budding and spore formation occur in the latter genus.

Mycelium of the Streptomycetaceae does not undergo fragmentation. In *Streptomyces* (Fig. 6–27D, E) special aerial branches bear chains of conidia that are quite distinct from the endospores of other bacterial orders. In their formation, bits of protoplasm are thought to be separated by crosswalls from the remainder of the filament. These portions then round off and are eventually released. Upon germinating, the conidium produces a germ tube, which develops into a new mycelium. Conidia of actinomycetes are not very resistant to heat as compared to endospores of other bacteria.

The Actinoplanaceae are relatively recently discovered organisms. These aquatic actinomycetes also produce hyphae, the tips of which bear minute sporangia. The mature sporangia rupture, releasing many small spherical or rod-shaped flagellated spores.

Many of the Streptomycetaceae and Actinomycetaceae are saprophytic soil organisms. They may also occur in decaying vegetation, in water, and in other habitats. A number of actinomycetes produce extremely important antibiotic substances, such as *streptomycin* and *actinomycin*. Vitamin B_{12} is obtained as a by-product of antibiotic production by species of *Streptomyces*.

OTHER ORDERS. Three additional orders of bacteria are recognized: the Mycoplasmatales, Virales, and the Rickettsiales. The Mycoplasmatales is a small group about which little is yet known. The Rickettsiales are responsible for a number of important diseases, including typhus and Rocky Mountain spotted fever in man. Some bacteriologists consider them more or less intermediate between true bacteria and the viruses, whereas others would consider them Virales. Rickettsias are extremely small but similar in shape to other bacteria. Many live in the bodies of rodents and are transmitted to man by various arthropod vectors; all are parasites that cannot reproduce in the absence of living host cells. They are found in the cytoplasm, or less commonly in the nucleus, of host cells and are either rod-shaped or spherical. The Virales (included with the Rickettsiales in the class Microtatobiotes in Bergey's classification) cannot be considered as closely related to bacteria.

RELATIONSHIPS

Simplicity of cell structure and small size seem to separate bacteria from most other groups or organisms. However, size in itself is of little value in determining relationships. Thus, some true fungi are smaller than the larger bacteria. In size and structure the blue-green algae appear to merge into the bacteria. In both groups, the simple cell structure, the lack of mitochondria, plastids, etc., and the low degree of complexity in nuclear organization are the same. Binary fission is the common means of reproduction, and little cellular differentiation occurs in either group. It has been suggested that these two divisions form a distinct evolutionary line and they have been treated together as the "lower protists." The "nuclei" of the Cyanophyta and Schizomycophyta have been designated as procaryotic in contrast to the eucaryotic nucleus of the other organisms. However, the Cyanophyta is a poorly known group in many respects. Additional studies of their chemistry, reproduction, and fine structure are required before there can be any certainty of their relationships to the bacteria. Bacteria were once considered to be related to the true fungi. However, the true fungi are equipped with cells of a high state of organization and differ in other respects.

Structural simplicity in the bacteria may not necessarily be due to primitiveness. Possibly some groups of bacteria are derived from more complex forms through regressive evolution. They can be regarded as simple only in structure; chemically, they are as complex as or more complex than many other organisms.

REFERENCES

Breed, R. S., Murray, E. G. D., and Smith, N. R., *Bergey's Manual of Determinative Bacteriology,* 7th Ed. London: Bailliere, Tindall & Cox Limited; Baltimore: Williams and Wilkins Co. (1957).

Brieger, E. M., *Structure and Ultrastructure of Microorganisms.* New York: Academic Press, Inc. (1963).

Cruickshank, R. (Ed.), *Mackie and McCartney's Handbook of Bacteriology.* Edinburgh: E. and S. Livingstone Limited (1962).

Frobisher, M., *Fundamentals of Microbiology.* Philadelphia: W. B. Saunders Co. (1962).

Gunsalus, I. C., and Stanier, R. Y. (Eds.), *The Bacteria.* Vol. I: *Structure.* New York: Academic Press, Inc. (1960).

Hawker, L. E., Linton, A. H., Folkes, B. F., and Carlile, M. J., *An Introduction to the Biology of Micro-organisms.* London: Edward Arnold (Publishers) Ltd. (1960).

Jacob, F., and Wollman, E. L., *Sexuality and the Genetics of Bacteria.* New York: Academic Press, Inc. (1961).

Perkins, H. R., "Chemical Structure and Biosynthesis of Bacterial Cell Walls." *Bact. Rev.,* 27(1): 18–55 (1963).

Skerman, V. B. D., *A Guide to the Identification of the Genera of Bacteria.* Baltimore: Williams & Wilkins Co. (1959).

Stanier, R. Y., Doudoroff, M., and Adelberg, E. A., *The Microbial World,* 2nd Ed. Englewood Cliffs, N. J.: Prentice-Hall, Inc. (1962).

Thimann, K. V., *The Life of Bacteria,* 2nd Ed. New York: The Macmillan Co. (1963).

Waksman, S. A., *The Actinomycetes.* Waltham, Mass.: Chronica Botanica (1950).

7 / ALGAL

GROUPS

At one time the organisms referred to as *algae* were grouped in one category. With increasing knowledge, resulting especially from studies of biochemistry and physiology, it is now apparent that the group "algae" is extremely artificial. The algae are generally considered to comprise several parallel lines of evolution that are only distantly related; thus, they are treated here as distinct divisions. However, these divisions have a few characteristics in common to distinguish them from other divisions of plants. Hence, the term alga, like the general term thallophyte, still has a useful place in the botanical vocabulary. It will undoubtedly continue to be used, although it is no longer considered a formal category.

DISTINGUISHING CHARACTERISTICS OF ALGAE

Typically, algae possess chlorophyll and are photosynthetic, whereas fungi and fungus-like organisms (including most bacteria) are not and are either saprobic or parasitic. Some algae are non-photosynthetic, but most of these can be shown to be derived from chlorophyll-bearing forms. Some algae may be autotrophic or heterotrophic, depending on the conditions to which they are exposed. Certain bacteria are also photosynthetic; but these usually produce sulfur or a sulfur compound as a by-product of their metabolic activities, whereas algae produce oxygen.

It is more difficult to distinguish some algae from the flagellated protozoa. Some naked and colorless organisms, as well as chlorophyll-bearing ones, can be considered either algae or protozoa. In fact, some authors consider these organisms in a group (Protista) separate from plant and animal kingdoms. Typically, the presence of a rigid cellulose wall in unicellular, flagellated organisms is sufficient to classify them as algae; but this is strictly arbitrary, since many photosynthetic flagellates do not have a cellulose wall.

Distinguishing algal groups from other plant groups is generally not difficult, if reproductive material is available for comparison. The reproductive structures in algae are unicellular with no layers of sterile cells. In a few instances, there are structures, which at maturity appear multicellular (as in bryophytes). But in following their development it is evident that there is no separation of inner fertile and outer sterile cell layers. One exception to this, and then only in the male reproductive organ, occurs in the Charophyceae (stoneworts—see Chapter 15). However, other morphological features place these plants in the algae.

In algae the zygote rarely develops into a multicellular embryo while still within the female plant. In fact, the male and female gametangia may both liberate gametes, with syngamy occurring in the water. The zygote is generally independent of the gametophyte from the time of its initiation.

Another distinguishing feature of the algae is the lack of a true vascular system. Thus, true roots, stems, and leaves are not present. In general, there is little tissue differentiation in algae. In one of the more complex algal groups, the Phaeophyta (brown algae), some multicellular genera have root-like, stem-like, and leaf-like parts (see Chapter 11). In some of these there are rather striking similarities to phloem and meristematic tissues of vascular plants.

Vegetative (or asexual) reproduction commonly occurs in the algae, and a variety of spores is produced. Flagellated spores are termed **zoospores (planospores),** whereas non-flagellated ones are referred to as **aplanospores.** In some species the cell contents round up and form a heavy wall. If the original cell wall is involved, the resulting spore is referred to as an **akinete;** if a new internal wall is formed, it is a **hypnospore.**

DISTINGUISHING CHARACTERISTICS OF ALGAL DIVISIONS

In this text, eight divisions of algae are distinguished. Each of the divisions Chrysophyta, Pyrrophyta, Xanthophyta, and Chlorophyta possesses two classes, whereas each of the others (Cyanophyta, Phaeophyta, Rhodophyta, and Euglenophyta) has only one class. Table 7–1 lists the main distinguishing characteristics of the divisions (and classes) of algae. For some divisions the data are still incomplete, since only a few forms have been studied. Whether these forms are representative of the whole division is still unknown. Within each group there are now organisms that may prove to be exceptions. After further study, some of these algae may have to be referred to a different category.

The primary criteria used in distinguishing the divisions are biochemical and relate to the pigments, storage products, and chemical composition of cell walls. The pigments include not only a variety of **chlorophylls** but also the other fat-soluble pigments, the **carotenoids** (**carotenes** and **xanthophylls**), and the water-soluble **phycobilins** (**phycocyanin** and **phycoerythrin**). The submicroscopic (or ultrastructure) of the **chloroplast**[1] is the same in all groups of plants. It is delimited by a double membrane and is composed of many compressed bands, or stacks of paired **lamellae** (see Fig. 10–2D, 11–4D, 12–2A, B, 14–2A, C, 15–2). The storage, or reserve, substances may be some type of carbohydrate, protein, or fat and oil. Other impor-

[1] The term *chloroplast* is used for all chlorophyll-bearing plastids with lamellar structure; the term *chromatophore* is restricted to nonlamellar bodies, as occur in bacteria and animals.

TABLE 7–1

MAJOR CHARACTERISTICS OF ALGAL CLASSES

DIVISION AND CLASS	PIGMENTS	STORAGE PRODUCTS	FLAGELLATION	CELL WALL
CYANOPHYTA *Cyanophyceae*	chlorophyll *a* β-carotene antheraxanthin flavacin lutein myxoxanthin myxoxanthophyll zeaxanthin allophycocyanin *c*-phycocyanin *c*-phycoerythrin	cyanophyte starch (=amylopectin; α, 1–6, 1–4 linkage) cyanophycin and other proteins no sterols reported	none	cellulose pectin
PYRROPHYTA	chlorophyll *a, c* diadinoxanthin dinoxanthin	starch (=amylose + amylopectin; α, 1–4, 1–6 linkage) fats, oils		cellulose pectin
Dinophyceae	β-carotene peridinin		2 lateral (or apical) insertion, 1 around girdle (flattened or ?tinsel), 1 trail- ing (whiplash)	
Cryptophy- *ceae*	α-, ε-carotene ?zeaxanthin x-*c*-phycocyanin * x-phycoerythrin †		2 lateral insertion, ?tinsel	
CHRYSOPHYTA	chlorophyll *a, c* † β-carotene diadinoxanthin diatoxanthin † dinoxanthin † fucoxanthin	chrysolaminarin (= leucosin; β, 1– 3, 1–6 linkage) fucosterol and others †		cellulose pectin
Chrysophy- *ceae*	α-carotene lutein		1, 2 apical (or sub- apical) insertion; 1 tinsel (or ?whip- lash) 2 equal, whiplash 2 unequal, sube- qual, longer tinsel	may be absent
Bacillariophy- *ceae*	α-, ε-carotene		reproductive cell (male) only, 1 tinsel ?2	silicon

* Phycobilins in Cryptophyceae studied are for the most part different from those occurring in the Rhodophyta and Cyanophyta.

† Too few algae examined to make accurate generalizations.

TABLE 7–1

MAJOR CHARACTERISTICS OF ALGAL CLASSES (Continued)

DIVISION AND CLASS	PIGMENTS	STORAGE PRODUCTS	FLAGELLATION	CELL WALL
PHAEOPHYTA *Phaeophyceae*	chlorophyll *a, c* α-, β-carotene flavoxanthin fucoxanthin lutein violaxanthin	laminarin (β, 1–3, 1–6 linkage) mannitol fucosterol and others	reproductive cells only 2 lateral insertion, forward tinsel, backward whiplash 1 forward tinsel	cellulose pectin alginic acid (algin) fucoidin
RHODOPHYTA *Rhodophyceae*	chlorophyll *a,* ?*d* α-, β-carotene lutein ?taraxanthin zeaxanthin allophycocyanin *b-, c-, r*-phycoerythrin *b-, c-, r*-phycocyanin	floridean starch (=amylopectin; α, 1–4, 1–6 linkage, + α, 1–3) floridoside mannoglycerate cholesterol ‡ fucosterol, sitosterol	none	cellulose pectin various mucilages (agar, carrageenin xylan) mannan (some with calcium or magnesium carbonate)
XANTHO-PHYTA	chlorophyll *a* β-carotene xanthophylls		2, apical insertion	
Xanthophyceae	chlorophyll ?*e*	chrysolaminarin (=leucosin; β, 1–3, 1–6 linkage) sitosterol	unequal; long, tinsel; short, whiplash	cellulose pectin
Chloromonadophyceae		oil	equal or unequal; forward, ?tinsel; trailing, ?whiplash	generally lacking
EUGLENO-PHYTA *Euglenophyceae*	chlorophyll *a, b* β-carotene antheraxanthin astaxanthin neoxanthin	paramylon (=paramylum; β, 1–3 linkage) ergosterol	1 (2 or 3) apical insertion, tinsel, single row of mastigonemes	generally lacking ?pectin
CHLORO-PHYTA	chlorophyll *a, b* β-carotene	starch (=amylose + amylopectin; α, 1–4, 1–6 linkage)	2, apical insertion, equal, whiplash	cellulose pectin (occasionally with calcium carbonate)
Chlorophyceae	α-carotene astaxanthin lutein neoxanthin siphonein § siphonoxanthin § violaxanthin zeaxanthin	ergosterol fucosterol, sitosterol, and others	also 4, 8, or a ring of flagella	mannan mucilages (xylan) chitin
Charophyceae	γ-carotene lycopene		male reproductive cell only	

‡ Almost all Japanese forms contain cholesterol, but the British forms contain sitosterol or fucosterol instead.
§ In siphonous forms only.

tant criteria relate to the presence or absence of motile **flagellated** cells: the number, relative length, morphology, and arrangment of the flagella of these cells (Fig. 7–1A–I). As in the Eumycota, flagella that are smooth and lack external hairs are known as **whiplash flagella** (Fig. 7–1A); flagella with many fine hairs (or **mastigonemes**) along the length are **tinsel flagella** (Fig. 7–1C F).

Additional characteristics used in distinguishing and characterizing algal divisions and classes relate to the degree of nuclear organization and whether cells are uninucleate or multinucleate; the type of sexual reproduction, if present (**isogamy**, **anisogamy**, or **oogamy**— Fig. 7–2); and the type of **alternation of generations** exhibited (location of syngamy and meiosis in the life history—Fig. 7–3).

PHYLOGENY OF ALGAE

The occurrence of phycobilin pigments in the Cyanophyta (blue-greens) and Rhodophyta (reds), and protoplasmic connections between cells of certain representatives, may indicate a common origin. The simplicity of the chloroplast structure of the Rhodophyta (see Chapter 12) may be significant in showing their close relationship to the Cyanophyta. However, other cytological and morphological details give the two groups an extremely divergent evolution. Because of the presence of phycobilins, the Cryptophyceae (cryptomonads) of the Pyrrophyta may also be related to the Cyanophyta and Rhodophyta. However, the phycobilin pigments may have developed independently in the Cryptophyceae, since flagella are present on a great many of the Cryptophyceae but are lacking in the other two divisions. The Cryptophyceae contain chlorophyll c in addition to chlorophyll a and the phycobilins. For this reason they may have evolved from a form that also gave rise to another line represented by the more typical Pyrrophyta, the Dinophyceae (dinoflagellates). This latter class, which lacks phycobilins, has an abundance of carotenoid pigments, as well as chlorophyll c, which also occurs in the Phaeophyta (browns) and

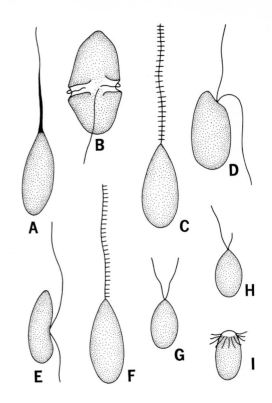

FIGURE 7–1   Types of flagellation of motile cells. A, C, F–I, apical insertion; B, D, E, lateral insertion. A, whiplash flagellum; B, encircling and trailing flagella; C, F, tinsel flagella; G, isokont (equal) flagella; D, E, H, heterokont (unequal) flagella; I, stephanokont (ring of) flagella.

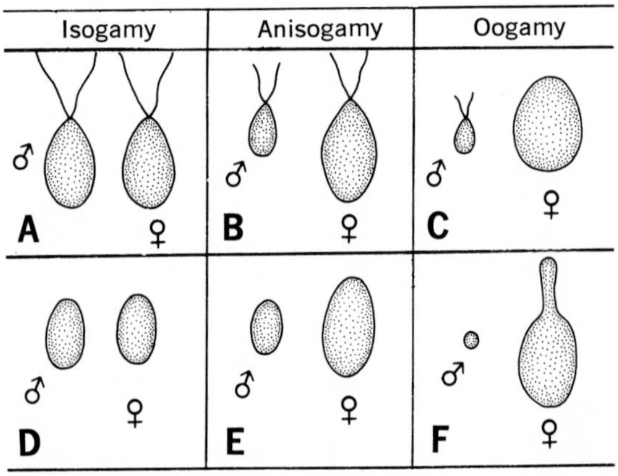

Isogamy		Anisogamy		Oogamy	
♂ A	♀	♂ B	♀	♂ C	♀
♂ D	♀	♂ E	♀	♂ F	♀

FIGURE 7–2   Types of sexual reproduction. A–C, at least one gamete motile. A, B, both gametes motile; C, male gamete motile. D–F, neither gamete motile.

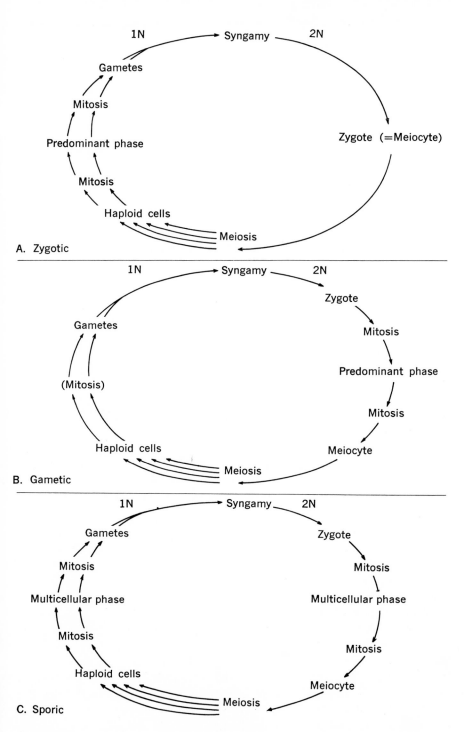

FIGURE 7–3   Types of alternation of generations. A, *Zygotic Meiosis:* predominant phase is haploid, zygote is only diploid stage and serves as meiocyte. B,
Gametic Meiosis: predominant phase is diploid, meiosis results in four haploid
cells that may function directly as gametes or divide mitotically to produce
gametes. C, *Sporic Meiosis:* haploid phase alternates with diploid phase, with
several mitotic divisions in each generation.

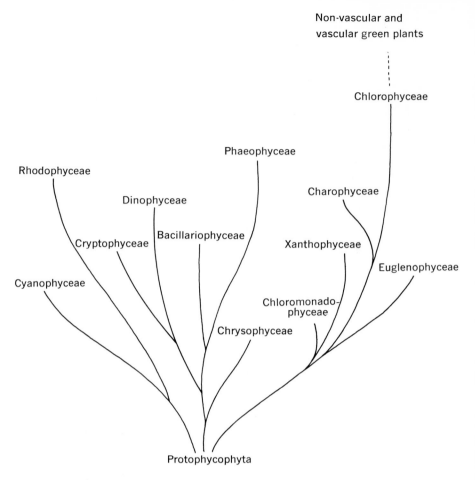

FIGURE 7–4   Diagram of possible interrelationships and phylogenetic arrangement of algal classes.

some members of the Chrysophyta (primarily the Bacillariophyceae or diatoms). Also in these two classes the carotenoid **fucoxanthin** is abundant. The storage product is **laminarin** or the closely related **chrysolaminarin.** These differ from the starch-like carbohydrates of the Rhodophyta, Cyanophyta, and Pyrrophyta in the type of linkage between the glucose molecules. Another similarity of the Phaeophyta and Chrysophyta is seen in the common occurrence of one whiplash flagellum and one tinsel flagellum. Whether all these forms have evolved from a common progenitor is highly debatable, although at least two distinct groupings exist.

The algae that lack masking pigments are also morphologically diverse, although possibly not as much as are those classes considered

previously. All photosynthetic algae have chlorophyll *a*. But some of these green-appearing algae may have only this one ubiquitous chlorophyll (Xanthophyta). In addition, chlorophyll *b* occurs in Chlorophyta (greens) and Euglenophyta (euglenids). These algae may have had a common ancestry, from which three distinct evolutionary lines have resulted. The Xanthophyceae store chrysolaminarin and possibly have diverged from the Chrysophyta–Phaeophyta line fairly early. The Euglenophyta possibly diverged soon after the development of chlorophyll *b*. Interestingly, some of the Euglenophyta have the same carbohydrate-splitting enzymes as the Phaeophyta, and the main storage product of the euglenids is starch-like.

Parallel evolution of morphological forms is evident in several classes of algae. In several divisions, variations seem to have occurred independently, including **rhizopodial, flagellated, palmelloid, coccoid, filamentous,** and **siphonous** forms.

Most botanists regard the Chlorophyta as the group from which higher plants have most likely originated. Certain modern genera in the Chlorophyceae illustrate features to support the hypothesis that all green plants (vascular and nonvascular) evolved from some green alga or green alga-like precursor. The Charophyceae represent a diverging evolutionary series from chlorophycean ancestry. Some botanists have considered the Charophyceae as a group from which bryophytes may be derived. A further discussion of these relationships will be presented in Chapter 15.

Figure 7–4 presents a diagram of possible interrelationships and phylogenetic arrangements of the algae.

REFERENCES

Blum, J. L., "The Ecology of River Algae." *Bot. Rev.,* 22: 291–341 (1956).

Bold, H. C., "The Cultivation of the Algae." *Bot. Rev.,* 8: 69–138 (1942).

Bold, H. C., *Morphology of Plants.* New York: Harper & Row, Publishers (1957). Pp. 11–138.

Burlew, J. S. (Ed.), *Algal Culture from Laboratory to Pilot Plant.* Publ. No. 600. Washington, D. C.: Carnegie Institute (1953).

Carson, R. C., *The Sea Around Us.* New York: Oxford University Press (1951).

Chapman, V. J., *Seaweeds and Their Uses.* London: Methuen & Co. Ltd. (1950).

Chapman, V. J., *The Algae.* London: Macmillan & Co. Ltd. (1962).

Chase, F. M., "Useful Algae." *Ann. Rept. Smithsonian Inst.* (1941): 401–452 (1942).

Coker, R. E., *This Great and Wide Sea.* Chapel Hill: University of North Carolina Press (1947).

Davis, C. C., *The Marine and Freshwater Plankton.* East Lansing: Michigan State University Press (1955).

Dawson, E. Y., *How to Know the Seaweeds.* Dubuque, Iowa: Wm. C. Brown Co. (1956).

Dittmer, H. C., *Phylogeny and Form in the Plant Kingdom.* Princeton, N. J.: D. Van Nostrand Co., Inc. (1964). Pp. 11–160.

Edmondson, W. T. (Ed.), *Freshwater Biology,* 2nd Ed. New York: John Wiley & Sons, Inc. (1959). ("Myxophyceae," by F. Drouet, pp. 95–114, figs. 5.1–5.43; "Algae," by R. H. Thompson, pp. 115–170, figs. 6.1–6.428; "Bacillariophyceae," by R. Patrick, pp. 171–189, figs. 7.1–7.57.)

Fogg, G. E., *The Metabolism of Algae.* London: Methuen & Co. Ltd. (1953).

Frey, D. G. (Ed.), *Limnology in North America.* Madison, Wisc.: University of Wisconsin Press (1963).

Fritsch, F. E., *The Structure and Reproduction of the Algae.* Vol. 1. Cambridge: Cambridge University Press (1935).

Fritsch, F. E., *The Structure and Reproduction of the Algae.* Vol. 2. Cambridge: Cambridge University Press (1945).

Guberlet, M. L., *Seaweeds at Ebb Tide.* Seattle: University of Washington Press (1956).

Hardy, A. C., *The Open Sea.* Cambridge: Houghton Mifflin Co. (1956).

Harvey, H. W., *The Chemistry and Fertility of Sea Waters,* 2nd Ed. Cambridge: Cambridge University Press (1960).

Huber-Pestalozzi, G., *Das Phytoplankton des Süsswassers.* Vol. 16, Pts. 1–5. In Thienemann, A. (Ed.), *Die Binnengewässer.* Stuttgart: E. Schweizerbart'sche Verlagsbuchhandlung (1938–1961).

Jackson, D. F. (Ed.), *Algae and Man.* New York: Plenum Press, Inc. (1964).

Johnson, J. H., *Limestone-building Algae and Algal Limestones.* Golden, Colo.: Colorado School of Mines (1961).

Lewin, R. A. (Ed.), *Physiology and Biochemistry of Algae.* New York: Academic Press, Inc. (1962).

Lund, J. W. G., and Talling, J. F., "Botanical Limnological Methods with Special Reference to the Algae." *Bot. Rev.,* 23: 489–583 (1957).

Moore, H. B., *Marine Ecology.* New York: John Wiley & Sons, Inc. (1958).

Palmer, C. M., *Algae in Water Supplies.* U. S. Dept. Health Service Publ. No. 657. Washington, D. C.: U. S. Government Printing Office (1959).

Papenfuss, G. F., "Classification of the Algae." In *A Century of Progress in the Natural Sciences,* 1853–1953. San Francisco: California Academy of Sciences (1955). Pp. 115–224.

Pascher, A. (Ed.), *Die Süsswasser-Flora Deutschlands, Österreichs, und der Schweiz.* Vols. 1–7, 9–12. Jena: G. Fischer (1913–1932).

Prescott, G. W., *How to Know the Freshwater Algae."* Dubuque, Iowa: Wm. C. Brown Co. (1954).

Prescott, G. W., "A Guide to the Literature on Ecology and Life Histories of the Algae." *Bot. Rev.,* 22: 167–240 (1956).

Prescott, G. W., *Algae of the Western Great Lakes Area,* Rev. Ed. Dubuque, Iowa: Wm. C. Brown Co. (1962).

Pringsheim, E. G., *Pure Cultures of Algae.* Cambridge: Cambridge University Press (1949).

Rabenhorst, L. (Ed.), *Kryptogamen-Flora von Deutschland, Österreich, und der Schweiz,* 2nd Ed. Vols. 7, 10–14. Leipzig: Akademische Verlagsgeschellshaft (1930–1944).

Ruttner, F., *Fundamentals of Limnology,* 3rd Ed. (Translated by D. G. Frey and F. E. J. Fry.) Toronto: University of Toronto Press (1963).

Scagel, R. F., *Marine Plant Resources of British Columbia.* Fisheries Research Board Bull. No. 127. Ottawa: Queens Printer (1961).

Smith, G. M., *Marine Algae of the Monterey Peninsula, California.* Palo Alto, Calif.: Stanford University Press (1944).

Smith, G. M., *The Freshwater Algae of the United States,* 2nd Ed. New York: McGraw-Hill Book Co., Inc. (1950).

Smith, G. M. (Ed.), *Manual of Phycology.* Waltham, Mass.: Chronica Botanica (1951).

Smith, G. M., *Cryptogamic Botany,* 2nd Ed. Vol. 1: *Algae and Fungi.* New York: McGraw-Hill Book Co., Inc. (1955). Pp. 12–345.

Starr, R. C., "Culture Collection of Algae." *Am. J. Bot.,* 51:1013–1044 (1964).

Taylor, W. R., *Marine Algae of the Northeastern Coast of North America,* 2nd Ed. Ann Arbor: University of Michigan Press (1957).

Taylor, W. R., *Marine Algae of the Eastern Tropical and Subtropical Coasts of the Americas.* Ann Arbor, Mich.: University of Michigan Press (1960).

Tiffany, L. H. *Algae, the Grass of Many Waters,* 2nd Ed. Springfield, Mo.: Charles C. Thomas, Publisher (1958).

Tiffany, L. H., and Britton, M. E., *The Algae of Illinois.* Chicago: University of Chicago Press (1952).

Tilden, J. E., *The Algae and Their Life Relations.* Minneapolis: University of Minnesota Press (1935).

Tressler, D. K., and Lemon, J. M., *Marine Products of Commerce,* 2nd Ed. New York: Reinhold Publishing Corp. (1951).

Tryon, C. A., and Hartman, R. T. (Ed.), *The Ecology of Algae; the Pymatuning Symposia in Ecology.* Special Publ. No. 2. Pymatuning Laboratory. Pittsburg: University of Pittsburg Press (1960).

Tseng, C. K., *Phycocolloids: Useful Seaweed Polysaccharides.* Pp. 629–734. In Alexander, J., *Colloid Chemistry.* Vol. 6. New York: Reinhold Publishing Corp. (1946).

8 / DIVISION

CYANOPHYTA

There are over 150 genera with about 1,500 species in the single class Cyanophyceae of the Cyanophyta (*blue-green algae*). Some authors consider these algae to be in the class Myxophyceae of the Myxophyta; others consider them related to the bacteria and classify them in the class Schizophyceae of the division Schizomyco-phyta. In this text they are considered as a separate division closer to the algal groups, although, because of current research, their affinities to the bacteria cannot be ignored.

CELL STRUCTURE

The blue-green algal cell wall is composed of at least two lay-ers (Figs. 8–1A, 2, 3A, B). The layer next to the protoplast is often stratified and may contain cellulose; outside this is a mucilag-inous **pectic** layer of varying thickness. Sometimes a prominent outer mucilaginous **sheath,** possibly pectic in nature or containing hemicelluloses, is secreted by the cell. The sheath may be very thick, stratified, and intensely colored. It may appear yellow, brown, red, blue, or violet; the color depends to some extent on the hydrogen ion, or pH, of the medium or substrate, as well as on the presence of numerous pigments.

The cell itself has very little of the cell differentiation charac-teristic of plants in general. With the light microscope the proto-plast often appears to consist of an inner colorless portion termed

156

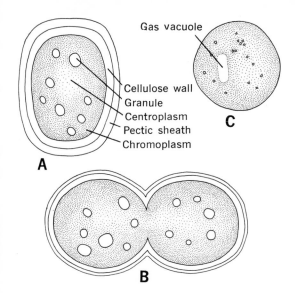

FIGURE 8–1   Typical Cyanophyta cell. A, vegetative phase, ×575; B, dividing phase, ×500; C, single cell of *Microcystis* showing gas vacuole, ×1,500.

the **centroplasm,** and an outer pigmented region called the **chromoplasm.** There is no central vacuole, or an organized nucleus with nuclear membrane and nucleoli. There is some difference of opinion as to the exact organization of the nuclear material, which may be distributed throughout the cell or restricted to the centroplasm. The nuclear material has been reported to occur as rod-like particles, or in a loose network. All accounts of chromosomes and spindle formation as known in other plants have been discredited. This lack of differentiation of the protoplasm into cell organelles is similar to that of the bacteria.

The chromoplasm pigments do not occur in definite plastids. The structure of the chromoplasm region, as determined with the electron microscope, seems to be a granular network and contains the nuclear material, the pigments in submicroscopic lamellae, and numerous other inclusions (Fig. 8–2, 3A, B). Among these inclusions are the food reserves,

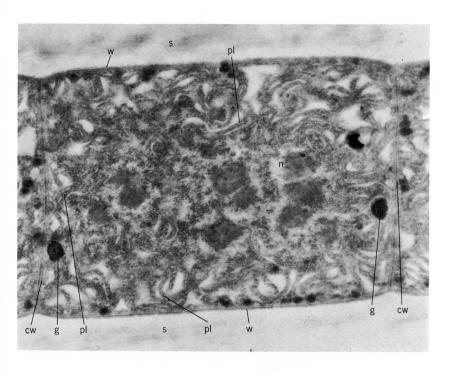

FIGURE 8–2   Electron micrograph of cell of *Calothrix parietina*, ×22,500. *n*, nucleoplasm; *pl*, photosynthetic lamellae; *g*, granules; *w*, wall; *s*, sheath; *cw*, cross wall. (Photograph courtesy H. Ris and R. N. Singh and with permission of the *Journal of Biophysical and Biochemical Cytology*.)

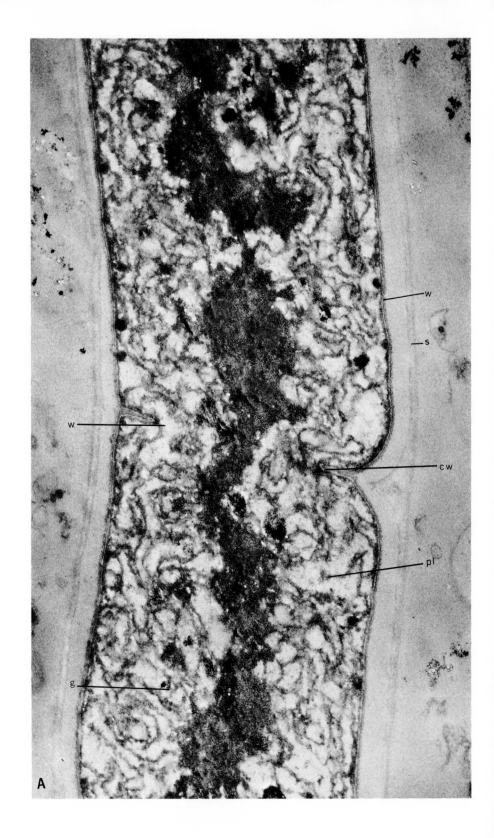

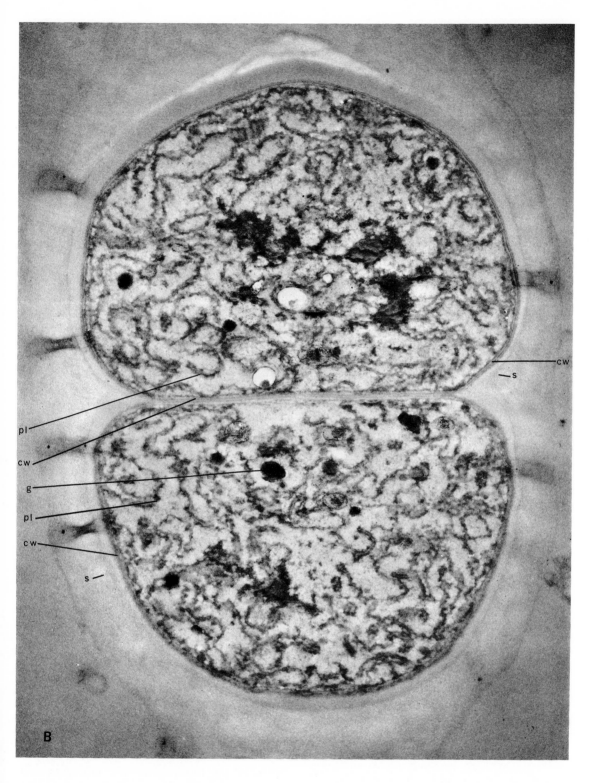

FIGURE 8–3   Electron micrographs of cells of *Mastigocladus laminosus*. A, early stage of cell division and invagination of the new wall, ×24,800; B, cell division completed, ×29,000. Symbols as for Fig. 8–2. (Photographs courtesy J. A. Chapman and M. R. J. Salton and with permission of *Archiv für Mikrobiologie*.)

which are stored as carbohydrates and proteins. The carbohydrate present is referred to as **cyanophyte starch;** it is the **amylopectin,** or branching factor of starch. Hyaline protein granules, sometimes referred to as **cyanophycin granules,** are also present. Oil or fat droplets are reported but no specific sterols have been isolated. Electron micrographs (Fig. 8–2, 3A, B) show that the diffuse pigments are present as small photosynthetic lamellae. In some instances the lamellae are open, forming vesicles; however, well-defined chloroplasts have not been established.

Chlorophyll *a* is the only green pigment present. In addition, there are carotenes, xanthophylls, and the proteinaceous phycobilins. The principal carotene is β-carotene; and the chief xanthophylls are flavacin, myxoxanthin, myxoxanthophyll, lutein, and zeaxanthin. Of the three phycobilins occurring in the blue-greens, blue *c*-phycocyanin is always present; the red *c*-phycoerythrin and blue allophycocyanin can occasionally be present. The presence of both chlorophyll and *c*-phycocyanin pigments gives many of the Cyanophyta their typical blue-green color. The alga will appear reddish when *c*-phycoerythrin is present in considerable amounts, although sometimes this reddish appearance is a result of nonphycobilin pigments in the sheath.

Under certain conditions small spherical or irregular gas vacuoles occur in the cell (Fig. 8–1C). These are particularly evident in free-floating species of such genera as *Microcystis* [1], *Aphanizomenon,* and others. It has been suggested that these gas vacuoles serve as a flotation mechanism and permit the alga to remain at or near the surface in optimum light conditions. The vacuoles also have been interpreted as indicative of unsatisfactory growing conditions.

Cell division results from splitting of the protoplast by a centripetal ingrowth of the inner wall layer. The septum apparently "pinches" the cell in half, dividing the contents equally (Fig. 8–1B, 3A, B). Regular movements of the nuclear material are not present, and the division is **amitotic.**

[1] The generic names used for the Cyanophyta are based upon usage by Smith (1950) and Prescott (1962). No attempt has been made here to use the taxa as set forth by Drouet and Daily (1956) and Drouet (1959).

MOVEMENT

Flagellated cells are never present, although in some filamentous species lacking a sheath (as *Oscillatoria* and *Spirulina*), the thallus undergoes some movement. The movement may be simple gliding or combined with rotation around a longitudinal axis, somewhat similar to the Myxobacteriales (see Chapter 6). The rate and direction of movement sometimes depend on light and temperature. Various theories proposed to explain these movements have included: streaming of protoplasm within the cell; secretion of mucilaginous material from the cell; and rhythmic longitudinal waves caused by alternate contraction and expansion of the cell membrane along the length of the filament resulting from osmotic changes. Another current theory relates gliding to a dynamic system of oscillations (at the submicroscopic level) formed by protoplasmic protein fibrils. According to this theory, the fibrils fixed to the surface cause a shift of secreted mucilage resulting in the gliding movement.

CLASSIFICATION AND MORPHOLOGICAL DIVERSITY

A number of systems of classification have been proposed for the members of the Cyanophyta. Because these algae lack cellular differentiation and are simple in form, few characteristics clearly distinguish higher levels of classification. This is especially true at the ordinal level, where from three to five orders are generally recognized. Thus, there is some difference of opinion concerning the validity of some of the proposed orders, suborders, and families. However, there appear to be two distinctive morphological lines of evolution: the

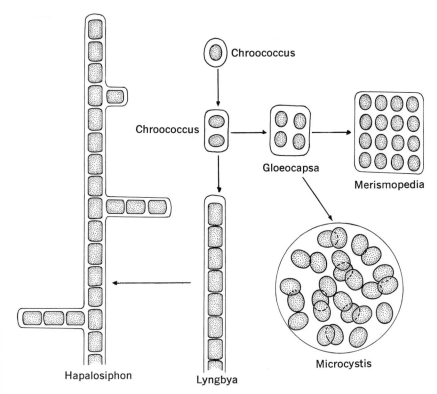

FIGURE 8–4   Diagram of possible evolutionary lines in Cyanophyta resulting from regular and irregular planes of cell division.

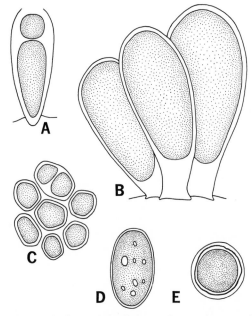

FIGURE 8–5   Unicellular Cyanophyta. A, *Chamaesiphon*, ×3,000; B, *Dermocarpa*, ×1,000; C, *Pleurocapsa*, ×830; D, *Synechococcus*, ×630; E, *Chroococcus*, ×415.

filamentous and nonfilamentous types (see Fig. 8–4). The simplest member of the division morphologically may be considered as a unicellular free-floating form, such as *Chroococcus* or *Synechococcus* (Fig. 8–5D, E). When a cell of these unicellular forms grows to a certain size, under appropriate conditions it divides and immediately separates to give rise to two new individuals. The unicellular *Chamaesiphon* is attached to the substrate, and there is a slight differentiation between the base and the apex (Fig. 8–5A). Some of these unicellular attached types may form small clusters, as in *Dermocarpa* (Fig. 8–5B), or dense aggregations, as in *Pleurocapsa* (Fig. 8–5C) on various substrates. From the unicellular type colonial forms have probably evolved. One line of evolution has led to the nonfilamentous forms (referred to as palmelloid), and the other to the filamentous types. Both have arisen from the same primitive unicellular stock but along divergent lines (Fig. 8–4).

The simplest type of colony, illustrated in *Gloeocapsa* and *Gloeothece* (Fig. 8–6B, C), results from the cells remaining fastened to each other after division. Each cell is enclosed within a discrete wall and all the cells of the colony are embedded in a common gelatinous sheath. The resulting palmelloid colony usually fragments before more than four to eight cells are produced. In *Merismopedia* (Fig. 8–6F) the cells divide regularly in only two planes. The cells remain fastened together in a single-layered, **monostromatic,** sheet of cells. If regular divisions occur in three directions, a cubical colony such as *Eucapsis* is produced (Fig. 8–6A). In some instances the division planes are irregular and the cells become oriented in quite a diffuse manner, as in *Microcystis* (Fig. 8–6D, E). In this genus some species form small spherical colonies (Fig. 8–6E) and others form large, diffuse, reticulate, or club-shaped colonies containing thousands of cells (Fig. 8–6D). The cells are held together by an extensive mucilaginous sheath. Each cell in these loosely organized colonies may be regarded as a separate individual, since the colony is devoid of any sort of differentiation.

In the filamentous line of evolution there are simple, unbranched as well as branched forms. Cell divisions in this series occur in only one plane in the unbranched forms (Fig. 8–7C, K, L). The filaments may be free or aggregated into various types of macroscopic, mucilaginous masses of regular or irregular form. These masses are in the form of cushions or balls, which can be free-floating or sessile on various substrates. In *Nostoc* the unbranched filaments (Fig. 8–7C) aggregate in a mucilaginous matrix, producing a body of considerable size (Fig. 8–8). In *Schizothrix* (Fig. 8–7D) several unbranched filaments may be laterally aggregated in a common sheath. Although divisions are mainly in one plane in branched forms, the cells occasionally divide longitudinally in a second plane. Thus, either a **uniseriate** branched thallus, as in *Hapalosiphon* (Fig. 8–7B), or a **multiseriate** branched thallus, as in *Stigonema* (Fig. 8–7G, I) may be produced. Branching of this type is referred to as *true branching*. In some of these, such as *Hapalosiphon*, conspicu-

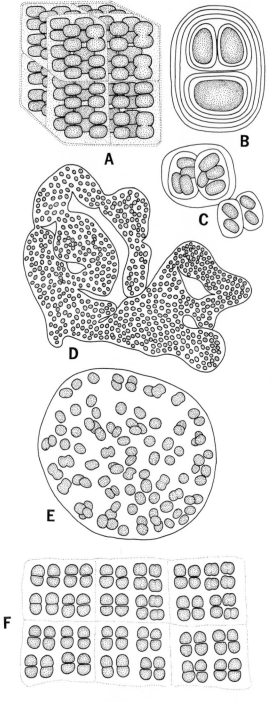

FIGURE 8–6   Colonial or palmelloid Cyanophyta. A, B, F, regular planes of division; C–E, irregular planes of division. A, *Eucapsis*, ×690; B, *Gloeocapsa*, ×2,250; C, *Gloeothece*, ×1,235; D, a large diffuse species of *Microcystis*, ×325; E, a small compact species of *Microcystis*, ×555; F, *Merismopedia*, ×1,175.

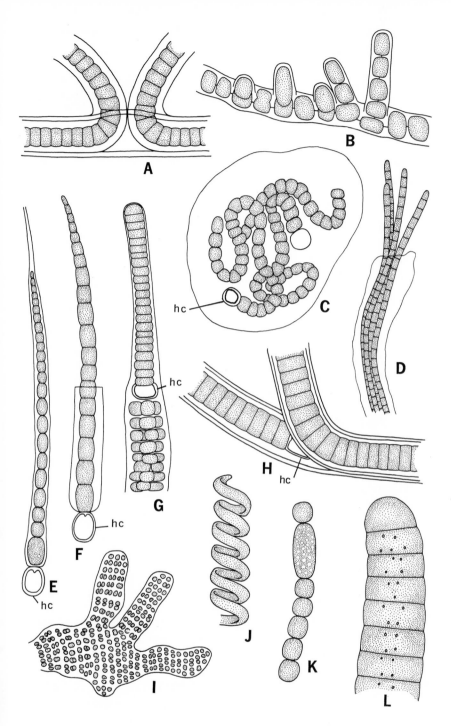

FIGURE 8–7   Filamentous Cyanophyta. A, H, false branching; B, G, I, true branching. A, *Scytonema*, ×570; B, *Hapalosiphon*, ×1,180; C, small colony of *Nostoc*, ×1,000; D, *Shizothrix*, showing several trichomes within a single sheath, ×1,000; E, *Rivularia*, with basal heterocyst, ×1,095; F, *Gloeotrichia*, with basal heterocyst, ×1,100; G, *Stigonema*, ×500; H, *Tolypothrix*, ×915; I, *Stigonema*, ×170; J, *Spirulina*, ×1,800; K, *Cylindrospermum*, showing large, subterminal akinete, ×880; L, *Oscillatoria*, ×2,355.

ous protoplasmic or primary **pit connections** form between cells as a result of incomplete cell division by the ingrowing septa (Fig. 8–7B).

In the few genera where so-called **false branching** occurs (as in *Scytonema* and *Tolypothrix,* Fig. 8–7A, H), the filament merely breaks at some point, and one or both ends resulting from the breakage grows out of the sheath into a "branch." The break may result from death of an intercalary cell or from extensive growth of the filament within its sheath (Fig. 8–7A, H).

In most of the filamentous forms cell division and growth occur throughout the filament, but in some genera cell division may be especially prevalent in the apical region. In the tapered forms, such as *Rivularia* (Fig. 8–7E), division and growth may be restricted to an intercalary region proximal to the long terminal cell, or so-called "hair." These forms with localized growth can be regarded as having primitive types of **intercalary meristems.**

In many of the filamentous species the filaments are uniform in diameter throughout, as in *Oscillatoria* (Fig. 8–7L). But in others, such as *Rivularia* (Fig. 8–7E), the filaments gradually taper from a broad, sometimes attached, specialized proximal cell to a narrow, distal, or free hair cell. In *Oscillatoria* the cells are uniform in length throughout the filament. But in *Rivularia,* in addition to being gradually tapered, the cells closest to the free end of the filament are generally longer as well as narrower. In some genera the cells are uniform in diameter throughout, although the terminal cells are usually tapered to the apex. Species may be separated from one another by cellular dimensions (short broad cells as opposed to long narrow cells). Most of the filamentous genera are more or less straight, but others, such as *Spirulina,* are helical in form (Fig. 8–7J).

REPRODUCTION

The chief method of vegetative reproduction is by fragmentation. But in addition, various types of nonflagellated spores or spore-like bodies are produced. Reproduction by frag-

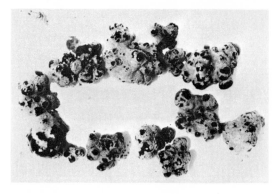

FIGURE 8–8   Macroscopic form of *Nostoc,* ×0.4.

mentation may occur by a simple breaking apart of a thallus into two or more units. Each fragment is then capable of continuing growth to produce a new colony. Fragmentation is the sole means of increase in numbers of individuals in the great majority of nonfilamentous forms.

In filamentous species, **hormogonia** are common in some genera, such as *Oscillatoria* (Fig. 8–9C). A hormogonium is not merely a fragment of a filament; rather, the filaments break into short multicellular segments, which may be capable of gliding movements. Hormogonia are liberated from the sheath under optimum growing conditions; they develop into new plants. The break in a filament to form a hormogonium may result from death of an intercalary cell. Such a place in a filament is known as a **separation disc,** and the biconcave shape is the result of a decrease in pressure in the adjacent cells (Fig. 8–9C). There is no conspicuous differentiation in the cells of the hormogonium in any way, except that the terminal cells are rounded. Hormogonia sometimes are dormant and act as resting stages. They may form under unfavorable conditions, and are frequently associated with rapid changes in temperature and desiccation such as when a pond or stream becomes dry.

Another type of reproductive structure formed in certain filamentous genera is the spore-like akinete (Fig. 8–9B), a single cell that develops directly from metamorphosis of a vegetative cell. Usually the akinete is considerably larger than the ordinary cell, and has a thickened wall outside the regular cell wall. The

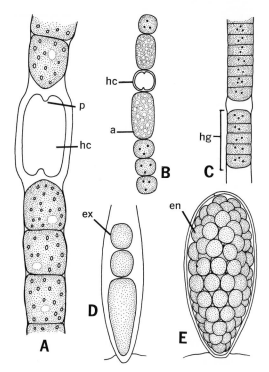

FIGURE 8–9   Reproductive structures in Cyanophyta. A, heterocyst (*hc*) with papillae (*p*) in *Aphanizomenon*, ×2,890; B, akinete (*a*) and heterocyst (*hc*) in *Anabaena*, ×1,800; C, hormogonium (*hg*) in *Oscillatoria*, ×1,800; D, exospores (*ex*) in *Chamaesiphon*, ×3,000; E, endospores (*en*) in *Dermocarpa*, ×1,000.

heterocysts are uniformly dense and generally yellowish; however, sometimes the protoplast remains a vivid blue-green. Heterocysts may be intercalary or terminal in position. The wall becomes thickened, and an inner swelling—or papilla—develops at the end attached to the rest of the filament. A median pore is present in each papilla and a delicate protoplasmic connection passes through it to the adjacent vegetative cell. Prominent, highly refractive granules called polar granules are often present in the heterocysts near these pores. A filament may fragment at the point of an intercalary heterocyst; thus, this structure is regarded as contributing to vegetative reproduction by fragmentation. In some filaments, the heterocysts persist after the adjacent vegetative cells die. In forms with both heterocysts and akinetes, the position of one is relative to that of the other.

Finally, true spore formation (aplanospores) within a cell is present in certain genera. One type of true spore is the endospore (Fig. 8–9E). In certain forms such as the epiphyte *Dermocarpa,* the protoplast divides endogenously into a number of units. The wall of the parent cell eventually breaks down and liberates these units as individual thin-walled spores, which are then capable of germinating and growing immediately into new plants. Heterocysts have been reported to germinate by production of endospores. Sometimes another type of aplanospore, the **exospore,** may be distinguished, although the distinction is not a striking one (Fig. 8–9D). Exospores are formed **basipetally** at the distal end of an attached unicellular alga, as in *Chamaesiphon,* by transverse divisions of the protoplast.

Sexual fusion, as known for most other algal groups, has not been observed in the blue-green algae. However, there are recent reports of exchange of genetic material. It is likely that any sexuality in the Cyanophyta will be found to be similar to that reported in bacteria.

DISTRIBUTION AND ECOLOGY

The extremely ubiquitous Cyanophyta appear as blue-green to brown or black smears,

akinete contains a rich accumulation of food reserves as cyanophycin granules, and is resistant to adverse conditions. On germination, the akinete develops into a new filament within the old cell wall. Some akinetes evidently germinate immediately after they are formed, but they may remain dormant for some time and can be extremely resistant to desiccation and high temperatures.

Another type of spore-like structure is the **heterocyst,** which is common in certain filamentous genera (Fig. 8–9A). There is some question whether all heterocysts behave in the same manner. The heterocyst, too, is apparently a metamorphosed vegetative cell, which in some instances functions to produce a new filament; in other instances it is a degenerate cell. In the latter instance, heterocysts may be archaic reproductive bodies that have lost their ability to function as such. The contents of macroscopic cushions, or layers on moist surfaces of rocks, soil, and trees. In desert areas, the lower surfaces of many rocks are covered with blue-green algae. They occur on all types of substrate and are free-floating **(planktonic)** in every conceivable type of aquatic environment. Although the blue-greens are abundant and important in the sea in certain parts of the world, particularly in tropical areas, the group as a whole is much more diverse and conspicuous in fresh-water habitats. Cyanophyta are also present in hot springs; in ice; in various types of associations with other plants and animals; and in the soil, either on or below the surface, to a depth of a meter or more.

Certain plankton species may occur in such large quantities as to color a body of water a brilliant blue-green or even red. The dense concentrations of planktonic forms, which are responsible for these **blooms,** are caused by certain species of the nonfilamentous *Microcystis* (Fig. 8–6D, E), and filamentous genera including *Aphanizomenon, Nostoc, Gloeotrichia,* and *Oscillatoria* (Fig. 8–9A, 7C, F, L). Optimum conditions for such blooms are the result of the interaction of many factors. When exposed to long hours of sunlight, shallow warm water, which is high in nitrogen and possibly phosphorus, will favor bloom conditions. Especially troublesome blooms occur in domestic drinking water supplies, such as reservoirs, where they tend to clog filters. In extreme conditions of algal growth the water may be unfit for human or livestock consumption, and may be toxic to fish or other aquatic organisms. If the concentration of algae is relatively low, there is only a disagreeable taste or smell. Livestock, including cattle and sheep, have been known to succumb from drinking water contaminated with certain species of *Microcystis, Anabaena,* and *Aphanizomenon.* No deaths among humans have been reported, although many instances of 24-hour (gastrointestinal) flu may be due to such toxic substances. The nature of the substance produced in *Microcystis* has been studied by workers at the laboratories of the National Research Council of Canada. The toxin, which is a mixture of five polypeptides in units of ten amino

acids, is retained within the algal cells. When the cells are broken, the toxin causes respiratory difficulties and breakdown of the liver tissues. In experiments with mice (dosage 80–120 mg/kg body weight), death occurs in one to two hours. Wild fowl are not susceptible to this toxin; however, they are susceptible to one secreted by a species of *Anabaena.* In similar experiments with *Microcystis,* this second toxin, which is excreted by the living cells, causes death of the experimental mice within two minutes (at a dosage of 640–1280 mg/kg body weight). Again, the effect is on the respiratory system and causes convulsions.

A few blue-greens occur as marine plankton. Several species of a filamentous form related to *Oscillatoria* have been known for a long time to cause extensive blooms in parts of the Indian Ocean, where they cause mass mortality in populations of marine fishes. The precise nature of the lethal action is uncertain. It may be a toxic condition in the water, similar to that brought about as a result of the blue-green algal activities described above. The algae may have essentially a suffocation effect on the fish as a result of clogging of the gills, preventing the intake of oxygen. Or, it may be that the respiratory demand of the dense concentrations of these blue-greens at night, in the absence of photosynthesis, lowers the oxygen tension in the water to a point where the fish suffocate from lack of oxygen. One of these species produces a reddish bloom; from this phenomenon the Red Sea derives its name. Most of the marine forms, however, occur in shallower coastal areas where they are attached to various substrates, or in extensive mats, in confined embayments, on mud flats, or in lagoons. Some genera are attached to the surfaces of many of the larger brown and red algae, whereas other species occur on rocks or within softer rocky substrates. The algae may secrete substances that dissolve and perforate soft rock, thus being important in the weathering of rock. Other genera inhabit the shells of fresh-water and marine molluscs.

A number of blue-green algae are believed responsible for many of the calcareous concretions or pebbles in standing fresh water, as well as in thermal areas. The Cyanophyta are also important in tropical marine reef formations, resulting in characteristic calcareous incrustations. The exact mechanism is not understood, but the algae apparently secrete calcium and magnesium carbonates and build up extensive deposits of travertine in a variety of forms. Blue-green algae of all morphological types have this ability and include several species of *Chroococcus, Oscillatoria, Hapalosiphon, Stigonema,* and *Rivularia.*

Blue-green algae are common in inland salt-water ponds and lakes. They are apparently able to tolerate relatively higher concentrations of salt than normally occur in the sea. The blue-greens are the most common algae in alkaline waters.

Numerous species of the Cyanophyta are common inhabitants of thermal springs tolerating high temperatures ranging from 60–85° C. Certain genera as well as species of more cosmopolitan genera occur in such areas. At the other extreme, certain species have been collected growing on snow as well as in the seas and lakes of the Arctic and Antarctic.

Some blue-green algae live intimately in association with other organisms. Within some colorless organisms occur certain unicellular species such as *Synechococcus.* In these forms, e.g., *Gloeochaete, Paulinella,* and *Cyanophora* (Fig. 8–10A–C), the blue-green algal cell divides at the same time as the colorless host cell. The process is similar to chloroplast division in some of the other algal groups. The nature of the association is not clearly known, although the algae derive nutrients and perhaps carbon dioxide from the colorless cell. In turn, the heterotrophic host obtains food material from the built-in food-manufacturing blue-green symbiont. Recent electron microscope studies have shown no direct connections between the host cell and the blue-green alga. Such an association is similar to that in certain ciliates and some invertebrate animals, such as corals, which have other endozoic algae.

Blue-green algae are also endophytic within other plant groups. Species of *Chroococcus, Gloeocapsa, Nostoc,* and other genera are common algal symbionts of some lichens.

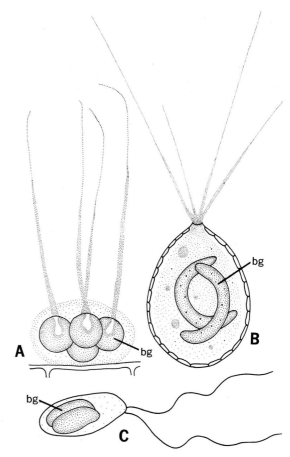

FIGURE 8–10   Symbiotic Cyanophyta and host cells. A, *Gloeochaete,* ×900; B, *Paulinella chromatophora,* ×750; C, *Cyanophora paradoxa,* ×2,-915. *bg,* blue-green alga.

Symbiotic relationships of certain species of *Nostoc* and *Anabaena* occur with other plants, such as the bryophytes *Ricciocarpus, Blasia,* and *Anthoceros;* the fern *Azolla;* the gymnosperms *Cycas* and *Zamia;* and the angiosperms *Gunnera* and *Trifolium.* In *Gunnera,* the blue-green algae are present in the cells of the leaf bases (Fig. 8–11). In *Trifolium* and *Cycas* they are present in root nodules. Although the association is not clear, there is some suggestion of nitrogen-fixation by the algae, thus making nitrogen available to the host plants.

A few species of colorless (presumably heterotrophic) blue-green algae are described. It has not been clearly established whether these species are capable of both heterotrophic and autotrophic metabolism. This is probably

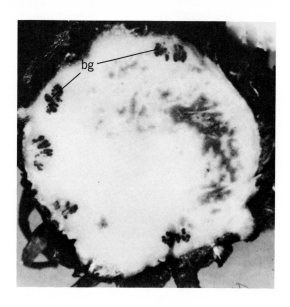

FIGURE 8–11   Transverse section of rhizome of *Gunnera* (vascular plant) with symbiotic *Nostoc* (*bg*), ×0.4. (Photograph by J. Kuijt.)

dependent on the conditions under which they live; thus heterotrophy may not be obligatory in some species. Some of these colorless forms may also be classed as bacteria, including such genera as the sulfur-fixing *Beggiatoa* and *Thiothrix* (see Chapter 6).

IMPORTANCE AND USES

The direct utilization of blue-green algae by man is at present rather limited. The Japanese eat certain fresh-water species as a confection after treating the algae with sugar. However, their chief importance is indirect. As a result of their primarily autotrophic activities, they undoubtedly play an important part as primary food producers in all the various environments in which they occur. One of their greatest contributions is as nitrogen-fixers in maintaining soil fertility; especially in areas where rice is cultivated, the presence of blue-greens in the paddies reduces the need for fertilizers rich in nitrogen. In certain desert soils, nitrogen-fixation is mainly due to the presence of blue-green algae. This ability to fix atmospheric nitrogen is widespread in the filamentous blue-green algae, occurring in certain species of *Nostoc, Anabaena, Tolypothrix,* and others. Scarcely any of the nonfilamentous forms is able to fix nitrogen.

The presence of photosynthetic algae in the water-clogged fields also prevents deterioration in aeration, and by increasing the available oxygen to roots, minimizes disease susceptibility. The filamentous blue-green algae have been used to reclaim lands exhausted from overuse and overirrigation. The land is flooded and the algae develop in extensive mats. After several months, the flooded area dries and the algal material is plowed into the soil. The algae thus serve as a beginning of the humus layer. Blue-green algae also form extensive mats on the soil surface, which bind the soil, absorb water, and thus reduce soil erosion.

PHYLOGENY

A number of fossil genera and species are reported from the Pre-Cambrian to the present. The oldest fossil algae are considered to be Cyanophyta. Most of the records from the Pre-Cambrian are extremely fragmentary and present no evidence of apparent phylogenetic significance. No heterocysts have been reported in the fossil condition. Many specimens exhibit a tubular structure and have been considered to be sheaths of blue-green algae. Some phycologists consider many of the described blue-green algal fossils invalid. In addition to these Pre-Cambrian records, specific fossils are known from the Paleozoic and Mesozoic eras. The significance of the Cyanophyta in the geologic past is probably great, judging from the ability of certain contemporary species to form calcium and magnesium carbonate deposits; the importance of some in reef formation today; and the ability of certain forms to fix nitrogen.

Very little evolution from the basic unicellular, little-differentiated type appears to have taken place within the Cyanophyta. The purported age, constancy in form, and absence of sexual reproduction are no doubt responsible for the high degree of uniformity present in the Cyanophyta.

REFERENCES

Desikachary, T. V., *Cyanophyta.* New Delhi, India: Indian Council Agric. Res. (1959).

Drouet, F., "Cyanophyta." In Smith, G. M. (Ed.), *Manual of Phycology.* Waltham, Mass.: Chronica Botanica (1951). Pp. 157–166.

Drouet, F., *"Myxophyceae."* In Edmondson, W. T. (Ed.), *Freshwater Biology.* New York: John Wiley & Sons, Inc. (1959).

Drouet, F., and Daily, W. A., "Revision of the Coccoid Myxophyceae." *Butler Univ. Bot. Studies,* 12: 1—218 (1956).

Fogg, G. E., "Nitrogen Fixation by Photosynthetic Plants." *Ann. Rev. Pl. Physiol.,* 7: 51–70 (1956).

Fritsch, F. E., *The Structure and Reproduction of the Algae.* Vol. 2. Cambridge: Cambridge University Press (1945). Pp. 768–898.

Geitler, L., *Cyanophyceae.* In Rabenhorst, L., *Kryptogamen-Flora von Deutschland, Österreich, und der Schweiz,* 2nd Ed. Band 14. Leipzig: Akademische Verlagsgeschellshaft (1932).

Geitler, L., *Schizophyzeen.* In Zimmermann, W., and Ozenda, P., *Handbuch der Pflanzenanatomie.* Vol. 6, Pt. 1. Berlin: Gebrüder Borntraeger (1960).

Huber-Pestalozzi, G., *Das Phytoplankton des Süsswassers.* Vol. 16, Pt. 1. In Thienemann, A., *Die Binnengewässer.* Stuttgart: E. Schweizerbart'sche Verlagsbuchhandlung (1938).

Singh, R. N., *Role of Blue-green Algae in Nitrogen Economy of Indian Agriculture.* New Delhi, India: Indian Council Agric. Res. (1962).

Smith, G. M., *Cryptogamic Botany,* 2nd Ed. Vol. 1: *Algae and Fungi,* New York: McGraw-Hill Book Co., Inc. (1955). Pp. 275–290.

Tilden, J. E., *Minnesota Algae.* Vol. 1. Botan. Ser. 8. Minneapolis: University of Minnesota Press (1910).

9 / DIVISION

PYRROPHYTA

There are about 125 genera and over 1,000 species of *pyrrophytes* referred to this division, many of which are marine. Most of the genera are unicellular motile flagellates; but some are nonmotile palmelloid forms, and a few are colonial or filamentous. The division has both colorless and pigmented forms, the latter being characteristically golden-brown or greenish-brown. Among the colorless forms, some are saprobes and others ingest particulate organic material. Some of the autotrophic species apparently can also be phagotrophic.

A number of different systems of classification have been proposed. The flagellate cryptomonad group is generally placed in a class by itself, the Cryptophyceae. Recent work concerning cytology and pigmentation indicates that the Cryptophyceae should probably be recognized as a separate division, the Cryptophyta; in this text, however, they are considered as a separate class in the Pyrrophyta. In this text the remaining forms are placed in a single class, the Dinophyceae; however, some authorities place them in two separate classes.

CLASS DINOPHYCEAE
(Dinoflagellates)

CELL STRUCTURE

The cell is either naked with a firm **peri-plast** or provided with a cellulosic membrane. The greatest diversity occurs in the motile forms that range in size from 25–500 microns. In the naked motile, or **unarmored,** forms such as *Gymnodinium* (Fig. 9–1B), the periplast may be smooth, striated, or ribbed. In **armored** forms, the cellulose layer may be composed of a number of discrete, **articulated,** sculptured plates cemented together tightly in a definite pattern. In *Glenodinium* (Fig. 9–1A) the plates are quite delicate, whereas in other armored forms, as in *Peridinium* and *Gonyaulax* (Fig. 9–1D, E), the plates may be perforated with one or more pores, and may be strikingly ornamented with horns, spines, papillae, or wing-like processes (Fig. 9–1C, E, 4). As far as is known, the cellulosic plates are formed on an inner delicate cell membrane.

The cells are uninucleate with a highly organized nucleus, which characteristically contains conspicuous **moniliform** (bead-like) threads of chromatin. One to several nucleoli may be present. A large vacuole, lying near the center of the cell, is present in some marine forms. This vacuole has two canals leading to the outside that do not pulsate, but change in size. Vacuoles similar to those in other plants occur in some forms. Some of the motile forms also may have a pigmented **eyespot** considered to be light sensitive.

The pigments, generally present in chloroplasts, give the cells a greenish-brown or golden-brown color. Usually two or more small, disc-shaped chloroplasts are present. In those forms considered primitive, only one or two large chloroplasts are present. In electron micrographs, the chloroplasts appear similar to those of the Chrysophyta (see Fig. 10–2D) and Phaeophyta (Fig. 11–4D). The chloroplasts are comprised of many compressed stacks or bands, each composed of three pairs of lamellae. Some forms contain a **pyrenoid** that is

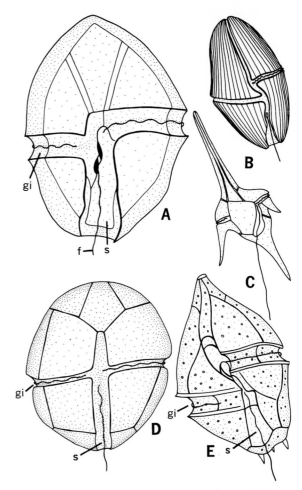

FIGURE 9–1   Motile representatives of Dinophyceae viewed from ventral side to show orientation of flagella (*f*), sulcus (*s*), and girdle (*gi*). A, *Glenodinium*, with a delicate armor, ×1,500. B, *Gymnodinium*, an unarmored form, ×250. C–E, armored forms. C, *Ceratium*, ×330; D, *Peridinium*, ×425; E, *Gonyaulax*, ×750. (A, B, E, after Schiller in Rabenhorst with permission of Akademische Verlagsgesellschaft, Geest and Portig K.-G., Leipzig.)

an integral part of the chloroplast. In nonphotosynthetic forms, pigments may occur as granules or may be dissolved in the cytoplasm.

The photosynthetic forms have two green pigments, chlorophyll *a* and *c,* as well as a number of carotenoid pigments. In addition to the almost universally present β-carotene, there are a number of xanthophylls, of which peridinin, and possibly dinoxanthin, are unique to this division. Peridinin is the brown pigment responsible for the characteristic color of the group. Diadinoxanthin, which occurs in the Chrysophyta, is also present.

The carbohydrate food reserves are stored in the form of starch, comparable to the starch of green algae and higher plants. Although little specific work has been done on dinoflagellate starch, it is assumed to consist of α, 1–4 (amylose) and α, 1–6 (amylopectin) linkages, The starch is formed on the periphery of the chloroplast; if a pyrenoid is present, starch is formed on the outside of it. Smaller starch grains are reported scattered in the cytoplasm adjacent to the chloroplast. Fat or oil is also stored, and may appear as bright red or yellow droplets.

Most types of nutrition are represented in the Dinophyceae. Those forms lacking photosynthetic pigments are saprobic or parasitic; some are phagotrophic. In the autotrophic forms studied, all require an external source of vitamins and are therefore auxotrophs. Some pigmented species have also been reported to be phagotrophic, but this is rare.

MOVEMENT

The motile cells are biflagellate and consist of two morphologically dissimilar flagella usually inserted laterally close together. In the armored forms, the flagella emerge through a common small pore, or in some, through separate pores in the cellulosic wall. A broad, ribbon-like flagellum encircles the cell in a transverse groove, the **girdle.** The other flagellum trails posteriorly, lying in a longitudinal groove, the **sulcus.** This trailing flagellum, which is the whiplash type, acts as a rudder and is responsible for forward movement as well as rotation of the cell. The transverse one may be tinsellated and has an undulatory movement that accounts for rotation and some forward motion. One small group with sulcus and girdle have the flagella apically inserted.

MORPHOLOGICAL DIVERSITY

The unicellular, biflagellate type is typical (Fig. 9–1) of the group and is by far the most common, although a few motile colonial forms, such as *Polykrikos* (Fig. 9–2A), occur in the marine phytoplankton. There are also unicellular, amoeboid forms, such as *Dinamoebidium* (Fig. 9–2B, C), which produce naked dinoflagellate zoospores. Nonmotile forms include the palmelloid *Urococcus* (Fig. 9–2F), the coccoid form *Cystodium* (Fig. 9–2D), the sessile unicellular *Stylodinium* (Fig. 9–2E), and the multicellular filamentous type, such as *Dinothrix* (Fig. 9–2G). In all the nonmotile forms, motile reproductive cells are produced with lateral flagellation typical of the motile forms (see Fig. 9–1A).

REPRODUCTION

The chief method of reproduction is by longitudinal cell division, which may occur while the cell is motile. In some, the flagella are shed just prior to division. Cell division of motile cells occurs in the plane that passes through the point of flagellar insertion. Usually each half receives one of the flagella, soon differentiating a second one. The cells may also become encysted and form thick walls, accumulate abundant food reserves, and become very resistant to environmental extremes. Such encystation is particularly common in fresh-water species.

As mentioned previously, the nonmotile forms produce biflagellate zoospores. In these, the cells round up and liberate one or more typical unarmored dinoflagellate cells.

Sexual reproduction has been reported in a few instances, but is apparently rare. In one report, a coccoid form produced naked unicellular motile cells that fused to produce a round zygote. Meiosis has been shown in some dinoflagellates to occur in zygote germination.

DISTRIBUTION AND ECOLOGY

Although the dinoflagellates are more numerous in the sea, they occur in fresh water, brackish water, and in beach sand. The most common (in both fresh water and the sea) are species of the genera *Peridinium* (Fig. 9–1D) and *Ceratium* (Fig. 9–1C, 4). Certain of the dinoflagellates contribute to the luminescence

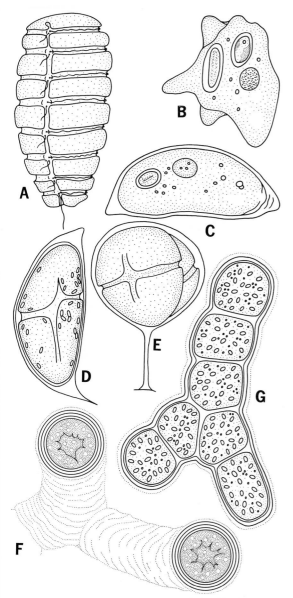

FIGURE 9–3   Tentacles of two sea anemones (*Condylactis*) containing symbiotic dinoflagellates. Upper, after exposure to darkness for 24 days; lower, after exposure to normal daylight for 24 days, ×0.8(Photograph courtesy P. A. Zahl and J. J. A. McLaughlin, and permission of *Journal of Protozoology.*)

resulting when sea water is disturbed at night, as in the wake of a ship. The marine naked forms are more common in the oceanic areas, whereas the armored forms are more common in coastal plankton.

In some sea anemones the various colors in the tentacles may be due to dinoflagellates. If the anemones are kept in the dark, they become a ghostly white (Fig. 9–3). Dinoflagellates also occur as parasites in fish and copepods, and as symbionts in the cells of various coelenterates and radiolarians.

The great diversity in ornamentation—particularly the development of horns, spines, sail-like, or wing-like structures in the armored photosynthetic dinoflagellates—may increase their ability to stay in the **photic zone.** These structures serve to increase the surface area of the cell in proportion to the cell volume. In so doing, there is an increase in friction, which slows down the rate of cell sinking and may help return the cell to a horizontal position. Thus, the dinoflagellate is assisted in maintaining itself in the surface waters where optimum light is available for photosynthetic activities. The flagellated forms are capable of swimming actively at rates of at least 0.8 cm/sec. But

FIGURE 9–2   Representatives of morphological types occurring in the Dinophyceae. A, *Polykrikos,* a motile colony, ×75. B, C, *Dinamoebidium,* an amoeboid type. B, vegetative stage, ×500; C, resting cyst stage, ×625. D, E, coccoid forms, each containing characteristic dinoflagellate cells. D, *Cystodium,* ×650; E, *Stylodinium,* ×900. F, *Urococcus,* palmelloid type with extensive mucilaginous matrix, ×245. G, *Dinothrix,* filamentous type, ×720. (A, D, E, after Schiller in Rabenhorst with permission of Akademische Verlagsgesellschaft, Geest and Portig K.-G., Leipzig; B, C, after Fott's *Algenkunde* with permission of G. Fischer; F, after Thompson with permission of John Wiley & Sons, Inc.)

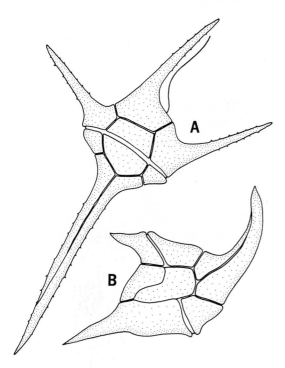

FIGURE 9–4   Variation in morphology of *Ceratium*, showing relative length of horns. A, a warm-water form, ×580; B, a cold-water form, ×465.

even this feeble movement may be inadequate to maintain the cells near the surface against other forces, including gravity and currents, which may tend to carry them below the depth of optimum light intensity. This relationship is apparent in comparing the morphological differences in the same species of *Ceratium* (Fig. 9–4). Cells from warmer water have a more prominent development of horns and spines (Fig. 9–4A), thus tending to sink more slowly in water of lower density. Cells of the same species in colder water have less conspicuous horns and spines (Fig. 9–4B) but sink slowly because the water is denser.

IMPORTANCE AND USES

The dinoflagellates are not used directly by man, but they are indirectly important. In general, especially in some warmer marine waters, dinoflagellates are considered second only to the diatoms in importance as **primary producers** in the sea. Thus, they are a source of food, directly or indirectly, for grazing popula-

tions of **zooplankton** and other animals. This statement may be modified when the representatives of the **nannoplankton** (less than 70–75 microns) are better known.

Because of rapid reproduction by cell division, extensive blooms of dinoflagellates can be produced in a very short time. Under optimum environmental conditions, cells may divide several times a day. Cell concentrations of marine species in natural waters are typically several million cells per liter. Thus, in this dense concentration they color the water green, brown, or red.

A number of dinoflagellates, including species in the genera *Glenodinium, Gymnodinium,* and *Gonyaulax* (Fig. 9–1A, B, E), are responsible for so-called red water or red tide. These conditions are particularly prevalent along the coasts of North America when water temperatures are unusually high and, in northern areas, when exceptionally long hours of sunlight occur. These conditions may result in tremendous numbers of dinoflagellates, which can lead to death of many marine animals. The species chiefly responsible for red tide along the Pacific coast of North America belong to the genus *Gonyaulax* (Fig. 9–1E). In Texas and Florida, species of *Gymnodinium* (Fig. 9–1B) are the main components of red tides. The way in which death is caused may be very comparable to that discussed in connection with blue-green algal pollution.

Another phenomenon related to such blooms is known as mussel poisoning or shellfish poisoning. In this instance, filter feeding invertebrates—such as clams, mussels, and oysters—extract cells of *Gonyaulax* from the water. Although there is apparently no lethal effect on the shellfish, these invertebrates remove and accumulate a toxic substance in certain tissues. The toxin may remain in the tissues for several months and is only gradually eliminated. When the shellfish are eaten by man, or other mammals, such as cats, dogs, or rodents, paralysis can result in distal parts of the body. The amount of paralysis depends on poison concentration in the invertebrate tissues, and in severe cases may result in death. Apparently the toxic material is closely related to the curare group of poisons produced by some tropical flowering plants.

PHYLOGENY

Phylogenetic trends within the group and the affinities of the group with other divisions are not particularly clear. An important means of distinguishing major groups within the division has been according to nutrition—that is, whether the organisms are autotrophic or heterotrophic. But this is a rather artificial criterion, because of the variety that may be encountered in species of the same genus. Classification has been largely according to the presence or absence of the cellulosic wall and the articulated plates; on this basis two rather distinct lines of evolution have been considered. One is confined to the unicellular armored motile types; the other has led from the unicellular unarmored motile types to the nonmotile and multicellular branched filamentous forms. The evolutionary sequence suggested is supported by the fact that the motile stages of the nonmotile and multicellular types revert to a simple naked stage morphologically comparable to simple unicellular genera.

The earliest of the many known fossil dinoflagellates are from the Ordovician Period of the Paleozoic Era. Over 100 genera of fossils referable to the Dinophyceae have been found in rocks of the Mesozoic and Tertiary. These fossils occur most commonly in marine sediments, but some, such as *Peridinium,* are found in rocks of fresh-water origin. A growing number of investigators are specializing in the study of fossil dinoflagellates. Although much has been learned, little has been contributed as yet to an understanding of relationships of genera or families within the class, or of the affinities of the Dinophyceae with other algae.

CLASS CRYPTOPHYCEAE
(Cryptomonads)

CELL STRUCTURE

This relatively small class is composed of fewer than 100 species in 24 genera. The ma-

jority of Cryptophyceae are biflagellate, dorsiventrally compressed unicells (Fig. 9–5C). In some forms a cellulose wall is present but many cells are naked with only a firm membrane, or periplast, which may be striated. The few non-motile genera are palmelloid or coccoid. Each cell has a single nucleus slightly posterior in position. At the cell's anterior end, there are one or several contractile vacuoles, which may lie alongside a **gullet** into which the vacuole empties. The gullet may be a shallow simple groove or it may be deeply tubular. It is lined with small tuberculate, spindle-shaped cavities containing **trichocysts,** whose exact function is unknown. In a few motile forms an eyespot is present.

The pigmented forms possess one or two laminate parietal chloroplasts. The ultrastructure shows the chloroplast bands to be composed of only two pairs of lamellae. This differs from most other organisms, including the Dinophyceae, in which the chloroplast bands contain three or four pairs of lamellae. Pyrenoids, present in some forms, either are embedded in the chloroplast or are free in the cytoplasm. In those forms studied with the electron microscope, starch grains are formed outside the chloroplast but are not free in the cytoplasm. Rather, they are held within a membrane that is part of the nuclear membrane. The chloroplast color varies from yellowish-green to brown to blue-green to red. The pigment complex is not well known, but chlorophyll a and c both occur. The carotenoids do not include β-carotene but rather α-carotene and ϵ-carotene. The xanthophylls known to be present include diadinoxanthin, dinoxanthin, and possibly zeaxanthin. In addition, several genera contain phycobilin pigments. However, the properties of the latter differ from those of the Cyanophyta and Rhodophyta.

The majority of the Cryptophyceae are photo-autotrophs, although those few forms investigated carefully have been shown to be auxotrophs. Some saprobic and phagotrophic forms also occur. The food reserves are stored as starch or starch-like substances. As mentioned previously, pyrenoids are present either in the chloroplast or in the cytoplasm. Similarly, starch granules may be associated

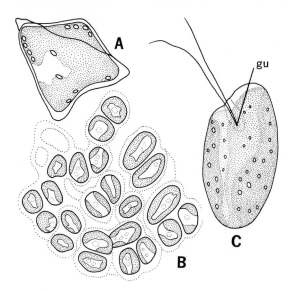

FIGURE 9–5 Representatives of morphological types in Cryptophyceae. A, *Tetragonidium,* a coccoid type, ×2,000; B, *Phaeoplax,* palmelloid type in mucilaginous matrix, ×1,000; C, *Cryptomonas,* motile type, with gullet (*gu*), ×3,650. (A, after Thompson with permission of John Wiley & Sons, Inc.; B, after Smith with permission of McGraw-Hill Book Co.)

with the pyrenoids or scattered throughout the cytoplasm. Fat has also been reported in some.

MOVEMENT

In motile cells, two slightly unequal flagella, thought to be tinsel flagella, are ribbon-shaped toward the proximal end. They are usually anteriorly inserted on the cell, but arise at the base of the gullet. The motile cells of those genera that have nonmotile stages are typically cryptomonad.

MORPHOLOGICAL DIVERSITY

The unicellular motile form, *Cryptomonas,* is the most common morphological type (Fig. 9–5C). Some of these motile genera may enter a palmelloid condition at times. Others, such as *Phaeoplax,* are typically palmelloid in the vegetative condition (Fig. 9–5B), liberating motile stages that have the typical flattened appearance and gullet of motile genera. The

coccoid type, as in *Tetragonidium* (Fig. 9–5A), has a thick wall containing cellulose. It produces zoospores similar to those in *Cryptomonas.*

REPRODUCTION

The chief method of reproduction is vegetative by longitudinal cell division. The cell may divide in the motile condition, or in a nonmotile condition where it comes to rest and becomes embedded in a mucilaginous matrix, forming a palmelloid mass by cell division. In some genera, thick-walled endogenous cysts have been reported. Sexual reproduction is doubtful and has not been confirmed in this class.

DISTRIBUTION AND ECOLOGY

The members of this class are found in fresh water and in the sea. In fresh water they are more common when some organic material is present, which may in part explain why those forms studied are known to require an external source of vitamins. A number of cryptomonads apparently occur as symbionts in radiolarians and corals, where they have been commonly referred to under the general term zooxanthellae.

PHYLOGENY

The affinities of this class are extremely vague. The presence of the water-soluble pigments does not necessarily indicate a close affinity to either the Cyanophyta or the Rhodophyta; rather, it suggests that these pigments developed more than once. One basis for placing the class with the dinoflagellates has been the presence of a gullet on the flattened side. It has been suggested that this gullet is analogous to the lateral one in dinoflagellates. The presence of chlorophyll *c* and sometimes cellulose, and starch as a food reserve, are other features that some cryptomonads have in common with the Dinophyceae. However, several features argue against including the class in the same division with the Dinophyceae. Cryptomonads have a more complex vacuolar apparatus and contain phycobilins. The flagellation differs, and the Cryptophyceae lack the moniliform nucleus characteristic of the dinoflagellates.

REFERENCES ON DINOPHYCEAE

Fritsch, F. E., *The Structure and Reproduction of the Algae.* Vol. 1. Cambridge: Cambridge University Press (1935). Pp. 664–720.

Graham, H. W., "Pyrrophyta." In Smith, G. M., *Manual of Phycology.* Waltham, Mass.: Chronica Botanica (1951). Pp. 105–118.

Huber-Pestalozzi, G., *Das Phytoplankton des Süsswassers.* Vol. 16, Pt. 3. In Thienemann, A. (Ed.), *Die Binnengewässer.* Stuttgart: E. Schweizerbart'sche Verlagsbuchhandlung (1950). Pp. 94–303.

Kofoid, C., and Swezy, O., "The Free-living Unarmoured Dinoflagellata." *Univ. Calif. Memoirs,* 5: 1–562 (1921).

Schiller, J., *Dinoflagellata (Peridineae).* In Rabenhorst, L. (Ed.), *Kryptogamen-Flora von Deutschland, Österreich, und der Schweiz.* Pts. 1–2. Leipzig: Akademische Verlagsgeschellshaft (1933–1937).

Schilling, A. J., *Dinoflagellata (Peridineae).* In Pascher, A. (Ed.), *Süsswasser-Flora Deutschlands, Österreichs und der Schweiz.* Heft 3. Jena: G. Fischer (1913).

Smith, G. M., *Cryptogamic Botany,* 2nd Ed. Vol. 1: *Algae and Fungi.* New York: McGraw-Hill Book Co., Inc. (1955). Pp. 148–164.

REFERENCES ON CRYPTOPHYCEAE

Fritsch, F. E., *The Structure and Reproduction of the Algae.* Vol. 1. Cambridge: Cambridge University Press (1935). Pp. 652–663.

Graham, H. W., *Cryptophyceae.* In Smith, G. M., *Manual of Phycology.* Waltham, Mass.: Chronica Botanica (1951). Pp. 117–118.

Huber-Pestalozzi, G., *Das Phytoplankton des Süsswassers.* Vol. 16, Pt. 3. In Thienemann, A. (Ed.), *Die Binnengewässer.* Stuttgart: E. Schweizerbart'sche Verlagsbuchhandlung (1950). Pp. 1–78.

Pascher, A., *Cryptomonadineae.* In Pascher, A. (Ed.), *Die Süsswasser-Flora Deutschlands, Österreichs und der Schweiz.* Vol. 2: *Flagellatae.* Jena: G. Fischer (1913). Pp. 96–114.

Pringsheim, E. G., "Some Aspects of Taxonomy in the Cryptophyceae." *New Phytologist,* 43(2): 143–150 (1944).

10 / DIVISION

CHRYSOPHYTA

The division Chrysophyta (*chrysophytes*) is a grouping of golden or yellow-brown algae and alga-like organisms. As more representatives are studied the limits of the division become better circumscribed. Thus, in this text the Chrysophyta consists of only two classes, the Chrysophyceae (yellow-brown or golden algae), and the Bacillariophyceae (diatoms). Another class, the Xanthophyceae (yellow-green algae), generally placed in the Chrysophyta, is considered here to have closer affinities with the Chlorophyta (see Chapter 15).

The pigments characteristic of the Chrysophyta are similar to some of those of the Pyrrophyta and include chlorophyll *a,* sometimes chlorophyll *c,* diadinoxanthin, and **fucoxanthin.** However, in the Chrysophyta, the food reserves are fats or oils and the polysaccharide **chrysolaminarin** (= leucosin). This carbohydrate, similar to laminarin (see Chapter 11) contains β, 1–3, and 1–6 glucoside linkages. In many forms the cell wall, when present, has scales or may consist of two overlapping halves, and be impregnated with silicon, calcium, or organic material. Motile cells have the flagella inserted apically or subapically.

CLASS CHRYSOPHYCEAE
(Golden Algae)

Over 75 genera with about 300 species are referred to several orders in this class. They are predominantly fresh-water algae; however, a number of marine species are significant as marine nannoplankton.

CELL STRUCTURE

Many of the simpler, unicellular forms are naked flagellates with a delicate periplast as in *Ochromonas* and *Chromulina* (Fig. 10–1D, F). Some have a characteristic **lorica,** which is open at one end, as in *Dinobryon* (Fig. 10–1A). When a well-defined wall is present, as in some motile and many of the nonmotile types, it consists chiefly of pectic substances and may be made of overlapping halves. Cellulose may be present in the wall of certain species, although its presence is not well established. The wall and periplast may have superficial scales (Fig. 10–1E)—either siliceous (Fig. 10–2A) or organic (Fig. 10–2B). There is an elaborate internal siliceous skeletal structure in the silicoflagellates (Fig. 10–1B); whereas heavily calcified discs, rings, or plates embedded in the wall are characteristic of the coccolithophores (Fig. 10–1H).

The Chrysophyceae owe their characteristic golden or golden-brown color to certain carotenoid pigments contained in one or two parietal smooth-edged chloroplasts. The ultrastructure of the chloroplasts is similar to that of the dinoflagellates and the brown algae. The chloroplast contains compressed stacks of three pairs of lamellae (Fig. 10–2D). Usually chlorophyll *c* is lacking in representatives of this class. The carotenoid pigments include chiefly β-carotene, α-carotene, and a number of xanthophyll pigments; the xanthophylls include those listed for the division and possibly lutein in addition. These pigments mask the chlorophyll to give the characteristic golden-brown color. An eyespot may be present in the anterior region of the chloroplast.

Pyrenoid-like structures in the chloroplasts are rare and, where present, are of unknown function. Various granules may be associated with the chloroplast and cytoplasm. Chrysolaminarin accumulates often as a large, refractive cytoplasmic granule posteriorly in the cell. Stored fats and oil are also present in the cytoplasm.

The cells are apparently uninucleate, and the nucleus has nucleoli and a distinct nuclear membrane. A large central vacuole is lacking; however, in the motile forms contractile vacuoles may be present near the flagellar insertion.

Most of the species are apparently photo-autotrophic, but many of those forms studied are auxotrophs. Colorless forms, which are saprobic or phagotrophic, are known. Some of the pigmented forms are also believed to be capable of ingesting particulate food.

MOVEMENT

In the motile cells, the one or two flagella are usually anteriorly inserted. In the biflagellate condition, one is generally tinsel and the other whiplash. If the two flagella are markedly unequal in length (Fig. 10–1D), the whiplash one is reduced; the reduction may be so complete that only the tinsel flagellum protrudes, as in *Chromulina* (Fig. 10–1F). One rather small group of biflagellate forms has two equal or almost equal flagella, both of which are whiplash. Triflagellate forms (*Chrysochromulina,* Fig. 10–1G) previously reported, are actually biflagellate cells of this latter whiplash series which have a coiled attaching structure—the **haptonema.** The ultrastructure of the haptonema consists of six or seven fibers surrounded by three concentric membranes (Fig. 10–2C) and thus differs from the flagellar structure of two central fibers and nine peripheral pairs surrounded by one membrane. The eyespot is apparently near a swollen flagellar base.

MORPHOLOGICAL DIVERSITY

The diversity in form of the Chrysophyceae is great, although most of the members are motile. These include unicellular amoeboid forms, such as *Chrysamoeba* (Fig. 10–3F); unicellular flagellates *Ochromonas, Mallomo-*

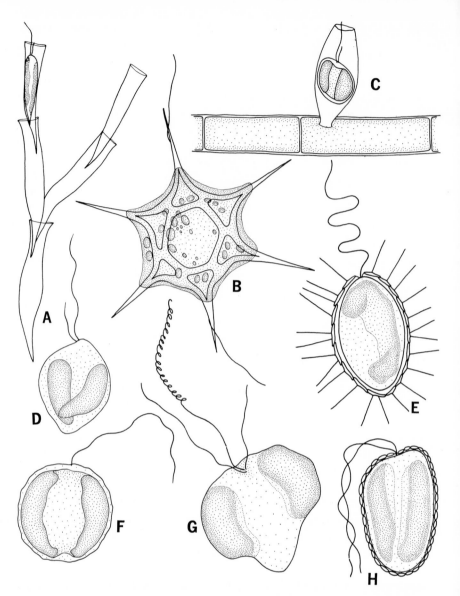

FIGURE 10–1   Morphological diversity of flagellated Chrysophyceae. A, colony with lorica, *Dinobryon,* ×1,085; B, *Distephanus,* a silicoflagellate with internal silicon skeleton, ×1,200; C, *Epipyxis,* with lorica attached to algal filament, ×1,000; D, *Ochromonas,* ×3,200; E, *Mallomonas,* with external scales and spines, ×1,000; F, *Chromulina,* ×2,700; G, *Chrysochromulina,* with coiled haptonema, ×700; H, *Hymenomonas,* coccolithophore with external calcareous discs, ×1,000. (B, after R. E. Norris.)

nas, and *Chromulina* (Fig. 10–1D, E, F); and colonial flagellates such as *Dinobryon* (Fig. 10–1A), which may also be unicellular, *Synura,* and *Uroglena* (Fig. 10–3A, C). Non-motile forms include the palmelloid colonies, such as *Hydrurus* and *Chrysocapsa* (Fig. 10–3D, E, H, I), the coccoid types, such as

Epichrysis (Fig. 10–3B), and the filamentous *Phaeothamnion* (Fig. 10–3G).

REPRODUCTION

In most forms zoospore production is common, with either one or two apical flagella

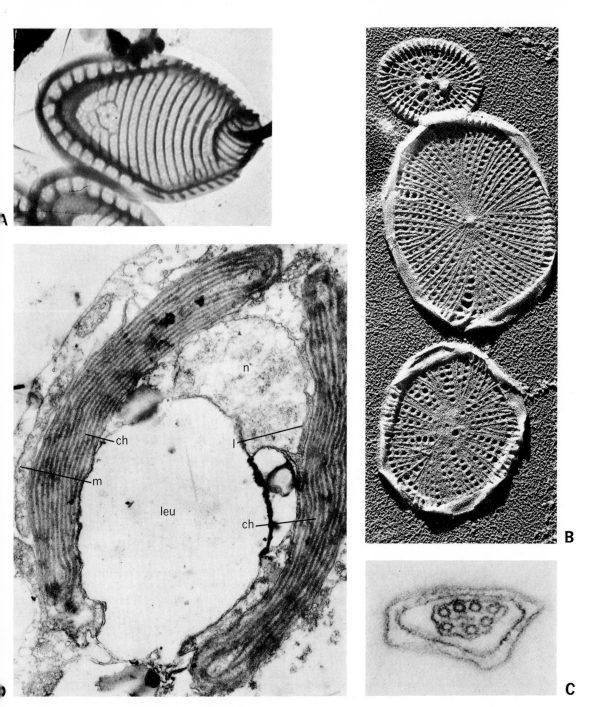

FIGURE 10–2   Ultrastructure of Chrysophyceae. A, *Mallomonas;* electron micrograph of scales, ×10,-000. B, *Chrysochromulina;* electron micrograph of three scales, seen from lower side, ×29,000. C, *Prymnesium,* ultrastructure of haptonema in transverse section, ×150,000; D, *Ochromonas* cell showing leucosin (*leu*) vacuole (=chrysolaminarin granule), mitochondrion (*m*), and large lamellate chloroplast (*ch*); tubules   are   present   in narrow space separating nucleus (*n*) from chloroplast, ×15,000. (A, photograph courtesy K. Harris and D. Bradley, and with permission of the University Press, Cambridge; B, photograph courtesy I. Manton, from Manton and Parke with permission of the Council of the Marine Biological Association of the United Kingdom; C, photograph courtesy I. Manton and G. F. Leedale, from Manton and Leedale, *Archiv für Mikrobiologie,* Vol. 45, pp. 285–303, 1963, Springer-Verlag, Berlin-Göttingen-Heidelberg; D, photograph courtesy Sarah P. Gibbs and with permission of *Journal of Cell Biology.*)

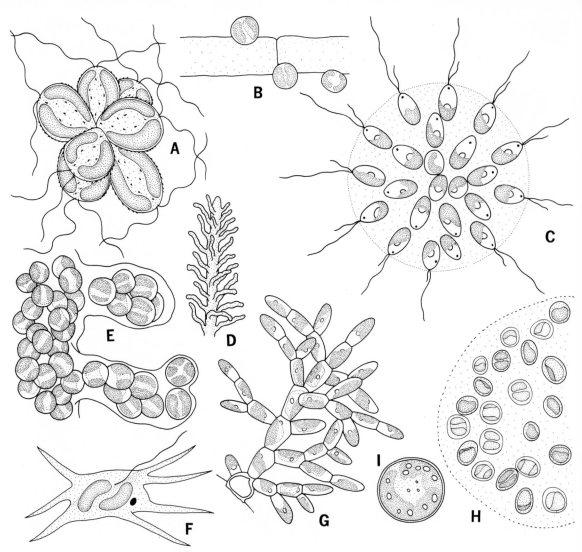

FIGURE 10–3   Morphological diversity in Chrysophyceae. A, C, motile colonial forms. A, *Synura,* ×2,700; C, *Uroglena,* ×600. B, coccoid form, *Epichrysis,* epiphytic on algal filament, ×930. D, E, H, I, palmelloid forms. D, E, *Hydrurus;* (D, habit, ×50; E, detail of colony, ×1,000). H, I, *Chrysocapsa* (H, colony, ×500; I, single cell, ×3,000). F, amoeboid form with flagellum (*Chrysamoeba,* ×1,200). G, branched filamentous form (*Phaeothamnion,* ×500).

present. In the motile genera, reproduction is by longitudinal cell division producing two zoospores. In the nonmotile forms, the zoospores generally resemble the biflagellate *Ochromonas* or the uniflagellate *Chromulina* (Fig. 10–1D, F).

In many Chrysophyceae a resting cell called a **statospore,** or cyst, occurs. A single statospore is formed within a cell and may become heavily silicified throughout, except for a small opening containing a nonsiliceous plug that closes the statospore (Fig. 10–4A, B). Under favorable conditions the resting statospore germinates, generally liberating one or two motile cells (zoospores), which escape through the pore left after the plug is dissolved (Fig. 10–4C).

Sexual reproduction is rare. It has been reported to be isogamous, with biflagellate gametes in some species. In the marine coccolithophores, an alternation of phases in the life history has been demonstrated. The motile

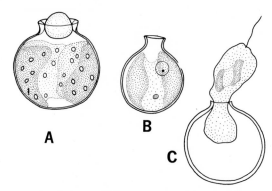

FIGURE 10–4 Statospore formation in Chrysophyceae. A, B, mature statospores. A, with plug
(*Chrysocapsa*, ×3,060); B, without plug (*Ochromonas*, ×1,000). C, statospore germination (*Chromulina*, ×1,000). (C, after Smith with permission
of McGraw-Hill Book Co.)

stage is evidently diploid and alternates with a
haploid nonmotile palmelloid or coccoid form.
The time of syngamy and meiosis in the life
history is unknown as yet.

DISTRIBUTION AND ECOLOGY

The fresh-water species of golden algae
are common in the plankton of lakes, particularly during the colder seasons of the year when
the algae may be abundant. One species of
Ochromonas gives a golden luster to shaded
woodland pools. The cells rest in a mucilaginous envelope on the upper surface of the water. Zoospores are released into the mucilaginous material and can then swim to another
place on the surface film. Some species are
also common in cold, fast-running mountain
streams, in springs, in spring pools, and in shallow ponds. Acid habitats, such as those present
in sphagnum or peat bogs, support a large variety of the smaller, delicate forms that may be
motile, free-floating, epiphytic, or endophytic.
Many occur in tide pools and salt marshes,
often in large enough numbers to color the water a golden-brown. The motile Chrysophyceae
in the nannoplankton of the North Sea are considered to be the most important primary food
producers. The coccolithophores are often the
predominant **phytoplankton** in the southern
Mediterranean and warm oceans such as the
Indian and tropical Atlantic.

IMPORTANCE AND USES

The Chrysophyceae are of no direct importance to man. However, as in all photosynthetic groups that have free-swimming or
free-floating species, they play an important
indirect role as primary producers in both fresh-
water and marine environments. An understanding of their importance will probably
increase with further knowledge of nannoplankton of colder waters.

PHYLOGENY

The Chrysophyceae have parallel characteristics in the Dinophyceae, Xanthophyceae,
and Chlorophyceae, and for this reason common precursors have been proposed for all
three classes. The Chrysophyceae are considered closely related to other flagellate groups.
Many zoologists treat them as protozoa because
of their protozoan-like naked forms. Some have
postulated that a nonpigmented chrysophycean
served as the progenitor of the metazoan line
that has ultimately culminated in mammals. It
has been postulated that auxotrophy may be
correlated with other animal-like tendencies.
Within the algal groups, the Chrysophyceae
have probably been an evolutionary dead
end. However, the similarities of pigmentation and flagellation of the Chrysophyceae
and the flagellated cells of Phaeophyceae have
led to speculation on a possible origin of the
brown algae from a golden-brown precursor.

The silicified parts of silicoflagellates and
the calcified parts of coccolithophores are important components in present-day depositions
of marine silicates and carbonates. Similarily,
the Chrysophyceae have been known for a long
time in the fossil record and many fossil species
are known to have contributed significantly to
marine deposits of the Cretaceous and later
periods.

CLASS
BACILLARIOPHYCEAE
(Diatoms)

About 190 genera with over 5,500 species
are referred to this class. Some estimates in-

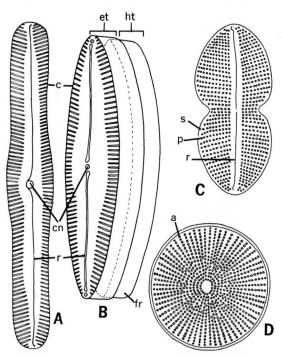

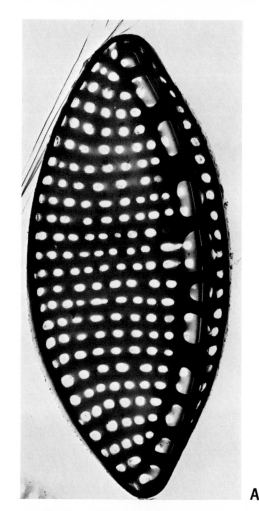

FIGURE 10–5   Symmetry and wall markings in Bacillariophyceae. A–C, pennate forms (A, B, *Pinnularia*, ×480; C, *Navicula*, ×590). A, valve view; B, view showing valve and girdle; C, valve view. D, centric form in valve view (*Coscinodiscus*, ×125). *fr*, frustule; *r*, raphe; *cn*, central nodule; *s*, stria; *c*, costa; *p*, puncta; *ht*, hypotheca; *et*, epitheca; *a*, aerola.

cluding fossil forms (which number about 70 genera) place the number of species as high as 10,000. The diatoms are conspicuous elements of both the present-day marine and fresh-water environments as well as represented in the fossil record. Certain genera occur in both fresh-water and marine habitats, whereas others are restricted to one or the other; some are known only from the fossil record.

FIGURE 10–6   Ultrastructure of diatom frustules. A, (above) *Nitzschia thermalis*, pennate form, ×17,000; B, (right, above) *Cyclotella cryptica*, centric form, ×18,000; C, (right, below) *Navicula pelliculosa*, pennate form, showing fine structure of puncta, ×66,000. (Photographs courtesy B. Reimann.)

CELL STRUCTURE

The diatom cell is quite complex, consisting of two overlapping walls that fit together like two halves of a box. These halves, often called **frustules,** generally contain large amounts of silicon, as much as 95 per cent of the wall. The outer frustule that partially overlaps the other is the **epitheca,** whereas the inner frustule is the **hypotheca** (Fig. 10–5B). Each

frustule consists of a flattened, or convex, valve with a connecting band attached along its edge. The overlapping walls form a **girdle** region and when observed from the side present the **girdle view.** Intercalated bands in the girdle may separate the two frustules and form a wide girdle area. The flat top or bottom surface of the cell is called the **valve** and when observed presents the **valve view.**

The silicon is deposited within wall material often considered to be a pectic substance. It varies in thickness and occurrence from one

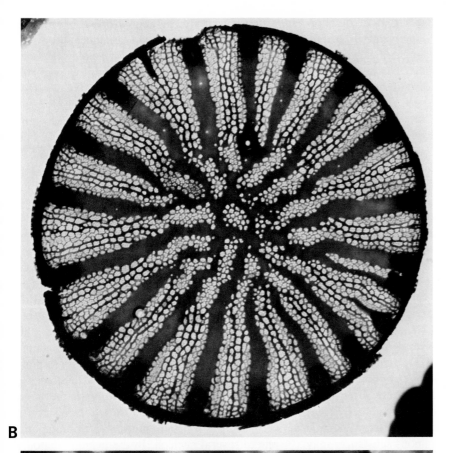

B

C

185

region to another, so that a pattern of alternating thin and thick regions results in a definite pattern of pores or elongated ridges, especially on the valve. In some diatoms the walls may be weakly silicified or only one valve may contain silicon.

The wall markings are of three types— **aerolae, costae,** and **punctae.** The aerolae (Fig. 10–6B) are thin areas bounded by ridges of siliceous material. Within an aerolar cavity is an aggregation of fine pores termed secondary aerolae, which in turn may have finer pores (Fig. 10–6C), or may have ingrowths from the aerolar edges. Punctae are actually small less-complicated aerolae. In many diatoms the punctae are in a linear order and are so close together that they appear as fine lines, termed **striae** (Fig. 10–5B, 6A, C). These striae may lie between well-defined ridges called costae (Fig. 10–5C, 6A, C). Generally most light microscope observations resolve only the primary aerolae (Fig. 10–5D), striae with possibly punctae (Fig. 10–5B), and the costae (Fig. 10–5C). As a result of these pores in the wall, the inner protoplasmic membrane is not completely protected from the external aquatic environment, and mucilaginous substances may be secreted through these pores. The whole cell or colony of cells is often enveloped in a mucilaginous layer of unknown nature. Those cells appearing round or triangular in valve view (radial symmetry) are classed as centric diatoms and those appearing more rectangular in valve view (bilateral symmetry) are pennate diatoms. Some consider classification based on symmetry to be artificial.

In the majority of pennate diatoms there is a vertical unsilicified cleft or groove in the valve, the **raphe** (Fig. 10–5B), which may be straight, undulate, or sigmoid. In some forms the raphe lies in a canal, the **keel.** Generally the raphe is present on both valves but may be confined to only one, or be absent altogether. In the central region of the raphe is a spherical thickening, the central nodule; and at each end of the groove may be similar swellings, the polar nodules (Fig. 10–5A, B). The raphe seems to be intimately associated with movement. In those pennate diatoms lacking a raphe, a clear area between the rows of striae or costae is referred to as a **pseudoraphe.**

The cell has a central vacuole and one, two, or many yellow or golden-brown parietal chloroplasts, which may be lobed, perforated, discoid, or ribbon-like. Centric diatoms generally have many chloroplasts, whereas pennate diatoms usually have only one or two. The ultrastructure of the chloroplast is similar to that of the Chrysophyceae (Fig. 10–2D), Dinophyceae, and the Phaeophyceae (Fig. 11–4D). The green pigments, chlorophyll a and chlorophyll c, are masked by carotenoids. These accessory pigments include three carotenes (α-cartotene, β-carotene, and ϵ-carotene), and certain xanthophylls that also occur in the Chrysophyceae. Diatoxanthin was originally considered unique to the Bacillariophyceae; however, it has recently been reported from a flagellated member of the Chrysophyceae. Fucoxanthin, the most abundant carotenoid pigment present, is responsible for the characteristic color of diatoms.

The cells are uninucleate, with the large well-organized nucleus centrally located in the cell. There is a definite nuclear membrane and one to several nucleoli. In the pennate diatoms the nucleus is often located on a cytoplasmic bridge across the middle of a large central vacuole. The cells of the Bacillariophyceae are apparently diploid in the vegetative condition. When cell division occurs, a new valve is secreted by each of the frustules at the point they were attached. Each frustule of the dividing cell becomes the epitheca of the two daughter cells.

The diatoms are chiefly autotrophic. In contrast to the golden algae, the majority of diatoms do not require an external source of vitamins. However, a number of the planktonic forms studied require vitamin B_{12}. Many pennate diatoms have been observed to grow heterotrophically, whereas this is uncommon in the centric diatoms tested. A few diatoms are colorless and are apparently saprobic.

Food reserves are stored as fats and oils, as well as chrysolaminarin. The fat droplets occur in the chloroplasts and in the cytoplasm as large round drops. Pyrenoid-like bodies occur in the chloroplasts of some diatoms, and electron micrographs show dense lipid globules congregated near these bodies, although not lying against them.

MOVEMENT

Only the pennate diatoms containing a raphe are able to move. Their movement is somewhat jerky, or a smooth, gliding motion. Rates of movement have been calculated at 0.2–25 microns/sec. The path taken seems to depend on the shape of the raphe, and the rate of movement is possibly light-dependent. The mechanism, incompletely understood, is believed to involve cytoplasmic streaming within the V-shaped raphe. The friction created by the moving cytoplasm, which may be in direct contact with the external environment, is believed to set up currents in the adjacent water causing movement of the cell. Other theories are concerned with a series of dynamic oscillations of the protoplasmic protein fibrils.

In the centric diatoms motile, uniflagellate or biflagellate planospores are produced. In most instances they have been interpreted as male gametes.

CLASSIFICATION AND MORPHOLOGY

Generally two orders are recognized, the Centrales, or centric diatoms, and the Pennales, or pennate diatoms (Fig. 10–5A–D). These two orders are separated on the basis of form, wall markings, chloroplast number, presence of motility, and occurrence of statospores. The two main evolutionary types of diatoms are analogous to the two orders recognized. The Centrales are radially symmetrical, usually with circular valves, as in *Coscinodiscus* (Fig. 10–5D), but sometimes they are triangular, as in *Triceratium* (Fig. 10–7A), or elongate, as in *Biddulphia* (Fig. 10–7B). The Pennales usually have bilateral symmetry with elongate valves, as in *Navicula* (Fig. 10–5C), but sometimes they may be asymmetrical in valve view, as in *Cymbella* (Fig. 10–7C) and *Gomphonema* (Fig. 10–7G). In the Centrales the sculpturing generally radiates out from a cen-

tral point of the valve (Fig. 10–5D); in Pennales the valve markings occur in two longitudinal series on either side of a median line (Fig. 10–5B). Also present in the Centrales are spines and external appendages, as well as intercalary bands in the girdle region. As already noted, a raphe or pseudoraphe is absent in the centric forms.

Many diatoms, including species of *Navicula, Pinnularia,* and *Coscinodiscus,* occur individually. Others, such as species of *Biddulphia,* may be loosely aggregated in irregular filamentous chains, with adjacent cells interconnected by mucilaginous pads joining the cells into a zig-zag colony. Species of *Gomphonema* form stalked, dendroid colonies, whereas *Asterionella* (Fig. 10–7H) is a star-shaped colony. Both the centric and pennate diatoms form long chain-like colonies of cells with the valve faces fastened end to end as in *Melosira* (Fig. 10–7D) and *Fragilaria* (Fig. 10–7F). Long spine-like valve processes assist in forming the filamentous colonies of some Centrales, as *Chaetoceros* (Fig. 10–7E). In one species of *Navicula* (often placed in a separate genus, *Schizonema*) there is an aggregation of long, loose mucilaginous tubes containing the diatom cells (Fig. 10–7I, J). These tubes, held together in a common mucilaginous matrix, result in macroscopic, branched, rope-like strands (Fig. 10–7I).

REPRODUCTION

The chief method of reproduction in diatoms is vegetative, by cell division. As in dinoflagellates, the rapid rate of division under optimum conditions can result in dense blooms, which give the water a distinct brown color over an extensive area. Silicon appears to be an absolute requirement for the cell division in many of the diatoms, with the number of cells being proportional to the amount of silicon dioxide present (assuming other nutrients are not limiting). Since the two frustules of the parent cell act as the epitheca for the two resulting daughter cells, there may be a gradual diminution in the size of some of the cells in the population. Ultimately, following fusion of two

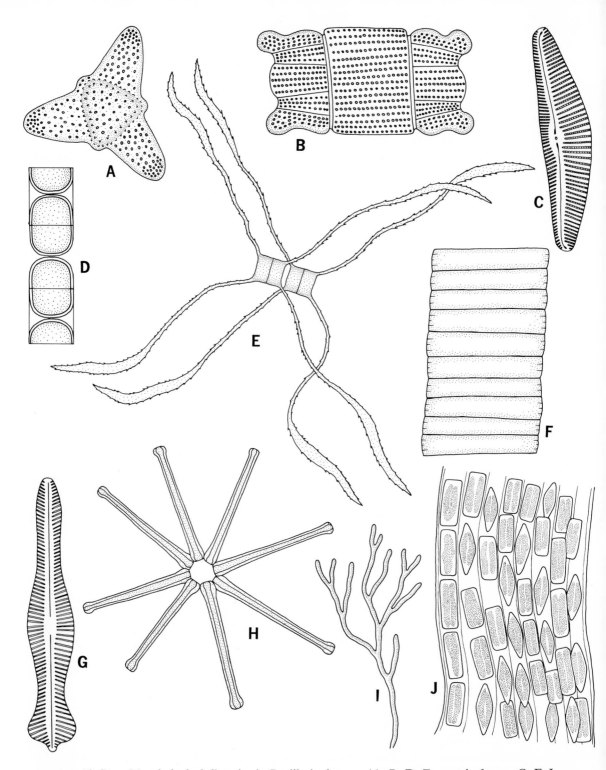

FIGURE 10–7   Morphological diversity in Bacillariophyceae (A, B, D, E, centric forms; C, F–J, pennate forms). A–C, G, unicellular representatives. A, *Triceratium,* valve view, ×545; B, *Biddulphia,* girdle view, ×475; C, *Cymbella,* valve view, ×545; G, *Gomphonema,* valve view, ×1,250. D–F, H–J, colonial representatives. D, *Melosira,* girdle view, ×640; E, *Chaetoceros,* girdle view, ×500; F, *Fragilaria,* girdle view, ×750; H, *Asterionella,* girdle view, ×1,000; I, J, *Navicula,* colonial species; I, habit, ×3.5; J, detail of colony, ×520.

protoplasts, new cells are produced, which restore the average size characteristic of the species (see below). Certain diatom populations do not show this diminution in size of some cells. The plasticity of the weakly silicified cells

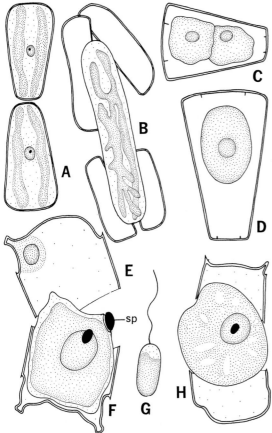

FIGURE 10–8   Sexual reproduction in Bacillariophyceae. A, B, auxospore formation between daughter cells (*Surirella,* ×300). C, D, auxospore formation involving single cell (*Gomphonema*); C, gametes, ×600; D, zygote, ×700. E–H, auxospore formation involving oogamy. E, F, H (*Biddulphia rhombus,* ×400); E, nonmotile sperm in frustule; F, fusion with sperm nucleus (*sp*) still separate. G, uniflagellate sperm (*Chaetoceros eibenii,* ×2,000); H, zygote being released from cell, ×400. (A, B, after Fott's *Algenkunde* with permission of G. Fischer; C, D, after Patrick from "Sexual Reproduction in Diatoms," in *Sex in Microorganisms,* copyright 1954 by the American Association for the Advancement of Science; E, F, H, after v. Stosch, *Archiv für Mikrobiologie,* Vol. 23, pp. 327–365 (1956), Springer-Verlag, Berlin-Göttingen-Heidelberg; G, after v. Stosch, *Die Naturwissenschaften,* 1958, p. 141, Springer-Verlag, Berlin-Göttingen-Heidelberg.)

may account for the ability to resume original size and shape after cell division. In laboratory populations no sexual reproduction occurs in cultures that maintain a constant cell size. However, in similar laboratory populations **auxospore** formation (as discussed below) occurs when cell size decreases.

The type of sexual reproduction varies throughout the class. It may be isogamous, anisogamous, or oogamous, with the vegetative cell diploid and meiosis occurring during gametogenesis. Generally only one or two gametes develop. The zygote resulting from syngamy is termed an auxospore. The Centrales may have fusion of two haploid nuclei from the same parental cell, resulting in autogamy (Fig. 10–8C, D). In the Pennales, auxospores generally result from a fusion of gametes—which may or may not be the same size—from two different individuals (Fig. 10–8A, B); generally these cells have been produced by the same mother cell. An auxospore increases two to three times the size of the original gamete-producing cell. Two mitoses take place, each with only one surviving nucleus. A new silicified shell is secreted after each mitosis so that the auxospore tends to have the maximum dimensions of the species. The auxospore wall may be smooth or have characteristic markings similar to or different from the vegetative cell. The process of auxospore formation occurs occasionally in a population, and in some genera possibly once every two to five years. It follows a prolonged period of vegetative reproduction by cell division. In some diatoms growing in **brackish** water (salinity less than that in the marine environment) auxospore formation will occur upon dilution of the medium.

In the centric diatoms such as *Biddulphia,* oogamy can occur (Fig. 10–8E–G). Some cells produce a single egg; others produce four to many flagellated sperm. The one (Fig. 10–8G) or two flagella may be anteriorly or laterally inserted. Oogamy has been reported only once in the pennate diatoms.

Statospores or endogenous cysts with walls in two parts are produced by some centric diatoms and are more common in marine forms.

Diatoms are widely distributed throughout the fresh-water and marine environments; the Centrales are primarily marine and more species of the Pennales occur in fresh water. These algae occur free-floating in the plankton, as well as on surfaces of solid substrates, on mud-flat surfaces, in salt marshes, and attached as epiphytes to other algae and aquatic plants. They also occur in the soil, on the bark of trees, on old brickwork, on rock walls, and almost any moist place. Their wide distribution somewhat correlates with the lack of auxotrophy in the majority and the wide specificity of those forms that do require vitamins.

Diatoms occur in vast numbers in the phytoplankton, and they may form extensive blooms. At times many million cells per liter may be present in marine coastal areas. The presence of many extremely small species of diatoms in the nannoplankton is of considerable significance in assessing the role of these minute organisms in primary production.

In colder marine waters diatoms often have two peaks of abundance. One occurs in late spring or early summer, when the water begins to warm up and the amount of sunlight increases. Later, as essential nutrients become limiting and small animals graze, production falls off rapidly. When the limiting nutrient materials are restored or regenerated in the surface waters in a form available to the diatoms, a second less-intense bloom occurs. This is generally in late summer or early autumn. Shortly afterward, the water becomes cooler, the amount of sunlight decreases, and the diatom population falls off, even though nutrients may no longer be limiting. In freshwater ponds and lakes, similar periods of abundance may occur.

Although the fresh-water algae occur in a wide range of habitats, most are encountered in standing bodies of water (lakes and ponds) and in flowing waters (rivers and streams). The distribution of these algae is related in both space (vertically and horizontally) and in time (seasonal periodicity). Temperature plays the most important role in ultimate distribution of the phytoplankton in standing waters of the temperate zone since there is an annual temperature cycle creating vertical stratification of the water mass. In the spring, the waters are constantly mixed due to winds and the cooling effect of lower air temperatures on the surface layers. This results in an unstratified water mass of relatively uniform temperature. When the surface waters warm, the upper layers gradually become stable, so that thorough mixing is impossible. This is the summer stagnation period. With autumn, the upper layers again become cooler and denser (water is most dense at 4° C rather than at 0° C), causing them to sink. Winds able to break down the stability of the upper layers contribute to the mixing that culminates in the fall overturn and complete mixing. The duration of this overturn depends on meterological conditions as well as the depth of the lake. If the lake is covered by ice, winter stagnation will exist since the warmer water is on the bottom. The ice covers the lake and prevents mixing by wind action. In the tropics there is generally a small annual temperature variation so that overturn occurs when periods of cooling follow one another quickly, or in areas where rainy seasons alternate with dry ones. In these, the overturn is associated with the dry season.

Although temperature is probably the most effective factor in vertical distribution of the fresh-water phytoplankton, light, oxygen, and nutrients must also be considered. For example, light intensity determines the lower limits at which photosynthesis occurs. When high light intensity is present, utilization of the excess light is temperature-dependent. Maximum photosynthesis then occurs at some depth below the surface, depending on the transparency of the water. Oxygen availability is related to temperature, since more oxygen is in solution at lower temperatures. Availability of nutrients may be limiting in a lake. As already noted, in highly transparent waters, active assimilation occurs at greater depths due to greater penetration of light of sufficient intensity for photosynthesis to occur in excess of respiratory requirements. Ample nutrients are generally available at such depths due to the proximity of the bottom where they accumulate.

The horizontal stratification is not as temperature-dependent and is less important in lakes of moderate size and depth. In shallow basins and those of irregular form, differences in horizontal distribution can be quite marked. Near the shore more species of algae occur in the shallow area around rooted aquatic vascular plants. The controlling factor may be availability of nutrients. However, in this protected zone, small differences in oxygen, light, temperature, and local water movements create microclimatic conditions that may also affect the over-all growth.

The action of water movement is of little consequence in bodies of standing water. But in flowing waters, the bottom and shore vegetation are continually receiving new water, whereas fresh-water plankton are carried downstream, ultimately to the sea and probable death. In slowly moving streams and rivers, the conditions are similar to those in standing water and thus the same types of algae may occur. Flowing waters are turbulent, containing eddies and currents at right angles to the direction of flow. At the bottom there may be a boundary layer of almost stationary water several millimeters thick. The thickness of this layer depends on the current (the faster the current the thinner the layer) and the density of water (the warmer and less dense the water, the thinner the layer). The effect of cascading water has been found to be important in gas exchange of the algae. More gas may go into solution because of the greater turbulence and resulting contact between air and water. However, the intensity of light reaching the algae in a stream is reduced with increased turbulence. In fast flowing waters, nutrient material is carried away quickly, thus limiting to some extent algal development. In slowly moving water, nutrients tend to settle, remaining available for a rich algal growth. On the leeward side of rocks, less turbulent areas support different algal populations for the same reason.

Seasonal changes in the fresh-water algal flora generally follow the same plan year after year. Such periodicity is best known from standing waters. Certain species that occur throughout the year may constitute as much as 40 per cent of the total population. For those forms not present at all times, a prerequisite is the ability to form resistant stages, such as auxospores, resting zygotes, akinetes, or hypnospores. Most of these species have a peak occurrence at the same time each year. The plankton forms usually have two maxima a year (spring and autumn) and two minima (winter and midsummer). The spring and autumn flora may be markedly different, since the water temperature usually changes more slowly than the light intensity. Nutrient supply is particularly important in determining seasonal abundance. In early spring, following the annual overturn and thorough mixing, nutrients from the bottom are redistributed and available in the upper layers. As summer stratification occurs and mixing is reduced, nutrients may be exhausted and become limiting. In late summer, mixing occurs and the nutrients again become available.

The general distribution of fresh-water algae is also correlated with the hydrogen-ion concentration, or pH, of the water. Acid habitats (pH 4.0–6.5) are richer in numbers of different species, although fewer of each are present. In contrast, alkali waters (pH 7.5–9.0) may have a greater abundance of only a few species. Bodies of water rich in organic materials tend to support greater algal populations (in both numbers and kinds) than waters with chiefly inorganic mineral nutrients.

Some diatoms have a narrow range of tolerance to temperature and salinity. Their distribution and physiological requirements are thus intimately related to the physical-chemical characteristics of the water. Therefore, they are useful as indicators of these conditions. In the sea they provide a means of following the path of ocean currents. In fresh-water habitats, the composition of the diatom communities is used as an indicator of varying ecological conditions. In particular, rivers free from pollution are composed of many species, each present in relatively small populations. In polluted waters the number of species is small due to the many limiting ecological factors imposed by the polluting materials.

Since the vegetative cells of the planktonic diatoms are not flagellated, as in the dinoflagellates, they have a great tendency to sink from the upper illuminated surface regions. However, the presence of oil and elaborate cell extensions help keep the cells afloat. The presence of setae with spine-like extensions, as in *Chaetoceros* (Fig. 10–7E), increases the surface area of the cell immensely, and tends to trap small bubbles of oxygen liberated in photosynthesis. The increased surface area and resulting increase in friction tends to decrease the rate of sinking. The filamentous, chain-like colonial habit of many marine species serves a similar function. The flotation mechanism provided by trapped bubbles also prevents sinking and tends to return the cell to the horizontal from the vertical position. The presence of oil food reserves in the cytoplasm is efficient in keeping the cell afloat, since oil is lighter than water. As long as conditions are optimum for photosynthesis and the oil reserves are not depleted, the diatom cell will remain buoyant.

IMPORTANCE AND USES

Diatoms are primary producers, and they are directly and indirectly important as food for other organisms in both fresh and marine waters. As mentioned, some diatom species are indicators of polluted waters, or of specific water conditions, such as hydrogen-ion concentration. However, man makes more direct use of diatoms deposited as fossils. In past geological ages diatom production was as important as now—if not more so. Under natural conditions, as the diatoms died, many of the empty silicified walls accumulated in great numbers as a diatomaceous ooze at the bottom of the sea and to some extent in lakes. Raised above sea level by geologic activity, these vast deposits of **diatomaceous earth** are now mined in various places. At Lompoc, California, surface quarrying may yield more than 6,000,000 frustules in 1 milliliter. At Lompoc, this surface accumulation of fossil diatoms, which is almost entirely composed of littoral marine species, is over 200 meters deep. Fresh-water deposits are rarely more than a meter thick. In other areas, extensive subterranean marine deposits vary from 10 meters to the exceptional deposits of 1,000 meters in the Santa Maria oil fields of California.

Diatomaceous earth is a soft, light crumbly material widely used for various types of filtration, especially in sugar refining; as a fine abrasive in silver polish, and toothpaste; as insulation shielding from the very high temperatures of blast furnaces and boilers; and in paints to increase visibility of pavement lines and traffic instructions. The deposits of diatomaceous earth are also used as an indication of oil- and gas-bearing strata.

PHYLOGENY

The Bacillariophyceae are a very old and successful group of plants. The two clear-cut lines of evolution are obviously closely related, and both the Centrales and Pennales are derived from a common ancestral stock. However, the diatoms have progressed very little during millions of years. From diatomaceous deposits we know that diatoms have been present since at least the Jurassic Period and possibly as far back as the Paleozoic Era. Apparently they became abundant in the late Cretaceous. There have been few changes in many of the species, with a large number of late Cretaceous specimens apparently identical to present-day species.

The fact that there have been so few changes in diatom species over such a long time may indicate they are well adapted to their environment. Sexual reproduction is known to occur in some diatoms, but it involves little genetic flexibility. Since the vegetative stage is diploid, meiosis results in segregation at gametogenesis; but the gametes from one cell (Centrales) or from sister cells (Pennales) usually fuse to produce the zygote. Thus, there is no recombination and subsequent segregation of new genetic material. Auxospore formation may be considered as a type of reproduction in which there is maintenance of a high degree of constancy in the species.

REFERENCES ON BACILLARIOPHYCEAE

Bourrelly, P., "Recherches sur les Chrysophycées, Morphologie, Phylogénie, Systématique." *Rev. Algol. Mem. Hors.-Série,* No. 1 (1957).

Fritsch, F. E., *The Structure and Reproduction of the Algae.* Vol. 1. Cambridge: Cambridge University Press (1935). Pp. 507–563.

Fritsch, F. E., "Chrysophyta." In Smith, G. M. (Ed.), *Manual of Phycology.* Waltham, Mass.: Chronica Botanica (1951). Pp. 86–92.

Huber-Pestalozzi, G., *Das Phytoplankton des Süsswassers.* Vol. 16, Pt. 2(1). In Thienemann, A. (Ed.), *Die Binnengewässer.* Stuttgart: E. Schweizerbart'sche Verlagsbuchhandlung (1941). Pp. 4–303.

Pascher, A., *Chrysomonadinae.* In Pascher, A. (Ed.), Die *Süsswasser-Flora Deutschlands, Österreichs, und der Schweiz.* Vol. 2: *Flagellatae* 2. Jena: G. Fischer (1913). Pp. 5–95.

Smith, G. M., *Cryptogamic Botany,* 2nd Ed. Vol. 1: *Algae and Fungi.* New York: McGraw-Hill Book Co., Inc. (1955). Pp. 184–193.

REFERENCES ON CHRYSOPHYCEAE

Cupp, E. E., "Marine Plankton Diatoms of the West Coast of North America." *Bull. Scripps Inst. Oceanog., Univ. Calif.,* 5(1): 1–238 (1943).

Fritsch, F. E., *The Structure and Reproduction of the Algae.* Vol. 1. Cambridge: Cambridge University Press (1935). Pp. 564–651.

Fritsch, F. E., "Chrysophyta." In Smith, G. M. (Ed.), *Manual of Phycology.* Waltham, Mass.: Chronica Botanica (1951). Pp. 92–101.

Helmcke, J., and Krieger, W., *Diatomeenschalen im Electronenmikroskopischen Bild.* Pts. I–IV. Weinheim, Germany: J. Cramer (1962).

Huber-Pestalozzi, G., and Hustedt, F., *Diatomeen.* In Huber-Pestalozzi, G., *Das Phytoplankton des Süsswassers.* Vol. 16, Pt. 2(2). In Thienemann, A. (Ed.), *Die Binnengewässer.* Stuttgart: E. Schweizererbart'sche Verlagsbuchhandlung (1942).

Hustedt, F., *Die Kieselalgen.* In Rabenhorst, L. (Ed.), *Kryptogamen Flora von Deutschland, Öesterreich, und der Schweiz,* 2nd. Ed. Vol. 7. Jena: G. Fischer (1930).

Lewin, J. C., and Guillard, R. L., "Diatoms." *Ann. Rev. Microbiol.,* 17: 373–414 (1963).

Macan, T. T., *Freshwater Ecology.* London: Longmans, Green & Co. Ltd. (1963).

Patrick, R. L., *Sexual Reproduction in Diatoms.* In *Sex in Microorganisms.* Washington, D. C.: American Association for the Advancement of Science (1954). Pp. 82–99.

Ruttner, F., *Fundamentals of Limnology,* 3rd Ed. (Trans. by Frey, D. G., and Fry, F. E. J.). Toronto: University of Toronto Press (1963).

Schönfeldt, H., *Bacillariales (Diatomeae).* In Pascher, A. (Ed.), Die *Süsswasser-Flora Deutschlands, Österreichs, und der Schweiz.* Vol. 10. Jena: G. Fischer (1913).

Smith, G. M., *Cryptogamic Botany,* 2nd Ed. Vol. 1: *Algae and Fungi.* New York: McGraw-Hill Book Co., Inc. (1955). Pp. 193–212.

11 / DIVISION

PHAEOPHYTA

The division Phaeophyta (*brown algae*) is a large, conspicuous group of algae containing about 240 genera and over 1,500 species. The representatives of this group are restricted to the sea, with the exception of a very few that occur in fresh water. The Phaeophyta may be considered to be in three separate classes or in one class. Separation into three classes is based on knowledge of life histories; however, many genera are not fully known. In this text the single class, Phaeophyceae, with 11 orders, is recognized.

CELL STRUCTURE

In general, the cell wall is composed of an inner firm, cellulose layer and an outer mucilaginous, pectic, or pectic-like layer. Various complex colloidal substances, termed **phycocolloids,** occur to varying degrees in the cell walls of many of the brown algae. These substances, including **algin** and **fucoidin,** occur in some of the larger genera of kelps (Laminariales) in sufficient quantity to be commercially important. In the more complex forms the phycocolloids may also accumulate in the intercellular spaces. Calcification of the cell wall occurs in *Padina* (Fig. 11–1).

The pigments in the cytoplasm are present in one (Fig. 11–3D) or more (Fig. 11–3B, C) usually peripheral chloroplasts, which vary to some extent in size and shape. Where they are numer-

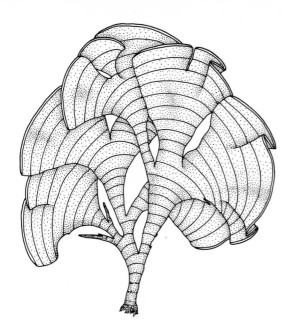

FIGURE 11–1   *Padina*, a tropical member of the Dictyotales with calcified cell walls, ×0.5.

ous in the cell, they are usually small and discoid (Fig. 11–3B, C); but they may be elongate, flattened, and irregular (Fig. 11–3A). Pyrenoid-like structures have been reported in some species. Electron micrographs (Fig. 11–4D) show the chloroplasts to be very similar to those of the Dinophyceae and the Chrysophyta (Fig. 10–2D). In the brown algae each group of three lamellar pairs is frequently separated from any other group.

The characteristic brownish color of these algae is due to the presence of the accessory xanthophyll pigment, **fucoxanthin.** Other accessory carotenoid pigments present are β-carotene and generally additional xanthophylls, including violaxanthin, neoxanthin, and possibly flavoxanthin. The green pigments, which are masked by the brown fucoxanthin, are chlorophylls *a* and *c*. According to the species and the conditions under which they occur, the brown algae range in color from olive-brown through a rich golden-brown to practically black. This variation is a reflection of the relative proportions of chlorophylls to other pigments present and in particular to fucoxanthin.

A central vacuole (Fig. 11–3A) may be present in the cell, or there may be several small

vacuoles (Fig. 11–2B). The food reserves are stored in the dissolved state, primarily as the polysaccharide **laminarin,** which is composed of β, 1–3, 1–6 linked glucosides. An integral part of laminarin is the sugar alcohol, **mannitol,** which oxidizes to produce the hexose sugar, mannose. Numerous refractive vesicles, usually aggregated about the nucleus, contain a tannin-like substance thought to be a waste product of metabolism. The substance is termed **phaeophyte tannin** (it has been referred to as fucosan, but it is not a polysaccharide). Fats and small amounts of other carbohydrates have been reported.

The cells are generally uninucleate; however, in certain regions of the thallus (as in certain of the holdfast cells of some kelps) they may be multinucleate. The nucleus with a well-defined nuclear membrane contains one or more nucleoli. Mitosis and meiosis are similar to that in higher plants, although the chromosomes are generally small and morphologically similar.

Most of the brown algae are autotrophic. A few forms occur as epiphytes and **endophytes.** The latter, especially, may be partially or wholly parasitic. Knowledge concerning nutritional. requirements of the brown algae is notoriously lacking.

MOVEMENT

None of the brown algae is motile although motile cells (zoospores and gametes) are produced. These motile cells are almost always laterally biflagellate and somewhat bean-shaped or pyriform. The flagella are unequal in length with the longer one generally projecting anteriorly and the shorter posteriorly (Fig. 11–2A, B, D). However, there are a few exceptions to this. In the Fucales the longer flagellum trails and the shorter one projects anteriorly; the flagellated cell (sperm) is also somewhat bell-shaped (see Fig. 11–2E, 4C). In the Dictyotales (Fig. 11–2C, 4E) one of the two flagella (the posterior one) is absent or rudimentary. In those brown algae studied with the electron microscope, the anterior flagellum is

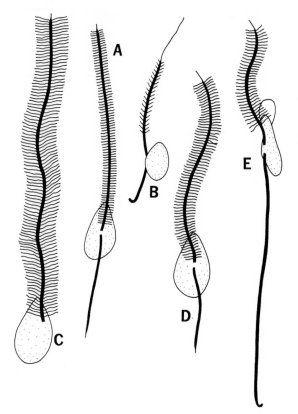

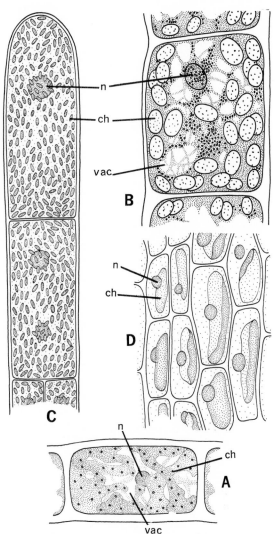

FIGURE 11–2   Arrangement of flagella of various Phaeophyta (anterior end toward top of each diagram). A, B, D, zoospores. A, *Pylaiella;* B, *Chordaria;* D, *Laminaria.* C, E, sperm. C, *Dictyota;* E, *Fucus.*

generally tinsel (Fig. 11–4A, B, E), with two rows of mastigonemes, and the posterior flagellum is whiplash (Fig. 11–2A, B, D, E).

FIGURE   11–3   Chloroplast types in Phaeophyta. A, reticulate (*Ectocarpus*), ×1,500; B, C, discoid (B, *Pylaiella,* ×690; C, *Sphacelaria,* ×320); D, laminate (*Scytosiphon*), ×300. *n,* nucleus; *ch,* chloroplast; *vac,* vacuole.

CLASSIFICATION AND MORPHOLOGICAL DIVERSITY

The 11 orders of Phaeophyta can be placed in a number of evolutionary lines based on life history and alternation of generations, on vegetative construction (Fig. 11–5, 6), and on reproductive characteristics. Since there are no motile or nonmotile unicellular or colonial forms of brown algae, the simplest organization is an unbranched or sparingly branched uniseriate filament. In the more specialized members, well-developed tissues are present, and

there may be considerable differentiation of cells in the thallus and method of growth from one phase to another in the life history. No other group of algae has attained the diversity of form, the complexity of vegetative construction, or the size of the Phaeophyta. They range from microscopic filamentous forms (less than 1 mm) to massive plants 50 to 70 meters or more in length. This diversity is achieved largely by the variety of types of growth in the brown algae (Fig. 11–5, 6).

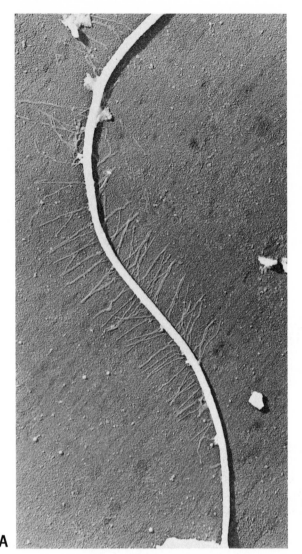

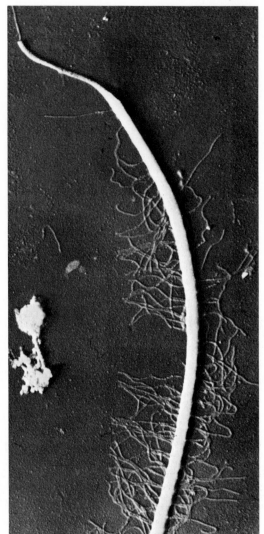

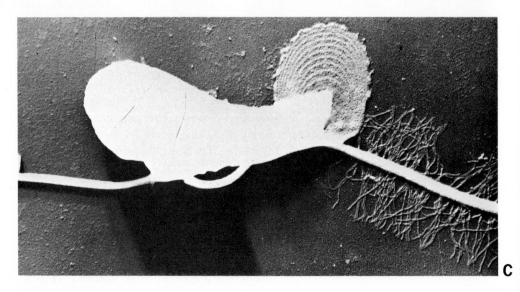

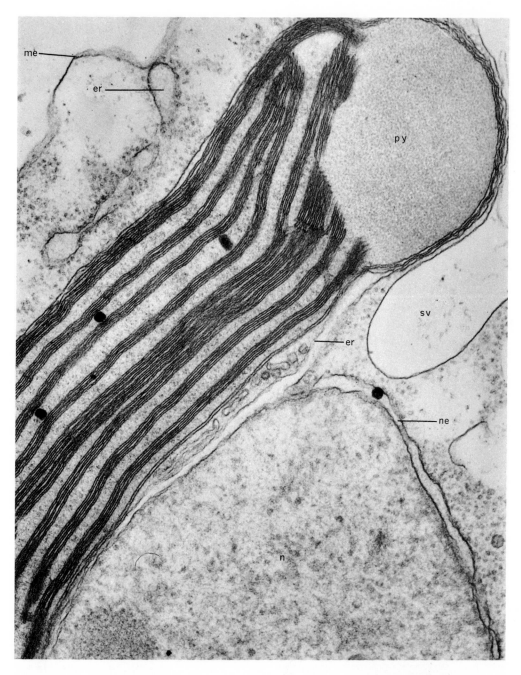

FIGURE 11–4A–D   Electron micrographs of flagella and chloroplast in Phaeophyta. A (left, above), anterior portion of tinsel flagellum of *Chordaria* zoospore, ×20,000. B (left, above), *Fucus* sperm showing distal portion of tinsel flagellum, ×28,000. C (left, below), *Fucus* sperm showing body of sperm, proboscis, and proximal portions of the posterior whiplash flagellum and the anterior tinsel flagellum, ×26,000. D (above), part of chloroplast of *Pylaiella* near pyrenoid (*py*), showing the characteristic compound lamellations, each composed of three parallel discs, and the dense lipid droplets lying between them (*n*, nucleus; *ne*, nuclear envelope; *er*, layer of endoplasmic reticulum surrounding chloroplast; *me*, membrane; *sv*, part of storage vesicle), ×54,600. (A, photograph courtesy J. B. Hansen, from Petersen, Caram, and Hansen, with permission of *Botanisk Tidsskrift;* B, photograph courtesy I. Manton, from Manton and Clarke, with permission of *Annals of Botany;* C, photograph courtesy I. Manton, from Manton and Clarke with permission of *Annals of Botany* and *Journal of Experimental Botany;* D, photograph courtesy L. V. Evans.)

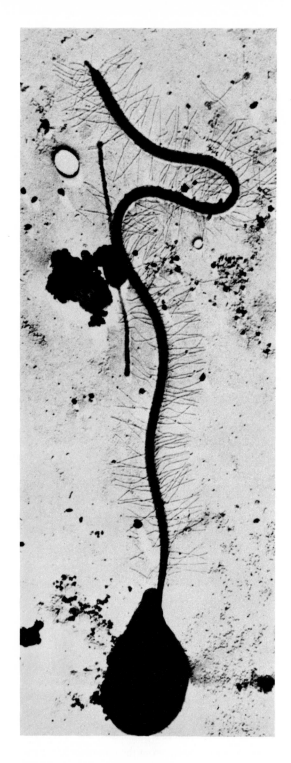

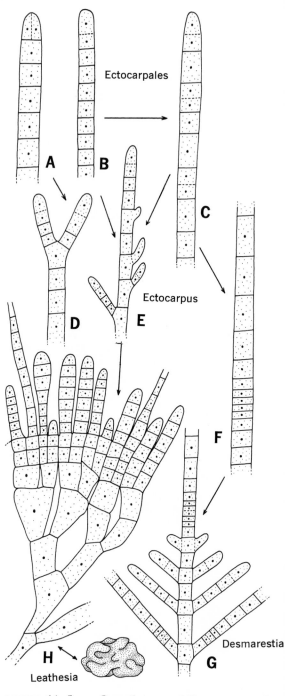

FIGURE 11–4E   Electron micrograph of *Dictyota* sperm, showing tinsel flagellum, ×7,500. (E, from Manton, Clarke, and Greenwood, with permission of *Journal of Experimental Botany*.)

FIGURE 11–5   Growth types of filamentous and pseudoparenchymatous Phaeophyta and possible evolutionary lines. A–F, unbranched and branched filamentous forms. A, B, D, E, with apical growth; C, with intercalary cell division in addition to apical growth; F, trichothallic growth. G, H, pseudoparenchymatous forms. G, trichothallic growth; H, apical growth.

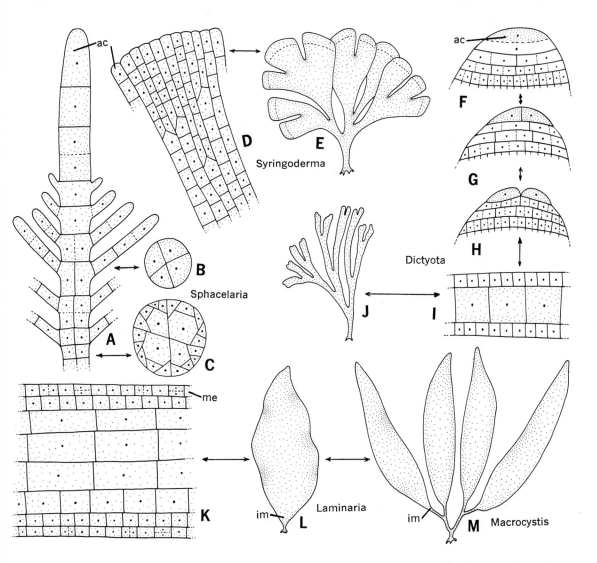

FIGURE 11–6   Growth types of parenchymatous Phaeophyta. A–J, apical growth followed by intercalary and parenchymatous cell divisions; B, C, transverse views of axis at points indicated in A by ar-
rows; A, F, with single apical cell at tip of axis; D, detail of portion of E showing marginal row of apical
cells. K–M, with meristoderm and intercalary meristem; K, detail of transverse section of lamina of L
and M. *me,* meristoderm; *im,* intercalary meristem or transition zone; *ac,* apical cell.

In the Ectocarpales the simplest type of
growth results from intercalary cell division in
one plane and only occasionally in a second
plane, resulting in a uniseriate, unbranched, or
rarely branched filament (Fig. 11–7G, H, *Pylaiella*). Some divisions (with varying degrees
of frequency and regularity) in a second plane
may result in a freely branching series of uni-

seriate filaments, as in *Ectocarpus* (Fig. 11–
7A, C). Erect unbranched filaments arising
from a prostrate branched system are characteristic of some genera (Fig. 11–7K, *Myrionema*).
This type of growth habit is referred to as
heterotrichy, and also occurs in the red algae
and green algae. In some instances there may
be an aggregation of only slightly branched

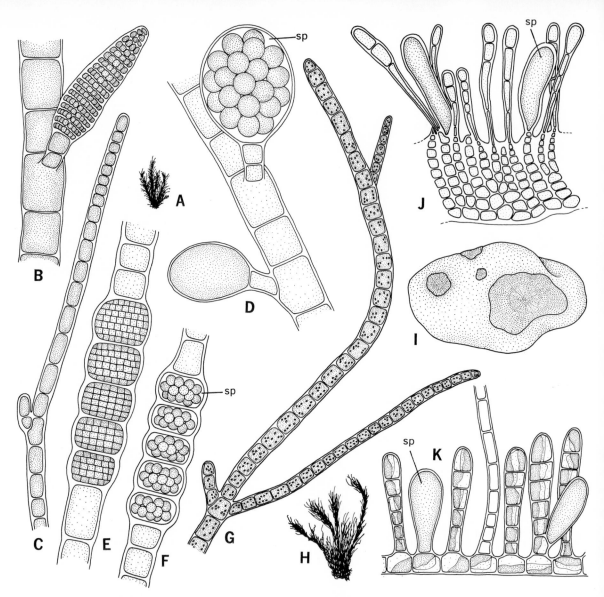

FIGURE 11–7   Filamentous forms of Phaeophyta with reproductive structures. A–D, *Ectocarpus*. A, habit, ×0.5; B, portion of filament bearing plurilocular structure, ×250; C, vegetative portion of thallus showing initiation of a branch, ×235; D, portion of filament showing immature (below) and mature (above) unilocular meiosporangia, ×250. E–H, *Pylaiella*. E, fertile portion of a filament, showing intercalary plurilocular structures, ×110; F, fertile portion of filament showing intercalary unilocular meiosporangia, ×110; G, vegetative portion of thallus, ×110; H, habit, ×0.5. I–J, *Ralfsia*. I, habit showing several encrusting thalli growing on a rock, ×0.5; J, transverse section through portion of encrusting thallus, showing erect compacted filaments and two unilocular meiosporangia (*sp*), ×225. K, *Myrionema*, showing prostrate basal system, erect vegetative filaments of cells, and two unilocular meiosporangia (*sp*), ×800.

filaments, which adhere laterally, forming a compact encrusting layer (Fig. 11–7I, J *Ralfsia*). In the Chordariales a **pseudoparenchymatous** thallus may be formed by an aggregation or intertwining of branched filaments, which may be loosely organized (Fig. 11–8C, D, *Leathesia*) or densely compacted (Fig. 11–8A, B, *Heterochordaria*). In the Sphacelariales, cells of a primary uniseriate axis may divide more than once to produce a **corticated**

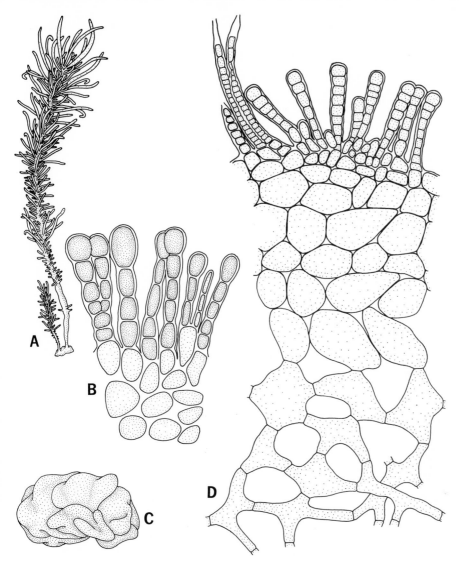

FIGURE 11–8   Pseudoparenchymatous forms. A, B, *Heterochordaria*. A, habit, ×0.5; B, transverse section through outer portion of thallus, showing pseudoparenchymatous medulla and free surface filaments, ×300. C, D, *Leathesia*. C, habit, ×0.5; D, transverse section through outer portion of thallus showing loose filamentous medulla, pseudoparenchymatous cortical region, and free surface filaments, ×155.

thallus, suggesting **parenchymatous** development (Fig. 11–9A–E, *Sphacelaria*). In the Dictyosiphonales, diffuse parenchymatous growth occurs as a result of divisions only in surface cells. **Periclinal** divisions in these surface cells increase the thickness of the thallus, and occasional **anticlinal** divisions permit the surface growth to keep pace with the increase in girth. The thallus may be a solid **foliose** one (as in *Phaeostrophion,* Fig. 11–10E, F) or it may

become hollow (as in *Scytosiphon,* Fig. 11–10C, D). The pseudoparenchymatous type, *Leathesia* (Fig. 11–8C, D), may also become hollow at maturity.

Growth is generally intercalary although in the Dictyotales, Sphacelariales, and Fucales there is a marked apical development of a thallus. There may be a single apical cell (Fig. 11–9C, *Sphacelaria*). In some of the Fucales there may be a group of several apical cells at a

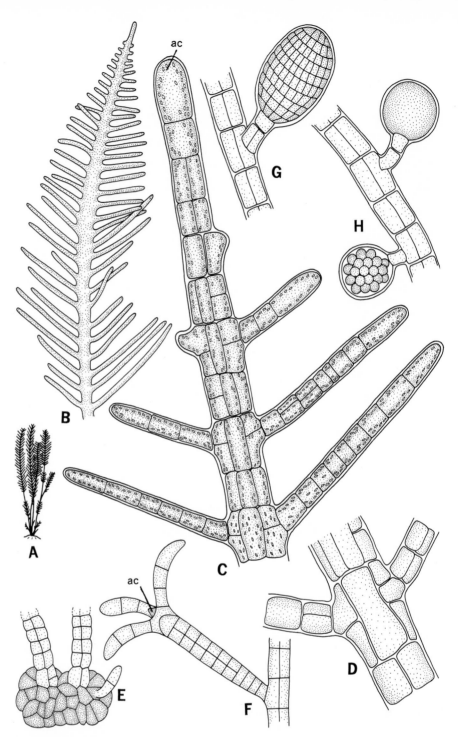

FIGURE 11–9   Parenchymatous form with apical growth. A–H, *Sphacelaria.*
A, habit, ×1; B, apical portion of thallus, ×30; C, apical portion of thallus,
showing apical cell (*ac*), branches, and parenchymatous development of main
axis, ×150; D, more mature portion of axis, showing cells in surface view,
×160; E, basal attachment region of a young thallus, showing prostrate basal
system and erect axes, ×120; F, portion of axis showing propagule, ×120. G, H,
filaments with reproductive structures. G, plurilocular structure, ×180; H,
immature (above) and mature (below) unilocular meiosporangia, ×180.

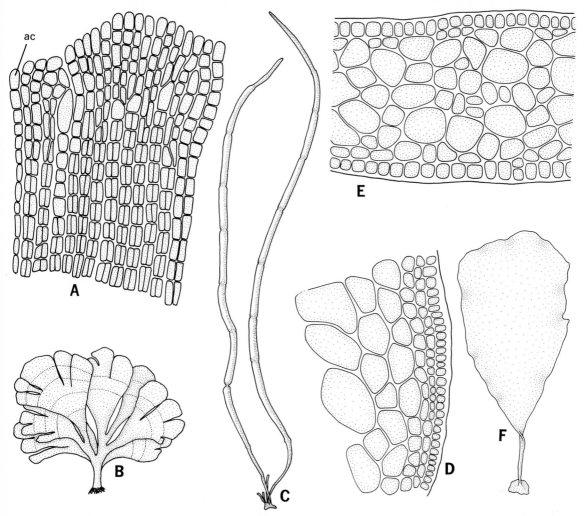

FIGURE 11–10   Parenchymatous forms of Phaeophyta. A, B, *Syringoderma*. A, outer region of mono-stromatic thallus, showing marginal row of apical cells (*ac*), ×125; B, habit of fan-shaped thallus, ×2.5. C, D, *Scytosiphon*. C, habit of hollow thallus, ×0.5, D, transverse section of outer portion of thallus, showing parenchymatous organization of cells, ×500. E, F, *Phaeostrophion*. E, cross section through portion of thallus, showing parenchymatous organization, ×300; F, habit, ×1.

branch apex, although most of them, as in *Fu-cus,* have a single apical cell. Some of the Dic-tyotales have a single apical cell (Fig. 11–11B, *Dictyota*), but in others there is a margin of apical cells (Fig. 11–10A, B, *Syringoderma*).

The ultimate in size and complexity in brown algae is achieved through meristematic activity in specific localized regions. Some of these meristems have potentialities similar to those of vascular plants. One type of meristem, unique to brown algae, results in **trichothallic** growth, which is the result of a special type of intercalary cell division in a filament. This is

characteristic of the Desmarestiales in particu-lar. Cell divisions are confined to a localized, subapical portion of the thallus apex at the base of hair-like, uniseriate filaments (see *Des-marestia,* Fig. 11–13E). Despite the relative simplicity of this type of growth (Fig. 11–13A–E), a complex pseudoparenchyma-tous organization (Fig. 11–13F) results and permits the development of a variety of mor-phological types (Fig. 11–12A, B).

The most highly developed type of meri-stematic activity occurs in the parenchymatous kelps, or Laminariales (Fig. 11–14O, P). A

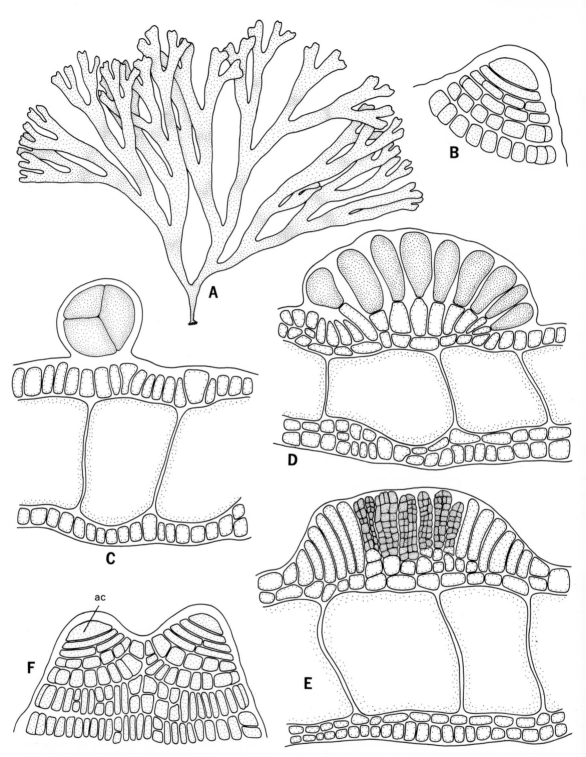

FIGURE 11–11   *Dictyota.* A, habit, ×0.5. B, F, apical region of branch (showing dichotomous division in F); B, ×300; F, ×215. C, transverse section through portion of thallus, showing mature meiosporangium, ×150. D, transverse section through portion of thallus, showing mature oogonia at surface, ×140. E, transverse section through portion of thallus, showing mature antheridia at surface, ×145.

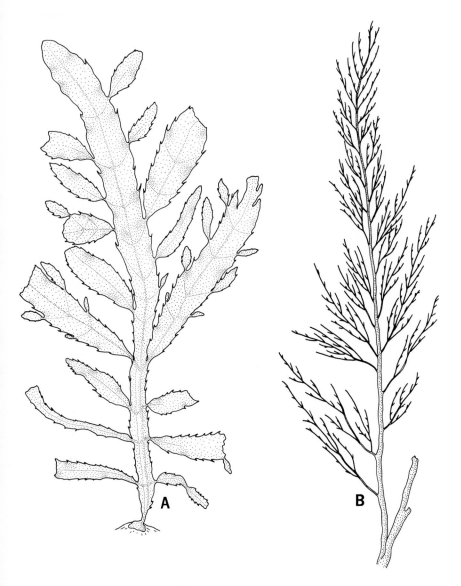

FIGURE 11–12   Species diversity of *Desmarestia*. A, habit of a flattened, strap-shaped species, ×0.3; B, habit of a terete species, ×0.3 (except for symmetry of thallus, anatomical detail is similar in all species and identical to that shown in Fig. 11–13).

primary meristem called the **transition zone** is an intercalary meristem located between the blade-like distal portion and the narrow, stem-like proximal region of the plant. In addition, surface meristematic activity occurs in the epidermal region, which is referred to as the **meristoderm** (Fig. 11–15A, C). It is also possible that in some forms there is an internal

meristematic region in the stem-like portion of the kelps similar to the cambium of vascular plants.

Most of the large conspicuous brown algae have these well-developed meristems, which accounts for their size. However, in two additional ways brown algae may attain macroscopic dimensions. (1) Forms with diffuse

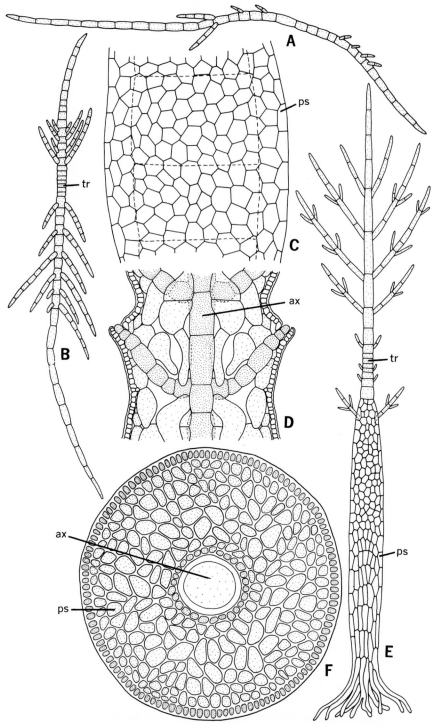

FIGURE 11–13   *Desmarestia,* a terete species. A, B, E, juvenile sporophytes.
A, early filamentous phase, ×150; B, filamentous phase, showing initiation of
trichothallic growth (*tr*), ×150; E, more mature, showing trichothallic growth
and pseudoparenchymatous habit (*ps*) of cortical filaments, ×110. C, enlarged
surface view of basal portion of E, showing pseudoparenchymatous cells surrounding central axis (broken lines), ×200. D, enlarged longitudinal section of
more mature portion of the thallus, showing axial row of cells (*ax*), ×250. F,
transverse section of mature portion of plant, ×150.

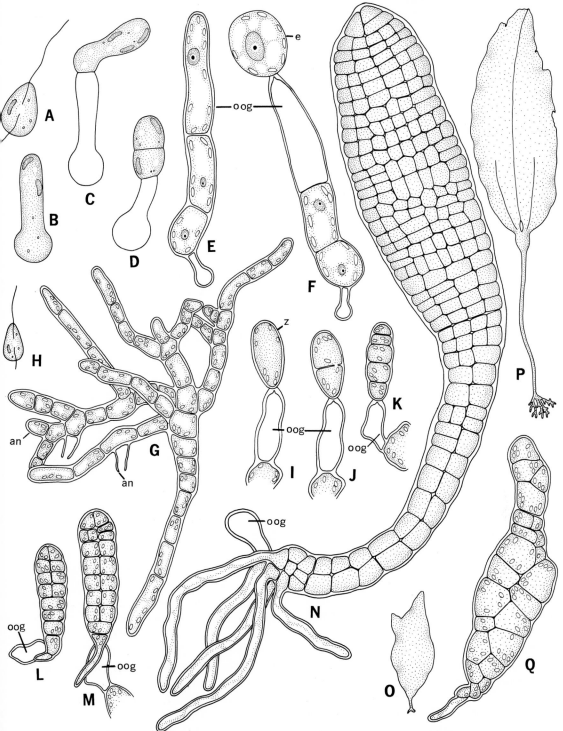

FIGURE 11–14   Stages in growth and life history in Laminariales. A–Q, *Nereocystis*. A, zoospore (meiospore), ×1,000; B, germinating zoospore ×1,000; C–E, stages in development of female gametophyte, ×1,000; F, mature female gametophyte with empty oogonium (*oog*) and discharged unfertilized egg (*e*), ×1,000; G, mature male gametophyte with immature and mature (empty) antheridia (*an*), ×1,000; H, sperm, ×1,000; I–K, zygote (*z*) and early divisions in young sporophyte attached to empty oogonium, ×1,000; L–N, stages in development of young sporophyte (L, M, ×800; N, ×400); O, P, later stages (macroscopic) of young sporophyte (O, × 0.5; P, ×0.3); Q, a young abnormal, parthenogenetically developed "sporophyte," ×1,000.

intercalary meristematic regions form an extensive multilayered, or parenchymatous, thallus by undergoing cell divisions in three planes, as in *Phaeostrophion* (Fig. 11–10E, F) and *Scytosiphon* (Fig. 11–10C, D). (2) Simple intercalary cell divisions, trichothallic growth, strict apical growth, or a combination of these may result in a basically filamentous thallus. However, an aggregation, lateral fusion, or intertwining of these branched filaments results in a large pseudoparenchymatous thallus, as in *Leathesia* (Fig. 11–8D) or *Desmarestia* (Fig. 11–12A, B). This second type is fundamentally simpler than the first but neither generally results in forms as large as those with intercalary meristems.

In *Fucus,* as well as other members of the Fucales, a variety of different types of growth occur during the ontogeny of the conspicuous generation. The embryo starts out as a short filament (Fig. 11–16A–E), which soon develops a definite polarity. Filamentous rhizoids develop at one end and a parenchymatous apex is soon established at the other. Although the surface cells continue to divide, following the development of a prominent apical depression, trichothallic growth becomes established (Fig. 11–16I, K). However, this method of growth soon ceases. The establishment of the first apical cell (Fig. 11–16K) in the apical depression initiates apical growth, which continues throughout the life of the mature plant.

Differentiation in the more complex brown algae, such as the Laminariales, is such that structures somewhat comparable to higher plant organs may be distinguished. Morphologically these parts are leaf-like, stem-like, and root-like (Fig. 11–18) but they do not function as true leaves, stems, or roots because they lack the features characteristic of a vascular system. The leaf-like part of a brown alga is referred to as a **lamina,** or blade; the stem-like part as a **stipe;** and the attachment part as a **holdfast,** often with root-like structures, the **haptera** (Fig. 11–19). Although these structures are not as complex as vascular plant roots, they are not necessarily composed of simple tissues. Definite anatomical regions may be differentiated as the meristoderm (epidermis), the cortex, and the innermost **medulla** (Fig. 11–15A–F). In the cortex, pitted elements (Fig. 11–15D) and **mucilage canals** (Fig. 11–15A, 17C) may occur, whereas phloem-like elements (Fig. 11–15B, D, 17D) may be in the medulla. Morphologically and chemically the phloem-like elements are very similar to the sieve elements of vascular plants. Some evidence using radioactive tracers shows that these sieve-like elements function in conduction. Some regions of the stipe may become hollow and develop into floats, or **pneumatocysts,** which hold the plant more or less erect in the water (Fig. 11–18).

REPRODUCTION AND LIFE HISTORIES

Although many brown algae are quite complex vegetatively, they all have relatively simple reproductive structures. Sexual reproduction varies greatly, but typically there is an alternation of two multicellular generations.

Vegetative reproduction may occur by simple fragmentation of the thallus, or by somewhat specialized multicellular portions, such as propagules of *Sphacelaria* (Fig. 11–9F). Fragmentation of the thallus is the only method of reproduction known in some free-floating species of *Sargassum* (Fig. 11–20). Species of this same genus found attached to the ocean bottom in coastal areas reproduce sexually; but unattached, free-floating species have apparently lost the ability and are perpetuated vegetatively (as in the Sargasso Sea). **Mitospores** (also termed neutral spores) from many-chambered **(plurilocular) mitosporangia** (Fig. 11–7B, E, 9G) may also occur as an accessory method of reproduction. Meiosis occurs in an unpartitioned **(unilocular) meiosporangium** (Fig. 11–7D, F, 9H, 11C). The meiospores (zoospores or aplanospores) are produced by free-nuclear division.

In sexual reproduction, plants with isogamy, anisogamy, and oogamy occur, and apparently these various types have evolved repeatedly along diverging evolutionary lines. Motile gametes are morphologically similar to

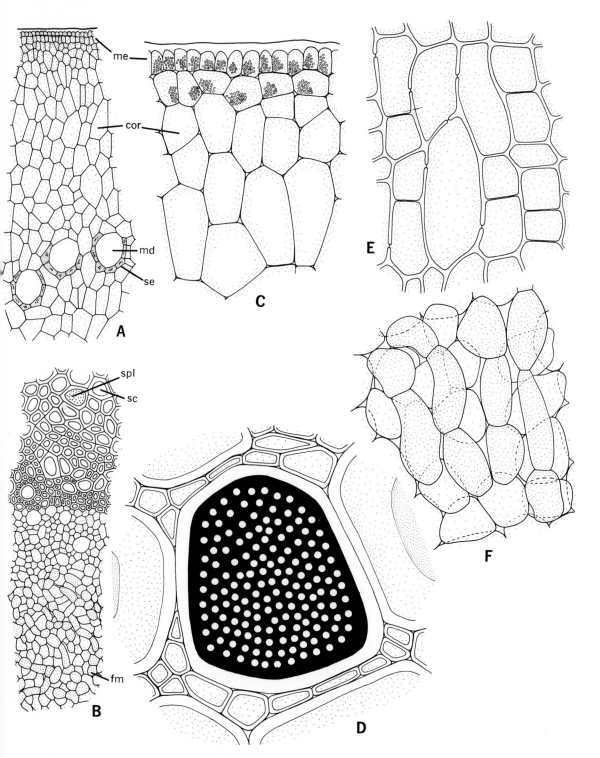

FIGURE 11–15   Anatomy of *Nereocystis* stipe. A–D, transverse sections. A, outer portion of stipe, showing surface meristoderm (*me*), compact cortex (*cor*), mucilage ducts (*md*), and secretory cell (*se*),
×150; B, inner portion of stipe, showing thick-walled sieve cells (*sc*), filamentous medulla (*fm*), and
sieve plate (*spl*), ×150; C, enlarged view of epidermal region, showing meristoderm (*me*), ×600; D,
enlarged transverse section of sieve plate, ×1,200. E, F, longitudinal sections. E, portion of outer cortex,
showing pitted cells, ×300; F, portion of filamentous medulla, ×450.

the zoospores of brown algae, although often smaller. Isogamous forms produce gametes morphologically alike and of the same size. Anisogamous gametes are also morphologically alike, but one gamete is consistently larger (the female) than the other (the male). In oogamous forms a nonmotile egg is fertilized by a small motile sperm. Generally syngamy occurs in the water, although an egg may remain fastened (Fig. 11–14F) on the haploid female plant. In oogamous species (Fig. 11–11, 14, 21) one to several eggs or sperm form in a gametangium. However, in some of the isogamous and anisogamous species (Fig. 11–7, 9) the gametangia are subdivided into many compartments, each of which produces a single motile gamete. These gametangia are referred to as **plurilocular** structures.

The sexual plants of brown algae generally produce either the male or the female gametangia. In some instances the male and female gametophytes are morphologically distinguishable (as shown in *Nereocystis,* Fig. 11–14E, G). In other brown algae, the gametophytes are indistinguishable (as in some species of *Ectocarpus,* Fig. 11–7A). Less commonly other species of algae produce both kinds of gametes on the same plant.

All brown algae but the Fucales may have an alternation of free-living multicellular gametophytic and sporophytic generations. In the simpler filamentous brown algae, such as the Ectocarpales, there is an alternation of **isomorphic** generations in which the haploid and diploid phases are morphologically identical and physiologically independent in the vegetative condition (Fig. 11–7B, D).

The motile isogametes (Fig. 11–22E, F) produced in many-chambered gametangia (Fig. 11–22C, D) fuse, forming the diploid zygote (Fig. 11–22H) that immediately divides to produce the diploid (sporophytic) generation (Fig. 11–22J). The sporophytic generation produces many-chambered mitosporangia (Fig. 11–22T) that in turn produce diploid mitospores (Fig. 11–22U) capable of maintaining the diploid generation by asexual means. Meiosis occurs in one-chambered meiosporangia (Fig. 11–22K–M). The resulting

meiospores (Fig. 11–22N, O) grow into two types of haploid gametophytes (Fig. 11–22Q, S, A, P, R, B), each producing one type of gamete (Fig. 11–22C–F).

In the more advanced orders, such as the Laminariales, there is typically an alternation of **heteromorphic** generations, in which the haploid phase is a free-living physiologically independent diminutive (although multicellular) generation and the diploid phase is the conspicuous, relatively large, generation (Fig. 11–23). Some of these large, more complex sporophytic generations may be annual, as in *Nereocystis,* but they still reach a length of 30 to 35 meters in less than four months. Others may be perennial as *Pterygophora* (Fig. 11–24), and reach a length of about 3 to 4 meters in ten to 15 years. Some evidence indicates that the free-living gametophytic generations of the Laminariales may also be perennial.

In the typical kelp, the haploid gametophytes are microscopic (Fig. 11–23A, B). The female gametophyte (Fig. 11–23B) produces one egg (per oogonium) which is held at the end of the oogonium (Fig. 11–23D). The male gametophyte (Fig. 11–23A) produces many motile sperm (one per cell usually) which swim to the egg (Fig. 11–23E). The resulting zygote (Fig. 11–23F), as in the Ectocarpales (Fig. 11–22H), undergoes mitosis to form the embryo sporophyte (Fig. 11–23G–I). The sporophyte continues growing into the typical kelp plant (Fig. 11–23J). In specialized areas on the blade of the sporophyte (Fig. 11–23J), meiosis occurs in one-chambered meiosporangia (Fig. 11–23K). The motile meiospores (Fig. 11–23M, N) settle to produce the two types of haploid gametophytes (Fig. 11–23A, B).

In the Fucales, the diploid generation is a multicellular conspicuous phase, whereas the haploid generation has been reduced to single cells that become the gametes themselves (Fig. 11–25). In other words, meiosis occurs at gamete formation (Fig. 11–25K, M) in the diploid plant. Thus, the gametangia (Fig. 11–25A, B) are comparable to the unicellular (and unilocular) sporangia of other brown algae. By com-

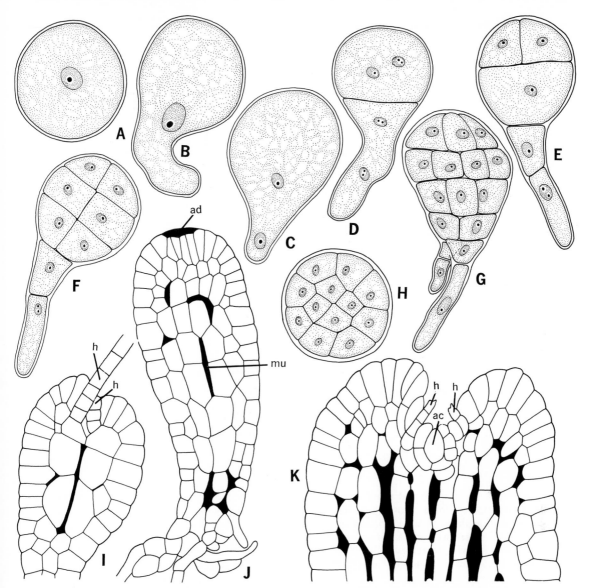

FIGURE 11–16   Early developmental stages of *Fucus*. A, zygote, ×600; B–G, stages in development of juvenile thallus, ×600; H, transverse section view of terminal portion of G, ×600; I, upper portion of more mature juvenile, showing two terminal hairs (*h*), ×325; J, juvenile, showing early development of apical depression (*ad*), filamentous medulla, and mucilage (*mu*), ×250; K, upper portion of more mature juvenile thallus, showing apical depression, remnants of terminal hairs (*h*), and initiation of apical cell (*ac*), ×325. (I, after Nienburg; J, K, after Oltmanns.)

parison with other Phaeophyceae, the spores essentially function as gametes, fusing immediately (Fig. 11–25D) instead of developing into free-living gametophytes.

The embryo undergoes a complex development (Fig. 11–16) before it becomes the typical dichotomously branched diploid thallus (Fig. 11–25G). At maturity, swollen tips (receptacles) on the thallus (Fig. 11–25H) produce numerous small cavities, called **conceptacles** (Fig. 11–25I), in which the gametangia (Fig. 11–25J, L) are formed. Meiosis occurs in the one-chambered female gametangium (oogonium—Fig. 11–25J–K) resulting in eight functional eggs; and in the one-chambered male gametangium (antheridium—Fig. 11–25L,

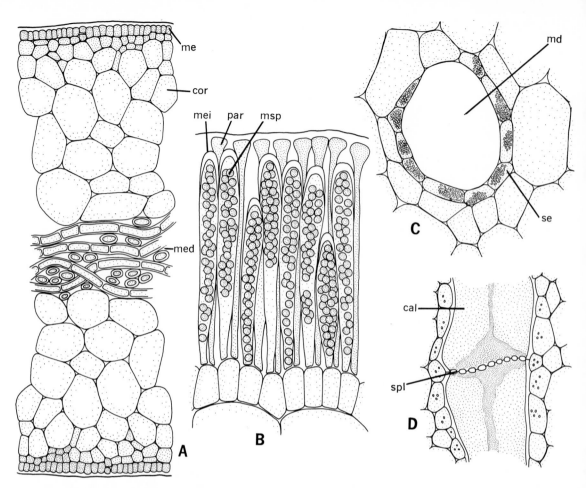

FIGURE 11–17   Anatomy and reproduction of *Nereocystis* sporophyte. A, transverse section through a sterile region of the lamina, showing meristoderm (*me*), cortex (*cor*), and medulla (*med*), ×350; B, transverse section through outer portion of fertile region of lamina, showing almost mature unilocular meiosporangia (*mei*) with meiospores (*msp*) and paraphyses (*par*), ×720; C, transverse section through mucilage duct, showing secretory cells (*se*) surrounding duct (*md*), ×400; D, longitudinal section through portion of stipe, showing region of sieve plate (*spl*) and adjacent cells (note heavy deposit of callose (*cal*) in sieve cells), ×650.

M), resulting in 64 sperm. This type of life history is somewhat comparable to that occurring in animals, with the organism diploid and the gametes the only haploid cells.

In no known examples is the diploid generation in the brown algae reduced to only a single cell, the zygote. But this reduction is common in the fresh-water forms of the yellow-green and green algae (Chapters 13 and 15).

In some brown algae, isogametes or anisogametes develop directly into haploid plants, thus behaving like mitospores. This suggests that vegetative reproduction is more primitive, that fusion of cells has occurred secondarily, and that sexuality is perhaps relative. For example, in some isogamous species of algae, both gametes are produced by the same plant; in other isogamous forms, the gametes fuse only with those from different plants. The next step in development of sexual differentiation was probably anisogamy. The most advanced type of sexual reproduction is oogamy. One of the advantages of oogamous sexual reproduction is that the large, nonmotile female gamete, or egg, can survive longer to be fertilized without exhausting its stored food re-

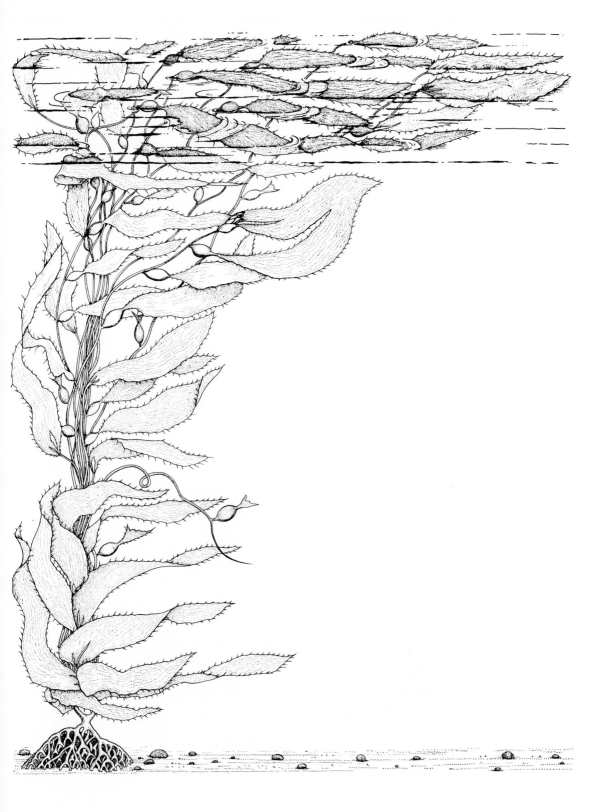

FIGURE 11–18   Habit view of *Macrocystis pyrifera*, showing branched holdfast of haptera, and erect stipes bearing leaflike lamina with basal floats, ×0.01. (Modified after a drawing by M. Neushul.)

FIGURE 11–19   Attached holdfast of *Macro-cystis integrifolia* at low tide in northern British Columbia, ×0.1.

FIGURE 11–20   Attached plant of *Sargassum muticum,* ×0.1.

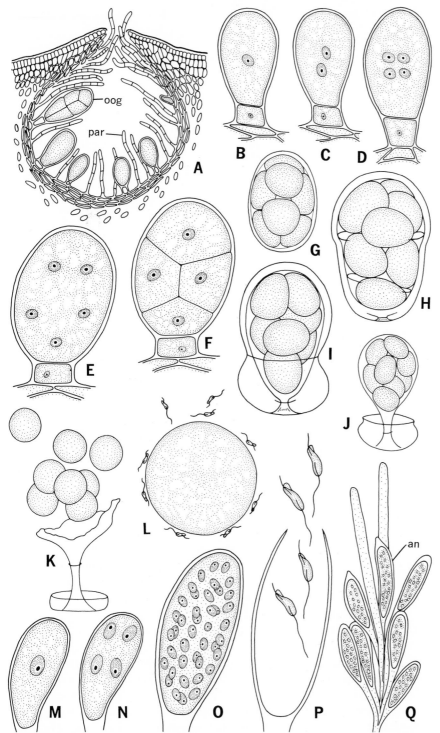

FIGURE 11–21   Reproduction in *Fucus*. A, transverse section of fertile portion of thallus, showing conceptacle containing immature and mature oogonia (*oog*),and paraphyses (*par*), ×125. B–K, stages in development and release of eggs in oogonium; B–F, ×500; G, ×400; H, I, K, ×500; J, ×350. L, sperm swimming about unfertilized egg, ×1,500; M–P, stages in development of antheridia and sperm release, ×1,800; Q, branch bearing several antheridia (*an*), ×800. (H–L, after Thuret.)

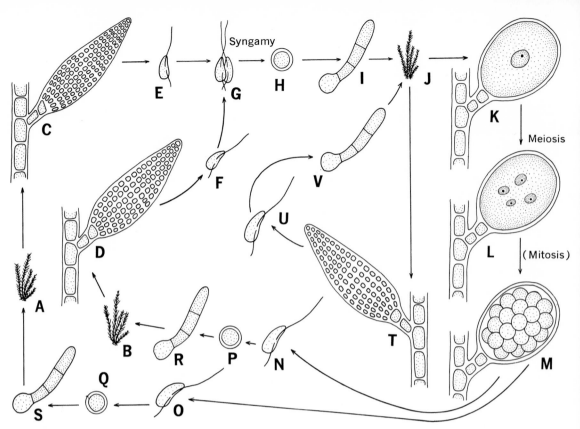

FIGURE 11–22   Life history of *Ectocarpus*. A, B, gametophyte plants; C, D, plurilocular gametangia; E, F, gametes; G, syngamy; H, zygote; I, developing sporophyte; J, mature sporophyte; K–M, maturation of meiosporangium; N, O, meiospores; P–S, developing gametophytes; T, plurilocular sporangium on sporophyte; U, mitospore; V, developing sporophyte. (For structural details and relative sizes of structures refer to Fig. 11–3A, 7A–D.)

serves. Also, because of the egg's relatively large contribution to it, the zygote too can survive longer before developing.

LINES OF EVOLUTION

Repeatedly, in the more highly evolved groups of algae, we find a trend from isogamy through anisogamy to oogamy. In the brown algae good evidence indicates that this trend has occurred along two or three quite distinct lines of evolution, especially within the orders where there is an alternation of heteromorphic generations. Three of these evolutionary series are particularly well distinguished.

The Ectocarpales contain the simplest morphological forms in the brown algae. A number of genera in other orders, especially in the Chordariales, merge with this basic group.

This is the chief reason why an arbitrary division into several classes does not result in a tenable phylogenetic arrangement. *Ectocarpus* illustrates well the primitive features of the brown algae and, at the same time, serves as a possible prototype from which all other groups of brown algae (with the possible exception of the Fucales) may be derived.

From the *Ectocarpus* type of life history (Fig. 11–22), forms with anisogamy and an alternation of isomorphic generations can readily be derived (as in *Sphacelaria,* Fig. 11–9). Similarly, a more advanced sexual reproduction, oogamy, still with an alternation of isomorphic generations (*Dictyota,* Fig. 11–11), is in a direct line of evolution from this basic group. Although vegetatively *Nereocystis* (Fig. 11–14G) has a reduced *Ectocarpus*-like filamentous gametophytic stage, the

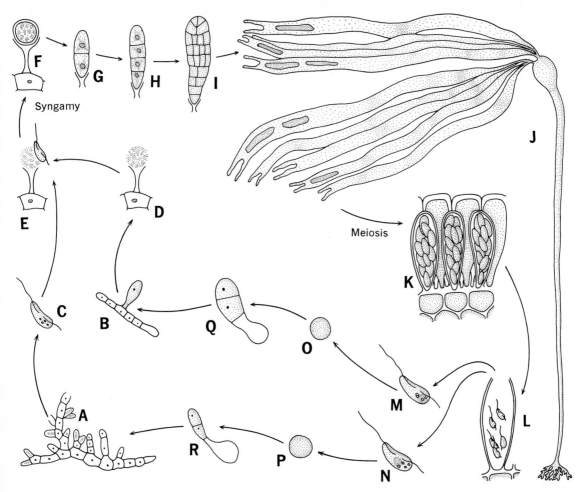

FIGURE 11–23   Life history of *Nereocystis*. A, male gametophyte with antheridia; B, female gameto-phyte with oogonium; C, sperm; D, unfertilized egg; E, syngamy; F, zygote; G–I, development of young sporophyte; J, mature sporophyte with dark, fertile sori on distal portion of lamina; K, meiosporangia; L, release of meiospores; M, N, meiospores; O–R, development of gametophytes. (For details and relative sizes of structures refer to Fig. 11–14, 15, 17.)

sporophyte has become a massive, complex, and highly developed sporophytic stage. *Fucus* (Fig. 11–25), on the other hand, has the ulti-mate in reduction in the haploid (1 *n*) phase, mainly the gametes, but also has a complex, highly developed diploid (2 *n*) phase.

DISTRIBUTION AND ECOLOGY

The brown algae are almost entirely ma-rine in distribution, including brackish water and salt marshes. Some species (such as *Sar-gassum*) occur free-floating far from shore in the North Atlantic (Sargasso Sea); and in the Sea of Japan other species may occur either attached or free-floating in salt marshes and lagoons or embedded in the sand. In the unat-tached condition, however, these algae gener-ally reproduce only by vegetative propagation. A number of large genera—such as *Nereocystis* and *Macrocystis*, which grow attached in deeper water (to 35 meters or more) in the North Pacific—form dense subtidal forests (Fig. 11–26, 27, 28). At times the distal branches of these large kelps float in dense mats along the sea surface. In tropical and semi-tropical regions the many species of *Sargassum* (Fig. 11–20, 29) also occur in dense beds.

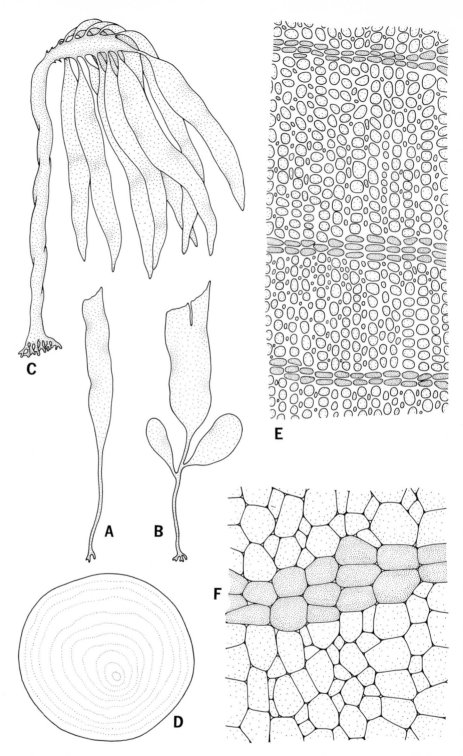

FIGURE 11–24   *Pterygophora.* A, B, young sporophytes, ×0.2; C, mature sporophyte, ×0.07; D, transverse section of stipe, showing "growth rings" formed by concentric rings of differentiated cells, ×0.5; E, enlarged view of a portion of stipe, showing distinct zones of differentiated cells, ×50; F, the same as D and E, but at higher magnification, ×150.

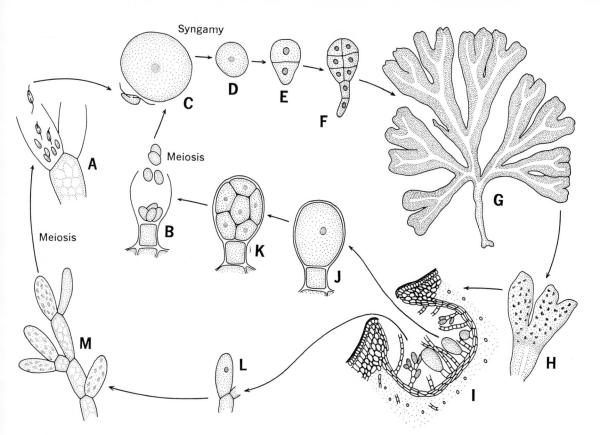

FIGURE 11–25   Life history of *Fucus*. A, mature antheridium liberating sperm; B, mature oogonium liberating eggs; C, mature sperm and egg prior to fusion; D, zygote; E, F, early development of thallus; G, mature thallus; H, fertile receptacle with numerous conceptacles; I, conceptacle with male and female structures; J, K, development within conceptacle of oogonium and eggs; L, M, development within the conceptacle of branch with several antheridia. (For structural details and relative sizes of structures refer to Fig. 11–16, 21.)

Such forests serve as breeding and grazing areas for many marine animals.

The most conspicuous brown algae belong to the Laminariales and Fucales. Although representatives of both these orders occur in northern and southern hemispheres, they appear to have had two distinct centers of distribution. The Laminariales are richest in genera and species in the North Pacific, and appear to have had a center of distribution in the northwestern part of the Pacific. The Fucales, on the other hand, are most abundant (in genera and species) in the southern hemisphere, and appear to have had a center of distribution in southern Australia and New Zealand. Certain genera in each of these groups occur in only one or the other region. In the Fucales, for example, the large *Durvillea* (Fig. 11–33) does

not occur in the northern hemisphere; it is found only in the colder waters of Australia, New Zealand, and in other subantarctic regions. *Fucus* (Fig. 11–32), on the other hand, occurs only in the northern hemisphere. The ecological niche occupied by *Fucus* in the northern hemisphere is occupied in the southern hemisphere by another member of the Fucales, *Hormosira* (Fig. 11–31). In the Laminariales, however, *Macrocystis* is found in both northern and southern hemispheres. But it does not occur in the western Pacific, or in the Atlantic Ocean, except for very restricted areas in the South Atlantic bordering South Africa and South America.

Although the sea is often thought of as a more uniform environment than the land, the topography and substrate beneath the sea are

FIGURE 11–26   Bed of *Nereocystis* at high tide in northern British Columbia.

FIGURE 11–27   Bed of *Nereocystis* at low tide in the Queen Charlotte Islands, British Columbia.

just as varied. As on land, variety in the marine environment is reflected by a diversified flora. The greatest number of marine species and individuals live on the rocky shores. The mud flats and sandy beaches generally have few seaweeds, because of the unstable bottom. The smoothness or roughness of the substrate may determine the type or size of plant that may be supported or anchored. The strength of the currents may also affect distribution. The marine algae do not have true roots. However, they may have extremely strong holdfasts, which anchor them under the most severe pounding surf and wave action.

Because of the varied conditions (both vertically and horizontally) which exist along

FIGURE 11–28   Bed of *Macrocystis integrifolia* at low tide in northern British Columbia.

FIGURE 11–29   Distal portion of *Sargassum muticum,* showing leaflike branches and spherical pneumatocysts (floats), ×1.

the rocky coasts where the brown algae predominate, a striking vertical zonation and geographical distribution of species is usually apparent. This zonation is related directly to the tidal phenomena that exist in the marine environment. The tidal pattern varies greatly in magnitude and character from one part of the world to another and from one part of an ocean to another, and even locally from one region to another. Many factors modify the characteristic tidal pattern in any given area. The most common pattern is referred to as a semidiurnal tidal cycle—one in which the sea level rises and falls twice within approximately 25 hours (Fig. 11–34). The seaweed collector must arrange his collecting trips to coincide with periods when the tide is low, because at this stage the greatest number and variety of seaweeds can be found and studied. Most of the **intertidal region**—that portion of the sea bottom exposed between the highest point to which the sea surface rises and the lowest point to which it falls—is exposed at low tide.

Tidal phenomena are related directly to the gravitational forces exerted on the earth by the moon and the sun and to the centrifugal force associated with the rotation of the earth-moon pair about their common center of

FIGURE 11–30   Basal portion of *Sargassum muticum,* showing straplike "leaves" and discoid holdfast, ×1.

gravity, and with the rotation of the earth-sun pair about their common center of gravity. Although smaller than the sun, the moon is much closer to the earth, and as a result its effect is about twice that of the sun (Fig. 11–35).

It is easiest to understand the influence of these bodies by considering them one at a time. For instance, the combination of the gravitational pull of the moon and the centrifugal force on the ocean causes a flow of water to raise the level—i.e., causes a high tide—both on the side of the earth nearest to the moon and simultaneously on the opposite side. Then as the moon rotates about the earth, the high tides rotate in synchronism. The semidiurnal rise to high tide and fall to low tide is a consequence. The sun exerts a similar effect, but because its rotation is not synchronized with the moon, the combined effect is more complicated than that which would be produced by either body alone. In addition, the shape of the ocean floor and shore influences the tidal flow of water and hence the character of the rise and fall. The over-all result may therefore be different in different geographic regions. For instance, around much of the Atlantic Ocean the succes-

sive high tides during a day are about the same height and the successive low tides are also similar in height. When the sun and the moon are approximately in line with the earth—i.e., at new moon and full moon—both combine to produce extreme high and low tides, called *spring* tides (Fig. 11–35), although these tides occur throughout the year. When the sun and moon are at right angles, their effects tend to cancel and high and low water are not so extreme. These are called *neap* tides (Fig. 11–35). Around much of the Pacific Ocean the tides are semidiurnal but the heights of successive high tides may be quite different, as may be those of successive low tides. These are called semidiurnal mixed tides, and they indicate the different response of the water of the Pacific Ocean basin to the same forces that cause the equal height tides in the Atlantic Ocean. In a few places, only one high and one low water occur in twenty-five hours—a so-called diurnal tide (Fig. 11–34).

Throughout the intertidal region, and extending down to a depth of 35 meters or more (depending on the transparency of the water), the brown algae may occur. However, they are

FIGURE 11–31 *Hormosira* in South Australia. A, dense bed at low tide; B, close-up showing conceptacles on swollen beadlike receptacles, ×0.5. (Photographs courtesy H. B. S. Womersley.)

more characteristic of the intertidal and shallower **subtidal** regions. Because of the constant ebb and flow of the tide through the intertidal region, which may cover a vertical distance of 8 meters or more in some areas, the plants in this zone are alternately submerged and exposed for varying periods of time. The physical-chemical conditions to which the algae are subjected in this zone vary greatly, sometimes over rather short vertical distances. Because the physiological requirements of marine algae differ, and because many of the algae have fairly narrow limits of tolerance to changes in temperatures, light, and salinity, a marked vertical distribution of genera and species in distinct bands is generally directly related to the tidal characteristics of a particular region. Since there are no true roots, stems, or leaves, and little conduction in most algae, the whole plant must be bathed in water for at least the greater part of the day in most instances. This is the only way in which it can obtain directly through its surfaces inorganic materials and other substances necessary for plant growth.

The vertical distribution of a marine alga may be controlled in part by the amount of light it requires, by wave action, by its ability to withstand freezing or desiccation, or by the amount of oxygen available. Since energy for synthesis of food substances by marine plants comes from the sun, the degree of penetration of sunlight into water (or the transparency of the water) is very important. Both quality and intensity of light change with depth in the water. Since the depth at which an alga grows depends on available light, the distribution of these plants may also vary with latitude. In lower latitudes light can penetrate to a greater depth than in higher latitudes. There may be specific light requirements of intensity, quality, and perhaps even duration. In the Mediterranean, where the water is highly transparent, **benthonic** algae are reported at depths approaching 100 meters; but in the northeastern Pacific, where the waters are rather turbid, significant algal development generally does not extend below 35 meters. These are only a few of the important factors that bring about a marked zonation of brown algae (and other attached groups such as red algae and green algae) along rocky shores.

In response to these vertical differences in the environment, certain species may occur only quite high in the intertidal area and may form narrow bands along the shore. Among these is the common rockweed, *Fucus* (Fig. 11–32), and related genera. Some of these plants may be exposed for hours or even for several consecutive days. The phycocolloids, such as algin, hold water within the plant tissues most effectively, helping such algae resist desiccation from exposure to the sun or to frost. In the middle intertidal region on exposed portions of the Pacific Coast, *Postelsia* forms a marked zone. Other species and genera, such as

FIGURE 11–32   Plant of *Fucus* showing wartlike appearance of conceptacles on swollen receptacles, ×0.3.

Pterygophora (Fig. 11–24), are only rarely exposed. Still others (some species of *Desmarestia,* Fig. 11–12) occur only in the subtidal region and are never exposed to the air.

There are also marked distributional patterns of marine algae related to the physical-chemical changes that occur horizontally as well as vertically. Certain marine algae are characteristic of water of high salinity; others may extend into brackish zones. On the whole, there is a marked progressive depletion of genera and species in the brown algal flora as one proceeds from the cold Arctic and Antarctic regions to the warmer waters of the tropics. Brown algae, in general, grow abundantly in the conditions suitable for most photosynthetic plants: optimum light, temperature, and a constant supply of inorganic nutrients and growth substances. These photosynthetic plants are found in the cold shallow waters of the continental shelf where drainage from the land, turbulence, and upwelling of deeper, nutrient-rich water provide the necessary constituents.

IMPORTANCE AND USES

The indirect importance to man of the brown algae in coastal regions is again related to their potential as primary producers. The plankton algae—such as the diatoms, dinoflagellates, and others—are the most important producers in the sea. A much greater area of

B

FIGURE 11–33   *Durvillea* in South Australia. A, photograph of bed at low tide, ×0.2; B, a single plant, ×0.1. (Photographs courtesy H. B. S. Womersley.)

the globe and volume of water is available for the support of these free-floating or free-swimming plants than for the benthonic algae. The benthonic, or attached marine algae (the seaweeds), cover a small area, primarily because of the relatively limited area of continental shelf or water shallow enough to allow sufficient light for plant growth to penetrate. Less than a tenth of the oceans, including adjacent seas, have a depth shallower than about 225 meters, and algae seldom grow to this depth. However, in coastal areas seaweeds such as kelps are important contributors to the economy of the sea. Their large plant bodies provide a substrate for small, sessile animals; among root-like branches, the holdfasts may house many diverse small animals. Dense subtidal forests may provide protection and spawning areas for larger, free-swimming animals, including fish. Some marine animals browse directly on the plant tissues of larger seaweeds and others indirectly make use of these large algae by feeding upon **detritus** originating from decaying plant tissues. Specimens of *Nereocystis* individually reach a length of over 35 meters and may weigh over 125 kilograms (fresh weight). Such plants provide an abundant source of detritus in coastal regions for filter-feeding animals. The larger algae also contribute signifi-

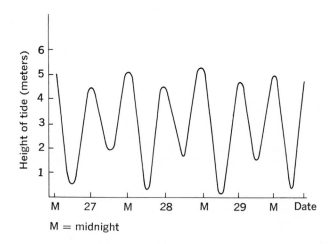

FIGURE 11–34   Typical tidal features over period of several days (June 27–29) at north end of Vancouver Island, British Columbia.

cantly to the phytoplankton at certain stages in their life history through their motile stages (zoospores and gametes). In dense beds of *Nereocystis,* through an average depth of about 20 meters, an estimated 3,000,000 zoospore cells (about 5 microns in diameter) may be produced per liter per day from June to September. The total primary production in such an area also includes the reproductive cells liberated by other smaller kelps and other algae growing around the holdfasts of the *Nereocystis* plants.

The larger brown algae are also directly important to man. Species of Laminariales have been used as food (called **kombu**) in the Orient since 1730. The algae are treated in a special way, dried, and pressed into blocks. For cooking, the blocks are cut into thin slices with a sharp knife and used in a variety of ways: soaked in fresh water, boiled, and served as a vegetable; cooked with meats, or powdered and used in soups or with rice and sauces; steeped as a drink or coated with sugar and eaten as a confection. Most kombu comes from Japan; although much of it is consumed by the Japanese, a large amount is exported to China and elsewhere.

Algin, or alginic acid, produced exclusively from seaweeds, occurs in the plant chiefly as a cell-wall constituent. Algin is a salt of a polyuronic acid (mannuronic acid). The

soluble salts (sodium, ammonium, potassium) of this polymer are referred to as algin. Valuable algin industries have developed in Britain and California, and to a limited extent in the Canadian Maritime Provinces and Australia. The greatest production of algin is from *Macrocystis* (Fig. 11–18) in California. Dense stands are harvested by mowers on floating barges. These mechanical harvesters can collect several hundred tons of seaweed a day by cutting through the beds at a depth of about 1 meter.

Although alginic acid as such is limited in use, its salts—the alginates—both in soluble and insoluble form, have a great variety of uses. Alginic acid can absorb ten to 20 times its own weight of water, but when dried it becomes so hard that it can be turned on a lathe. It produces viscous or gummy sols with water. Being a weak acid, it forms a wide variety of alginates having interesting properties, as well as complex compounds of the plastic type. For example, ammonium alginate is used in fireproofing fabrics; calcium alginate in plastics and as a laundry starch substitute; and sodium alginate as a stabilizer in ice cream and other dairy products.

There are many other uses of alginates and their derivatives in industrial processes. They are used as a binder in printer's ink; in soaps and shampoos; in molding material for artificial limbs; and in the manufacture of but-

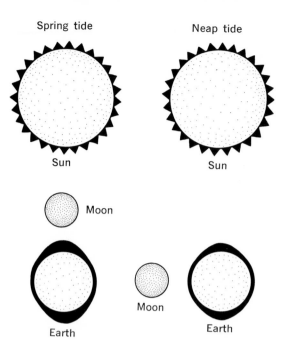

FIGURE 11–35 Positions of sun, moon, and earth at spring tide and neap tide, and showing relative effect on tidal height by black band around earth.

tons. They are used in photography for film coatings; in paints and varnishes; in dental impression materials; in leather finishes; in insecticides. Pharmaceutical preparations such as toothpaste, shaving cream, lipsticks, medicines, and tablets are manufactured from alginates. As mentioned previously, they are widely used in the food industry as stabilizers; they are also used as a clarifier in the manufacture of beer.

Brown algae have been used at times for fertilizer, although cheaper sources of supply are now available. A considerable part of the value of seaweed as fertilizer lies in the provision of trace nutrients and organic growth substances. Marine algae accumulate certain substances, such as potassium salts, in significantly higher concentrations than these substances are present in sea water. Because of the great number of elements present in sea water, which are found also in the algae, deficiency diseases in land plants can often be remedied with seaweed fertilizer. The total amount of fertilizing constituents in fresh seaweed is said to be comparable to the amount present in barnyard

manure, although seaweed contains more potassium salts, less phosphorous, and about the same proportion of nitrogen. For this reason it is particularly good for crops such as beets and potatoes. Iodine was reclaimed from seaweeds on a large scale in the last century until cheaper sources of supply were discovered. This industry too has largely disappeared, although it still exists to a small extent in Japan.

PHYLOGENY

No fossils can be referred to the brown algae with any degree of certainty from periods earlier than the Triassic, although fossils more or less resembling *Fucus* apparently occur in the early Paleozoic Period. Some phylogeneticists have suggested a possible origin for brown algae in the Proterozoic or late Archeozoic Periods. In general, there is little paleobotanical evidence of a geological history for the group. The brown algae are obviously not closely related to any other group of living algae. Most likely they are derived from some laterally biflagellate ancestral stock comparable to the characteristic motile cells of brown algae. The fact that there are no modern, free-living forms of unicellular flagellates referred to the Phaeophyta does not necessarily mean that they do not exist in the sea. Our knowledge of the marine nannoplankton is still too fragmentary to preclude the possibility of finding a prototype for the brown algae among living flagellates. Because of the similarity in flagellation to some of the Chrysophyceae, a common ancestry has been suggested for the brown algae and the Chrysophyceae. This suggestion is further supported by the presence of chlorophyll *c* and fucoxanthin in the Chrysophyceae and Bacillariophyceae (see Chapter 10). A more distant relationship of brown algae to the Pyrrophyta (see Chapter 9) has also been suggested because of the presence of chlorophyll *c* in the majority of the Dinophyceae. If these three divisions had a common origin, it is likely that the brown algae have had some prechrysophyte ancestor (see Fig. 7–4).

The most primitive order of brown algae is

thought to be the Ectocarpales. From this assemblage or an *Ectocarpus*-like ancestry, all other orders of brown algae, with the possible exception of the Fucales, may have evolved (Fig. 11–7). The strikingly different shape and flagellation of the sperm suggests a different origin for the order Fucales; but the biochemical characteristics, including pigment complex, support a common origin for the Fucales within the same division, possibly at some early stage in evolution. Some believe that the Fucales do not belong properly in the Phaeophyta. A more realistic proposal might be to place the Fucales in a separate class in the division Phaeophyta and, as already suggested, refer all other orders to the Phaeophyceae.

REFERENCES

Fritsch, F. E., *The Structure and Reproduction of the Algae*. Vol. 2. Cambridge: Cambridge University Press (1945). Pp. 17–396.

Papenfuss, G. F., "Phaeophyta." In Smith, G. M. (Ed.), *Manual of Phycology*. Waltham, Mass.: Chronica Botanica (1951). Pp. 117–158.

Scagel, R. F., "The Role of Plants in Relation to Animals in the Marine Environment." In the *Twentieth Annual Biology Colloquium: Marine Biology*. Corvalis: Oregon State College (1959). Pp. 9–29.

Setchell, W. A., and Gardner, N. L, "The Marine Algae of the Pacific Coast of North America, III: Melanophyceae." *Univ. Calif. Publ. Bot.*, 8: 383–898 (1925).

Smith, G. M., *Marine Algae of the Monterey Peninsula, California*. Palo Alto, Calif.: Stanford University Press (1944). Pp. 77–157.

Smith, G. M., *Cryptogamic Botany*, 2nd Ed. Vol. 1: *Algae and Fungi*. New York: McGraw-Hill Book Co., Inc. (1955). Pp. 217–274.

Taylor, W. R., *Marine Algae of the Northeastern Coast of North America*, 2nd Ed. Ann Arbor: University of Michigan Press (1957).

12 / DIVISION

RHODOPHYTA

The division Rhodophyta (*red algae*) is an extremely large and diverse group of algae with over 400 genera and nearly 4,000 species. This group is generally considered as one class, the Rhodophyceae, with two subclasses, the Bangiophycidae and the Florideophycidae. Each of these subclasses has several orders. Some of the orders of the latter are poorly known, and will undoubtedly be further subdivided when the genera now included are more completely studied.

No flagellated cells occur in the red algae. Although the vegetative plant is relatively simple, most of these algae have a complex reproductive system. This is especially true of the female reproductive system, post-fertilization processes, and embryogeny. The characteristics associated with the female reproductive system provide the primary basis for distinguishing orders in the Florideophycidae. The red algae as a whole are distinguished by having oogamous sexual reproduction. A nonmotile female gamete, retained on the haploid gametophyte, is fertilized *in situ* by a nonmotile male gamete carried by water currents. Various types of spores are also produced, some as a result of mitosis and others as a result of meiosis. The species may produce male and female reproductive structures on the same thallus; or the structures may be on separate thalli with male and female plants vegetatively indistinguishable. Most of the genera have an alternation of free-living generations and, in addition, there is generally a morphologically

231

and cytologically distinct diploid generation, which may be essentially parasitic, remaining attached to the haploid female gametophyte.

The complexities of the reproductive system and variety of life histories have resulted in a specialized terminology. The antheridium is referred to as a **spermatangium;** and the non-motile male gametes are called **spermatia.** The oogonium, called a **carpogonium,** usually has an elongate, emergent, thread-like receptive portion called the **trichogyne.** The carpogonium may be borne at the end of a special filament, the carpogonial branch.

The male nucleus from the spermatium enters the trichogyne and passes down into the enlarged base of the carpogonium, where it fuses with the female nucleus, effecting fertilization. The cytoplasm in the carpogonium does not become a discrete female gamete, nor does the cytoplasm of the fertilized carpogonium form a discrete zygote. Subsequent events involve the zygote nucleus in a variety of phenomena.

Division in the zygote nucleus results directly or indirectly in the production of **carposporangia,** which produce **carpospores.** If the division is meiotic, the carpospores are haploid, and if the division is mitotic, they are diploid. The carposporangia may occur on filaments called **gonimoblast filaments** and produce haploid or diploid carpospores. The gonimoblast filaments, including the carposporangia, make up the **carposporophyte,** which is also referred to as a **gonimoblast.**

In the simpler members of the Florideophycidae the gonimoblast filaments arise directly from the fertilized carpogonium, or from a cell very near it, into which the diploid nucleus has been transferred. In the more specialized members, the diploid nucleus is generally transferred by a connecting filament to one or more specialized cells called **auxiliary cells,** which are often remote from the carpogonium. From the auxiliary cell the gonimoblast filaments then emanate.

The carpospores that arise from haploid carposporangia generally give rise directly to gametophyte generations. The carpospores that arise from diploid carposporangia generally give rise directly to a free-living sporophyte generation—the **tetrasporophyte.** The tetrasporophyte is generally morphologically similar to the free-living gametophytes in the life cycle, and it is in this diploid phase that meiosis occurs. The meiosporangium of the Florideophycidae is referred to as a **tetrasporangium,** and each produces four **tetraspores.** The tetraspores then germinate into free-living gametophytes.

CELL STRUCTURE

The red algal cell wall is typically differentiated into an inner cellulose and an outer pectic layer. A number of complex colloidal substances, such as **agar** and **carrageenin,** may also occur in the cell wall and intercellular spaces of many of the more specialized red algae. These complex compounds are actually mixtures of sulfated polysaccharides. In certain genera, such as the coralline algae, there is a heavy calcification of the outer part of the cell wall, which is composed chiefly of calcium carbonate but may also contain magnesium carbonate. In some coralline genera the whole thallus is encrusted with lime (**encrusting** forms, such as *Lithothamnium*). In other genera, certain regions of the plant remain uncalcified (articulate forms, Fig. 12–1).

The cells in simple forms are usually uninucleate. In the more advanced forms they are generally multinucleate, except for young or reproductive cells. In some instances the large cells of red algae may contain hundreds of nuclei; these nuclei have a well-defined nuclear membrane and a nucleolus. Central (**axile**) or peripheral (**parietal**) chloroplasts are also present. In some simple forms, there may be only one chloroplast, with or without pyrenoid-like structures. Generally the more complex forms have numerous small discoid chloroplasts in each cell, although irregular or band-like ones also occur. In electron micrographs the chloroplast appears similar to that of other algae, having a narrow double membrane, small dense granules, and larger lipid-like granules. However, the Rhodophyceae examined show only

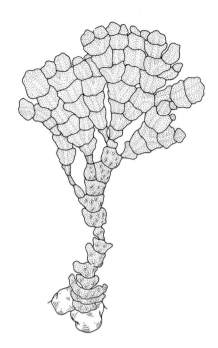

FIGURE 12–1   *Bossiella,* an articulated coralline member of Florideophycidae, ×1.

single, unstacked pairs of lamellae (Fig. 12–2). This may be a primitive feature linking the Cyanophyceae and Rhodophyceae, since the former has lamellae primarily in the chromoplasm part of the cell (see Fig. 8–2, 3A, B).

The red algae owe their characteristic color to the presence of accessory phycobilin pigments. These are generally *r*-phycoerythrin, which is red; and *r*-phycocyanin, which is blue. Some reds contain *b*-phycoerythrin, allophycocyanin, and *c*-phycocyanin. The phycobilins are very similar, but not chemically identical to the phycobilins of Cyanophyceae or Cryptophyceae. Accessory carotenoid pigments are also present. These include two carotenes, α-carotene and β-carotene; and the xanthophylls lutein, zeaxanthin, and possibly taraxanthin. The green pigments include the universal chlorophyll *a* and possibly another reported in only a few red algae—chlorophyll *d,* which may be only a derivative of chlorophyll *a* and an artifact of the extraction techniques. The green pigments are generally masked by the accessory pigments. However, depending on the environmental conditions, the red algae exhibit a va-

riety of shades from green, through red-brown, bright red, blue, purple-red, and even black. These shades depend on the relative amounts of the pigments present.

The food reserves are stored as a polysaccharide, generally referred to as **floridean starch.** This starch is essentially identical to the branched, or amylopectin, fraction of starches that occur in green algae and other plants, but a slightly different staining reaction with iodine–potassium-iodide solution is obtained when testing for presence of floridean starch. Possibly other polysaccharide reserves may be present. On the basis of X-ray diffraction techniques, the starch in certain species of red algae apparently cannot be distinguished from potato starch. Other reserve substances of low molecular weight include the saccharides trehalose, floridoside, mannoglyceric acid, and sucrose. Certain polyhydroxy alcohols are abundant in some forms. Fats stored include cholesterol, sitosterol, and fucosterol. There may be some relation between environment and sterol content.

Most red algae are autotrophic. A number occur as epiphytes or endophytes; some of these may be very pale in color, or completely white, and it is presumed that they are in part, if not wholly, dependent on the host for their nutrition.

Because the two subclasses of Rhodophyta are so different in morphology, reproduction, and alternation of generations, they will be considered separately.

SUBCLASS BANGIOPHYCIDAE

CLASSIFICATION AND MORPHOLOGICAL DIVERSITY

The Bangiophycidae is a small subclass with 70 or more species in some 20 genera. They are the simplest of all red algae, both vegetatively and reproductively. Most of them are marine and occur on rocks or as epiphytes.

The simplest type of thallus is unicellular (Fig. 12–3A). A number of the genera are filamentous. These may be erect, uniseriate un-

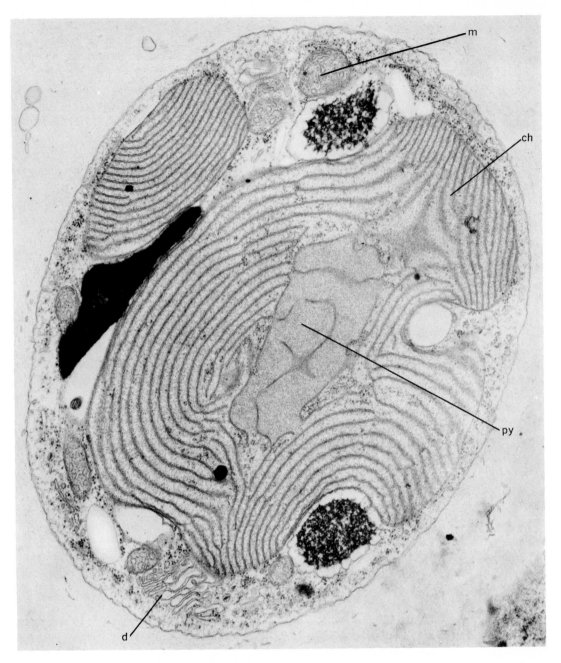

FIGURE 12–2A   Ultrastructure of whole cell of *Porphyridium*, ×25,000. *ch*, chloroplast; *d*, dictyosome; *m*, mitochondrion; *py,* pyrenoid. (Photograph courtesy A. D. Greenwood.)

branched (Fig. 12–3B, C), branched (Fig. 12–3D), or prostrate and monostromatic (Fig. 12–3H). In others there may be a few regular divisions in the erect simple branches, indicative of parenchyma (Fig. 12–3F). The most advanced growth attained in the group is the foliose type (Fig. 12–4A, D). The cells divide in two planes to form a monostromatic plant body (Fig. 12–4A–C), or in three planes to form a **distromatic** thallus (Fig. 12–4D, E). The lines along which these various types may have evolved are diagrammatically illustrated in Fig. 12–5.

The thallus may be attached by a simple

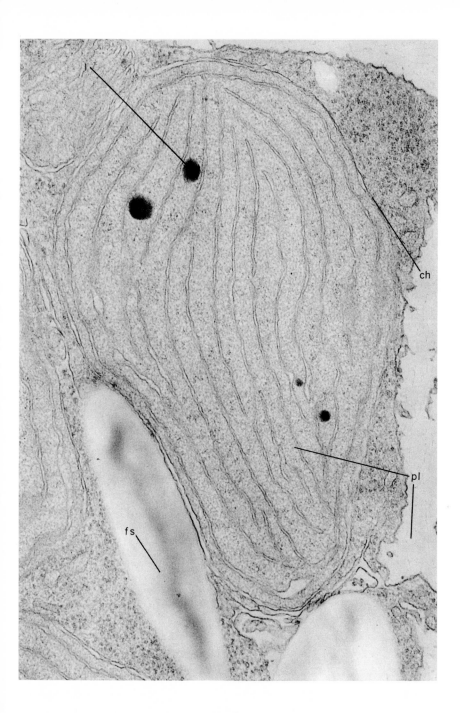

FIGURE 12–2B   Ultrastructure of chloroplast of cortical cell in *Ceramium*,
×53,000. Note that simple internal lamellae (*pl*), consisting of single membrane
pair, are not elaborately layered as is typical of other algal chloroplasts (see Fig.
10–2D, 11–4C, 15–2A, C); also compare this chloroplast ultrastructure with
photosynthetic lamellae in Cyanophyta (Fig. 8–2, 3A, B). The large translucent
areas are floridean starch granules (*fs*) outside the chloroplast (*ch*). *l*, lipoid
globule. (Photograph courtesy A. D. Greenwood.)

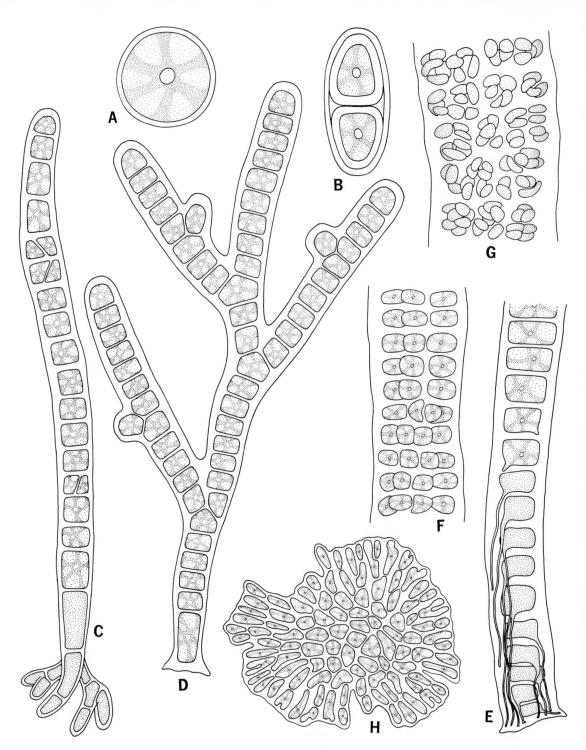

FIGURE 12–3   Morphological diversity in Bangiophycidae. A, B, unicellular forms (A, *Porphyrid-ium*, ×2,500; B, *Chroothece,* after division, ×1,200); C, D, unbranched and branched filamentous forms (C, *Erythrotrichia,* ×825; D, *Goniotrichum,* ×800); E–H, parenchymatous types (E–G, *Bangia;* E, basal region of thallus with rhizoidal cells, ×500; F, distal vegetative portion of parenchymatous region of thallus, ×500; G, fertile portion of thallus, ×500; H, *Erythrocladia,* viewed from above, ×1,000).

236 / *NONVASCULAR PLANTS*

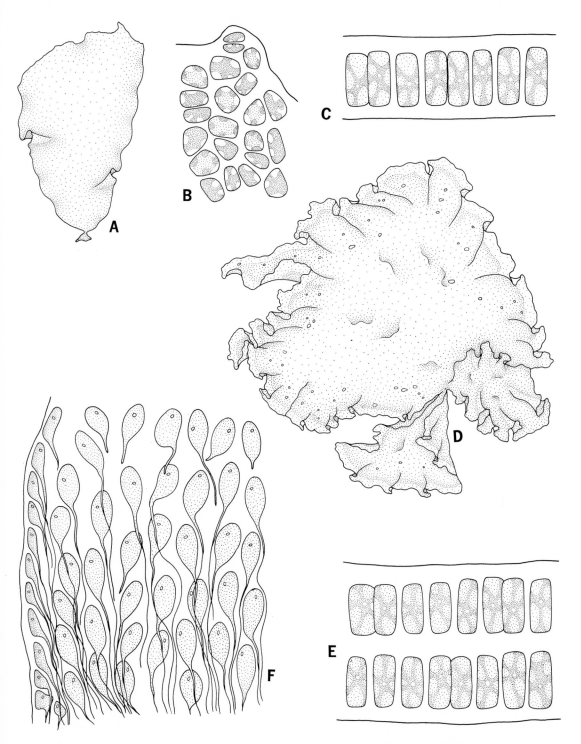

FIGURE 12–4   Morphological diversity in parenchymatous Bangiophycidae (*Porphyra*). A–C, monostromatic species. A, habit, ×1.5; B, surface view of cells, ×500; C, transverse section through portion of thallus, ×500. D, E, distromatic species. D, habit, ×0.5; E, transverse section through portion of thallus, ×500. F, portion of basal attachment region of thallus as seen in longitudinal section showing rhizoidal cells, ×500.

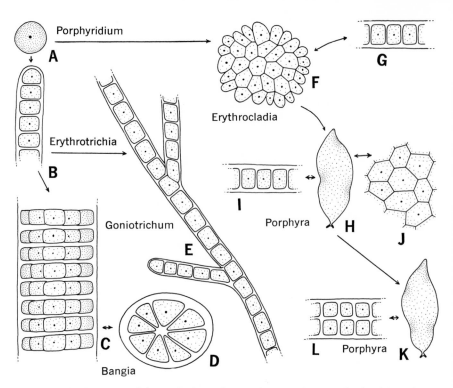

FIGURE 12–5   Possible evolution of growth types in Bangiophycidae, from unicellular (A) to filamentous (B, E) or to parenchymatous (C, D, F–K) types.

holdfast cell (Fig. 12–3D), by a few basal rhizoidal multicellular filaments (Fig. 12–3C), or by rhizoidal filaments sent out by a number of cells at the base of the thallus (Fig. 12–3E). These filaments anchor the thallus to the substrate. There may be a very extensive production of nonseptate, rhizoidal processes aggregated to form a massive holdfast structure (Fig. 12–4F).

LIFE HISTORIES AND REPRODUCTION

Vegetative reproduction by fragmentation is common. Various spore types are also formed. A single spore, produced by simple metamorphosis of a vegetative cell, is called a **monospore** and the cell a **monosporangium.**

Sexual reproduction is unknown in the simpler forms, although it is well established in certain other genera. The species generally produce separate male and female plants that are vegetatively indistinguishable.

Each spermatangium in the Bangiophycidae divides mitotically, producing a number of spermatia. Each carposporangium also divides mitotically and gives rise to a number of carpospores in members of the Bangiophycidae. The production of many spermatia and carpospores per cell distinguishes this subclass from the Florideophycidae.

The reproductive structures in the Bangiophycidae are relatively simple and are well illustrated by species of the genus *Porphyra* (Fig. 12–6D, G). The carpogonium and spermatangium are merely metamorphosed vegetative cells. Each cell of the thallus (except for the rhizoidal holdfast cells) is capable of becoming a gametangium; however, some generally remain vegetative. In the spermatangium, by mitotic divisions, a large number (16, 32, 64, 128, depending on the species) of almost colorless spermatia are formed (Fig. 12–6D). Plants producing spermatia appear whitish along the margins, where the thallus first becomes fertile. The female gametangium—the

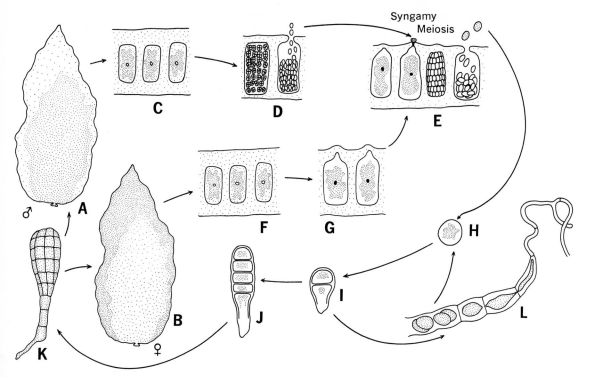

FIGURE 12–6 Life history of *Porphyra* (monostromatic species). A, male gametophyte with fertile margin; B, female gametophyte with fertile margin; C, F, vegetative gametophyte cells; D, formation and liberation of spermatia from spermatangium; G, carpogonium development; E, fertilization (left) and formation of carpospores (right) from zygote on female gametophyte; H–K, germination of carpospore to form gametophyte; L, filamentous *Conchocelis*-phase developed from germinated carpospore (monospores being produced). (For details and relative sizes of structures, refer to Fig. 12–4.)

carpogonium—undergoes a slight modification to form a rudimentary trichogyne that is little more than a receptive portion of the cell (Fig. 12–6G); the carpogonium is uninucleate. If a spermatium contacts the trichogyne, and its nucleus passes into the cytoplasm of the carpogonium, fusing with the female nucleus (Fig. 12–6E). Immediately after fusion, it is believed that the zygote nucleus undergoes meiosis, followed sometimes by a number of mitotic divisions. The cytoplasm then cleaves to form a number of uninucleate haploid carpospores (Fig. 12–6E). The number produced varies in different species (4, 8, 16, 32, or 64). Most of the carpogonia are apparently fertilized and give rise to carposporangia.

The carpospores may germinate and grow directly into new foliose multicellular gametophytes (Fig. 12–6H–K, A,B). However, a number of alternatives are evidently possible.

These appear related to the environmental conditions at the time of carpospore production and may not be true for all species. Under optimum conditions, the carpospores may grow directly into the mature foliose plant. However, when conditions are not optimum, several different patterns of development occur. The carpospores may germinate and begin to grow into a foliose phase; but instead of continuing to maturity, the foliose thallus becomes arrested as a diminutive but multicellular stage. Each cell in this plant, except for the rhizoidal ones, may round up and liberate a monospore, which behaves exactly the same as a carpospore. Under other conditions, a second type of development can occur. The carpospore may germinate, developing into a branched filamentous stage, which at maturity produces somewhat swollen cells. These function as monosporangia, each producing a single monospore that is also potentially similar to a carpospore in function. This filamentous stage forms reddish patches on shells of dead molluscs, and some of the filaments actually penetrate the shell (Fig. 12–6L).

As far as is known, the alternate phases are not cytologically different; meiosis is believed always to occur immediately following syngamy. The developmental pattern of the carpospore is apparently plastic enough to permit (to a limited extent) vegetative reproduction under less than optimum conditions. The filamentous stages of *Porphyra* were known for a long time as a separate genus, *Conchocelis,* before their affinities were recognized. Essentially the same characteristics of reproduction and life history have also been shown to occur in *Bangia.*

SUBCLASS FLORIDE-OPHYCIDAE

CLASSIFICATION AND MORPHOLOGICAL DIVERSITY

The Florideophycidae is a large subclass with over 3,500 species in about 375 genera. Most are marine, but a few genera with about 200 species occur in fresh-water habitats. They grow on rocks or other usually solid substrata. The Florideophycidae are also vegetatively simple, although somewhat more complex than the Bangiophycidae.

The Florideophycidae have primary pit connections between adjacent cells, in contrast to the Bangiophycidae where primary pit connections are uncommon. Primary pit connections result from an incomplete wall formation between two daughter cells (Fig. 12–7A–C). In more complex thalli secondary pit connections may occur between adjacent cells in the same filament and between cells in adjacent filaments (Fig. 12–7D–H), or in parasitic genera between the cells of the parasite and the host (Fig. 12–8). The formation of secondary pit connections is complex. When a nucleus in a cell (uninucleate or multinucleate) divides, one of the daughter nuclei migrates to the periphery of the cell, and a protuberance in the cell wall is

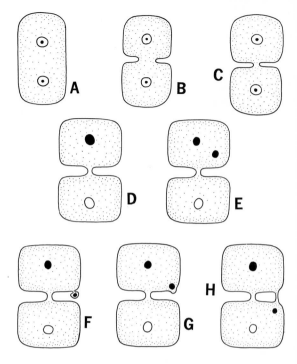

FIGURE 12–7   Formation of pit connections in Florideophycidae. A–C, formation of primary pit connection; D–H, formation of secondary pit connection.

formed, with the daughter nucleus migrating into it. As this protuberance elongates, it establishes a connection with a second cell and the daughter nucleus passes into it. This connection, known as a secondary pit connection, is a permanent one. The function of the pit connection has not been clearly established. Possibly it provides a means for transferring food from one cell to another. Although primary and secondary pit connections differ in method of formation, they are essentially similar in mature morphological characteristics. However, the precise nature of the connection seems to vary from species to species. In some instances there seems to be a direct cytoplasmic connection, whereas in others it is less distinct. Electron micrographs have shown that some pit connections between cells are protoplasmic ducts with thickenings in the end walls. Other pit connections are an aggregation of fine protoplasmic strands that traverse the loose, continuous microfibrils of the cell wall. Either type may occur in primary or secondary pit connections.

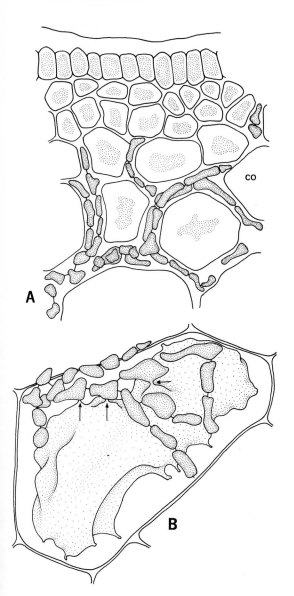

FIGURE 12–8   Parasitic Florideophycidae. A, cortical tissue (*co*) of *Odonthalia*, showing intercellular filaments of parasite *Harveyella mirabilis*, ×250; B, medullary cell of *Odonthalia*, showing intracellular filaments of *Harveyella* (arrow indicates pit connections between host and parasite cells), ×350.

There are no unicellular members in this subclass. The simplest are uniseriate, branched forms (Fig. 12–9A, B). The more complex forms are basically filamentous, but the branches are laterally fused to varying degrees so that a pseudoparenchymatous thallus results (Fig. 12–10A–D). There is little tissue differen-

tiation, although the aggregation of filaments often results in a compact, small-celled cortex and a medulla that may be loose and filamentous (Fig. 12–10A–D, 11A–E), or large-celled (Fig. 12–12A, B). Growth of each filamentous branch is by means of a simple apical cell. In rare instances (subfamily Nitophylleae) intercalary cell divisions occur, resulting in a type of marginal growth.

The pseudoparenchymatous and loosely branched forms may have either **uniaxial** or **multiaxial** type of growth. In the former the main axis consists of a single row of large cells (Fig. 12–9D). In multiaxial types the main axis is composed of a number of parallel or almost parallel filaments (Fig. 12–10B, 11B). The lines along which the uniaxial and multiaxial types may have evolved are diagrammatically illustrated in Figure 12–13 and Figure 12–14.

Considering the relatively simple vegetative growth that occurs in the Florideophycidae, the tremendous variety in gross morphology is remarkable. The scope in symmetry and branching habit vie in complexity with that found in the flowering plants. They vary from filamentous microscopic plants to large, profusely branched or foliose plants about 4 meters long.

LIFE HISTORIES AND REPRODUCTION

With some more complex thalli, vegetative reproduction is common and perennial at the base. The erect branches die back to the base and new branches arise later from a basal undifferentiated region. A variety of spores are produced, especially in some of the simpler forms. As in the Bangiophycidae, monospores (Fig. 12–9J) may be formed, or highly differentiated sporangia may divide to produce a number of mitospores, often called **polyspores.** These vegetative spores germinate, reduplicating the thallus that bore them.

Sexual reproduction is well established in the Florideophycidae, with usually an alternation of free-living generations. When a free-living tetrasporophyte occurs, it is usually vegetatively indistinguishable from the haploid

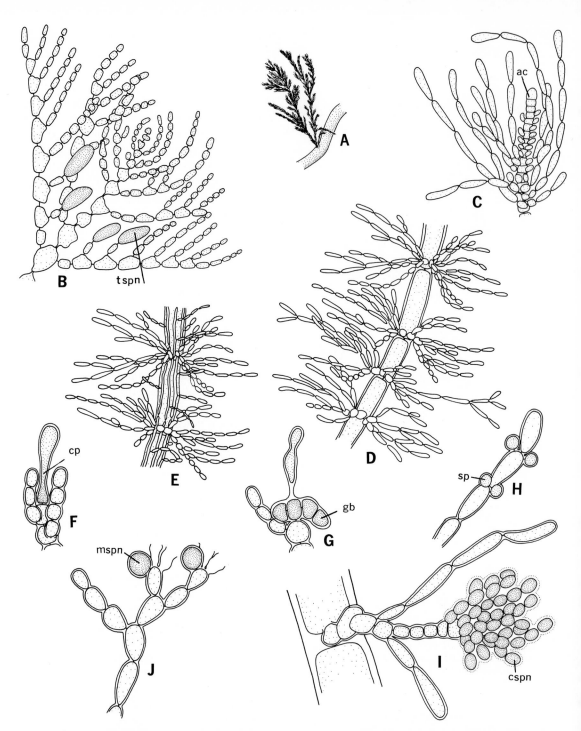

FIGURE 12–9   Morphology and reproduction in uniaxial Florideophycidae. A, B, *Antithamnion*. A, habit epiphytic on kelp stipe, ×0.5; B, terminal portion of thallus, showing uniaxial, loose, filamentous construction, and immature tetrasporangia (*tspn*), ×240. C–I, *Batrachospermum*. C, apical region of thallus, showing apical cell (*ac*) and filamentous branches, ×475; D, portion of main axis, showing uniaxial construction and whorls of filamentous branches, ×165; E, more mature portion, showing development of corticating filaments that cover the axial row of cells, ×165; F, unfertilized carpogonium (*cp*), ×915; G, post-fertilization stage showing initiation of gonimoblast filaments (*gb*), ×915; H, branch bearing several mature spermatangia (*sp*), ×960; I, later stage of gonimoblast development, showing chains of carposporangia (*cspn*), ×790. J, portion of thallus showing mature and empty monosporangia (*mspn*), ×790.

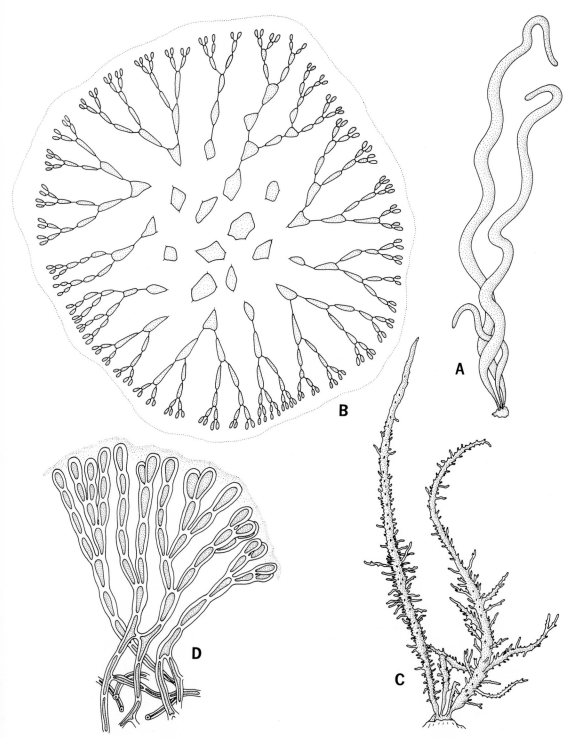

FIGURE 12–10   Morphology of simple multiaxial Florideophycidae. A, B, *Nemalion*. A, habit of cluster of plants, ×0.7; B, transverse section through thallus, showing multiaxial construction and organization of branched filaments embedded in mucilaginous matrix, ×415. C, D, *Cumagloia*. C, habit of a cluster of plants, ×0.5; D, transverse section through portion of thallus, showing multiaxial construction and filamentous organization, ×350.

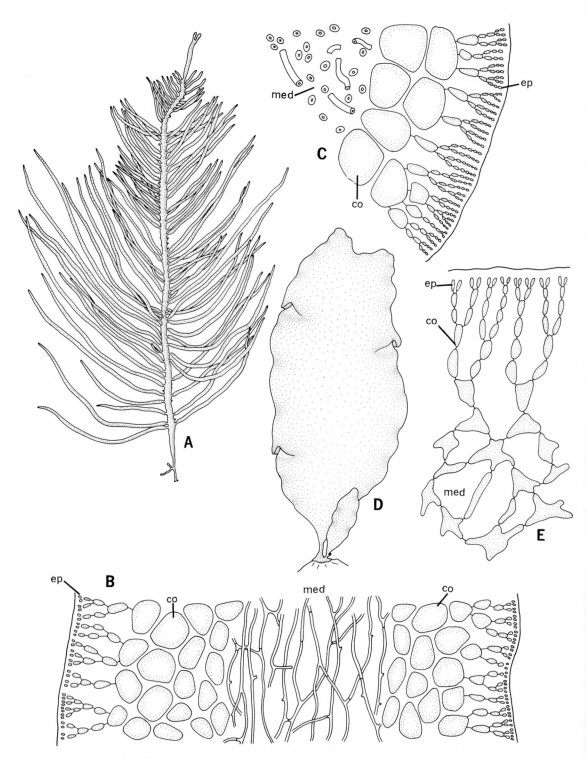

FIGURE 12–11.   Morphological diversity of complex multiaxial Florideophycidae. A–C, *Agardhiella.* A, habit, ×0.5; B, longitudinal section through portion of thallus, showing filamentous medulla (*med*) and pseudoparenchymatous cortex (*co*), ×60; C, transverse section through outer portion of thallus, showing filamentous medulla and pseudoparenchymatous cortex, ×70. D, E, *Rhodoglossum.* D, habit of plant, ×0.5; E, transverse section of outer part of thallus, showing loose filamentous inner, medulla region (*med*), and more compact outer small-celled cortex (*co*), ×700. *ep,* epidermis.

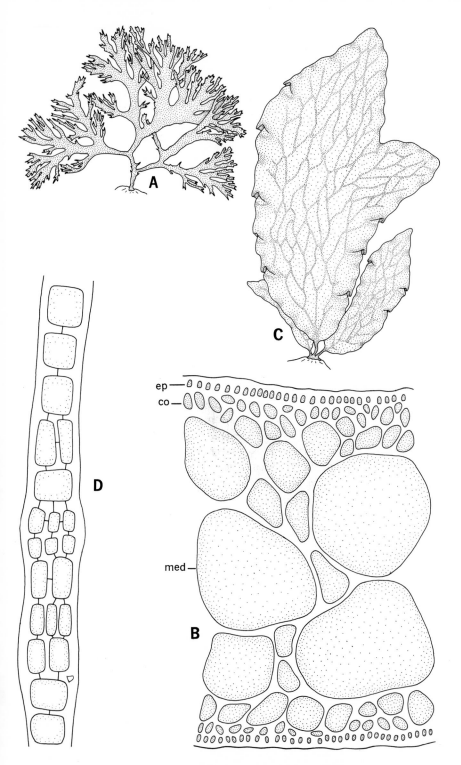

FIGURE 12–12   Morphological diversity in Florideophycidae. A, B, *Callo-phyllis*. A, habit of multiaxial thallus, ×0.5; B, transverse section through portion of thallus, showing pseudoparenchymatous organization with compact large-celled medulla (*med*) and small-celled cortex (*co*) and epidermis (*ep*), ×150. C, D, *Polyneura*. C, habit of membranous, veined thallus, ×0.5; D, transverse section through portion of thallus in vicinity of vein, ×250.

245

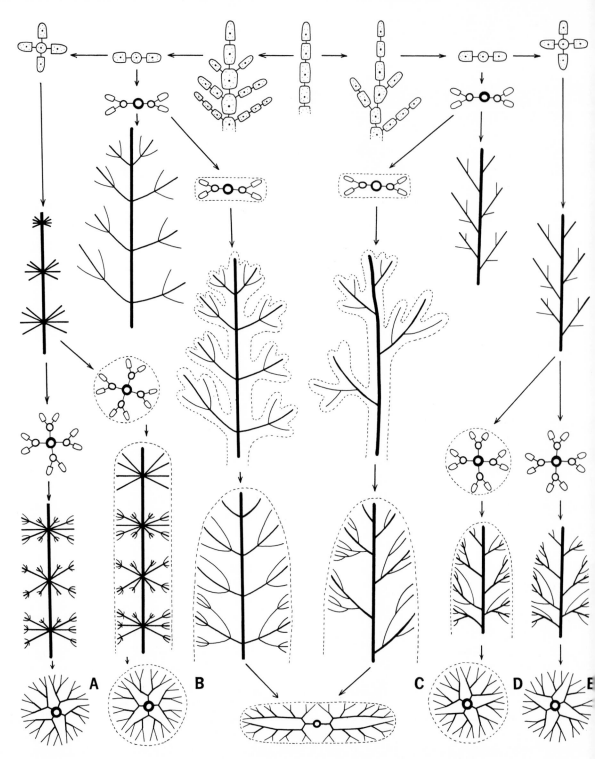

FIGURE 12–13   Growth types in uniaxial Florideophycidae, showing possible evolutionary lines leading to freely branched (A, E) and pseudoparenchymatous (B–D) types with radial (A, B, D, E) and bilateral (C) symmetry.

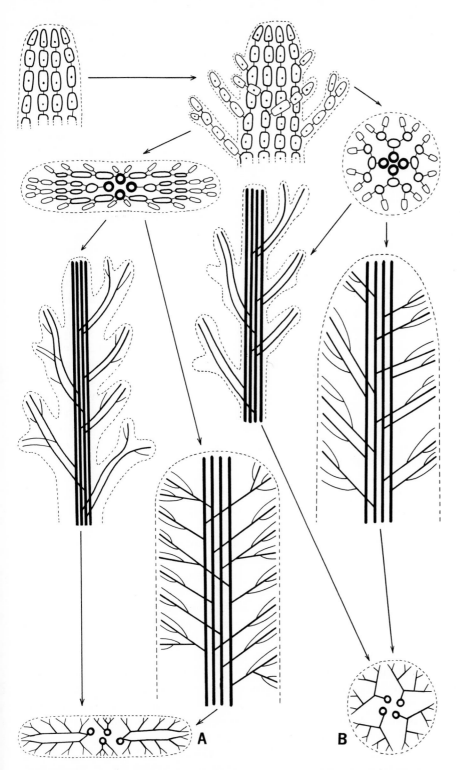

FIGURE 12–14   Growth types of multiaxial Florideophycidae, showing possible evolutionary lines leading to bilaterally (A) and radially (B) symmetrical pseudoparenchymatous forms with varying amounts of fusion of filaments.

gametophytes. Unlike the Bangiophycidae, each spermatangium gives rise to a single spermatium. Similarly, each carposporangium gives rise to only one carpospore in the Florideophycidae.

The female sexual apparatus and fertilization processes are extremely complex and variable in the Florideophycidae. It is impossible to summarize in this respect the characteristic variation that occurs in the subclass. As a result of such complexities, there is a great deal of specialized terminology. The cytological evidence for the alternating phases in red algae is still far short of that desirable to justify any generalizations. **Genotypic sex determination** has been demonstrated in a few of the Florideophycidae; that is, from a single tetrasporangium producing four tetraspores by meiosis, two of the spores produce male gametophytes and two produce female ones. However, there are anomalous situations where male, female, and tetraspore structures have been found on the same thallus. This situation has not yet been cytologically clarified.

In the simpler forms the life history is similar to that of some of the Bangiophycidae. For example, in *Nemalion* (Fig. 12–10A, B, 15) the gametophyte is the conspicuous generation—the only diploid cell being the zygote, and it is never freely liberated. The first division of the zygote nucleus is meiotic. Colorless spermatia are produced superficially in spermatangia borne on the tips of filamentous branches (Fig. 12–9H, 15C, E). The carpogonia, also freely exposed at the tips of filamentous branches, have a well-defined, diminutive trichogyne (Fig. 12–9F, G, 15D, F, G). The spermatium rests on the trichogyne, and the nucleus passes to the enlarged basal part of the carpogonium, where it fuses with the female nucleus (Fig. 12–15F, G). After meiosis of the zygote, daughter nuclei are cut off in cells, which then divide repeatedly, forming chains of cells. These make up the gonimoblast filaments, or carposporophyte, which are thus haploid cells (Fig. 12–9I, 15J, K). The carposporophyte is freely exposed and the terminal cells mature to develop directly into carposporangia, each of which produces a single haploid carpospore (Fig. 12–15L, M). The carpospores germinate and develop into free-living gametophytes. In other members of this simple group, the Nemalionales, the zygote nucleus is transferred to a cell beneath the carpogonium and from this lower cell the gonimoblast filaments emanate.

Also, a few members of this simple group have a more complex life history. For example, in *Bonnemaisonia* the free-living gametophytes are fairly large plants (Fig. 12–16A, B), somewhat more complex vegetatively but with sexual reproduction similar to that of *Nemalion*. However, in *Bonnemaisonia,* meiosis apparently does not occur immediately after syngamy, and the gonimoblast filaments are thus diploid cells. The unexposed diploid carposporophyte that produces diploid carpospores is surrounded by an urn-shaped structure, the **pericarp** (Fig. 12–16D). This is composed of female gametophytic cells that envelop the developing carposporophyte to form a protective filamentous covering. The diploid carpospores grow to produce a free-living, diminutive, filamentous generation, which is so strikingly different that it was known for a long time as a distinct genus, *Trailiella* (Fig. 12–16E). The *Trailiella* phase produces tetrasporangia, and meiosis is believed to occur during tetraspore production. The liberated tetraspore germinates and develops into the typical *Bonnemaisonia* plant.

This type of life history, the most common encountered in the Florideophycidae, has free-living gamete-producing generations (male and female) alternating with a free-living tetraspore-producing generation, and an intermediate diminutive diploid carposporophyte remaining *in situ* on the female gametophyte. However, in most instances the diploid tetrasporophyte is morphologically identical to the haploid gametophytes and is not vegetatively distinct, as in the *Trailiella*-stage of *Bonnemaisonia*. The customary type of life history in most Florideophycidae comes close to an alternation of isomorphic generations (Fig. 12–17), except for the introduction of an additional diploid generation, the carposporophyte. This additional diploid generation evidently occurs as a result of

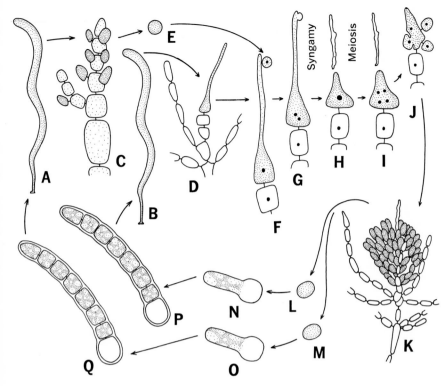

FIGURE 12–15   Life history of *Nemalion*. A, B, gametophytes; C, branch of
male gametophyte with several spermatangia and one released spermatium (E);
D, branch of female gametophyte with carpogonium; F, spermatium adjacent to
trichogyne; G, spermatium nucleus in base of carpogonium; H, syngamy completed; I, after meiosis, trichogyne degenerates; J, initiation of gonimoblast
filaments from fertilized carpogonium; K, mature gonimoblast with numerous
carposporangia; L, M, carpospores; N, O, germinating carpospores; P, Q,
filamentous germlings. (For details and representative sizes of comparable structures refer to Fig. 12–9C–I, 10A, B.)

delay in the time and place of meiosis. In a few
species one or another of these phases appears to
have been lost (or perhaps is not yet known).

The characteristics of the female reproductive system and events following fertilization vary markedly in the advanced Florideophycidae. Only one example (*Polysiphonia*)
will be cited.

In *Polysiphonia* there is an alternation of
free-living, vegetatively similar haploid male
and female gametophytes with a morphologically identical diploid tetrasporophyte. A diminutive diploid carposporophyte, which remains attached to the female gametophyte and
produces diploid carpospores, precedes the initiation of the free-living tetrasporophyte. The
tetraspores (meiospores), produced on the free-

living tetrasporophyte, germinate and develop
into the free-living gametophytes. It is assumed
that genotypic sex determination occurs and
two of the tetraspores from each tetrasporangium give rise to male gametophytes and the
other two give rise to female gametophytes.
The cytological alternation, as outlined above,
accompanies the morphological alternation of
generations.

The mature plant of *Polysiphonia* is a
branched thallus with cells in regular tiers.
Each mature tier, or segment, consists of a
central cell surrounded by a number of **pericentral** cells of equal length. This is often referred to as a **polysiphonous** construction. The
number of pericentral cells in the vegetative
axes is usually constant in any one species,

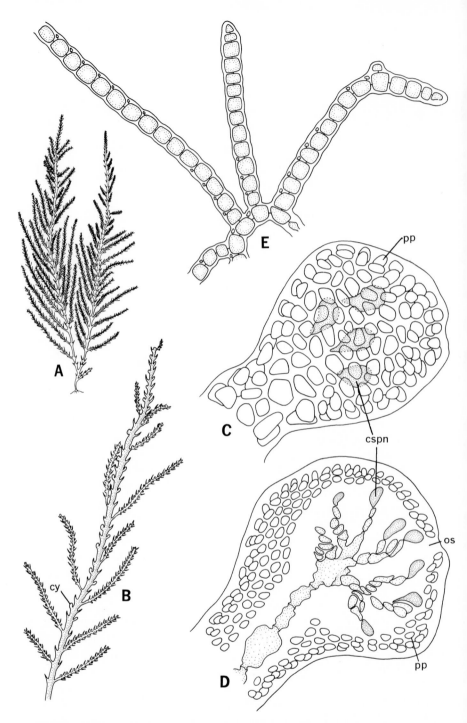

FIGURE 12–16   Morphology of *Bonnemaisonia*. A, habit, ×0.3; B, thallus at higher magnification, showing branching habit and position of fertile regions with cystocarps (*cy*), ×1; C, surface view of cystocarp, showing sterile pericarp wall (*pp*) through which some terminal carposporangia (*cspn*) of gonimoblast are seen, ×300; D, transverse section of cystocarp showing outer sterile pericarp wall, ostiole (*os*), and enclosed gonimoblast, ×250; E, *Trailiella*-stage, ×220.

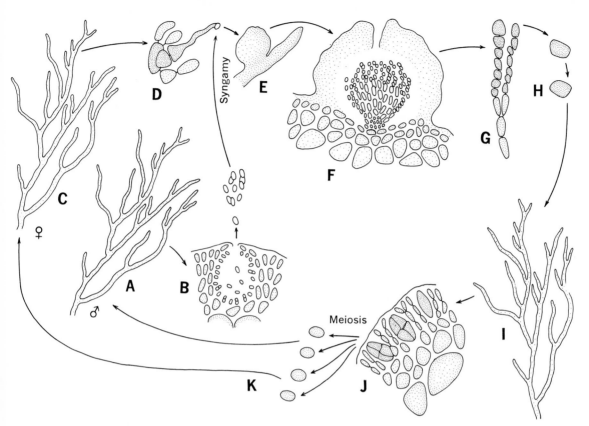

FIGURE 12–17   Life history of *Gracilaria*. A, male gametophyte; B, conceptacle of spermatangia liber-ating spermatia; C, female gametophyte; D, spermatium attached to trichogyne of carpogonium before fertilization; E, immature cystocarp; F, transverse section through mature cystocarp, showing gonimoblast enclosed within ostiolate sterile pericarp wall of gametophytic tissue; G, portion of gonimoblast, showing chains of carposporangia; H, carpospore; I, tetrasporophyte; J, tetrasporangia (meiosporangia) in surface region of mature thallus; K, tetraspores (meiospores).

although it varies in number from species to species, with five a common number. Even where the number of pericentral cells in the vegetative axes is more than five, the reproductive axes revert to the basic five (Fig. 12–18O, 19B).

Growth in *Polysiphonia* is strictly apical, and the apical cell cuts off cells from its posterior face. If the apical cell segment is to produce only a central cell and five pericentral cells, the daughter nuclei in the dividing apical cell line up along the longitudinal axis (Fig. 12–18A–D). The cell wall that follows this nuclear division develops at right angles to the longitudinal axis. The primary cell undergoes division in a regularly alternating sequence within a few segments of the apical cell—that

is, from left to right of the first cell cut off. This results in the typical arrangement of a central cell surrounded by five pericentral cells (Fig. 12–18J–O).

If the apical cell segment is to produce a branch, the daughter nuclei in the dividing apical cell line up diagonally and the cell wall is oblique to the longitudinal axis. From the high side of the resulting wedge-shaped cell, a protuberance rises that initiates the branch (Fig. 12–18H–I). The primary cell thus first forms a branch initial. Subsequently the primary cell divides in the typical fashion, producing a central cell surrounded by five pericentral cells. The branch initials may be indeterminate and repeat the development of the main axis; or they may be determinate and of limited devel-

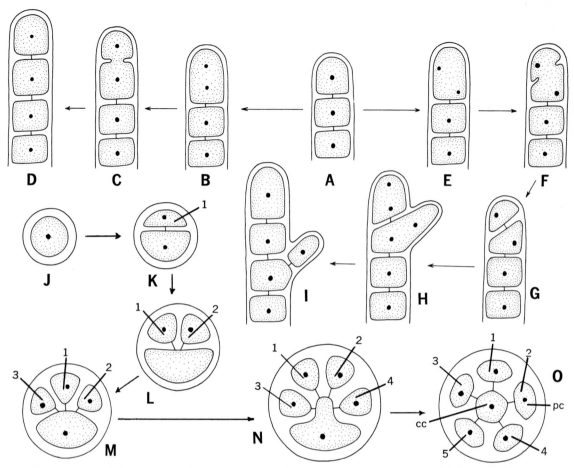

FIGURE 12–18   Apical growth and polysiphonous structure in *Polysiphonia*. A–D, stages in division of apical cell to produce non-branch-forming segments; E–I, stages in division of apical cell (note position of nuclei in apical cell) to produce a branch-forming segment. J–O, divisions in segments (as seen in transverse section) cut off from the apical cell, resulting in polysiphonous structure of axis with central (axial) cell and several (in this example, five) pericentral cells. Sequence in division is indicated by number. *cc,* central cell; *pc,* pericentral cell.

opment, remaining partially or wholly mono-siphonous. These monosiphonous determinate branches are referred to as **trichoblasts** and may be further branched. The trichoblasts may be sterile or fertile. The sexual structures are formed on this determinate type of branch, with quite distinctive female and male trichoblasts (Fig. 12–20C, D, N–Q).

On the female trichoblast, usually only the basal three segments next to the supporting axis become polysiphonous; the distal portion, which may be simple or branched, remains monosiphonous and is generally rather evanescent. It is the first segment above the basal one that becomes fertile, and the last-formed peri-

central cell in the segment that produces the carpogonial branch. Before considering the ontogeny of the female reproductive system, note that there is a vegetative development of some adjacent cells. The last-formed pericentral cells of both the basal segment and the segment above the fertile one cut off series of vegetative cells. Similarly, the pericentral cells on each side of the fertile one also cut off a series of vegetative cells (Fig. 12–20D–G). The filamentous series of cells resulting from these four vegetative pericentral cells fuse laterally to form an urn-shaped pericarp, which encloses the developing female reproductive system (Fig. 12–19E). These filaments do not fuse

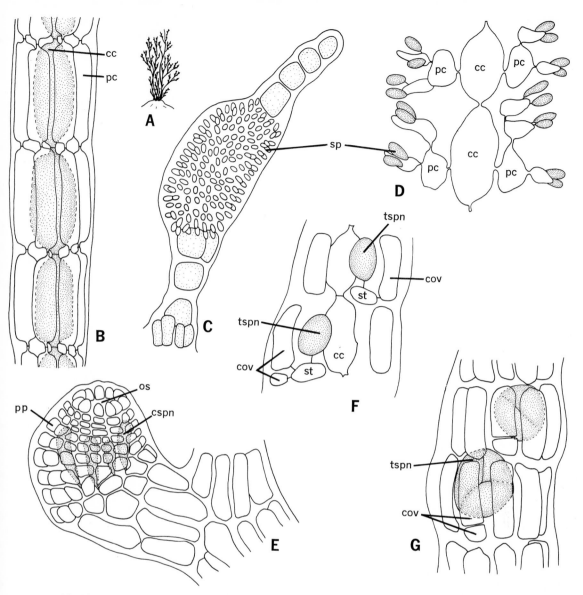

FIGURE 12–19   Structure and reproduction in *Polysiphonia*. A, habit, ×1; B, polysiphonous sterile portion of thallus, showing central series of cells (*cc*) surrounded by pericentral cells (*pc*), ×250; C, mature male branch, or trichoblast, showing dense mass of spermatangia (*sp*), ×200; D, transverse section through two fertile segments of male trichoblast, showing derivation of spermatangia from pericentral cells, and relationship to central cells, ×500; E, cystocarp, showing ostiolate (*os*) and outer sterile pericarp wall (*pp*), through which some of fertile terminal carposporangia (*cspn*) of gonimoblast are shown, ×150; F, longitudinal section through two fertile segments of tetrasporophyte, showing attachment of immature tetrasporangia (*tspn*) with stalk (*st*) and cover cells (*cov*), ×250; G, surface view of fertile portion of thallus, showing mature tetrasporangia as seen through protecting cover cells, ×250.

completely; at the apex a small pore, or ostiole, remains and the trichogyne extends through it into the water. This development of the sterile pericarp precedes fertilization, but it is accelerated after fertilization, keeping pace with the developing carposporophyte within it.

Prior to fertilization, the fertile pericentral cell enclosed within the pericarp undergoes three primary divisions. The first cuts off a cell to one side and results in a lateral sterile cell;

the second cuts off toward the top the carpogonial branch initial; and the third cuts off a basal sterile cell toward the base. The remaining portion of the fertile pericentral cell, which is attached to the central cell of the fertile segment, is referred to as the **supporting cell.** Thus, there are three initials attached to the supporting cell at this stage. The lateral and basal sterile cells each divide a few times to form short filaments of sterile cells. These may later serve as a source of nutriment for the developing carposporophyte, but apparently have no other function. The carpogonial branch initial divides to produce a four-celled carpogonial branch, the terminal cell of which develops into the carpogonium (Fig. 12–20G–H). It has a long narrow trichogyne that emerges through the pericarp ostiole into the water, forming a receptive structure for the spermatium.

The male reproductive system matures about the same time as the female. In contrast to the female trichoblast, the male trichoblast forms a large number of spermatia. The basal segment of the fertile trichoblast generally remains monosiphonous—as does the often-branched distal portion. However, between these two monosiphonous regions several segments divide to form a central cell and five pericentral cells. All five pericentral cells in each of these fertile polysiphonous segments become fertile (Fig. 12–19C, D, 20N–Q).

Each fertile pericentral cell undergoes a number of transverse divisions to produce three or more spermatangial mother cells. In turn, each of these divides obliquely, cutting off two or more spermatangia, which at maturity liberate a single colorless naked spermatium (Fig. 12–19D). Due to the number of divisions resulting in successively smaller cells, the mature male trichoblast appears as a stalked club-shaped structure with a large number of small, almost colorless, refractive cells (the spermatangia) on its surface. The spermatia are carried passively by water currents, coming to rest on the trichogyne (Fig. 12–20H).

When a spermatium comes in contact with the trichogyne, the male nucleus passes down the trichogyne to the base of the carpogonium, where it fuses with the female nucleus. As soon as fertilization occurs, the trichogyne degenerates and a cell is cut off from the top of the supporting cell. This is the auxiliary cell (Fig. 12–20I). A protuberance, very much like that of a secondary pit connection, arises from near the base of the fertilized carpogonium and the diploid zygote nucleus migrates into it, eventually being transferred to the auxiliary cell (Fig. 12–20J). The haploid nucleus of the auxiliary cell apparently degenerates, and the diploid (zygote) nucleus now present divides mitotically. The first true diploid cell of the carposporophyte generation is formed when a diploid daughter nucleus is cut off in the gonimoblast initial (Fig. 12–20K); this initial cell then divides repeatedly by mitosis to produce a multicellular gonimoblast or carposporophyte. The terminal cells of the filamentous gonimoblast become much enlarged and develop into carposporangia. At maturity, each carposporangium liberates a single elongate, densely pigmented, naked carpospore (Fig. 12–19M), which escapes through the ostiole. The carpospore is then carried passively in the water and, on contacting a suitable substrate, germinates and develops into a free-living tetrasporophyte generation morphologically identical to the gametophyte generations.

Reproduction in the free-living tetrasporophyte is somewhat less complicated than that of the gametophytic phase. The tetrasporangia (meiosporangia) are produced in the ordinary vegetative polysiphonous axes of the plant (Fig. 12–19F, G, 20T). However, when the plant becomes fertile a large number of consecutive segments toward the apex of the branches become fertile. Each segment generally produces one tetrasporangium, which arises indirectly from one of the pericentral cells. The fertile pericentral cell undergoes a number of divisions, somewhat comparable to the primary divisions that occur in the development of the female reproductive system. Three cells, two usually larger than the third, are cut off from the outer face of the fertile pericentral cell. Each of these is a sterile cover cell (Fig. 12–19F, G). Then from the upper portion of the fertile pericentral cell, a single cell, the tetra-

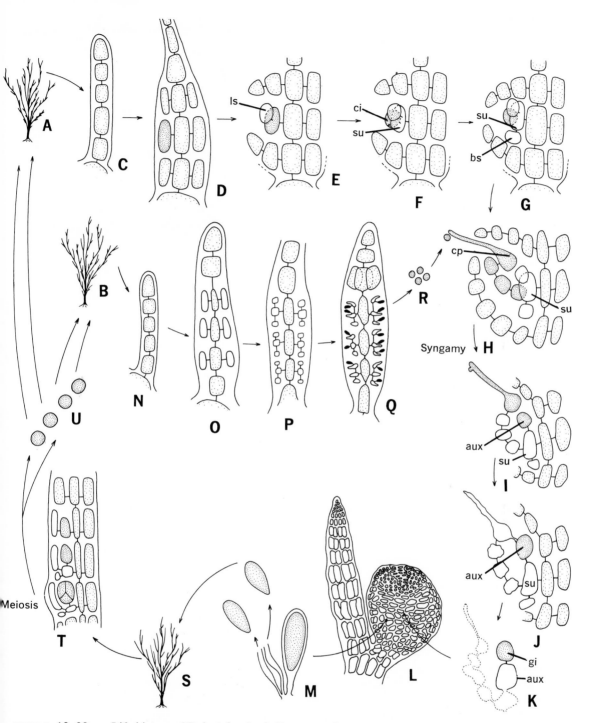

FIGURE 12–20   Life history of *Polysiphonia*. A, B, gametophytes. C–H, stages in development of female trichoblast, showing formation of lateral sterile cell (*ls*), carpogonial branch initial (*ci*), and basal sterile cell (*bs*). The four-celled carpogonial branch with carpogonium (*cp*) in H is fully developed and attached to supporting cell (*su*). N–R, stages in development of male trichoblast, showing formation of spermatangia and release of spermatia. I, fertilization is complete and auxiliary cell (*aux*) is cut off. J, diploidization of auxiliary cell. K, cutting off gonimoblast initial (*gi*). L, cystocarp maturation. M, carposporangia. liberating carpospores. S, tetrasporophyte. T, fertile branch of tetrasporophyte with tetrasporangia forming (lowest tetrasporangium mature). U, tetraspores(meiospores). (For structural details and representative sizes of structures refer to Fig. 12–19A–G.)

sporangium, is cut off and protected by the external cover cells. The small cell, to which the tetrasporangium and the three cover cells remain attached, is the stalk cell and is comparable to the supporting cell of the carpogonial branch. The tetrasporangium enlarges considerably, and its diploid nucleus divides meiotically to form four haploid nuclei. The cytoplasm then divides into four uninucleate portions (Fig. 12–19G). At maturity the wall of the tetrasporangium breaks down, the intercellular material between the cover cells breaks down, and the naked tetraspores (meiospores) are liberated from between the cover cells. These meiospores are carried about passively in the water, and they germinate to develop into the free-living gametophyte generations (Fig. 12–20A, B).

DISTRIBUTION AND ECOLOGY OF RHODOPHYTA

The red algae are predominantly marine and are more widely distributed than the brown algae. Some, such as *Porphyridium,* are terrestrial, forming reddish scums on damp surfaces in greenhouses or around the margins of drying garden pools. Many of the fresh-water species are confined to cold, fast-running streams. They are seldom characteristically red; instead, they are a green, blue, or sometimes brown to black.

The marine Rhodophyceae are most abundant and have attained great diversity in form and color. They are also the most widely distributed geographically and vertically of all the larger algae. Although more species of red algae occur in tropical waters, they are well represented in colder waters, but seldom are as conspicuous as the larger brown algae. Most of the tropical species are relatively small and inconspicuous, whereas some of the cold-water reds attain considerable size. The red algae are generally much more extensive in vertical distribution than the brown algae. Some of them, such as *Porphyra* (Fig. 12–21) and *Gloiopeltis,* occur high in the intertidal region

FIGURE 12–21   At low tide, *Porphyra* on rocks high in intertidal zone in British Columbia, ×0.1.

where they may be exposed sometimes for several consecutive days and dry out until they are brittle, but without adverse effect. Other red algae occur at great depths, especially in the tropics where they have been recorded below 120 meters.

The extreme range in color in marine red algae follows the vertical variations in the habitat with respect to light conditions. The intertidal forms achieve the greatest diversity in color. Depending on the relative proportion of the various pigments present, they range from a dull green, or black high in the intertidal zone to purplish-red, brown, or rosy-red lower in the intertidal zone. Those from greater depths are generally a bright rosy-red with the phycoerythrin masking and exceeding the chlorophyll present. The presence of the accessory phycobilin pigments permits photosynthesis at great depths. Light of shorter wave lengths (blue light) penetrates deepest in water. The phycobilin pigments absorb most of this light. The light energy absorbed by the accessory pigments is transferred to the chlorophyll *a* in a manner not clearly understood, thus permitting photosynthesis to occur.

Although coralline algae of both the encrusting and articulated types (Fig. 12–1) are widespread in cold as well as in warm waters, they are most abundant and conspicuous in the tropics. They are particularly significant in coral reef areas, where the cementing action of the encrusting coralline algae is thought to be primarily responsible for maintenance of reef structure. The corals (animals) would probably be reduced to rubble if it were not for the cementing action of the algae, which binds together the calcium carbonate plant and animal remains.

IMPORTANCE AND USES

In addition to the importance of the coralline algae in reef building, the red algae provide, directly and indirectly, a source of detritus and food for marine animals. The reproductive cells of the red algae, although nonmotile, are liberated in profusion and form a part of the phytoplankton. They are certainly less significant on the whole in this respect in cold-water regions than the brown algae, but can be significant. For example, it has been estimated that a single plant of the foliose *Rhodymenia pertusa,* which can reach a length of a meter or more, may produce about 12,000,000 carpospores; and a single tetrasporophyte of the same species may produce about 100,000,000 tetraspores.

The red algae are also used directly by man and are important for industrial and domestic uses. Man uses a number for food. **Dulse,** prepared in several countries from a species of *Rhodymenia,* is used in many ways. It is eaten like candy, used as a relish with potatoes, or cooked in soups. *Porphyra,* known as purple **laver,** is also used widely as food. The Japanese have artificially cultivated beds of this red alga for many years (Fig. 12–22A, B). It is undoubtedly one of the most valuable maritime industries in Japan, where it is commonly known as **nori** and is prepared as a dry flavored product. It is often used for wrapping pieces of fish or meat rolled in rice as a type of sandwich, known as a **sushi.** It is also used in the preparation of Japanese macaroni and in soups and sauces.

A more valuable use of red algae is based on the presence of certain phycocolloids. There are a number of these substances, the best known of which are **funori,** carrageenin, and agar. Funori, which is obtained from *Gloiopeltis,* is a water-soluble sizing. It is used in the preparation of certain water-base paints, as an adhesive in hair dressings, and as starch in laundering. It has an advantage over starch in retaining a certain degree of flexibility when dry.

Carrageenin is a mucilaginous extract obtained chiefly from *Chondrus crispus* of the North American Atlantic Coast. It was first used by the people of Northern Ireland, who simply wrapped the seaweed in cloth and boiled it in water. The extract obtained was flavored, cooled, and when the mixture was firmly set it was used as a dessert like **blanc mange.** Carrageenin extracted commercially is still used as food in much the same way. It is also used in the food industry as a stabilizing or thickening agent in chocolate milk, cheese, ice cream, and jellied foods; and is used in cosmetics, insect sprays, and water-base paints.

Agar is probably the most widely used and most valuable product obtained from red algae. It has been known since 1760 in Japan and, prior to World War II, was almost exclusively produced from *Gelidium.* Although Japan is still the largest producer, agar is now available in commercial quantities from a number of genera from several countries, including South Africa, Australia, New Zealand, the United States, and Russia. Agar has many of the physical properties of animal gelatin, but it is chemically quite different. It has certain advantages over gelatin, especially since it is firm at much higher temperatures than gelatin. Agar has many of the same uses as carrageenin, and many additional uses. It is widely used in microbiology in the preparation of media for culture work. It is a useful therapeutic agent in intestinal disorders since it is a nonirritant bulk producer that can absorb and hold water and at the same time act as a mild laxative. It is used also to make capsules to enclose antibiotics, sulfa compounds, vitamins, and other substances where a slow release of the medicant is desired at a point beyond the stomach. It is used as a dental impression material. In certain special breads for diabetics, agar replaces starch; however, agar itself is not good for

FIGURE 12–22   Nori culture in Tokyo Bay, Japan. A, net (partly submerged) suspended from bamboo poles with meshes covered by growth of *Porphyra* plants. B, Japanese "fisherman" at low tide tending emergent nets covered with growth of *Porphyra* plants. (Photographs by A. Miura, courtesy S. Ueda, Botanical Laboratory, Tokyo University of Fisheries.)

human consumption because it is relatively indigestible.

PHYLOGENY

Although some of the red algae have left excellent fossil records, the origin of the group as a whole is quite obscure and apparently very ancient. Some phylogeneticists believe that the red algae probably had their origin during the Archeozoic Era. Fossil red algae are well known from the Cretaceous Period and onward, but there are a few records also from the Triassic. Other somewhat questionable calcareous forms, thought by some paleobotanists to be red algae, have been recorded from the Ordovician Period. Most of the fossil records are of the lime-encrusting forms, such as the coralline algae. It is quite apparent that the encrusting coralline algae, such as *Lithotham-*

nium, were as important and active in reef building in past periods as they are today.

The red algae are so different in many respects that they must be regarded as taxonomically remote from other groups of algae. Because phycobilin pigments occur in the Rhodophyta and Cyanophyta, it has been suggested that the blue-green algae may have given rise to some simple nonsexual type of red alga. This origin could have led to the Bangiophycidae, some of which apparently have no sexual reproduction; again, the Florideophycidae may have evolved from some sexually reproducing proto-type in the Bangiophycidae. The putative chlorophyll *d* in red algae and absence in blue-green algae, does not necessarily support the hypothesis of the origin from blue-green algae; however, the nature of chlorophyll *d* is debatable. On the other hand, the floridean starch of red algae is considered closely related to cyanophycean starch of blue-green algae, which lends support to the hypothesis. The similarity of the sexual reproductive processes of some of the Florideophycidae to certain ascomycetous fungi has led some botanists to suggest that fungi may have descended from a red algal prototype.

REFERENCES

Drew, K. M., "Rhodophyta." In Smith, G. M. (Ed.), *Manual of Phycology.* Waltham, Mass.: Chronica Botanica (1951). Pp. 167–191.

Drew, K. M., "Reproduction in the Bangiophycidae." *Bot. Rev.,* 22: 553–611 (1956).

Fan, K., "Morphological Studies of the Gelidiales." *Univ. Calif. Publ. Bot.,* 32: 315–368 (1961).

Fritsch, F. E., *The Structure and Reproduction of the Algae.* Vol. 2. Cambridge: Cambridge University Press (1945). Pp. 397–767.

Hommersand, M. H., "The Morphology and Classification of Some Ceramiaceae and Rhodomelaceae." *Univ. Calif. Publ. Bot.,* 35: 165–366 (1963).

Johnson, J. H., "The Algal Genus *Lithothamnion* and its Fossil Representatives." *Quart. Colorado School Mines,* 57(1) (1962).

Kylin, H., *Die Gattungen der Rhodophyceen.* Lund, Sweden: Gleerup Fölag (1956).

Norris, R. E., "Morphological Studies on the Kallymeniaceae." *Univ. Calif. Publ. Bot.,* 28: 251–334 (1957).

Scagel, R. F., "A Morphological Study of Some Dorsiventral Rhodomelaceae." *Univ. Calif. Publ. Bot.,* 27: 1–108 (1953).

Smith, G. M. *Marine Algae of the Monterey Peninsula, California.* Palo Alto, Calif.: Stanford University Press (1944). Pp. 159–381.

Smith, G. M., *Cryptogamic Botany,* 2nd Ed. Vol. 1: *Algae and Fungi.* New York: McGraw-Hill Book Co., Inc. (1955). Pp. 291–343.

Sparling, S. R., "The Structure and Reproduction of Some Members of the Rhodymeniaceae." *Univ. Calif. Publ. Bot.,* 29: 319–396 (1957).

Taylor, W. R., *Marine Algae of the Northeastern Coast of North America,* 2nd Ed. Ann Arbor: University of Michigan Press (1957). Pp. 200–347.

Wagner, F. S., "Contributions to the Morphology of the Delesseriaceae." *Univ. Calif. Publ. Bot.,* 27: 279–346 (1954).

13 / DIVISION

XANTHOPHYTA

Until recently, members of this division (*xanthophytes*) have been considered as part of the Chrysophyta. However, differences in pigmentation and flagellation are now considered significant enough to place the yellow-green algae (Xanthophyceae) in a division with affinities closer to the Chlorophyta. Also treated separately will be a class of uncertain systematic position, the Chloromonadophyceae. The number of genera in this group of green monad forms is quite small, and there is little information about them. Further investigation of the chloromonads is needed to ascertain their affinities with the other algal groups.

CLASS XANTHOPHYCEAE
(Yellow-Green Algae)

There are over 75 genera with some 400 species referred to the class Xanthophyceae. They occur predominantly in fresh-water habitats, including soil, but there are a few marine species.

CELL STRUCTURE

Little is known concerning the cell-wall components of the Xanthophyceae. However, the chief materials are cellulose and pectic substances, and are in some instances impregnated with silicon. In some forms the cell wall is composed of two overlapping equal or unequal halves.

One to several discoid, smooth-edged, green or yellow-green chloroplasts occur in a parietal location in the cells (Fig. 13–1). The main green pigment is chlorophyll *a*. The reported occurrence of the unique chlorophyll *e* is possibly only a result of extraction techniques. The carotenoid pigments that mask the green pigment to some extent are β-carotene and at least three uncharacterized xanthophylls. Pyrenoid-like structures may be associated with the chloroplast in some genera but are probably not concerned with the accumulation of reserve foods. The polysaccharide chrysolaminarin, present in Phaeophyta and Chrysophyta, is probably the chief storage product of the Xanthophyta. Since starch is lacking, the chloroplast appears smooth-edged; this may be distinguished from the granular chloroplast of the Chlorophyta. In a few genera the fat sitosterol is present either alone or in addition to the chrysolaminarin. Very little is known of the food reserves in the Xanthophyceae.

The nucleus has one to several nucleoli. Most genera are uninucleate, but a few have a multinucleate, coenocytic thallus (Fig. 13–2E). A central vacuole may be present. Most of the members of this class are apparently autotrophic. A few colorless heterotrophic forms are saprobic or phagotrophic. There are reports of pigmented forms capable of ingesting food particles. Again, few investigations have been concerned with the nutritional requirements of the yellow-green algae.

MOVEMENT

In motile forms or motile stages of nonmotile species, the cells have two unequal anteriorly inserted flagella (Fig. 13–1G). The term **heterokont** is used to describe this unequal situation, and thus the Xanthophyceae may be referred to as the heterokonts. The shorter flagellum, which may be trailing, is of the whiplash type, whereas the longer one is anteriorly

directed and usually tinsellated with a double row of mastigonemes. This longer flagellum is considered responsible for forward propulsion. In a few instances the uniflagellate condition has been reported; however, the second very short flagellum may have been overlooked. In the genus *Vaucheria* an unusual, large, multinucleate, and multiflagellate zoospore is produced. The flagella arise in pairs, with one member of each pair slightly longer than the other. It is thought that this zoospore is a compound one, composed of many typical heterokont units. The sperm of *Vaucheria* has the typical heterokont flagellation (Fig. 13–3D, G, H, 4J).

MORPHOLOGICAL DIVERSITY

The majority of genera of Xanthophyceae are unicellular, nonmotile forms, including *Chloridella,* which is free-floating (Fig. 13–1I); *Characiopsis,* which is attached (Fig. 13–1D, E); and *Ophiocytium,* which is either free-floating or attached (Fig. 13–1B, C). The morphological diversity is similar to that of the Dinophyceae (Chapter 9), Chrysophyceae (Chapter 10), and the Chlorophyceae (Chapter 15), although there are fewer representatives in the Xanthophyceae. Motile biflagellate unicellular forms include those with a delicate periplast, such as *Xanthophycomonas* and *Heterochloris* (Fig. 13–1F, G), or a lorica, such as *Pseudomicrosportella* (Fig. 13–1A). A few unicellular amoeboid forms occur, such as *Rhizochloris* (Fig. 13–1H), as well as palmelloid colonies such as *Mischococcus* and *Chlorosaccus* (Fig. 13–2C, D). The most commonly encountered yellow-green algae are the filamentous, free-floating or attached, unbranched *Tribonema* (Fig. 13–2B), and the coenocytic, multinucleate forms, *Botrydium* (Fig. 13–2A) and *Vaucheria* (Fig. 13–2E).

REPRODUCTION

The chief method of reproduction is by cell division, but various types of spores may also occur. Zoospores and aplanospores are

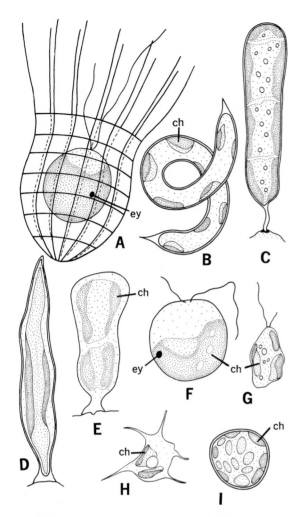

13–3B), as well as statospores similar to those of the Chrysophyceae (Fig. 13–3E). In some genera the entire cell may store reserve material and secrete a heavy wall forming an akinete (Fig. 13–3A).

Sexual reproduction is not widespread in the group, although it is common in a few genera. It is isogamous in *Tribonema*, isogamous or anisogamous in *Botrydium* (Fig. 13–4A–F), and oogamous in *Vaucheria* (Fig. 13–4G, H). In the fresh-water forms studied, meiosis apparently occurs on germination of the zygote.

DISTRIBUTION AND ECOLOGY

The yellow-green algae are widespread but relatively inconspicuous, and they are predominantly fresh-water algae. There are a few marine species recorded, some of which are quite abundant. The class is possibly more important in the sea than is presently apparent, since the nannoplankton are not well known. One form (*Ostreobium*) occurs in the shells of dead marine molluscs. In the fresh-water habitat they are especially common in standing water, sometimes appearing as scums on ponds and occasionally forming dense blooms. In alpine areas many of the small ponds seem to abound with Xanthophyceae; however, most of these appear to be delicate and are not easily collected or preserved. The filamentous form *Tribonema* may occur in dense free-floating masses, generally in cool spring water. Some Xanthophyceae occur on the surface of moist soil or drying mud, as in *Botrydium*, or grow on tree trunks, damp walls, or intermingle with mosses and liverworts. Many forms are epiphytes on the surfaces of larger algae and other aquatic plants.

IMPORTANCE AND USES

The members of this group are not directly important to man. However, they too are an essential component of the fresh-water and marine phytoplankton as primary producers. As noted previously, their significance in the little-known marine nannoplankton is unknown.

FIGURE 13–1   Morphological diversity of Xanthophyceae. A, F, G, motile forms. A, *Pseudomicrosportella,* ×3,300; F, *Xanthophycomonas,* ×2,150; G, *Heterochloris,* ×560. B–E, I, coccoid forms. B, C, two species of *Ophiocytium;* B, ×500; C, ×235. D, E, two species of *Characiopsis;* D, ×2,200; E, ×1,800. I, *Chloridella,* ×940. H, amoeboid form (*Rhizochloris,* ×830). *ch,* chloroplast; *ey,* eyespot. (G, H, after Pascher, in Rabenhorst with permission of Akademische Verlagsgesellschaft, Geest and Portig K.-G., Leipzig.)

produced singly in the cell, or the protoplast may divide to produce several spores. The zoospore has the unequal flagellation characteristic of the Xanthophyceae (Fig. 13–3F), although that of *Vaucheria* is an exception (Fig. 13–3D). In the multicellular genera, fragmentation may also occur. Endogenous cysts with two overlapping halves may be formed (Fig.

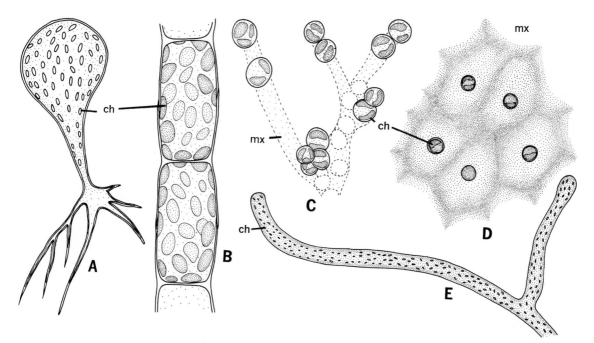

FIGURE 13–2   Morphological diversity of Xanthophyceae. A, E, coenocytic forms. A, *Botrydium,*
×250; E, *Vaucheria,* ×60. B, filamentous form (*Tribonema,* ×915). C, D, palmelloid forms with mucilaginous matrix (*mx*). C, *Mischococcus,* ×855; D, *Chlorosaccus,* ×650. *ch,* chloroplast.

PHYLOGENY

The relationships of this class to the class
Chrysophyceae are rather distant. They undoubtedly have affinities with the animal flagellate groups. The parallel morphological diversity in the Xanthophyceae, Chrysophyceae,
Dinophyceae, and—as will be seen later—the
Chlorophyceae, is also rather striking. These
similarities in form suggest a parallel evolution
of these groups, possibly from some common
ancestral stock. In each group there is a sequence from simple, unicellular, motile (and
nonmotile) forms to the colonial (nonfilamentous and filamentous) types. Insofar as sexual
reproduction occurs in the group, there is a similar advance from isogamy through anisogamy
to oogamy.

Because of their delicate nature, the
yellow-green algae have contributed little to the
fossil record. The presence of silicon in the
walls of some species suggests that some may
have been preserved. However, the present information concerning the history of the Xanthophyceae is quite meager.

CLASS CHLOROMONADO-PHYCEAE

(Chloromonads)

This group of unicellular alga-like flagellates is very poorly known. It is a small group of
less than a dozen genera, usually placed in one
order. The affinities of the chloromonads to
other algae are not clear. They may be allied
with the Cryptophyceae or, as in this text, with
the Xanthophyceae. Many of the small, motile,
unusual unicellular forms considered as Chlorophyceae may actually belong to this group.
None of the species has been completely
studied, and little is known about the group as a
whole.

CELL STRUCTURE

The cell is relatively large (50 to 100
microns) for a flagellate organism. It is naked
with a delicate periplast and is plastic in form.
It may be somewhat circular in outline in side-

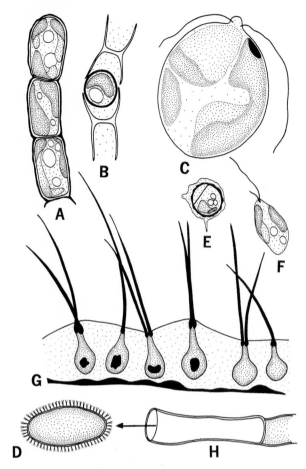

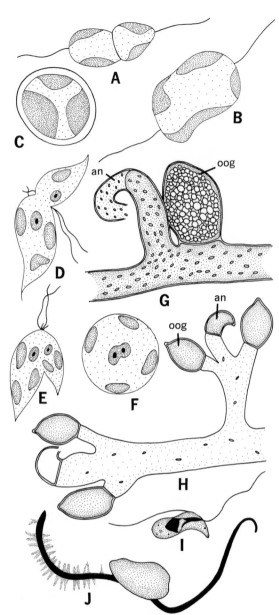

FIGURE 13–3   Asexual reproduction in Xanthophyceae. A, akinetes (*Bumillaria*, ×450); B, endogenous cyst (*Tribonema*, ×400). D, G, H, *Vaucheria* (D, multiflagellate zoospore, ×400; G, detailed structure of outer area of part of zoospore, showing flagellar apparatus, ×1,240; H, empty sporangium, ×400). E, statospore (*Chloromeson*, ×710); C, F, heterokont zoospores (*Tribonema*); C, ×180; F, ×800. (A, B, E, after Pascher in Rabenhorst with permission of Akademische Verlagsgesellschaft, Geest and Portig K.-G., Leipzig; G, redrawn by permission of William J. Koch and *Journal of Elisha Mitchell Scientific Society*.)

view, but is usually compressed; frequently there is a longitudinal groove in one surface (Fig. 13–5B). A large centrally located nucleus is present. On the flattened (ventral) surface is a reservoir where the flagella are inserted. In many of the genera **ejectosomes** (also known as trichocysts) occur in the outer cytoplasm either throughout the cell (Fig. 13–5B) or in localized areas (Fig. 13–5A). These sen-

FIGURE 13–4   Sexual reproduction in Xanthophyceae. A–C, isogamy (*Botrydium*, ×145). D–F, anisogamy (*Botrydium*, ×1,500). G, H, oogamy (two species of *Vaucheria*; G, ×145; H, ×135). I, J, sperm of *Vaucheria*; I, ×1,240; J, ×2,030 (J, stained to show tinsel on shorter anterior flagellum). *an,* antheridium; *oog,* oogonium. (A–C, after Rosenberg, "Die geschlechtliche Fortpflanzung von *Botrydium granulatum*," *Österreichische Botanische Zeitschrift,* 1930; I, J, redrawn by permission of William J. Koch and *Journal of Elisha Mitchell Scientific Society;* D–F, after Moewus with permission of Biologische Zentralblatt, VEB Georg Thieme, Leipzig.)

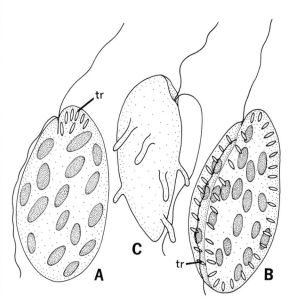

FIGURE 13–5   Morphological diversity of Chloromonadophyceae. A, B, photosynthetic species of *Gonyostomum* (A, with restricted trichocysts (*tr*), ×460; B, trichocysts over entire cell, ×550); C, *Rickertia*, nonphotosynthetic form with pseudopodia, ×540.

sitive organelles are released, often as fine threads, when the organism is disturbed.

Usually the cell is anteriorly biflagellate with the swimming flagellum (probably tinseltype) directed forward, the other (of the whiplash type) trailing posteriorly. The flagella may be the same length or one may be shorter. Often the trailing flagellum is delicate and difficult to discern. One or more contractile vacuoles usually occurs close to the reservoir and no eyespot is apparent. Numerous small discoid bright green or yellowish green chloroplasts are evident. The pigment complex is not well known, but there is an abundance of xanthophylls, and it is most likely that chlorophyll *a* and β-carotene are also present. Pyrenoids or similar structures are lacking. The food reserves are stored as minute droplets of oil, never as starch. A few colorless forms, such as *Rickertia* (Fig. 13–5C), are known; these ingest particulate food, often by pseudopodia.

REPRODUCTION

Vegetative reproduction occurs by longitudinal cell division. Sometimes the cells become temporarily nonmotile; the flagella are lost and the cell rounds up, secreting a muciliaginous wall. Repeated cell division in this condition produces extensive palmelloid colonies with a copious mucilaginous matrix. Spherical cysts also are formed when the cells round up and secrete a heavy wall.

DISTRIBUTION AND ECOLOGY

The chloromonads occur both in freshwater and marine habitats. They are rarely abundant, although the marine genus *Horniella* has been responsible for fish mortality in one area of the Indian Ocean. The fresh-water forms occur often in the mud and are apparently most common in water where there is an abundance of larger aquatic plant growth.

PHYLOGENY

Some authors have treated the chloromonads as a class of Pyrrophyta, closely related to the Cryptophyceae. However, the chloromonads seem to be more closely related to the Xanthophyceae, because they have an abundance of xanthophyll and food reserves in the form of oil. Their cell structure, particularly the occurrence of a reservoir and ejectosomes, is much more complex than that in the Xanthophyceae. Until the group has been more carefully studied and the pigment complex is better known, the Chloromonadophyceae must be considered of uncertain relationship and of questionable position in the Xanthophyta. Current studies of the nannoplankton show that several green algal forms lack the characteristic chlorophyll *b* and starch of the Chlorophyceae. With the refinement in cultural procedures it is now possible to study these forms, so their relationships may soon be better known.

REFERENCES ON XANTHOPHYCEAE

Fritsch, F. E., *The Structure and Reproduction of the Algae*. Vol. 1. Cambridge: Cambridge University Press (1935). Pp. 470–506.

Fritsch, F. E., "Chrysophyta." In Smith, G. M. (Ed.), *Manual of Phycology*. Waltham, Mass.: Chronica Botanica (1951). Pp. 84–86.

Huber-Pestalozzi, G., *Das Phytoplankton des Süsswassers*. Vol. 16, Part 2(1). In Thienemann, A. (Ed.), *Die Binnengewässer*. Stuttgart: E. Schweizerbart'sche Verlagsbuchhandlung (1941). Pp. 304–356.

Pascher, A., *Heterokontae*. In Pascher. A. (Ed.), *Die Süsswasser-Flora Deutschlands, Österreichs, und der Schweiz*. Vol. 11. Jena: G. Fischer (1925). Pp. 1–118.

Pascher, A., *Heterokonten*. In Rabenhorst, L. (Ed.), *Kryptogamen Flora von Deutschland, Oesterreich, und der Schweiz*, 2nd Ed. Vol. 11. Leipzig: Akademische Verlagsgeschellshaft (1939).

Smith, G. M., *Cryptogamic Botany*, 2nd Ed. Vol. 1: *Algae and Fungi*. New York: McGraw-Hill Book Co., Inc. (1955). Pp. 166–184.

Venkataraman, G. S., *Vaucheriaceae*. New Delhi: Indian Council Agric. Res. (1961).

REFERENCES ON CHLOROMONADOPHYCEAE

Huber-Pestalozzi, G., *Chloromonadinen*. In Huber-Pestalozzi, G., *Das Phytoplankton des Süsswassers*. Vol. 16, Pt. 3. Thienemann, A. (Ed.), *Die Binnengewässer*. Stuttgart: E. Schweizerbart'sche Verlagsbuchhandlung (1950). Pp. 79–93.

Pascher, A., *Chloromonadinae*. In Pascher, A. (Ed.), *Die Süsswasser-Flora Deutschlands, Österreichs, und der Schweiz*. Vol. 2. Jena: G. Fischer (1913). Pp. 175–181.

14/DIVISION

EUGLENOPHYTA

There are about 25 genera and 450 species of algae or alga-like organisms referred to this division (*euglenids*). Most of these genera are unicellular and motile; very few are sessile. This group is considered one of the most primitive groups of flagellates, with forms having both plant- and animal-like features. Only one class, Euglenophyceae, is recognized.

CELL STRUCTURE

The cell lacks a firm wall; the protoplast is contained in a membrane referred to as the periplast, or **pellicle.** This membrane may be quite flexible, with a plastic cell outline, as in *Euglena* (Fig. 14–1C); such a cell is said to exhibit **metaboly,** or be metabolic. Or the periplast may be more rigid with delicate diagonal or longitudinal striations, as in *Phacus* (Fig. 14–1D). In a few forms, such as *Trachelomonas* (Fig. 14–1A), the cell is within a firm lorica with only the flagellum projecting. In *Euglena* the pellicle consists of a system of semirigid submicroscopic rings that probably slide into one another as rings of a collapsible cup (Fig. 14–2A). The rings are separated by a noncellulosic membrane.

At the anterior end of the motile cell there is usually an invagination or gullet with a narrow tube-like portion and an enlarged posterior **reservoir.** From the base of the reservoir arise the flagella, which project freely through the tube-like part. In some of the colorless genera, as in *Peranema* (Fig. 14–1E), rod-like structures lie parallel to the long axis of the gullet. These rod organelles, or **pharyngeal rods,** probably function in ingesting food. However, their presence is not essential to species that ingest particulate matter.

The flagellum is usually tinsel with unilateral mastigonemes. In some uniflagellate species, the basal part of the flagellum (within the reservoir) is bifurcate. In many forms there are two flagella within the gullet; however, one is rudimentary, barely protruding beyond the gullet, if at all. This second flagellum is thought to serve as a rudder, whereas the first is a locomotor organelle. On the flagella of some euglenids a swelling, called the **paraflagellar body** or **photoreceptor,** is evident; it has been shown to lie within the flagellar membrane.

Near the point of attachment of the flagella there may be a reddish eyespot, believed to be light sensitive. It is not universally present, although generally it is evident in photosynthetic forms. Electron micrographs show that the fine structure consists of numerous granules packed together. These granules, about 100 to 300 millimicrons in diameter, form a mosaic (Fig. 14–2B). The eyespot does not seem to be within the chloroplast membrane, as it is in the green algae (Chapter 15).

A typical nucleus with one or more nucleoli is often centrally located in the cell. Mitotic division of the chromosomes is similar to that of other algae and the chromosomes have been counted. Complex organelles, which form an intimate connection between the nucleus, the vacuolar system, and the flagella, have been shown to be present in some euglenids. At the base of the flagellum there may be another organelle, the blepharoplast, which may be attached to the nucleus by a delicate cytoplasmic thread. At the nuclear end of the thread is another organelle, the **centriole,** common to most animal cells.

The Euglenophyceae consists of both green (Fig. 14–1A, C, D) and colorless forms (Fig. 14–1B, E). Many of the colorless genera are identical to the pigmented forms except for chloroplasts and eyespots. In pigmented forms

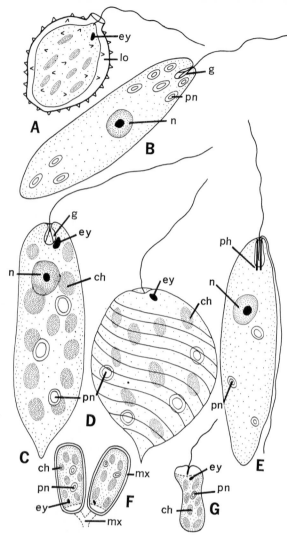

FIGURE 14–1   Morphological diversity in Euglenophyta. A–E, motile forms. A, *Trachelomonas,* with lorica (*lo*), ×1,000; B, *Astasia,* ×1,915; C, *Euglena,* ×1,550; D, *Phacus,* ×155; E, *Peranema,* ×1,485. F, G, nonmotile form *Colacium.* F, vegetative stage with matrix (*mx*), ×800; G, zoospore, ×530. *ch,* chloroplast; *ey,* eyespot; *g,* gullet; *n,* nucleus; *ph,* pharyngeal rods; *pn,* paramylon.

numerous bright green chloroplasts are irregularly scattered throughout the cytoplasm. Often the chloroplasts are most abundant at the posterior end of the cell. Their ultrastructure consists of a series of two to five closely lamellar pairs similar to developing grana in chloroplasts of higher plants. The pairs form a series of bands lying in an irregularly granular material, the matrix (Fig. 14–2C). In some, a central pyrenoid extends across the width of the chloroplast and seems to have a denser matrix than the chloroplast itself (Fig. 14–2C).

The pigments present are primarily chlorophyll *a* and *b*. The main carotene is *β*-carotene and the xanthophylls include two known from the Chlorophyta, astaxanthin and neoxanthin; antheraxanthin is specific to the Euglenophyceae. Other carotenoids present have not been characterized as yet. Several euglenids, including some species of *Euglena*, often contain numerous red granules referred to as **hematochrome.** This is actually the carotenoid astaxanthin, known previously as euglenarhodone.

Some of the Euglenophyta are truly autotrophic. However, many of the pigmented forms are auxotrophs. The unpigmented euglenids are obligate heterotrophs and may be phagotrophic. Some of the pigmented forms are facultative heterotrophs (or mixotrophs).

The typical food reserve is an insoluble polysaccharide, **paramylon** (or paramylum). It is present in the form of small granules of various shapes. In pigmented forms it may be free in the cytoplasm or adjacent to the chloroplast but not enclosed in any membrane (Fig. 14–2A). When a pyrenoid is present, paramylon granules may be closely associated with it, although not within the membrane. Fat droplets also are often distributed throughout the cytoplasm.

Contractile vacuoles occur near the reservoir. Several small contractile vacuoles empty into a larger one that empties into the reservoir. Some believe the reservoir is a vacuole itself and that the smaller reservoirs emptying into it are secondary vacuoles.

MOVEMENT

The motile euglenids exhibit two basic types of movement. One is the well-known swimming movement, in which the flagellar action is in the form of a helix or spiral. Thus, the cell moves forward as well as rotates on its long axis (Fig. 14–3H–I). The over-all result is

that the organism moves in a spiral pathway. In the other basic movement, the euglenid creeps or glides, apparently because the flagellum is held in front of the cell rather than at an oblique angle (Fig. 14–3F–G). Thus, no cell rotation occurs. If a long second flagellum is present it trails the cell, beating only at the tip.

Some euglenids constantly change shape or exhibit metaboly (Fig. 14–3A–E), probably because of a sliding of the semirigid rings composing the pellicle. The mechanics of metabolic movement are in need of further study.

CLASSIFICATION AND MORPHOLOGICAL DIVERSITY

The single class Euglenophyceae is generally divided into two orders. These may be based on morphological form (motile or palmelloid) or on mode of nutrition (phagotrophic or nonphagotrophic). Depending on the system employed, different genera are included in the orders. In the nutritional system the families are distinguished from one another on mode of nutrition and type of movement. In the morphological system the families are separated primarily according to flagellation and cell motility.

Although the majority of Euglenophyceae are motile and unicellular, there is a very small group of nonmotile forms. In the vegetative condition these cells are attached to the substrate by a mucilaginous stalk, as in the genus *Colacium* (Fig. 14–1F, G). In vegetative reproduction the cells (zoospores) become motile and are typically euglenid in form (Fig. 14–1G).

REPRODUCTION

Reproduction in this group occurs by longitudinal cell division while the cell is actively motile. Two immediately motile daughter cells are produced. Near the end of nuclear division the blepharoplast divides. The parental flagellar

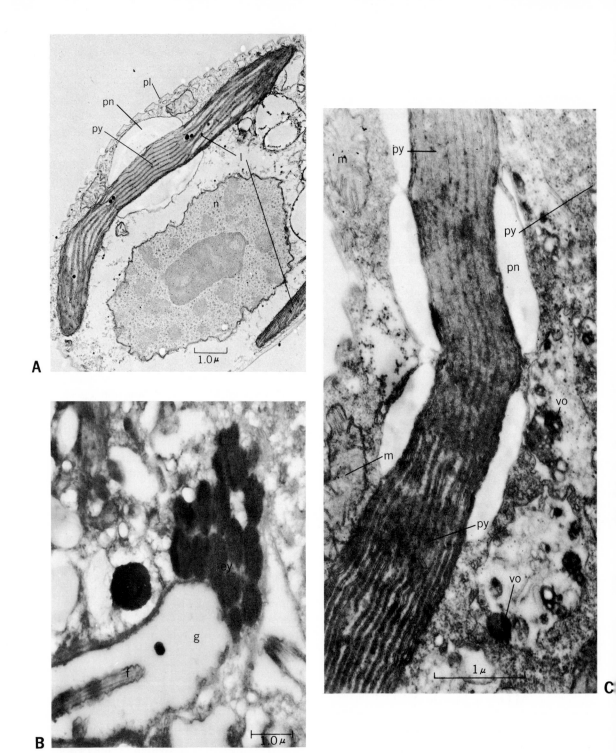

FIGURE 14–2   Ultrastructure of *Euglena*. A (above, left), longitudinal section, indicating chloroplast lamellae (*l*), pyrenoid (*py*), nucleus (*n*) with dark nucleolus, paramylon (*pn*), and pellicle (*pl*). B (above, right), detail anterior end showing eyespot granules (*ey*), gullet (*g*), and base of flagellum in longitudinal section (*f*). C , a longitudinal section of portion of the cell, showing the pyrenoid region (*py*), paramylon (*pn*), vacuoles (*vo*), mitochondrion (*m*). (A, B, photographs courtesy J. J. Wolken and with permission of Rutgers University Press; C, photograph courtesy Sarah P. Gibbs and permission of *Journal of Ultrastructure Research*.)

apparatus may remain attached and become that of one daughter cell. Under some conditions the cell may become nonmotile, undergoing repeated division in a palmelloid condition. Such stages are rare in the nonpigmented forms. In unfavorable conditions a cell may encyst and be very resistant to extreme environmental conditions. The wall of the cyst, composed of an unidentified carbohydrate, is sometimes stratified and often ornamented. In the encysted form some cells accumulate considerable amounts of astaxanthin (hematochrome), thus appearing red. Germination of thick-walled cysts usually results in only one motile cell. However, in the thin-walled cysts, the contents often divide into a number of cells.

Sexual reproduction, if it does occur, is rare and not well authenticated. The few records reporting union of gametes or nuclei are generally not accepted by phycologists as valid evidence. These reports are for the most part unsubstantiated and some are apparently due to the presence of other organisms or to misinterpretation of stages in mitosis. Recently there has been a report of the occurrence of meiosis in some euglenids, but this evidence is not yet conclusive.

DISTRIBUTION AND ECOLOGY

Most of the genera in this division occur in fresh water, particularly in water that is rich in decaying organic material. In fact, species of *Euglena* are some of the most tolerant of polluted conditions. They may occur in sufficient numbers to produce extensive bright green, yellow-brown, or red blooms (or scums) in the water. The red color results from the dispersion of astaxanthin granules throughout the cell. Euglenids often occur in the soil, on damp mud along streams, and in salt marshes, causing intensive coloration when in large numbers. Some are common in brackish water and there are a few marine representatives.

The nonphotosynthetic forms, such as *Astasia* (Fig. 14–1B), generally occur where putrefaction is present. Phagotrophic forms,

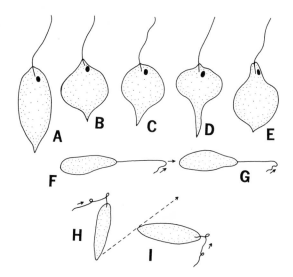

FIGURE 14–3   Swimming movements in Euglenophyta. A–E, metaboly in *Euglena*. F, G, direction of movement and flagellar position in *Peranema;* H, I, in *Euglena*. (F–I, adapted from T. L. Jahn, "Euglenophyta" in *Manual of Phycology—An Introduction to the Algae and Their Biology,* edited by Gilbert M. Smith, copyright 1951, The Ronald Press Company, New York.)

such as *Peranema* (Fig. 14–1E), are common where debris and other small plankton are present to provide particulate food. The exact nature of phagotrophy in the Euglenophyceae is not thoroughly understood.

Some euglenids, generally the nonpigmented or very pale forms, live within the bodies of other organisms, including various invertebrates such as rotifers, nematodes, flatworms, oligochaetes, and copepods. One euglenid occuring with or without pigment is known only from the intestinal tract of some frog tadpoles.

IMPORTANCE AND USES

As primary producers of carbon compounds and as a source of food for other herbivorous animals, the Euglenophyceae are particularly important in the phytoplankton of fresh-water areas. There is little direct use by man; however, certain euglenids have been used as bio-assay organisms (especially for cobalamine or vitamin B_{12}) and thus play a useful role in precise physiological and nutritional studies. Several genera occur under anaerobic conditions in sewage disposal tanks where they possibly play a role in the general breakdown of complex organic materials in sewage.

PHYLOGENY

Except for the close affinities to the flagellate protozoan line of evolution (see Fig. 7–4), there are no clear-cut relationships shown between the euglenids and any other division of algae. The Euglenophyceae have the same chlorophylls as the Chlorophyta and higher plants. However, they do not appear morphologically related to the simple unicellular green algae. Similarly, the delicate nature of the euglenid cell makes it appear unlikely that there will be much fossil evidence to clarify the relationships to other groups. The fact that some euglenids are typically photosynthetic whereas others, obviously closely related, are colorless does not aid in establishing a phylogenetic trend within the group or with other algal groups. It is difficult to say which euglenids are primitive and which are derived forms. Generally it is considered that colorless forms arose from chlorophyll-bearing forms and that some of the colorless forms eventually became phagotrophic. That colorless strains of *Euglena* may be derived from pigmented forms in laboratory studies, and the obvious similarity of these to the colorless *Astasia* substantiates the hypothesis that the colorless forms are derived. On the other hand, the fact that some species are mixotrophs suggests that possibly primitive colorless flagellates might be precursors to chlorophyll-bearing species. This latter theory obtains some support from the photosynthetic forms unable to carry on metabolic activities without organic growth substances. But, again, this requirement may be a derived one.

REFERENCES

Fritsch, F. E., *The Structure and Reproduction of the Algae.* Vol. 1. Cambridge: Cambridge University Press (1935). Pp. 724–744.

Gojdics, M., *The Genus* Euglena. Madison: University of Wisconsin Press (1953).

Jahn, T. L., "The Euglenoid Flagellates." *Quart. Rev. Biol.,* 21: 246–274 (1946).

Jahn, T. L., "Euglenophyta." In Smith, G. M. (Ed.), *Manual of Phycology.* Waltham, Mass.: Chronica Botanica (1951). Pp. 69–81.

Pringsheim, E. G., "Contributions towards a Monograph of the Genus *Euglena.*" *Nova Acta Leopoldiana,* 18: 1–168 (1956).

Smith, G. M., *Cryptogamic Botany,* 2nd Ed. Vol. 1: *Algae and Fungi.* New York: McGraw-Hill Book Co., Inc. (1955). Pp. 139–147.

Wolken, J. J., *Euglena, an Experimental Organism for Biochemical and Biophysical Studies.* New Brunswick, N. J.: Rutgers University Press (1961).

15 / DIVISION

CHLOROPHYTA

The *green algae* are predominantly fresh-water forms; however, they are common and sometimes relatively conspicuous in the sea. In general, the marine forms are much larger than the fresh-water; but macroscopic and microscopic green algae occur in both habitats. There are nearly 7,000 species of green algae in about 450 genera. Vegetatively, the Chlorophyta are relatively simple, but they exhibit a greater variety in life history and in reproduction than any other division of plants. There is some difference of opinion as to the systematic arrangement of this group. The system followed here recognizes two classes, the Chlorophyceae and the Charophyceae. The latter contains only one order, whereas the Chlorophyceae has 11 or 12 orders. The classification of the Chlorophyceae at the family level and recognition of genera is fairly uniform among most phycologists.

The green algae are generally considered to be the progenitors of embryo-producing green plants and to be part of the main line of evolution to vascular plants. For this reason the Chlorophyta has been left until last among the algal divisions for discussion. The two classes will be considered together in the discussion of the cell structure. However, the morphology and reproduction in the Charophyceae are so distinct that they will be treated separately.

273

CELL STRUCTURE

Most of the green algae have a rigid cell wall composed of an inner firm cellulosic layer (sometimes laminated) and an outer, less firm pectic layer. In some forms the cellulose may be partially replaced by xylan (formerly referred to as callose) or even by a thin chitinous outer layer. The pectic layer is impregnated with calcium carbonate in most Charophyceae, most desmids, and some representatives of the Siphonales, Dasycladales, and Siphonocladales.

The cells of most of the green algae are uninucleate, and the nucleus contains one or more nucleoli. However, in some the thallus is typically multicellular with multinucleate cells; and in others it is multinucleate and a coenocyte. Generally there is a large vacuole traversed by cytoplasmic strands. Motile cells may have contractile vacuoles, which are near the point of flagellar insertion. Other contractile vacuoles in the cytoplasm have been noted between the chloroplast and the cell membrane (Fig. 15–1).

The pigments of green algae occur in well-organized chloroplasts that may occur singly or may be numerous. When numerous, they are usually small, discoid, and possibly interconnected. When only one or two chloroplasts are present they may be shaped like a cup, a band, a ring, a net, a spiral, or a star (Fig. 15–1). When single, they are generally parietal in the cell, but they may be axile in position. Electron micrographs show that the chloroplast possesses bands of two to six appressed lamellar pairs that generally traverse the chloroplast (Fig. 15–2). In the Zygnematales, large and small lamellar units alternate similarly to grana in higher plants. Associated with the chloroplast may be the pyrenoid (Fig. 15–2), which is generally traversed by chloroplast lamellae. In motile cells a single eyespot may occur at one side of the chloroplast. The ultrastructure of the eyespot has been shown to consist of three to eight rows of densely packed granules; these rows are intimately associated with the photosynthetic lamellae. No lens structure has been demonstrated.

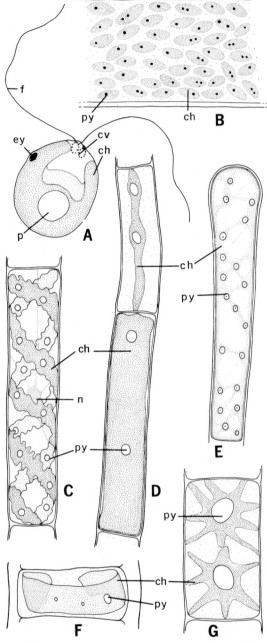

FIGURE 15–1   Chloroplasts of Chlorophyta. A, B, C, E, F, parietal in position; D, G, axile in position. A, cup-shaped (*Chlamydomonas*), ×2,750; B, discoid (*Bryopsis*), ×255; C, spiral-shaped (*Spirogyra*), ×530; D, band-shaped (*Mougeotia*), ×510; E, net-shaped (*Oedogonium*), ×280; band- or ring-shaped (*Ulothrix*), ×2,450; G, star-shaped (*Zygnema*), ×735. *ch,* chloroplast; *cv,* contractile vacuole; *ey,* eyespot; *f,* flagellum; *n,* nucleus; *py,* pyrenoid·

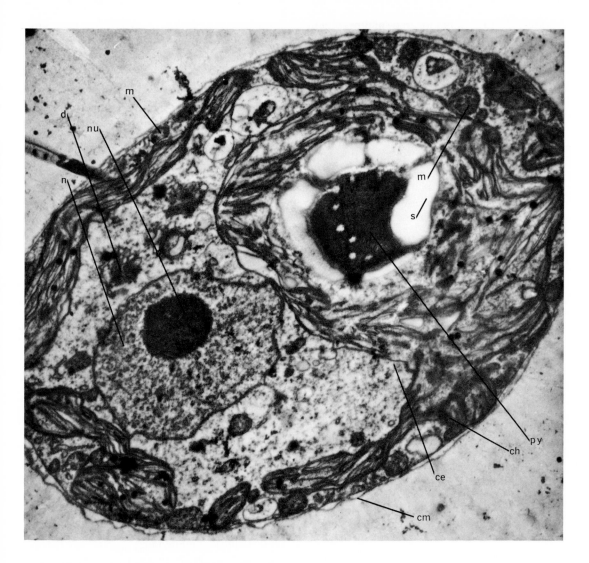

FIGURE 15–2   Electron micrograph of cell of *Gonium* (oblique section through middle of cell), ×14,000.
ce, two-layered chloroplast envelope; *ch,* chloroplast composed of lamellae; *cm,* cytoplasmic membranes;
d, dictyosome; *m,* mitochondrion; *n,* nucleus; *nu,* nucleolus; *py,* pyrenoid; *s,* starch plate.

The characteristic grass-green color of this group is due to the presence of chlorophyll *a* and cnlorophyll *b.* In addition there are the carotenoid pigments, which differ in the two classes. The carotene pigments always include β-carotene and either α-carotene in the Chlorophyceae or γ-carotene and lycopene in the Charophyceae. In the Chlorophyceae the main xanthophylls are, for the most part, the same as higher plants and are lutein, neoxanthin, violaxanthin, and zeaxanthin. In the Siphonales some genera possess certain unique xantho-

phylls, siphonein, and siphonaxanthin. As in the Euglenophyta, some Chlorophyceae may possess a red carotenoid pigment that masks the green color. The pigment has been shown in some instances to be astaxanthin (as in the Euglenophyta); however, its true nature is not known for all forms in which it occurs. As in most of the other algal divisions, some genera, classed as Chlorophyceae, are devoid of pigments.

Most of the green algae are autotrophic, although as noted there are a few heterotrophic colorless forms. Some of the photosynthetic species are nutritionally auxotrophic or mixotrophic. Carbohydrate reserves are stored as starch, and starch formation is usually intimately associated with the pyrenoids. The Chlorophyta appear to be the only algal group in which the pyrenoid is surrounded by a "shell" of starch grains lying within the chloroplast (Fig. 15–2). Some forms lack pyrenoids and, as in higher plants, store starch in **leucoplasts.** Fats and oil similar to those in other algae may be present as a reserve in some green algae.

MOVEMENT

When present, motile cells are generally anteriorly biflagellate (or quadriflagellate). The flagella are whiplash and generally are equal in length (the **isokont** condition). Somewhat lateral insertion of flagella and possibly tinsel flagellation occur in a few atypical forms in the Volvocales; however, current studies of these show a different biochemical composition. These forms may well have closer affinities to the Xanthophyceae or the Chloromonadophyceae, or they may be in a separate class. In the order Oedogoniales and in *Derbesia,* the motile cells always possess an anterior circlet of short flagella of equal length, termed **stephanokont.** Recent electron micrographs of *Oedogonium* show that such a flagellum is attached to a basal body. The ring of basal bodies alternates with flagellar roots that extend into the colorless apical portion of the cell. No connections between the flagella and the nucleus have been demonstrated in these stephanokont algae.

CLASS CHLOROPHYCEAE

CLASSIFICATION AND MORPHOLOGICAL DIVERSITY

The Chlorophyceae are extremely diversified morphologically (Fig. 15–3), ranging from unicellular motile or nonmotile forms to motile or nonmotile colonial forms; from multicellular simple or branched filaments to massive parenchymatous types. Aggregations of coenocytic filaments also occur, resulting in large forms. Certain genera may regularly exhibit heterotrichy. Growth is intercalary to a large degree, and apical growth is rare in the group as a whole. In the Chlorophyceae the gametangia are freely exposed and often are simply metamorphosed vegetative cells.

There are three fairly distinct main lines of evolution within the Chlorophyceae, and with a few exceptions the orders can be arranged in phenetic series within these. The Oedogoniales and Zygnematales, and certain marine orders (Dasycladales and Siphonocladales), are so different that they are regarded as taxonomically remote from others in the green algae; their precise origin is quite obscure. The three general lines of evolution are usually referred to as the **volvocine line,** the **tetrasporine line,** and the **siphonous line** (Fig. 15–3).

THE VOLVOCINE LINE. Vegetatively the simplest typical green alga can be illustrated by the unicellular motile form *Chlamydomonas* (Fig. 15–4C). This alga is representative of the primitive stock from which all other groups of green algae are thought to have evolved. *Chlamydomonas* is a biflagellate motile cell; but under certain conditions it may revert to a nonmotile state, becoming embedded in a gelatinous matrix, and dividing vegetatively to form a dense amorphous mass, the palmelloid state. The cells never have any organization or connection with one another or definite arrangement in these aggregations.

In the volvocine line, exemplified by the order Volvocales, a series of colonial forms has evolved from the *Chlamydomonas*-like type (Fig. 15–4C). Although there are a variety of types, possibilities are limited; in the evolutionary sense, this line has apparently been a blind alley with regard to other forms. In the colonial forms, each cell in the colony is typically like a motile vegetative *Chlamydomonas* cell. As the cell divides, the daughter cells are oriented in a definite manner and remain fastened together by a common mucilaginous matrix. In some

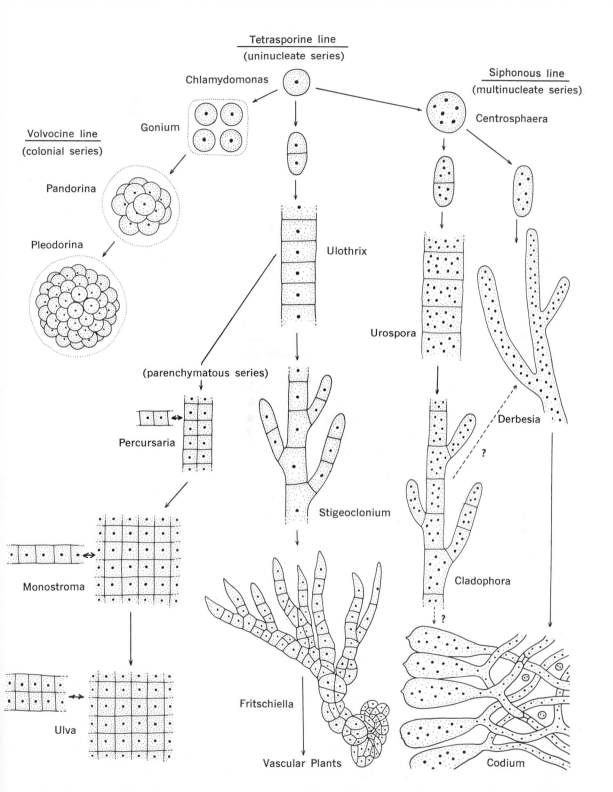

FIGURE 15–3   Habit types resulting from plane of cell and nuclear divisions in Chlorophyta. (Flagella not included in motile forms; surface and transverse sectional views shown for parenchymatous series.)

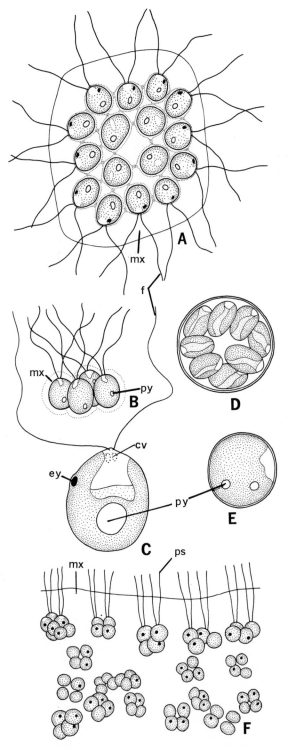

instances the cells are interconnected by cyto-plasmic strands (Fig. 15–7C). The colony is also termed a **coenobium,** since the number of cells in a colony is constant and does not change from the juvenile colony to the adult. In the simpler forms each cell of the colony is vegetatively similar and has the same reproductive potentiality. In the more advanced types, certain cells or groups remain vegetative whereas others become differentiated and specialized for reproduction. Hence, in the volvocine series, there is a trend toward a gradual increase in the number of cells in the colony with a tendency toward some division of labor.

In *Gonium* (Fig. 15–4A, B) a flat plate-like colony of 4, 8, 16, or 32 cells (depending on the species) is produced, and all cells are reproductive. In *Pandorina* (Fig. 15–5A) a spherical or ellipsoidal colony of 8, 16, or 32 tightly packed cells is formed. In *Eudorina* (Fig. 15–5B) a spherical colony of 16, 32, or 64 somewhat separated cells results; in some species the front tier of cells remains vegetative and the remaining cells become reproductive. *Pleodorina* (Fig. 15–6)—sometimes not recognized as separate from *Eudorina*—is also a spherical colony of 32, 64, or 128 cells, in which the smaller cells are only vegetative and the larger ones are reproductive. The ultimate in this line of evolution is *Volvox* (Fig. 15–7A–C) where 500 to 50,000 cells form a hollow spherical colony with only a few scattered reproductive cells. In sexual reproduction there is also an evolutionary series apparent. *Gonium* and *Pandorina* are isogamous and the gametes are *Chlamydomonas*-like. These gametes may be of different sizes, but there is no regularity in fusion of a large and small gamete. *Eudorina, Pleodorina,* and *Volvox* are oogamous with a small, ellipsoid, yellow-green sperm and a large round green egg.

THE TETRASPORINE LINE. From the palmelloid prototype of a chlamydomonad cell

cellular and colonial forms (tetrasporine line). D, *Chlorococcum,* daughter cell formation, ×1,040; E, *Chlorococcum,* vegetative cell, ×1,040; F, *Tetraspora,* in mucilaginous matrix (*mx*), ×625. *cv,* contractile vacuole; *ey,* eyespot; *f,* flagellum; *ps,* pseudocilia; *py,* pyrenoid.

FIGURE 15–4   Morphological diversity in chlorophyceae. A–C, motile unicellular and colonial forms (volvocine line). A, *Gonium* (surface view), ×1,215; B, *Gonium,* side view, ×1,215; C, *Chlamydomonas,* ×2,810. D–F, nonmotile uni-

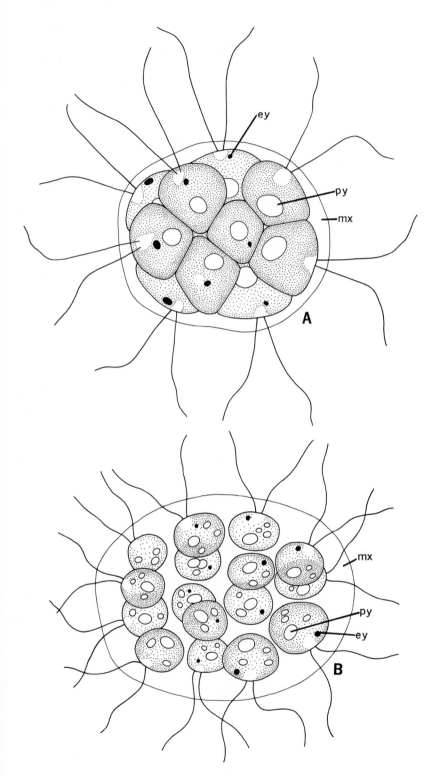

FIGURE 15–5   Morphological diversity in Chlorophyceae. Motile colonial forms (volvocine line). A, *Pandorina*, ×2,000; B, *Eudorina*, ×1,075. (Symbols as in Fig. 15–4.)

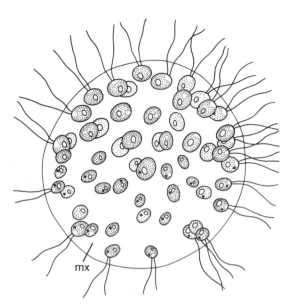

FIGURE 15–6 Morphological diversity in Chlorophyceae. Motile colonial form (volvocine line). *Pleodorina*, ×445. *mx*, matrix.

there are series of forms in the tetrasporine line ranging from the unicellular, nonmotile condition to more complex multicellular thalli (Fig. 15–3). Motile cells similar to the motile chlamydomonad form are produced but only during reproductive phases. In the tetrasporine line of evolution there are limitless possibilities, in contrast to the volvocine line. The main feature of this line is the uninucleate condition of the cells. The orders included in the tetrasporine line are the Ulotrichales (in the broadest sense including the Ulvales of some authors) and part of the Chlorococcales.

The nonmotile vegetative cell is illustrated by *Chlorococcum* (Fig. 15–4D, E). There is repeated division of cells in the vegetative condition to form a large macroscopic colony of undifferentiated cells, such as those in *Tetraspora* (Fig. 15–4F).

A more orderly series of vegetative division leads to the filamentous colony. If a nonmotile cell divides and its derivatives continue to divide in the same plane, a simple uniseriate filament of cells—as in *Ulothrix*—results (Fig. 15–8F). This is essentially a simple type of intercalary cell division. If this regular division of the basic uniseriate type is supplemented by an occasional division of a cell in a second plane, a branch initial arises. This leads to the branched uniseriate type of thallus, as seen in

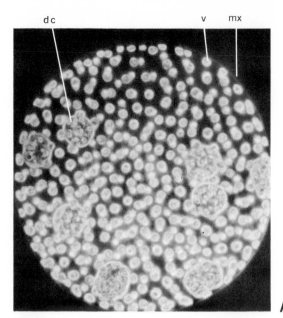

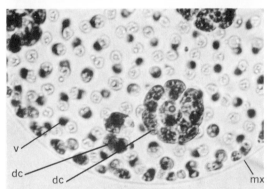

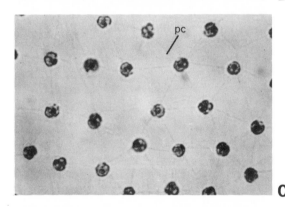

FIGURE 15–7 Photomicrographs of *Volvox*. A, dark field illumination showing boundary of matrix (*mx*), vegetative cell (*v*), and young daughter colony (*dc*), ×115. B, bright field illumination showing boundary of matrix (*mx*), vegetative cells (*v*), two-celled daughter colony, and older daughter colony (*dc*), ×160. C, phase contrast illumination showing protoplasmic connections (*pc*), ×200.

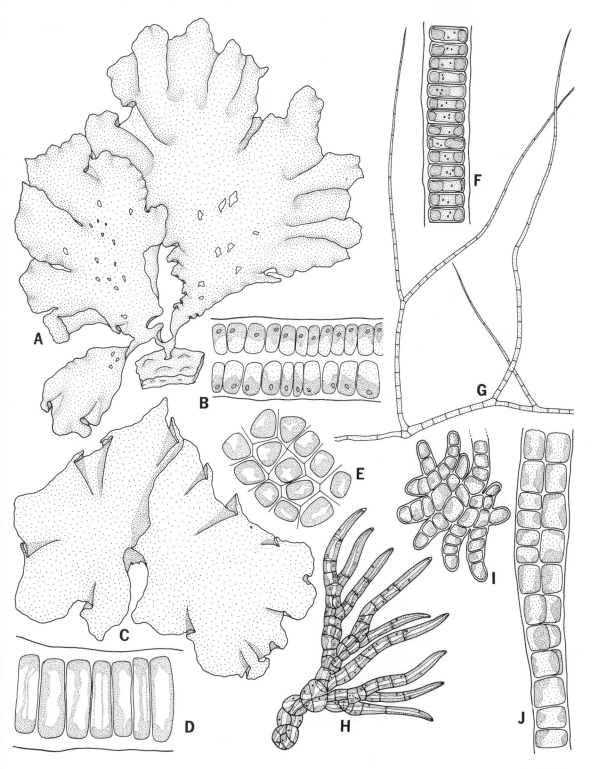

FIGURE 15–8   Morphological diversity in Chlorophyceae. Filamentous and parenchymatous forms (tetrasporine line). A, B, *Ulva* (A, habit, ×0.5; B, transverse sectional view, ×500). C–E, *Monostroma* (C, habit, ×0.5; D, transverse sectional view, ×530; E, cell arrangement in surface view, ×750). F, *Ulothrix*, ×560. G, *Stigeoclonium*, ×75. H, *Fritschiella*, ×375. I, J, *Percursaria* (I, basal attachment region, ×350; J, distal portion, ×350).

Stigeoclonium (Fig. 15–8G). However, if every cell in a primary, unbranched, uniseriate axis divides once in a second plane, a biseriate thallus comparable to *Percursaria* results (Fig. 15–8I, J). And if, in addition, division occurs repeatedly in the second plane, one can readily see how the monostromatic thallus typical of *Monostroma* can be derived (Fig. 15–8C–E). Finally, if cells divide regularly (but only once) in a third plane, a foliose thallus similar to that of *Ulva* is formed (Fig. 15–8A, B). Further division of certain cells in the third plane results in a partially parenchymatous thallus, as in *Fritschiella* (Fig. 15–8H). This division in three planes is the basis for true parenchymatous growth, making possible the development of complex tissues in higher plants.

Paralleling the filamentous to parenchymatous lines of development is the presence of heterotrichy, which is considered a precursor to certain characteristics of higher plants. In *Stigeoclonium* (Fig. 15–9F) both the prostrate and the erect systems are equally well represented. In *Fritschiella* (Fig. 15–9D) both systems develop and the prostrate portion is further differentiated into septate rhizoids, which anchor the plant in the mud. However, in other genera one or the other of these systems may be reduced or even completely eliminated. In *Draparnaldia* (Fig. 15–9E) the basal system is completely suppressed, and in some species of *Coleochaete* (Fig. 15–9A) the erect system is almost completely absent. In the very common *Pleurococcus,* which occurs generally on tree trunks, the filamentous form itself is somewhat suppressed, resulting in small packets of cells (Fig. 15–9B, C). As in the volvocine line, there is also an evolutionary series with regard to sexual reproduction. Such forms as *Ulothrix, Stigeoclonium,* and *Fritschiella* are isogamous; whereas *Ulva* may be isogamous or anisogamous and *Coleochaete* is oogamous.

THE SIPHONOUS LINE. Along a third line of evolution the multinucleate nature of the cell has resulted in several clearly distinct series of green algae with the typically multinucleate nature of the cell an outstanding feature (Fig. 15–3). Among the simple unicellular forms it is easy to imagine how a multinucleate genus such as *Centrosphaera* (Fig. 15–10A–C) might have arisen. This could occur simply by failure of septa to form following one or more nuclear divisions. In some instances an occasional septation followed by a number of nuclear divisions has given rise to a colonial thallus as in the coenobial *Pediastrum* (Fig. 15–10F). In *Hydrodictyon* (Fig. 15–10D, E) the young cells of the thallus are uninucleate, but as the cell matures and elongates, nuclear division occurs so that many hundred nuclei are present in each adult cell. A simple filamentous multinucleate form, as in *Urospora* (Fig. 15–11F, G), would also result from regular septation. As in the filamentous uninucleate series, occasional divisions to produce branch initials result in a branched thallus of multinucleate cells, as in *Cladophora* (Fig. 15–11A). A third line from the *Centrosphaera*-type, in which no septations are formed except when reproductive cells are formed, would produce a coenocytic multinucleate thallus (Fig. 15–10A–C). From the *Centrosphaera* type might develop *Valonia* (Fig. 15–11B, C), which is an irregularly branched or spherical cell up to 5 cm in diameter. Further elongation and nuclear division results in a coenocytic tube, as in *Derbesia* (Fig. 15–11E). Regularity in branching of the coenocytic thallus results in forms such as *Bryopsis* (Fig. 15–12A, B), which also lacks septa and has free branching. There may be an aggregation of profusely branched filaments to form a dense intertwined mass, as in *Codium* (Fig. 15–12D, E), resulting in a massive thallus of definite gross morphology. In *Halimeda* (Fig. 15–12C) the filaments become so densely aggregated that they form a pseudoparenchymatous structure.

As seen in Fig. 15–3, the siphonous line is not a linear series. Rather, it probably is composed of several parallel lines of evolution, resulting in a number of rather distinctive orders—Cladophorales, Siphonales, Dasycladales, Siphonocladales, and part of the Chlorococcales. The last order has representatives that fit also in the tetrasporine line. An evolutionary sequence with regard to sexual reproduction is not as evident in the siphonous series, although

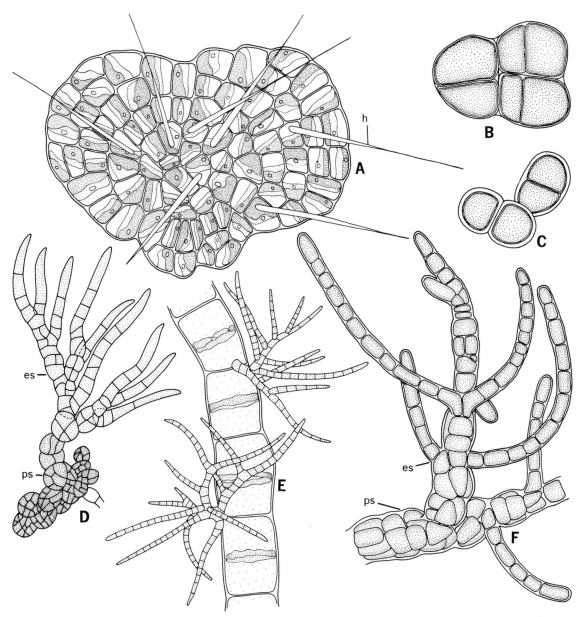

FIGURE 15–9   Morphological diversity in Chlorophyceae. Filamentous forms (tetrasporine line). A, *Čoleochaete*, a prostrate species showing hairs (*h*), ×435; B, C, *Pleurococcus*, showing reduced filamentous nature, ×2,150; D, *Fritschiella*, showing heterotrichy with prostrate parenchymatous and erect filamentous regions, ×375; E, *Draparnaldia*, showing main axis of erect form, ×290; F, *Stigeoclonium*, showing heterotrichous habit, with prostrate system (*ps*) and erect system (*es*), ×500.

forms exhibiting isogamy, anisogamy, and oogamy do occur.

REPRODUCTION AND LIFE HISTORIES

Vegetative reproduction occurs commonly by fragmentation in multicellular forms and by cell division in unicellular forms. Motile forms may revert to a nonmotile, palmelloid phase under certain circumstances and by repeated cell division produce a large amorphous aggregation of nonmotile cells. Mitotic divisions producing one to several aplanospores or zoospores occur throughout the Chlorophyceae. The

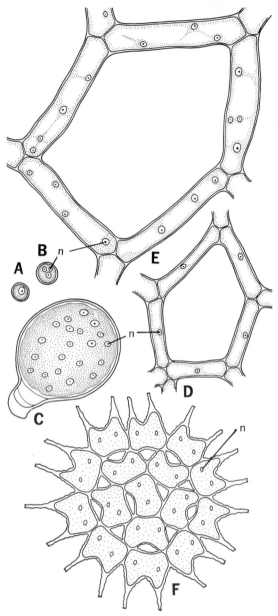

FIGURE 15–10 Morphological diversity in Chlorophyceae. Siphonous, multinucleate forms (siphonous line). A–C, *Centrosphaera*, showing change from uninucleate (A) to multinucleate (B, C) condition, ×500. D, E, *Hydrodictyon*, showing uninucleate stage (D), ×650, and multinucleate stage (E), ×540. F, *Pediastrum*, ×950. *n*, nucleus.

spores are not usually produced in specialized sporangia, but within metamorphosed vegetative cells. In some of the fresh-water forms, akinetes or hypnospores may be produced when the contents of an entire cell round up and form a heavy wall.

Sexual reproduction is well established in the Chlorophyceae as a whole, although it is completely lacking in some genera. As noted earlier, reproduction includes isogamy (Fig. 15–13B, C), as in *Gonium, Stigeoclonium,* or *Fritschiella;* anisogamy (Fig. 15–13E, F), as in *Bryopsis, Codium,* or species of *Ulva;* and oogamy (Fig. 15–13A), as in *Eudorina, Volvox,* or *Coleochaete.* In the genus *Chlamydomonas,* different species illustrate all three types of sexual reproduction. Generally gametes are produced in metamorphosed vegetative cells, although in *Codium,* for example, there are clearly differentiated gametangia. However, reproduction may occur only in terminal cells, as in *Cladophora;* or in ordinary branches, as in *Bryopsis* (Fig. 15–13D). Both gametes can be produced by one plant, or two separate plants may be necessary.

There is usually sexual reproduction and an alternation of generations in green algae. For the majority of genera the conspicuous generation is the haploid, with the zygote the only diploid cell in the life cycle, as in *Chlamydomonas* (Fig. 15–14). In fresh-water forms the zygote usually becomes a thick-walled resting structure; however, in marine forms it is usually a thin-walled structure that germinates immediately. The first division of the diploid zygote is meiotic; one or more viable haploid meiospores are formed.

An alternation of isomorphic generations also occurs in some marine and fresh-water forms. Hence, there may be one or two haploid gametophytes alternating with a morphologically similar but cytologically different diploid sporophyte (Fig. 15–16). There are also certain pleomorphic genera where the haploid and diploid phases are morphologically dissimilar (heteromorphic generations—see Fig. 15–17).

A third type of life history occurs, as in *Codium,* in which the diploid phase is the conspicuous generation (Fig. 15–18). Meiosis occurs at gametogenesis, with the haploid gametes being the only haploid cells in the life cycle.

Finally, an unusual type of life history is

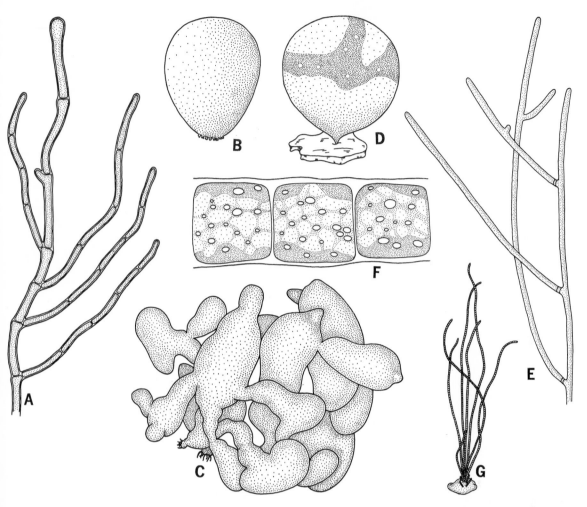

FIGURE 15–11   Morphological diversity in Chlorophyceae. Siphonous multinucleate forms (siphonous line). A, *Cladophora*, ×80; B, C, *Valonia* spp. (B, ×0.5; C, ×1). D, E, *Halicystis* (D, saclike *Halicystis*-stage, ×5; E, filamentous *Derbesia*-stage, ×120). F, G, *Urospora* (F, vegetative cells, ×460; G, habit, ×9).

exhibited in *Prasiola* where the gametophytic phase is essentially developed *in situ* on the sporophytic phase.

REPRESENTATIVE GENERA

The range of structure and reproduction is so great in the green algae that only a few examples will be considered in detail. The following types illustrate some of the fundamental characteristics of this class.

In the unicellular *Chlamydomonas,* vegetative reproduction takes place by cell division,

often while the parent cell is in the motile condition, forming 4, 8, or 16 biflagellate daughter cells (mitospores—Fig. 15–14C). Although these are morphologically similar to the parent cell, they are smaller when liberated by parental-wall breakdown but grow to the characteristic adult size. As noted, all three types of sexual reproduction occur in *Chlamydomonas*. The vegetative cell merely metamorphoses to function as a gametangium. In the most commonly occurring isogamous forms, the protoplast divides and 4, 8, 16, or 32 biflagellate gametes are formed. Morphologically, the gametes of *Chlamydomonas* are similar to zoo-

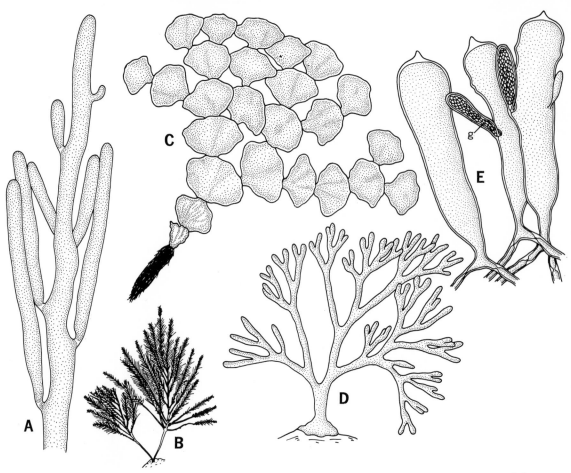

FIGURE 15–12   Morphological diversity in Chlorophyceae. Siphonous multinucleate forms (siphonous line). A, B, *Bryopsis* (A, enlarged view of branch, ×120; B, habit, ×1.5). C, *Halimeda* (habit), ×0.5: D, E, *Codium* (D, habit, ×1; E, vesicles with gametangia (*g*), ×115).

spores, except for their smaller size. However, when they are released they swim about in the water and fuse with morphologically similar gametes (Fig. 15–14H). After syngamy, for a brief period the zygote may be motile and possess four flagella (Fig. 15–14I). The flagella soon disappear; the cell rounds up and secretes a heavy, often strikingly sculptured cellulosic wall (Fig. 15–14J). This resting zygote, or zygospore as it is sometimes called, is dormant in most fresh-water species, permitting the species to tolerate extreme changes in moisture and temperature that may occur over a period of time. When appropriate conditions of moisture, light, and temperature are provided, the zygote will germinate (Fig. 15–14K). The nucleus divides meiotically (and sometimes sub-

sequently mitotically) to produce at least four biflagellate zoospores (meiospores)—(Fig. 15–14L–O). When these are released, each zoospore merely enlarges to form a vegetative cell whose size and morphology is typical of the species. Although the mitospores and meiospores differ in the way they arise, they are both haploid and are otherwise quite similar in morphology and behavior. Genetically, however, they may differ—the result of recombination of genes during syngamy and segregation during meiosis.

Control of the sexual processes has been studied extensively in a few species of *Chlamydomonas*. The haploid stage may be maintained in a mineral medium in liquid or on agar. Cells grown on agar, when suspended in water

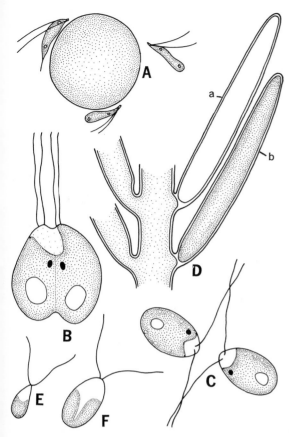

FIGURE 15–13   Sexual reproduction in Chlorophyceae. A, oogamy (*Volvox*), ×700. B, C, isogamy (*Gonium*), ×1,150. D–F, anisogamy (*Bryopsis*). D, empty (*a*) and immature (*b*) gametangia, ×50; E, F, anisogametes, ×1,250.

and illuminated, become flagellated. Within two to four hours these motile cells behave as gametes; when they are mixed with gametes of the opposite type (plus or minus), mating occurs. At first the gametes clump in large groups; then gametes of opposite mating types pair. Fusion may occur very rapidly. If the resting zygote is placed in the dark within 24 hours of formation, germination may occur after one week. When the dark-matured zygote is transferred into the light on a fresh medium, meiosis will occur with subsequent production of zoospores.

Sexuality can be induced in one species (*Chlamydomonas reinhartii*) by depletion of nitrogen in the medium, and sexual activity is lost when assimilable nitrogen is provided. However, another species (*C. moewusii*) re-

tains sexual activity in a nitrogen-containing medium as well as a nitrogen-free medium. It has been postulated, for the latter species, that sexual activation and photosynthesis are interrelated. In *C. reinhartii,* however, the effect of photosynthesis is indirect and important only in providing energy for mating and carbohydrates to tie up excess nitrogenous compounds.

In the colonial forms—such as *Gonium, Pandorina,* and *Eudorina*—each cell of the colony is capable of producing daughter colonies identical (although smaller) to the parental colony. In more advanced types, such as *Pleodorina* and *Volvox,* where division of labor occurs, only certain cells become reproductive. In all these volvocalean genera a constant number of cells is achieved; thus, the colony is a coenobium.

In most of these colonial motile forms the cells of the developing daughter colony are oriented with the apical, or flagellar, end pointing inward. It is thus necessary for the entire daughter colony to turn inside out so the flagella are on the outside of the colony. This is best seen in the large cells of *Volvox.* After the daughter colony is formed, the new coenobium inverts, as shown in Figure 15–15A–D, so that the flagella are ultimately on the outer surface of the colony. After this inversion, the daughter colony escapes from the mucilaginous matrix of the original cell and remains in the hollow center of the parent colony until the breakdown of the parental colony.

Oogamous sexual reproduction occurs in *Volvox,* with most cells remaining vegetative. A fertile cell loses its flagella, enlarges, and gives rise by mitosis to the male or female gametes. In the development of the sperm, the enlarged fertile cell forms a large number of small cells that become biflagellate sperm. Depending on the species, 16, 32, 64, 128, 256, or 512 sperm arise from repeated divisions of a single cell and are eventually liberated as a sperm packet into the water. They swim as a unit to the egg cell, which is simply a considerably enlarged vegetative cell that has lost its flagella. The sperm packet breaks down the matrix and the wall around the egg and one sperm effects syngamy *in situ.*

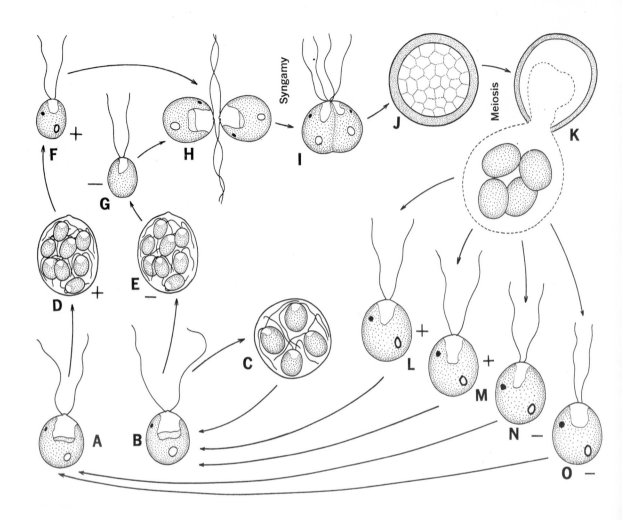

FIGURE 15–14   Zygotic life history (*Chlamydomonas*). A, B, vegetative condition; C, mitospore production; D, E, gamete production; F, G, gametes; H, fusion of isogametes (syngamy); I, planozygote; J, resting zygote; K, germinating zygote (meiosis); L–O, meiospores. (+ and − indicate mating types.)

The zygote develops a heavy wall, which is also often strikingly sculptured, pitted, or covered with spines. As is typical in fresh-water green algae, this zygote is a resting stage and meiosis occurs upon germination, resulting in one or four haploid zoospores. These zoospores initiate a new colony by repeated division similar to the formation of a daughter colony. Where only one zoospore is produced, three of the haploid nuclei formed at meiosis apparently degenerate.

In *Ulothrix* each cell of the filament, except the basal holdfast cell, is capable of producing gametes or zoospores, and a resting zygote follows syngamy. In this genus and many others in the Ulotrichales, the zoospores are quadriflagellate and the gametes biflagellate. In *Percursaria, Monostroma,* and *Ulva* each cell of the thallus may become fertile and produce gametes or zoospores, although usually the basal cells forming the holdfast remain sterile.

In *Ulva* there is usually an alternation of isomorphic generations, with sexual reproduction being isogamous or anisogamous, depending on the species (Fig. 15–16). The juvenile vegetative thallus starts out as a uniseriate filament, but divisions soon occur in the second

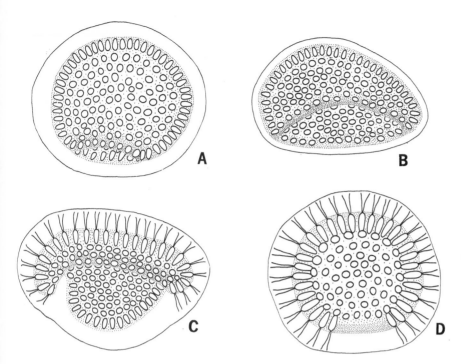

FIGURE 15–15   Daughter colony development within mother cell of *Volvox* showing one type of inversion, ×225. A, invagination beginning at lower end of colony; B, further invagination of colony; C, cells at upper end of colony evaginated so that flagella are directed outward; D, inversion almost complete with flagella directed outward.

and third plane to build up a more complex thallus, consisting of two layers. At maturity there is close contact between the two cell layers, resulting in a flat foliose plant body. The basal cells of the plant are rhizoidal and are aggregated to form a compact holdfast. Vegetatively there is little morphological difference between the haploid gametophyte (male and female) plants and the diploid sporophytic plants. In anisogamous species the male will appear orange due to the abundance of pigments in the smaller male gametes. Except for the basal cells, which usually remain sterile, all cells are potentially capable of becoming fertile and producing gametes, zoospores, or aplanospores.

The uninucleate cells of the haploid gametophytes (Fig. 15–16A, B) undergo nuclear division to produce 8, 16, or 32 terminally biflagellate gametes that are released through a pore in the wall (Fig. 15–16C, D). Syngamy occurs in the water, and for a brief period the

zygote may be quadriflagellate (Fig. 15–16H). The flagella soon disappear and the thin-walled zygote germinates, immediately forming by repeated mitotic divisions a uniseriate multicellular filament (Fig. 15–16J, K). Subsequently this filament gives rise to the typical flat foliose thallus (Fig. 15–16L). Although this phase is morphologically identical to the gametophyte, it is cytologically different, since it has diploid cells. At maturity, all cells of the thallus, except those near the base, are potentially capable of functioning as meiosporangia. Meiosis, followed by a number of mitotic divisions, produces 4, 8, or 16 terminally quadriflagellate zoospores (Fig. 15–16N, O) or aplanospores. These spores are released the same way as gametes and then settle down, losing the flagella. The spores germinate immediately, again forming by mitotic divisions first a uniseriate filament and then the typical foliose plant (Fig. 15–16A, B), which is the new gametophyte generation.

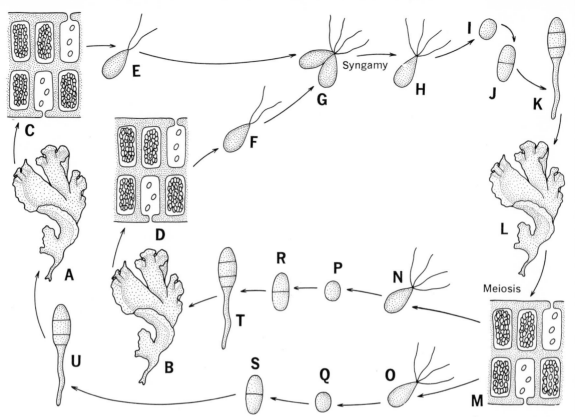

FIGURE 15–16   Sporic life history (*Ulva*) with alternation of isomorphic generations. A, B, mature gametophytes (pale margin indicates region of gamete discharge). C, D, gamete production. E, F, gametes. G, fusion of isogametes (syngamy). H, planozygote; I, zygote. J, K, filamentous juvenile sporophyte. L, mature sporophyte (pale margin indicates region of meiospore discharge). M, meiospore production (meiosis). N, O, motile meiospores. P–U, filamentous juvenile gametophytes.

In some of the forms allied to *Ulva,* quadriflagellate mitospores have also been reported in the diploid phase as an accessory method of reproduction. These zoospores apparently develop into the same type of plant from which they arose, similar to the zoospores that arise from the plurilocular sporangia of *Ectocarpus.* Possibly, haploid mitospores may also occur on the gametophytes, but this has not been demonstrated. Development of unfertilized gametes into gametophytes has been reported in some species.

An alternation of heteromorphic generations occurs in two marine forms that were considered as separate genera until their affinities became apparent from laboratory studies (Fig. 15–17). Morphologically these plants, *Derbesia* and *Halicystis,* are quite distinctive. In the *Halicystis*-stage, or gametophytic phase (Fig. 15–17A, B), the thallus is spherical and attached by coenocytic rhizoidal branches. The plants are unisexual and the gametangial regions are quite distinctive at the surface of the multinucleate thallus. The male gametangial regions are lighter in color than the female. Anisogamous, biflagellate gametes are forcibly ejected at maturity through well-defined pores in the gametangial region. The gametes fuse in the water (Fig. 15–17E) and the zygote (Fig. 15–17F) germinates immediately to form a coenocytic, multinucleate, branched thallus known as a species of *Derbesia* (Fig. 15–17G–J). At maturity the *Derbesia* stage forms well-defined sporangia, in which meiosis probably occurs. Many spores are produced in each sporangium, and at maturity these zoospores (meiospores) are liberated. In contrast to the biflagellate nature of the

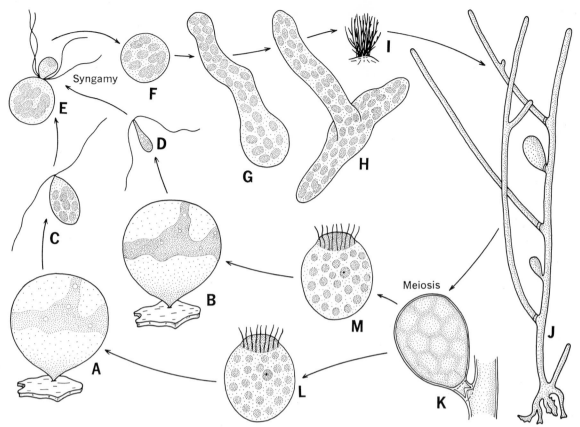

FIGURE 15–17   Sporic life history (*Halicystis*) with alternation of heteromorphic generations. A, mature female gametophyte; B, mature male gametophyte; C, female gamete; D, male gamete; E, fusion of anisogametes (syngamy); F, zygote; G, H, filamentous juvenile sporophyte; I, J, mature *Derbesia*-stage; I, habit; J, mature sporophyte with two meiosporangia; K, mature meiosporangium (meiosis); L, M, meiospores.

gametes, the zoospores are stephanokont with an anterior circlet of flagella of equal length (Fig. 15–17L, M). When these zoospores settle down after a brief swimming period, they germinate and give rise to the gametophytic *Halicystis* stage. This pleomorphic genus should now be known as *Derbesia,* since this form was described first.

In the marine form *Codium* there is a different type of life history (Fig. 15–18). In this genus, which is anisogamous, the gametes are produced in large numbers in clearly differentiated gametangia (Fig. 15–18I, J) as a result of meiosis. Syngamy (Fig. 15–18C) again occurs in the water and the resulting zygote is a thin-walled structure (Fig. 15–18E). It germinates immediately to form the massive diploid thallus of aggregated coenocytic filaments (Fig.

15–18G). Development of a thallus from an unfertilized gamete has also been reported in *Codium.*

Other orders of the Chlorophyceae that are not part of the three lines of evolution are the well-known fresh-water Zygnematales and Oedogoniales. The Zygnematales includes filamentous forms such as *Spirogyra, Zygnema,* and *Mougeotia* (Fig. 15–19A–C) and the desmids *Micrasterias, Staurastrum, Cosmarium,* and *Closterium* (Fig. 15–19D–G). No flagellated cells are produced by any members of the order. Sexual reproduction results from conjugation of somewhat amoeboid gametes, and the zygote is again a resting cell (Fig. 15–20D, C). Vegetative division is by fragmentation or cell division. In the desmids the vegetative cell is composed of two halves, or semicells, which are

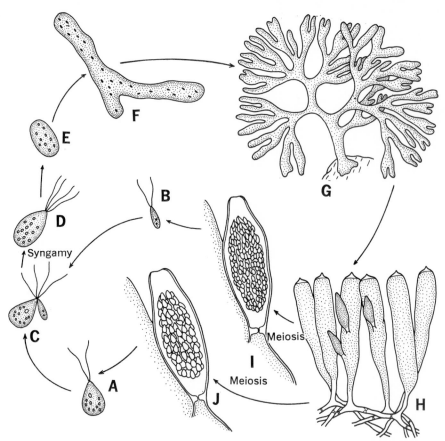

FIGURE 15–18   Gametic life history (*Codium*). A, female gamete; B, male gamete; C, fusion of anisogametes (syngamy); D, planozygote; E, zygote; F, filamentous juvenile stage; G, mature diploid thallus; H, vesicles with gametangia; I, male gametangium (meiosis); J, female gemetangium (meiosis).

mirror images. After nuclear division, each semicell regenerates itself (Fig. 15–21), producing two new identical daughter cells.

In the filamentous Oedogoniales (Fig. 15–22), both the zoospores (mitospores and meiospores) and sperm have stephanokont flagellation (Fig. 15–22C). In this order oogamy occurs and gametes are produced in specialized gametangia (Fig. 15–22B, D, E). In some species a special type of haploid mitospore **(androspore)** is produced that settles near the oogonium and forms a dwarf filament that produces sperm (Fig. 15–22E). In one species it has been shown that this special spore becomes attached to certain cells—cells that also control the direction of growth of the dwarf filament—ultimately forming an oogonium just above the point of spore attachment. The dwarf male

plant evidently produces a substance that triggers the division, resulting in the oogonium. A gelatinous material that encases the antheridia is produced by the oogonium, thus trapping the sperm. The sperm itself is further attracted to the opening in the oogonium by a substance produced at the opening.

CLASS CHAROPHYCEAE
(Stoneworts)

MORPHOLOGICAL DIVERSITY

The Charophyceae is a relatively small group commonly known as stoneworts; they occur submerged and attached to the bottom

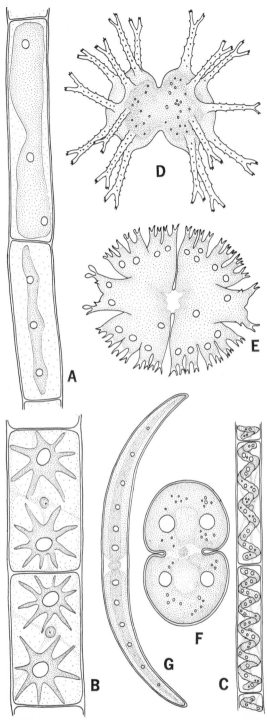

primarily in fresh water. Although there are only six genera with about 250 living species, other genera and numerous species are known only from the fossil record. Most of the forms in this class have heavily calcified walls.

This group of algae is so distinctive morphologically especially in the structure of the male reproductive organ, that some botanists place them in a separate division. The stoneworts are taxonomically remote from the other groups of green algae, but judging from their biochemical characteristics they probably have a common evolutionary origin with the Chlorophyceae there is a differentiated system of botanists consider the stoneworts closer to the bryophytes than to the algae.

The Charophyceae are morphologically distinguished by an apical growth and are differentiated into nodal and internodal regions (Fig. 15–24A, B). From the nodes, whorls of branches of limited growth arise. In some genera, as in *Chara* (Fig. 15–23B), the internodal region is covered by corticating filaments of cells, which also arise from the nodes and extend up and down over the internodal cells. In *Nitella* (Fig. 15–23A), cortication is absent. At the base of the branched thallus in Charophyceae. It is interesting to note that some branched septate rhizoidal filaments. Most of the cells are uninucleate, but the large internodal cells are often multinucleate.

REPRODUCTION AND LIFE HISTORY

Vegetative reproduction occurs by fragmentation of specialized groups of cells, but zoospores are never produced. Oogamous sexual reproduction is the chief method of reproduction, and most species produce both male and female reproductive organs on the same thallus (Fig. 23B). The oogonia (Fig. 15–24C) may be considered unicellular; however, the male reproductive organs are multicellular and structurally complex (Fig. 15–24D, E).

In *Chara,* the oogonium, containing a single egg, is borne at a nodal region of the thallus

FIGURE 15–19   Morphological diversity in Zygnemales. A–C, filamentous types. A, *Mougeotia,* ×510; B, *Zygnema,* ×735; C, *Spirogyra,* ×215. D–G, unicellular desmids. D, *Staurastrum,* ×264; E, *Micrasterias,* ×274; F, *Cosmarium,* ×220; G, *Closterium,* ×524.

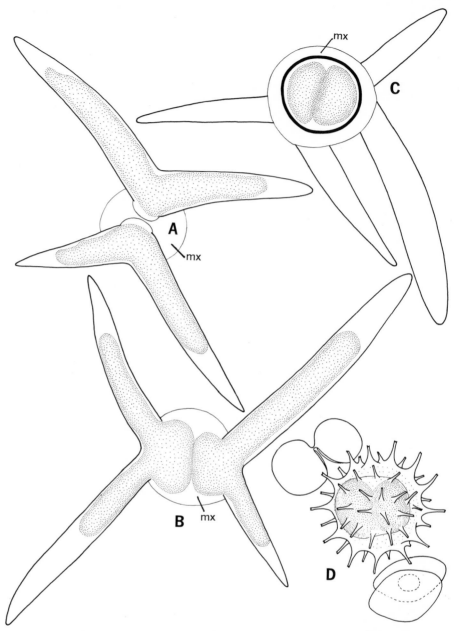

FIGURE 15–20　　Sexual reproduction in desmids. A, B, fusion of amoeboid gametes of *Closterium* within mucilaginous matrix (*mx*). C, D, zygotes. C, young zygote of *Closterium*, ×350; D, resting zygote of *Cosmarium*, ×350.

on a short stalk-like cell. There are five sterile vegetative sheath cells, which originate beneath the oogonium and grow up in a spiral fashion around the oogonium to form a protecting sheath of cells. At maturity the sheath cells reach to and cover the tip of the oogonium. At the end of each sheath cell one or two small cells, called **coronal** cells, are cut off (Fig. 15–24C). The sperm must penetrate between these coronal cells to come in contact with the egg cell. The entire female reproductive structure, including its outer protective cells, is commonly referred to as a **nucule.**

In contrast to the relatively simple devel-

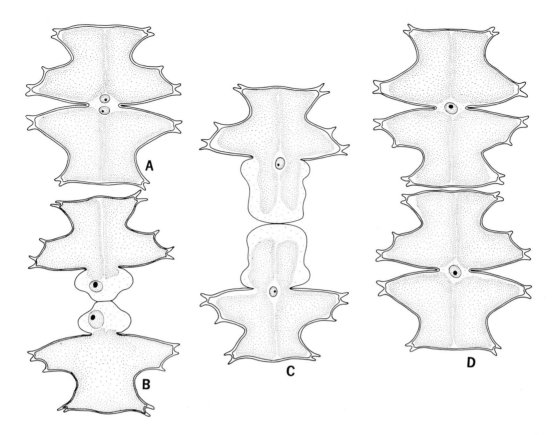

FIGURE 15–21   Asexual reproduction in desmids showing semicell regeneration in *Micrasterias,* ×350. A, binucleate condition of cell; B, C, stages in regeneration of new semicells (note chloroplast and nucleus positions in new semicell); D, regeneration of semicells complete.

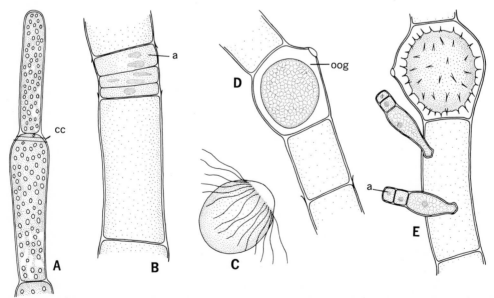

FIGURE 15–22   Morphology of *Oedogonium.* A, part of vegetative filament showing ring or cellulose cap (*cc*), ×290; B, filament with narrow, immature antheridial cells (*a*), ×740; C, multiflagellate sperm, ×1,700; D, filament with mature oogonium (*oog*) containing single egg, ×740; E, filament with spiny resting zygote and epiphytic dwarf male plants, each with two antheridia, ×875.

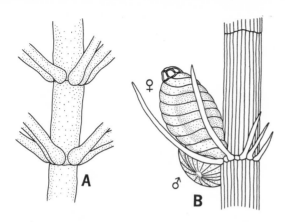

FIGURE 15–23   Morphology of Charophyceae. A, uncorticated axis of *Nitella,* ×300; B, corticated axis of *Chara* with female gametangium (above) and male gametangium (below) attached at the nodal region, ×300.

opment of the female reproductive organ, the male reproductive structure of *Chara* is the most complex in the algae. It is also borne at a nodal region of the thallus and generally appears as a spherical structure attached by a short stalk-like cell. At an early stage in its development (Fig. 15–24D) there is an outer sterile layer of cells cut out and differentiated from an inner fertile group of cells. This is very similar in theory to the development of a bryophyte antheridium. The outer cells enlarge and at maturity form eight sterile cells. Attached to the inner surface of each of these cells is a small cell, from which ultimately arise cells that form one or more antheridial filaments (Fig. 15–24E). Each cell of the antheridial filament produces a single coiled sperm, which has two coiled flagella extending backward from the apical point of attachment. This type of sperm, which is comparable to that of some higher plants, is possibly indicative of the close affinity of the stoneworts and bryophytes. Each cell of the antheridial filament, or the whole structure (the **globule**), may be interpreted as being a separate antheridium.

Syngamy occurs *in situ* after the sperm passes between the coronal cells, and the zygote secretes a heavy wall. The zygote with the remnant of the surrounding sheath generally persists as a resting stage. At germination, the zygote nucleus divides meiotically to produce

four haploid nuclei. Three of these apparently degenerate, and the functional nucleus produces first a filamentous stage, the **protonema** (Fig. 15–24B), which eventually gives rise to the typical thallus with apical growth.

DISTRIBUTION AND ECOLOGY OF CHLOROPHYTA

Few other groups of algae have such a wide range of distribution and variety of habitat as the Chlorophyta. They may occur wherever there is some moisture and light available. Green algae are common free-floating or swimming in the plankton of lakes, ponds, rivers, streams, and to a lesser extent in the oceans. However, they can be very abundant in tide pools. In confined areas, or where there are dense blooms of planktonic green algae, the water may appear grass-green. There are many larger attached forms, especially in the ocean where the Chlorophyta have a broad vertical range of distribution through the intertidal zone into deeper water. In colder waters, they are more conspicuous in the shallower regions and in the intertidal zone; but in warm waters they may extend to depths exceeding 100 meters.

Although most green algae are aquatic, some—such as *Fritschiella* and the ubiquitous *Pleurococcus*—are terrestrial and occur on damp surfaces, such as the trunks of trees, moist walls, and the surfaces of leaves. Some, such as *Chlorococcum,* occur in the soil or as the algal component of lichens. The commonest cause of "red snow" is due to the presence of cytoplasmic hematochrome in representatives of the Volvocales and Chlorococcales. Some orders—such as Siphonocladales and Dasycladales—are strictly marine, whereas the Zygnematales and Oedogoniales occur only in fresh water. Most of the other orders occur in both habitats. Similarly some genera are strictly marine, as are *Codium, Acetabularia, Siphonocladus, Dictyosphaeria,* and *Chamaedoris;* others are strictly freshwater, such as *Volvox* and *Fritschiella;* and still others have both fresh-

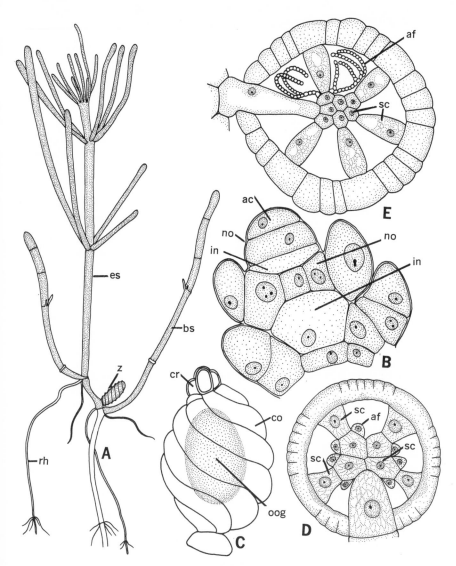

FIGURE 15–24   Morphology of *Chara*. A, juvenile thallus originating from germinating zygote (*z*) with protonemal basal system (*bs*), rhizoids (*rh*), and erect system (*es*) with whorls of branchlets, ×225. B, apex of thallus, showing apical cell (*ac*) and initiation of alternating nodal (*no*) and internodal (*in*) regions, ×395. C, nucule (female gametangium) with twisted cover cells (*co*) and short coronal cells (*cr*) protecting oogonium (*oog*). D, immature globule (male gametangium) with preantheridial filaments (*af*) and sterile cells (*sc*), ×845. E, mature globule with antheridial filaments and sterile cells, ×750. (A, D, after Smith with permission of McGraw-Hill Book Co.)

water and marine species, such as *Cladophora*.

Some of the nonplanktonic green algae occur epiphytically on larger algae or aquatic seed plants; others occur in large free-floating or submerged mats. Some Chlorophyceae occur inside the shells of molluscs, or within the tissues of higher plants. Others (*Zoochlorella*) live symbiotically within the cells of certain protozoa and other invertebrates. As noted earlier, some Chlorophyceae are colorless and occur as saprobes or as plant or animal parasites.

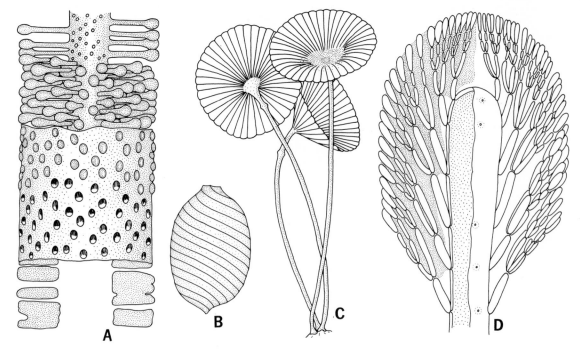

FIGURE 15–25   A–D, living and fossil Chlorophyta. A, C, D, Dasycladales (A, *Rhabdoporella*, fossil, ×180; C, *Acetabularia*, living, ×1.5; D, *Paleodasycladus*, fossil, ×25). B, fossil *Chara* nucule showing spirally twisted cover cells, ×30. (A, B, after Pia in Hirmer's *Handbuch der Paläobotanik,* with permission of R. Oldenbourg.)

IMPORTANCE AND USES

The green algae, like all green plants, are important primary producers. Although the planktonic Chlorophyceae are apparently less important in the sea than other phytoplankton, they are one of the important groups of algae in the fresh-water phytoplankton. The attached forms are also important in this respect in shallower regions of both fresh water and the sea. The planktonic forms may be more important in the sea than is apparent, but these green algae are still poorly known in the marine environment. In confined areas the motile stages of multicellular attached marine forms may be quite abundant and conspicuous.

Man rarely uses green algae directly. Species of marine genera, such as *Ulva* (sea lettuce) and *Monostroma,* have been used as food (laver) in some countries (especially Japan and Wales), but green algae as such are not generally used as food. Culture studies have demonstrated the feasibility of using some of the smaller planktonic forms, such as *Chlorella,* as a source of food; this has been tried to some extent in Japan and Israel.

Some Chlorophyceae may become contaminants in domestic supplies of fresh water and give a disagreeable flavor to the water. Plankton forms of green algae are often useful in oxidation ponds in sewage treatment plants. As a result of their photosynthetic activity, these minute forms may produce an abundance of oxygen, which is necessary to achieve rapid decomposition of raw sewage by bacteria. The nutrients so released are used by the algae for growth.

PHYLOGENY

Various fossil green algae of uncertain taxonomic affinities are reported from as far back as the Pre-Cambrian Period. However, a number of groups have left an excellent record; some of these are clearly related to modern

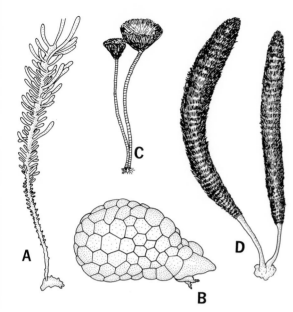

FIGURE 15–26   Living members of Dascladales, Siphonocladales, and Siphonales. A, *Siphonocladus*, ×3.5; B, *Dictyosphaeria* (young), ×6; C, *Chamaedoris*, ×0.6; D, *Dasycladus*, ×3. (B, after Egerod with permission of University of California Press.)

representatives of the Chlorophyceae. The earliest of these fossils is found in the Ordovician Period, but the Chlorophyta are well represented throughout the geological record up to modern times. Forms that can be unquestionably identified with the Dasycladales have been particularly well preserved. These groups are most closely related to the siphonous line of evolution. Characteristically they have an outer layer of calcium carbonate, which at the death of the alga remains as a mold in which further calcite is deposited. In this way are left recognizable fossils, which have contributed significantly to the formation of certain limestones. The Dasycladales are particularly abundant in Permian, Triassic, and Tertiary deposits. They apparently reached their greatest diversity and complexity in the Triassic and Jurassic periods, but have declined since then. Of some 70 genera referred to the Dasycladales, about 60 are known only from the fossil record. The remainder comprise six genera known only as living forms, and four with both living and fossil representatives, such as *Acetabularia*

(Fig. 15–25C). The fossil genus *Rhabdoporella* (Fig. 15–25A) is apparently the most primitive known member of the Dasycladales. It is a slender cylindrical calcareous thallus studded with pores, and occurs in Ordovician and Silurian rocks. Also from the Ordovician and Silurian are forms very similar to living genera, such as the fossil *Paleodasycladus* (Fig. 15–25D), which closely resembles the living *Dasycladus* (Fig. 15–26D).

Certain of the Siphonales, especially forms similar to the lime-encrusted living genus *Halimeda* (Fig. 15–12C), have been very important. They probably occurred as far back as the Ordovician Period, but they definitely occur in the Permian and have been abundant in many areas in the Tertiary. *Halimeda* is believed to have been important in the past (as well as in the present) in reef building, although subsidiary to the encrusting coralline red algae. In the Siphonales, the fossil genus *Dimorphosiphon* from the Ordovician is thought to be closely related to *Halimeda;* it is a calcareous form with a nonseptate, branched, filamentous thallus.

The Charophyceae have also left a substantial fossil record from the Silurian Period on, although the records are fragmentary and restricted largely to the oogonia (Fig. 15–25B). These fossil structures, which resemble the oogonia of present-day *Chara,* are particularly abundant in Lower Tertiary beds. Many genera are known only from the fossil record, but there are others, such as *Nitella* and *Chara,* which have numerous living as well as fossil representatives.

Thus, the green algae is undoubtedly an extremely ancient group of plants. Some believe that they are derived from photosynthetic bacteria and that all other groups of algae, except the Cyanophyta and the Rhodophyta, may have been derived from the Chlorophyta. If all these complex fossil types of green algae have had a common origin with the simpler, colonial, unicellular types, then the prototype of the division must indeed have had its origin in some very ancient stock. At the same time, most botanists agree that higher plants must have evolved from the green algae. The structure of the green algae is not as complex as that of some of the Rhodophyta or Phaeophyta. However, it must be remembered that the more highly evolved Chlorophyceae probably gave rise to land plants such as mosses or ferns. The nature of the pigment complex, the biochemical nature of both the cell walls and the food reserves offer some support for this view.

It is also apparent in this direct line of evolution that a number of significant offshoots have occurred. In some instances, these have terminated in rather complex forms that, although advanced, have features that are actually "dead ends" in an evolutionary series. This termination of a line is somewhat self-imposed, since the complexities produced are the ultimate that a group of organisms can achieve from a basic stock. The volvocine line is one of the most complete and striking examples of this. The very simple *Chalmydomonas* serves as a starting point for several lines. The motile colonial forms, culminating in *Volvox,* indicate a greater and greater degree of specialization. The ultimate and subsequent end form is the large round colony with hundreds of cells, most of which are vegetative. The Zygnematales and Oedogoniales also seem to have been offshoots from the main lines of evolution; their precise origin is very obscure. Similarly, the siphonous line (Siphonales, Dasycladales, and Siphonocladales), although giving rise to very complex genera, has not led to other plant groups. The siphonous line appears to have been more successful in the past and at present is diminishing in numbers (Fig. 15–26). On the other hand, since the parenchymatous and heterotrichous habits and oogamous sexual reproduction have become well developed in the tetrasporine line, it may have been the stock from which higher plants have evolved.

REFERENCES

Borge, O., and Pascher, A., *Zygnemales.* In Pascher, A. (Ed.), *Die Süsswasser-Flora Deutschlands, Österreichs, und der Schweiz.* Vol. 9. Jena: G. Fischer (1913).

Egerod, L. E., "An Analysis of the Siphonous Chlorophycophyta, with Special Reference to the Siphoncladales, Siphonales, and Dasycladales of Hawaii." *Univ. Calif. Publ. Bot.,* 25: 325–454 (1952).

Friedmann, I., "Structure, Life-history, and Sex Determination of *Prasiola stipitata* Suhr." *Ann. Bot., N. S.,* 23: 571–594 (1959).

Fritsch, F. E., *The Structure and Reproduction of the Algae.* Vol. 1. Cambridge: Cambridge University Press (1935). Pp. 60–469.

Gemeinhardt, K., *Oedogoniales.* In Rabenhorst, L. (Ed.), *Kryptogamen-Flora Deutschlands, Österreichs, und der Schweiz,* 2nd Ed. Vol. 12. Leipzig: Akademische Verlagsgeschellshaft (1938–1940).

Heering, W., *Chlorophyceae 3.* In Pascher, A. (Ed.), *Süsswasser-Flora Deutschlands, Österreichs, und der Schweiz.* Vol. 6. Jena: G. Fischer (1914).

Heering, W., *Chlorophyceae 4.* In Pascher, A. (Ed.), *Süsswasser-Flora Deutschlands, Österreichs, und der Schweiz.* Vol. 7. Jena: G. Fischer (1921).

Huber-Pestalozzi, G., *Das Phytoplankton des Süsswassers.* Vol. 16, Pt. 5. In Thienemann, A. (Ed.), *Die Binnengewässer.* Stuttgart: E. Schweizerbart'sche Verlagsbuchhandlung (1961).

Iyengar, M. O. P., "Chlorophyta." In Smith, G. M. (Ed.), *Manual of Phycology*. Waltham, Mass.: Chronica Botanica (1951). Pp. 21–67.

Kolkwitz, R., and Krieger, H., *Zygnemales*. In Rabenhorst, L. (Ed.), *Kryptogamen-Flora von Deutschland, Österreich, und der Schweiz*. Vol. 13(2). Leipzig: Akademische Verlagsgeschellshaft (1941–1944).

Krieger, W., *Desmidiaceen*. In Rabenhorst, L. (Ed.), *Kryptogamen-Flora von Deutschland, Oesterreich, und der Schweiz*. Vol. 13(1). Leipzig: Akademische Verlagsgeschellshaft (1937).

Krieger, W., and Gerloff, J., "Die Gattung *Cosmarium*." *Nova Hedwigia*, Suppl. 1 (1962).

Lemmerman, E., Brunnthaler, J., and Pascher, A., *Chlorophyceae 2*. In Pascher, A. (Ed.), *Süsswasser-Flora Deutschlands, Österreichs, und der Schweiz*. Vol. 5. Jena: G. Fischer (1915).

Levine, R. P., and Ebersold, W. T., "The Genetics and Cytology of *Chlamydomonas*." *Ann. Rev. Microbiol.*, 14: 197–216 (1960).

Pascher, A. and Printz, H., *Chlorophyceae 1*. In Pascher, A. (Ed.), *Süsswasser-Flora Deutschlands, Österreichs, und der Schweiz*. Vol. 4. Jena: G. Fischer (1927).

Randhawa, M. S., *Zygnemaceae*. New Delhi, India: Indian Council Agric. Res. (1959).

Rawitscher-Kunkel, E., and Machlis, L., "The Hormonal Integration of Sexual Reproduction in *Oedogonium*." *Am. J. Bot.*, 49: 177–183 (1962).

Smith, G. M., *Marine Algae of the Monterey Peninsula, California*. Palo Alto, Calif.: Stanford University Press (1944). Pp. 25–76.

Smith, G. M., *Cryptogamic Botany*, 2nd Ed. Vol. 1: *Algae and Fungi*. New York: McGraw-Hill Book Co., Inc. (1955). Pp. 12–130.

Starr, R. C., "A Comparative Study of *Chlorococcum* Meneghini and Other Spherical, Zoospore-producing Genera of the Chlorococcales." *Indiana Univ. Publ. Sci. Ser. No. 20* (1955).

Taylor, W. R., *Marine Algae of the Northeastern Coast of North America*, 2nd Ed. Ann Arbor: University of Michigan Press (1957). Pp. 36–95.

Tiffany, L. H., *Oedogoniaceae, a Monograph*. Columbus, Ohio: Published by the Author (1930).

Tiffany, L. H., *Oedogoniales: Oedogoniaceae*. North Amer. Flora, 11(1). New York: New York Botanical Garden (1937).

Transeau, E. M., *The Zygnemataceae*. Columbus, Ohio: Ohio State University Press (1951).

West, G. S., West, W., and Carter, N., *A Monograph of the British Desmidiaceae*. Vols. 1–5. London: Ray Society (1904–1923).

Wood, R. D., "A Review of the Genus *Nitella* (Characeae) of North America." *Farlowia*, 3: 331–398 (1948).

16 / DIVISION

BRYOPHYTA

The mosses and moss allies belong to a single division, the Bryophyta. This division includes the most primitive of the green land plants; in both morphology and anatomy *bryophytes* are structurally simple. Both gametophyte and sporophyte are relatively conspicuous, and each has evolved a number of distinctive features. Bryophytes are a potentially significant, but generally neglected, source of information concerning chromosomal influence on the morphology of both diploid and haploid generations.

Often the bryophytes are described as archegoniate plants. Like the primitive vascular plants, bryophytes possess a peculiar multicellular female sex organ, the **archegonium,** in which the egg is enclosed (Fig. 16–1B, C). In bryophytes the archegonium is always flask-shaped, whereas in flowering plants a discrete flask-shaped organ is replaced by a much-reduced structure of more complex cytological development.

Some authors use the name Atracheata in preference to Bryophyta for this division of plants. This name avoids the confusion caused by the different applications of the term Bryophyta and emphasizes that the plants lack a vascular system. Some authors restrict the division Bryophyta to include only the mosses. In such instances, the hepatics and hornworts belong to a single division, the Hepatophyta; or the hepatics are placed in a separate division, the Hepatophyta, and the hornworts in yet another, the Anthocerophyta. In this text the division Bryophyta includes liverworts, hornworts, and mosses—each of which is accorded a separate class.

The Bryophyta form an isolated group; they are not closely related to any other plant group nor have they served as ancestors to other groups of plants. Of all of the plant groups, the Psilophyta and Pterophyta appear to show closest relationships. On this basis the bryophytes are believed to have originated from psilophyte or pre-psilophyte ancestors. Another view is that bryophytes may have evolved from a green algal ancestor rather than from a primitive vascular plant group.

The Bryophyta are generally divided into three classes: Hepaticae (liverworts), Anthocerotae (hornworts), and Musci (mosses). The Hepaticae are represented by approximately 9,000 species in 240 genera; the Anthocerotae by five genera and approximately 100 species; the Musci include approximately 670 genera and nearly 14,500 species.

All Bryophyta are small: the largest erect forms are less than 60 cm tall; some creeping or aquatic mosses are more than a meter long; and in cool rain forests some epiphytic mosses reach lengths of more than 60 cm. The smallest bryophytes are nearly microscopic; the moss *Ephemerum serratum* is about 1 to 2 mm high, and some species of the hepatic *Cephalozia* are barely visible to the unaided eye.

Most bryophytes are strictly terrestrial and grow in humid environments; however, some grow in arid sites and a few are essentially aquatic. No bryophytes grow submerged in salt water and none will tolerate the heat in hot springs. However, some—such as *Grimmia maritima*—are largely restricted to the seashore, and others grow well near hot springs.

Bryophytes have no special absorptive structures for mineral and water uptake and, in most, no complex internal conducting system for circulating raw materials for photosynthesis. A number of mosses, but rarely liverworts, possess a central conducting strand in the stem. In such mosses, water containing nutrients is absorbed from the substrate by rhizoids and is conducted to the leaves and the rest of the plant through the conducting strand. Most bryophytes absorb water rapidly, and some, especially *Sphagnum,* can absorb immense quantities. However, all bryophytes desiccate very rapidly when in a dry atmosphere.

GAMETOPHYTE

The **gametophyte,** the conspicuous generation in most bryophytes, is thallose (strap-shaped) or leafy. In the latter case, the main shoot (or **caulid**) bears lateral flattened leaves (or **phyllids**). The leaves are generally a single cell thick but may be several cells thick in some forms. Usually, the stem is also a simple structure. The outer (cortical) cells tend to be larger or smaller than those of the central cylinder. Initially these cortical cells generally contain chlorophyll, but in most bryophytes the green pigment is lost as the gametophyte ages.

The gametophyte is either annual or perennial. In some bryophytes, much of the thallus dies back during the unfavorable season, but portions persist and regenerate the gametophyte with the return of favorable conditions.

The gametophyte is generally attached to the substrate by means of rhizoids. In most bryophytes these rhizoids have no absorptive function. They are either branched or unbranched filaments of cells; or each is an elongated tube-like cell arising from either the stem or leaves and extending into or over the substrate.

In bryophytes the female sex organ (Fig. 16–1B, C) is microscopic, flask-shaped, and multicellular. The **neck** is generally five or six cells in circumference, and this outer **unistratose** (one cell thick) layer surrounds an inner filament of cells which fills the **neck canal.** The lower swollen portion of the archegonium is the **venter,** which is often more than one cell thick and encloses the single egg. The archegonium often has a short multicellular stalk. The neck canal of the mature archegonium ultimately contains the semifluid remains of disintegrated neck canal cells, which diffuse out when water surrounds the archegonium. Generally, each gametophyte produces several archegonia,

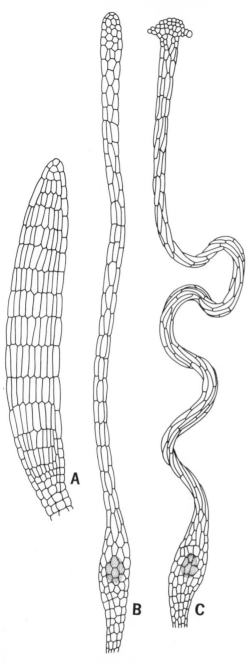

phyte by a stalk, is always multicellular, and is either elongate or spherical. The outer jacket of cells is always sterile, and each of the many inner cells gives rise to a single sperm. When the antheridium is mature and wet, the jacket bursts by turgor pressure, releasing hundreds of anteriorly biflagellate, coiled sperm. One of these unites with an egg to form the zygote.

SPOROPHYTE

Although some bryophytes are not known to produce sporophytes, most develop a sporophyte by mitotic division of the zygote, differentiating to produce a morphologically distinct structure. As the sporophyte develops, the venter and stalk cells of the archegonium also divide to form an enclosure—the **calyptra**—which protects the developing sporophyte. In most sporophytes the basal cells, or **foot,** form an haustorial connection with the gametophyte, so that food manufactured by the gametophyte is available to the developing sporophyte. The sporophyte itself usually contains chlorophyll until the spores are produced. However, as the sporophyte matures, the chlorophyll disappears.

LIFE HISTORY

The basic life cycle of a bryophyte begins with the germination of the haploid spore, which generally produces a photosynthetic gametophyte (Fig. 16–2, 3). The gametophyte begins as a much-branched, filamentous **protonema** in most mosses; but in most liverworts and hornworts it begins as a very simple, few-celled protonema that produces a more highly differentiated thallose or leafy gametophyte. The protonema is a relatively undifferentiated multicellular structure that precedes the development of the leafy or thallose gametophyte. The gametophyte bears the antheridia and archegonia. The sperm, expelled from the mature antheridia, at first swim randomly in the water immersing the antheridia. But as a sperm enters the neck cell fluid diffusing from the

FIGURE 16–1   Sex organs of bryophytes. A–C, *Polytrichum formosum*. A, antheridium, ×180; B, archegonium showing egg (surrounded by venter), and the elongate neck, ×180; C, archegonium after fertilization, ×180. (After Schimper.)

which are often surrounded by a protective sleeve or an envelope of leaves.

The male sex organ, the antheridium (Fig. 16–1A), is generally attached to the gameto-

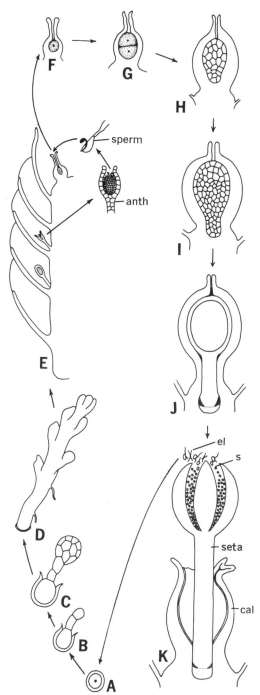

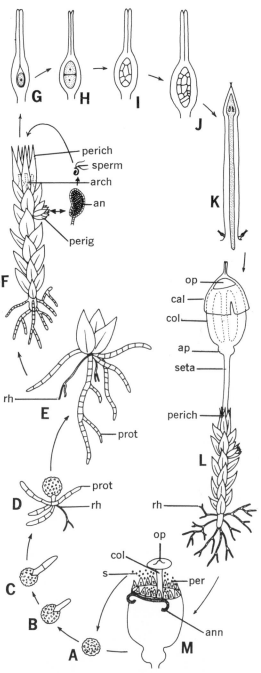

FIGURE 16–2   Life cycle of typical leafy hepatic. A–D, germination of spore and development of gametophyte; E, detail of apex of fertile shoot showing antheridia, archegonium, and fertilization; F–J, development of zygote and differentiation of sporophyte; K, mature sporangium bursting to shed spores. *an*, antheridium; *cal*, calyptra; *el*, elater; *seta*, seta; *s*, spore; *sperm*, sperm. (After Schuster with permission of *American Midland Naturalist*.)

FIGURE 16–3   Life cycle of typical moss. A–E, germination of spore and development of gametophyte; F, mature gametophyte showing antheridium, archegonia, and fertilization; G–K, development of zygote and differentiation of sporophyte; L, gametophyte bearing mature sporophyte; M, detail of sporangium, showing spore release. *ann*, annulus; *an*, antheridium; *ap*, apophysis; *arch*, archegonium; *cal*, calyptra; *col*, columella; *op*, operculum; *per*, peristome tooth; *perich*, perichaetium; *perig*, perigonium; *prot*, protonema; *rh*, rhizoid; *seta*, seta; *s*, spore; *sperm*, sperm.

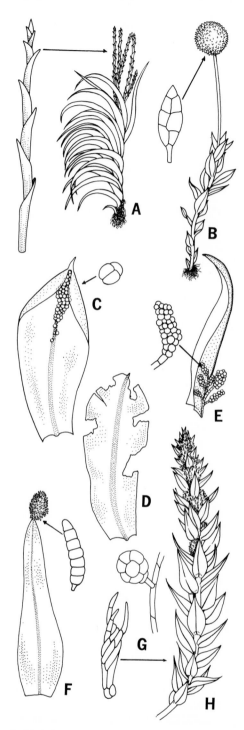

archegonium, it moves toward the area of greater concentration of this material, and consequently travels down the neck of the archegonium to the egg. The fusion of sperm and egg (syngamy) results in the zygote, the first cell of the diploid ($2n$) sporophyte generation. In most bryophytes the sporophyte differentiates into a **seta** (or stalk), which raises the **capsule** (spore case) above the gametophyte. In some bryophytes this seta is short or absent. However, in all bryophytes the sporophyte produces both sterile cells and **spore mother cells.** The details of differentiation are significant in distinguishing the major classes and subclasses. The spore mother cells undergo meiosis, and each produces a tetrad of meiospores, which are released from the mature capsule. The spore wall is often sculptured or pitted in a pattern characteristic to the species. In some bryophytes the spore develops into a multicellular mass while within the capsule; in such instances, a protonema is not produced. In most cases the spore is wind-borne and, if it lands in a suitable environment, germinates to produce the gametophyte.

Many bryophytes can also reproduce by vegetative means. Any young cell in the gametophyte or sporophyte of most bryophytes is capable of producing an entire gametophyte. In some bryophytes, nearly any part of a gametophyte—special branches, paraphyses, rhizoids, leaves, or stems—can produce special asexual reproductive bodies such as **gemmae** (Fig. 16–4, 5). Structure and position of these reproductive bodies is constant for any species. A gemma differentiates into a new gametophyte, or into a filamentous protonema, from which the gametophyte ultimately arises.

NUTRITION AND DISTRIBUTION

Little is known about nutrition in bryophytes, but they obtain much of their basic

FIGURE 16–4   Asexual reproduction in mosses. A, *Dicranum flagellare*, with deciduous flagelliferous shoots, ×2; B, *Aulacomnium androgynum*, with gemmiferous shoot, ×3; C, *Tortula papillosa*, leaf with gemmae on costa, ×5; D, *Tortula fragilifolia*, showing gaps, fragments from which serve as propagants, ×5; E, *Grimmia torquata*, with gemmiferous clusters at costa base, ×4; F, *Ulota phyllantha*, with gemmae at costa apex, ×5; G, rhizoidal gemma of *Bryum violaceum*, ×25; H, gemma clusters of *Pohlia camptotrachela*, ×4.

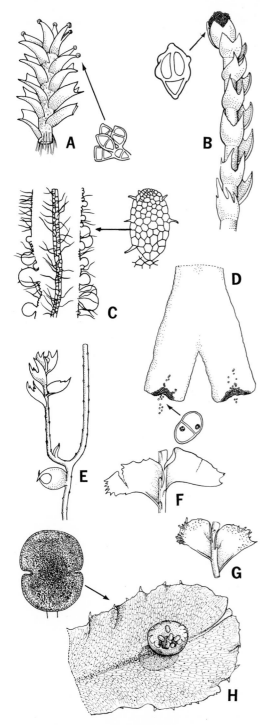

nutrient requirement from substances dissolved in atmospheric moisture. Some substances are probably absorbed directly from the substrate by diffusion through the cells of the gametophyte. Since most bryophytes possess chlorophyll, they manufacture their own food by photosynthesis. Only one, the hepatic *Cryptothallus mirabilis,* lacks chlorophyll; it is nutritionally dependent on fungi associated with it. As in other land plants, bryophytes store food in the form of carbohydrates, fats, and proteins. In a number of hepatics, elaborate oil bodies are conspicuous in cells of the leaves or other parts of the thallus (Fig. 16–8).

In the tropics bryophytes reach their greatest diversity, but they occur in all parts of the world. In frigid climates mosses are more common than hepatics, and in the North Temperate Zone the vegetation of moist habitats is made up largely of mosses. In temperate coniferous forests the growth of moss carpets is often extensive. In North America the richest bryophyte flora and vegetation is found in the humid parts of the Pacific Coast and in the high rainfall areas of the southern Appalachian Mountains; in these areas deep masses of bryophytes often cover the forest floor and cliffs, and epiphytic bryophytes festoon the trees.

ECOLOGY

Like all land plants, bryophytes vary in the climates and substrates where they can thrive. Some bryophytes grow only on a particular kind of wood in a certain stage of decay; others occur only in acid bogs or alkaline fens. Some species grow either on cliffs of acidic rock

FIGURE 16–5   Asexual reproduction in hepatics. A, *Lophozia ascendens,* with gemmae on apical leaf lobes, ×15; B, *Sphenolobus minutus,* with gemmiferous mass at apex of shoot, ×45; C, *Metzgeria* sp., with marginal gemmae on thallus, ×15; D, fragment of gemmiferous section of *Riccardia palmata* thallus, showing terminally produced gemmae, ×15; E, *Plagiochila tridenticulata* shoot showing barren stem from which propagating caducous leaves have fallen, ×14; F, *Plagiochila yokogurensis fragilifolia* shoot sector showing partially caducous leaves that can propagate new gametophytes, ×9; G, *Plagiochila virginica* shoot sector with gemma-bearing leaves, ×6; H, *Marchantia polymorpha* thallus with gemma cup containing gemmae, ×2. (A–G, after Schuster with permission of *American Midland Naturalist.*)

or on the smooth hard acidic bark of living trees.

Many bryophytes are significant pioneers on newly exposed substrates. Many mosses and leafy liverworts colonize bare rock surfaces. By building up organic material, they produce a water- and mineral-retaining substrate on which vascular plants can grow, ultimately entirely covering a site with vegetation. In the aquatic environment bryophytes are also important pioneers—for example, the moss *Sphagnum* in acid lakes, and species of the mosses *Drepanocladus* and *Calliergon* in alkaline waters.

Some bryophytes can grow in deep shade, but others flourish in direct sunlight. Most hepatics grow in fairly deep shade; those that grow in bright sunlight often are deeply pigmented. Although the pigment is confined to the cell walls, it obscures the chlorophyll, making the gametophytes appear dark red, brown, or nearly black.

Many bryophytes with sufficiently plastic morphology exhibit different growth forms in different environments. Thus, bryophyte growth forms can be used, to a certain degree, to determine the nature of the microclimate. For example, small cushions are most frequent in environments where water may be limiting; weft-forming mosses, which consist of interwoven gametophytes closely appressed to the substratum, tend to be more conspicuous in more humid shaded situations. These two growth forms are relatively common, but other species form two kinds of turfs: short turfs in a velvety mass of closely packed erect gametophytes or tall turfs in a loose thick carpet of erect gametophytes. Among the mat-forming species are those composed of relatively large much-branched plants. In these mats the creeping gametophytes interweave to form a loose springy carpet. These mats abound in humid coastal forests in some parts of North America.

In some species of leafy hepatics, such as *Scapania,* the morphology of the gametophyte is altered when growing in extreme environments and appears superficially like other species commonly found in that environment. The morphology of the more stable sporophyte betrays the true identity of the plant.

CLASS HEPATICAE
(Liverworts)

Most hepatics possess a dorsiventrally flattened gametophyte that is either a strap-shaped branching thallus or is leafy. In the latter instance the larger leaves are arranged bilaterally on the stem; and a row of small leaves, or **amphigastria,** is ventrally located on the stem (Fig. 16–7E, F). In some genera amphigastria are absent; in others they are indistinguishable from the lateral leaves.

Since the leaves always lack a true midrib or **costa,** they are generally one cell thick throughout. Leaves are frequently notched at the tip or variously lobed. The cells are generally isodiametric. In some genera the corners of the cell wall are thickened, restricting the cell protoplast. These corner thickenings, found only in hepatics, are termed **trigones** (Fig. 16–8E).

The gametophyte generally develops directly from the spore without any extensive preliminary protonema. Thus, an apical cell is differentiated early, dividing in several planes and producing a recognizable **thallose** or leafy gametophyte. When present, rhizoids are unicellular and lack chlorophyll.

The sporophyte may possess little chlorophyll, and it has a very short maturity (generally only a few days). The archegonium sheaths the developing sporophyte until the spores are mature and the capsule is fully developed. However, when the seta elongates, the capsule is pushed through the apex of the archegonium, which has grown to produce a sleeve. The seta is often colorless, whereas the mature capsule is usually dark brown.

The cells of the capsule wall frequently possess transverse thickenings and stomata are absent. In the differentiation of the capsule, the outer cells **(amphithecium)** produce the capsule jacket. The inner cells **(endothecium)** differentiate further into spore mother cells and sterile cells. The sterile cells, termed **elaters,** usually possess spiral thickenings and are hygroscopic —i.e., they coil and uncoil in response to changes in humidity. These sterile cells often effectively help to discharge spores from the capsule. In some hepatics—e.g., *Frullania*—contraction of the elaters just before capsule dehiscence is responsible for explosive discharge of the spores. In all hepatics, spores are discharged as soon as the capsule wall ruptures, although some may be expelled later by hygroscopic movement of the elaters. The capsule jacket usually splits open by four longitudinal slits derived from previously differentiated lines of weakness.

All hepatics possess apical growth. Many thallose forms branch dichotomously. In leafy, and many thallose forms, branching appears superficially irregular, although the branches are generally bilaterally arranged on the main stem. Growth continues through the favorable season, which normally coincides with the highest annual humidity and with temperatures well above freezing. During the later stages of this growth the sporophytes generally mature and release their spores.

Most hepatics are relatively small. Some thallose forms, such as *Conocephalum conicum,* occasionally produce a thallus 30 cm or more long. Some pendulous, epiphytic leafy forms may be equally large. Growth is slow in most hepatics, although under favorable conditions the gametophyte will grow as much as 30 cm in a year. The death and disintegration of the previous year's growth usually means that only the most recently produced fragment of the plant persists from one year to the next. By this mode of growth and decay, hepatics build up a layer of organic material. The continued growth of the tips of each of the branches fragments the single plant and results in vegetative reproduction.

The Hepaticae can be conveniently separated into six well-differentiated orders. The most primitive of these is generally considered to be the Calobryales and the most advanced the Marchantiales.

ORDER CALOBRYALES. This is an order of two families (Fig. 16–6). The most primitive

family, Takakiaceae, contains a single genus, *Takakia* with two species. The family Haplomitriaceae has two genera, *Haplomitrium* and *Calobryum*. *Takakia* is found only locally in alpine regions of Japan, North Borneo, India, and in the Queen Charlotte Islands of British Columbia, Canada. The genus *Calobryum* is predominantly tropical, and is best represented in Australasia, Malaysia, and South America, where it is very local. *Haplomitrium* has one rare north temperate species and one species in Australia.

In all Calobryales the gametophyte consists of erect leafy photosynthetic shoots arising from pale rhizomatous shoots lacking rhizoids. The leaves are at first spirally arranged in three ranks, but this arrangement is frequently distorted as the shoot elongates. Mucilage hairs of unknown function are present near the axils of the leaves and often around the sex organs. In *Takakia* the pale shoots possess characteristic curved mucilage cells. The exudate from these is often colonized by fungi, which may in some way benefit the hepatic. These peculiar cells are absent in the Haplomitriaceae.

The Haplomitriaceae have flattened and unistratose leaves that vary in shape from nearly round to elliptic. The margins are often irregular, but the leaves are never lobed. In *Takakia* the leaves are simply short determinate branches forming elongated cones of cells tipped by a single cell (Fig. 16–6D, E). These leaves are readily deciduous **(caducous)** and form an effective means of vegetative reproduction. In the Haplomitriaceae the upper leaves are often more than 1 mm long and nearly as wide; in *Takakia* the upper leaves rarely exceed 0.5 mm. In all of the Calobryales the earliest-formed lower leaves are smaller than those near the apex of the shoot. In some of the Haplomitriaceae there is just a suggestion of amphigastria and lateral leaves. The leaf cells are thin-walled and, when mature, contain many chloroplasts. Numerous spherical oil bodies are also present.

The gametophyte of the Calobryales is always small. The largest, *Calobryum blumei* is occasionally 3.5 cm tall; the smallest, *Takakia lepidozioides,* is often less than 1 cm tall. They

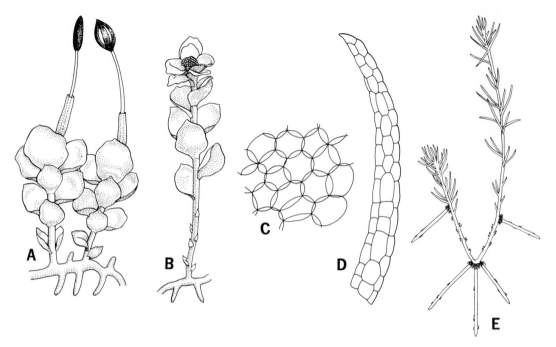

FIGURE 16–6   Morphology of Calobryales. A–C, *Calobryum*. A, habit showing sporophytes with elongate calyptra sheathing base of seta, ×4; B, habit showing terminal cluster of antheridia, ×4; C, leaf cells, ×70. D, E, *Takakia*. D, leaf, ×70; E, habit, ×7. (A, B, modified from Schiffner in Engler, *Die natürlichen Pflanzenfamilien*, Vol. 1, Pt. 3, p. 61, Fig. 35A, C, 1909.)

tend to grow in relatively dense colonies. For example, in *Takakia lepidozioides* the gametophytes form a short bright green turf.

Any detached fragment of the gametophyte appears to be capable of producing an entire gametophyte, but no specialized asexual structures are present.

Archegonia are apical and generally occur on a dome-shaped receptacle surrounded by enlarged leaves (Fig. 16–6A). In some instances occasional lateral archegonia are present, as in *Takakia*. The archegonia are similar to those of other bryophytes. Antheridia are terminal in *Calobryum;* they are spherical to ovoid and each is borne on a short multicellular stalk (Fig. 16–6B). Antheridia are unknown for *Takakia,* but in *Haplomitrium* they may be lateral or in the axils of the upper leaves. Members of the Calobryales are either **unisexual** or **bisexual.**

In *Takakia* the sporophyte is unknown. In *Calobryum,* as the embryo develops, gameto-phytic tissue also develops outside the archegonium, forming a protective cylindrical sleeve, the **perigynium.** Within the perigynium the venter of the archegonium develops to form the calyptra. The calyptra is left at the base of the colorless seta as the latter elongates, extending the cylindrical capsule through the perigynium and above the gametophyte. *Haplomitrium* lacks a perigynium, but the calyptra is very large. The mature capsule usually dehisces by four valves, which generally remain attached at their apex, and the spores are sifted out through the slits (Fig. 16–6A). Characteristic elaters occur among the spores.

The simple structure of the gametophyte emphasizes the primitive nature of the order. In *Takakia* the gametophyte shows little differentiation; structurally, the leaves are barely different from the stem. The radial arrangement of appendages is a more generalized design than the bilateral arrangement in the Jungermanniales. In most Calobryales the number of sex organs is high; this and the absence of rhizoids are considered to be primitive features. But in *Takakia* the curious mucilage cells on the pale shoots are rather specialized structures and the number of archegonia is low.

ORDER JUNGERMANNIALES. The order Jungermanniales (scale mosses) contains over two thirds of all known liverworts; 180 genera and 8,000 species belong to more than 20 families. These are distributed from the arctic to the tropics, reaching their greatest variety in the tropics. They occur predominantly in moist environments on earth, peat, logs, or rock; some species grow in water, and some are epiphytes.

The gametophyte is generally dorsiventrally flattened with two rows of lateral leaves; on the ventral surface of the (normally) reclining stem is usually a row of ventral leaves termed amphigastria. If present, the amphigastria are generally simpler in outline than the lateral leaves. Leaf arrangement is transverse, **incubous,** or, in most instances, **succubous** (Fig. 16–7). The leaves are unlobed or variously lobed; the margins are toothed, entire, or bear long multicellular **cilia.** Leaves are usually unistratose, and in most genera the cells are isodiametric and have the same shape throughout the leaf. The cell walls vary from thin to thick. In many genera trigones are present. In some genera the leaf cells contain oil bodies of a characteristic form useful in determining species (Fig. 16–8). These oil bodies, usually colorless, are sometimes vivid blue (as in *Calypogeia trichomanis*) or brownish. They disappear soon after the death of the leaf cell. Rhizoids present in most Jungermanniales are smooth-walled and arise from the cortical cells of the stem. In the most primitive Jungermanniales, rhizoids are few or absent; in less primitive genera the rhizoids are scattered on the ventral surface of the stem; and in more advanced genera they are restricted to specific parts of the stem or leaves.

The stem is structurally very simple. The outer cells forming the cortex are generally chlorophyllose and possess oil bodies; often these cells have a somewhat thickened outer wall. The inner cells forming the medulla generally lack chloroplasts, but oil bodies may occur.

Branching is rather variable, never truly dichotomous, and frequently irregular or **pinnate** with the branches arising along the single axis of the main stem and generally in the same plane as the lateral leaves. Branching may be **postical,** in which branches originate in the plane of the amphigastria; or **endogenous,** where a branch originates from internal cells of the stem and pushes through the mature stem cells.

Antheridia are normally spherical or ovoid and borne on a multicellular stalk, singly or in groups and surrounded by lateral leaves that differ from others of the gametophyte. These leaves are the **perigonial leaves** and, with the included antheridia, are termed **perigonia** (Fig. 16–7F). In some genera, specialized branches are composed only of perigonia.

Archegonia are always at the apex of the main shoot, and the apical cell is utilized in producing the archegonia. Jungermanniales are thus said to be **acrogynous.** The archegonia are frequently surrounded by a specialized sleeve, the **perianth** (Fig. 16–7A–F, I), which develops while the archegonia are differentiating. In primitive genera the perianth is absent (Fig. 16–7H); in advanced genera it is formed of larger leaves; and in the most highly evolved genera it is bottle-shaped, produced by fused upper leaves. In primitive genera the number of archegonia is large; in more advanced genera the number is greatly reduced. Often, specialized larger leaves surround the perianth. Within the perianth in some genera a sleeve-shaped **perigynium** is sometimes developed from an extension of stem tissue, instead of being derived from specialized leaves, as is the perianth; in such a species, then, a developing sporophyte may be surrounded by the calyptra (developed from the archegonium), by the perigynium (of stem tissue), by the perianth (of specialized leaf tissue), and by **perichaetial leaves** (enlarged leaves arising below the perianth).

Gametophytes are unisexual or bisexual. The position of the antheridia in relation to the archegonia is often useful in recognizing a species.

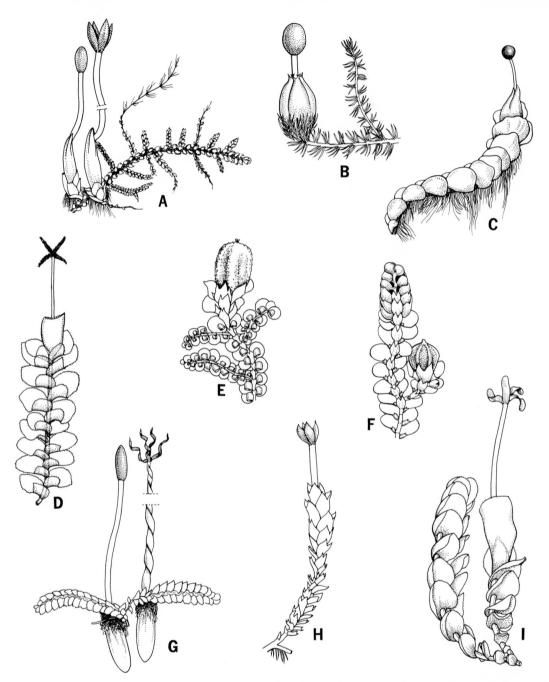

FIGURE 16–7   Morphology of Jungermanniales, showing various sporophytes and gametophytes. A, *Lepidozia reptans* shoot with ripe sporangia, ×5; *B, Blepharostoma trichophyllum* shoot with sporophyte, ×12; C, *Plectocolea hyalina* shoot with sporophyte, ×8; D, *Scapania nemorosa* shoot with open sporangium, ×5; E, *Frullania dilatata* shoot with perianth (note also the helmet-shaped lobules and the notched amphigastria), ×9; F, *Lejeunea flava* shoot, showing terminal perigonial branch and lateral perianth-bearing branch (note also notched amphigastria and lobules of lateral leaves), ×15; G, *Calypogeia fissa* shoot, showing fleshy subterranean perigynium and emergent sporophytes, ×4; H, *Marsupella sprucei* shoot with mature sporophyte, ×12; I, *Plagiochila asplenioides* shoot with flattened perianth and emergent sporophyte, ×4. (A, C–E, G, after Müller with permission of Akademische Verlagsgesellschaft, Geest and Portig K.-G., Leipzig; H, after Schiffner in Engler, *Die natürlichen Pflanzenfamilien*, Vol. 1, Pt. 3, p. 77, Fig. 41A, 1909; F, I, after Schuster with permission of *Journal of Elisha Mitchell Scientific Society* and *American Midland Naturalist*.)

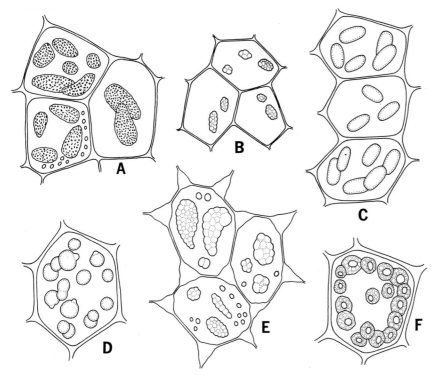

FIGURE 16–8   Oil bodies of hepatics. A, *Solenostoma crenuliformis;* cells from somewhat immature leaf of apical part of plant, ×600. B, *Calypogeia meylanii:* cells from leaf middle, ×275. *Solenostoma sphaerocarpa:* cells near lateral leaf margin, ×440. D, *Lophozia grandiretis:* cell from leaf middle, ×515. E, *Cryptocolea imbricata:* median cells showing trigones, ×35. F, *Lophozia silvicola* median cell, ×850. (After Schuster with permission of *American Midland Naturalist.*)

Asexual reproduction is frequent. Deciduous masses of undifferentiated cells are often budded off the leaves or stem; these are gemmae and can produce new gametophytes (Fig. 16–5A, B). In some genera the brittle leaves break into fragments, in others entire leaves break off and can produce new gametophytes (Fig. 16–5E). In other genera, leaf cells often produce small leafy gametophytes while the leaf is still attached; these small plants ultimately fall off and grow independently (Fig. 16–5G). In some instances the caducous perianth develops a new gametophyte, as in *Gymnocolea.*

The mature sporophyte normally has a long colorless seta that carries the capsule well beyond the perianth (if present) and the calyptra. The capsule is either spherical or cylindrical, depending on the genus (Fig. 16–7A–C, G). In the early development of the capsule the cellular organization is simple, with a single layer of outer cells (amphithecium) surrounding a single layer of inner cells (endothecium). The amphithecium differentiates into two to eight layers (depending on the species) to form the sterile jacket of the capsule. The outer and generally the inner cells of this jacket have thickenings that give the wall a dark brown color. The capsule jacket generally dehisces by four longitudinal slits, separating four valves, which in turn release the spores. The endothecium differentiates to form sterile cells and **archesporial** cells. When the sterile cells lose their chlorophyll, the walls generally develop spiral brown thickenings; these cells become hygroscopic elaters. These unicellular elaters are usually cylindrical and tapered at both ends, varying in length and in the number of spiral thickenings. They average 8 microns thick and 100 microns long, but they may be as long as 420 microns; in some species the elaters are as broad as the spores. Elaters are usually very numerous and scattered among the spores.

Spore discharge is often aided by the nature and position of the elaters (Fig. 16–9A, B, D). In many cases the elaters contract in length as they dry out, coiling the spirals of the thickened walls very tightly. When the strain is too great, the tensile water column inside is ruptured and the elater uncoils rapidly, throwing out adjacent spores as it springs into the air.

Each of the spore mother cells has four lobes and undergoes meiosis, producing a tetrad of spherical spores. Spores are always unicellular, although some, as in *Porella,* develop precociously before they are released from the capsule. The walls are often variously sculptured, but this characteristic is usually of little taxonomic value. The spores contain chloroplasts and food reserves in the form of oils and starch. Spores vary from 6 to 90 microns in diameter.

A few tropical genera of Jungermanniales possess a thallose protonema, indicating the close relationship of this order to the Metzgeriales. The latter order is frequently included in the Jungermanniales as the Jungermanniales anacrogynae, and in that case the present order is considered to be the Jungermanniales acrogynae.

ORDER METZGERIALES. The order Metzgeriales contains 20 genera and approximately 550 species in ten families. The Metzgeriales are found throughout the world but are most abundant in the humid tropics. They grow predominantly in damp shaded habitats but are also found in more exposed sites.

The gametophyte is generally thallose and is one to several cells thick (Fig. 16–10, 11). In the chiefly unistratose gametophytes a distinct **multistratose** costa generally occurs; this costa is similar in structure to the stem of Jungermanniales. In the multistratose forms the central portion of the thallus is thicker than the margin. The thallus frequently branches dichotomously in a single plane. The tissue of the thallus is almost uniform, although the upper cells gen-

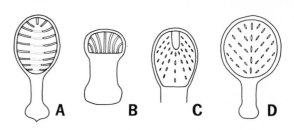

FIGURE 16–9   Location of elaters in sporangia of hepatics. A, *Cephalozia bicuspidata;* B, *Frullania;* C, *Riccardia;* D, Jungermanniaceae. (After Goebel with permission of G. Fischer.)

erally have more chloroplasts than the lower ones. In some Metzgeriales, such as *Petalophyllum ralfsii,* one zone contains fungal hypae. In other Metzgeriales, such as *Blasia pusilla,* there are endophytic colonies of the blue-green alga *Nostoc* (Fig. 16–11G). In *Cryptothallus mirabilis,* chlorophyll is absent and the hepatic is nutritionally dependent on the fungi contained in it. As in the Jungermanniales, the rhizoids are simple and unicellular; they arise from epidermal cells on the lower surface of the thallus. In leafy Metzgeriales, the stems of the gametophytes have lateral leaves, as in the Jungermanniales, but the stems lack the amphigastria characteristic of that order (Fig. 16–10). Lateral leaves are generally simple in outline, but in some—*Treubia,* for example—there is a small **lobule.** Cells of the gametophyte never possess trigones.

The thallose gametophytes occasionally have marginal hairs, or the entire thallus may be hairy, as in *Metzgeria pubescens* (Fig. 16–11F). Generally the thallus margin is plane and entire, but it is occasionally somewhat toothed; it may be ruffled, as in *Moerkia flotowiana;* or as in *Petalophyllum ralfsii,* it may bear unistratose flaps emerging on the dorsal surface of the thallus (Fig. 16–11C). Rarely thalli have two rows of dorsal scales near the costate region of the thallus, as in *Moerkia hibernica.* Growth of the thallus is indefinite even after the production of the sex organs, which arise behind the apical cell and are borne on the dorsal surface.

Antheridia structurally similar to those of the Jungermanniales are borne on the dorsal surface of the thallus and are on short branches

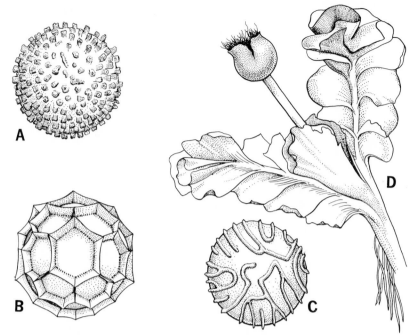

FIGURE 16–10 Metzgeriales: *Fossombronia,* showing variety of spores. A, *F. mittenii,* ×640; B, *F. angulosa,* ×640; C, *F. wondraczeki,* ×640; D, *F. cristata* habit showing sporophyte on gametophyte, ×25. (D, after Schiffner in Engler, *Die natürlichen Pflanzenfamilien,* Vol. 1, Pt. 3, p. 59, Fig. 34A, 1909.)

(*Riccardia,* Fig. 16–11D), in a globose sac formed from a branch (*Metzgeria,* Fig. 16–11F), buried in a chamber (*Pellia,* Fig. 16–11B), naked (some species of *Fossombronia*), or each covered by a single scale (*Moerkia blyttii*).

Archegonia are also structurally similar to those in the Jungermanniales. They are borne on a special dorsal branch and enclosed in a pseudoperianth (*Riccardia*), are naked (*Fossombronia*), or in a pocket-like cavity (*Pellia*). Gametophytes may be unisexual or bisexual.

The sporophyte resembles that of the Jungermanniales. In some genera of the Metzgeriales the spore sculpturing is highly characteristic. For example, in *Fossombronia,* species are distinguished most readily by spore sculpturing (Fig. 16–10A–C). In *Pellia* the spores germinate precociously and are multicellular when released. Asexual reproduction is usually by fragmentation of the thallus, but in some genera there are specialized asexual reproductive

structures (Fig. 16–5C, D, 11G). In *Metzgeria,* marginal gemmae are produced (Fig. 16–5C), and in *Blasia* gemmae are extruded from remarkable gemma bottles (Fig. 16–11G).

ORDER MONOCLEALES. This order contains a single family, Monocleaceae, with one genus, *Monoclea,* and two tropical species (Fig. 16–12).

The gametophyte is a green to olive-green thallus and may be as long as 20 cm and as wide as 5 cm, making it one of the largest thallose liverworts known. The thallus is of homogeneous parenchyma cells and lacks air spaces; in this way it resembles the Metzgeriales. The upper cells of the thallus are chlorophyllose, whereas those lower down contain starch grains as well as chloroplasts (Fig. 16–12C). Some scattered cells contain a single brown oil body—a feature shared by the thallus of Marchantiales. Fungi are sometimes abundant in the lower cells of the thallus. Rhizoids occur over the entire ventral surface of the

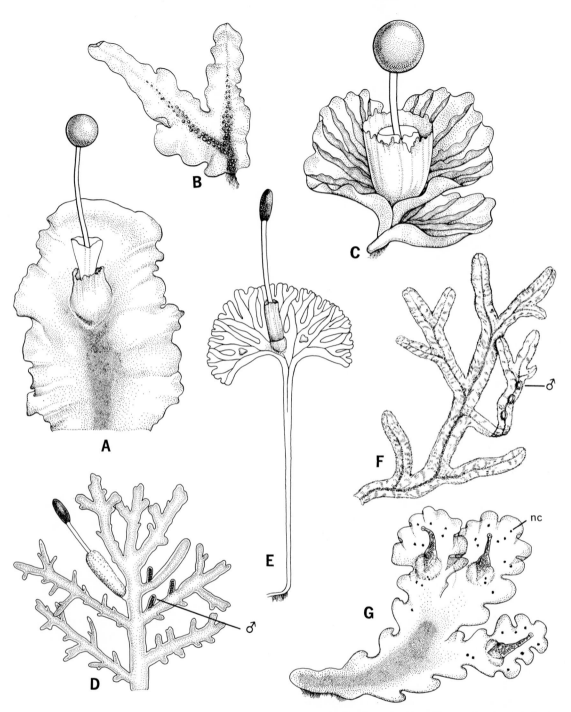

FIGURE 16–11   Metzgeriales; habits of a variety of morphological types. A, *Pellia neesiana* sporophyte-bearing thallus lobe, ×6; B, *P. neesiana* antheridial thallus, ×6; C, *Petalophyllum ralfsii* thallus with lamellae on upper surface (note calyptra surrounded by campanulate perigynium from which sporophyte emerges), ×6; D, *Riccardia multifida*, portion of thallus with sporophyte and antheridial lobes, ×5; E, *Hymenophytum flabellatum* thallus with sporophyte, ×3; F, *Metzgeria pubescens* thallus with antheridial branches on under surface, ×8; G, *Blasia pusilla* thallus with gemma "bottles," ×5. *nc, Nostoc* colonies. (E, after Cavers with permission of Trustees of *New Phytologist* and Messrs. Dawsons of Pall Mall, who reprinted F. Cavers' *The Inter-Relationships of the Bryophyta* in 1964.)

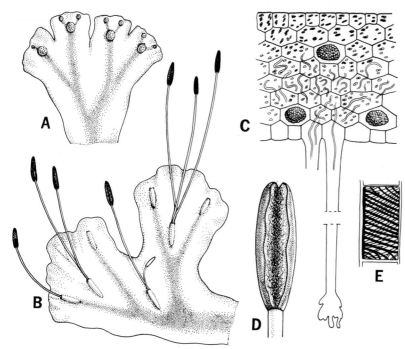

FIGURE 16–12   Monocleales: *Monoclea forsteri*. A, portion of thallus with antheridial pads, ×0.75; B, portion of thallus with sporophytes, ×0.75; C, cross section of thallus, showing oil bodies, fungal hyphae among cells, and ventral rhizoid, ×120; D, detail of dehiscing sporangium, ×4; E, cell of capsule wall from longitudinal section of capsule, showing thickenings of walls, ×100. (After Cavers with permission of Trustees of *New Phytologist* and Messrs. Dawsons of Pall Mall, who reprinted F. Cavers' *The Inter-Relationships of the Bryophyta* in 1964.)

thallus and, as in Marchantiales, are of two types: some rhizoids are oriented parallel to the length of the thallus, others are vertical and serve to anchor the thallus. A few rhizoids have rudimentary peg-like thickenings, suggestive of those found in rhizoids of the Marchantiales.

Monoclea produces unisexual gametophytes. The male thallus possesses small pad-like receptacles, generally found behind the growing point of each dichotomy of the thallus (Fig. 16–12A). The antheridia are embedded in the antheridial pad, each in a small chamber that opens by a pore to the dorsal surface. Cylindrical sleeve-like chambers occur in the same general location on the female thallus as the antheridial pads on the male thallus (Fig. 16–12B). Each chamber contains several archegonia and opens by a small pore that faces the growing point of the dichotomy.

Often three or four sporophytes emerge from each archegonial tube. The colorless seta elongates rapidly and carries the cylindrical sporangium high above the thallus. The capsule, whose wall is unistratose, dehisces by a single vertical slit and opens into a spoon-like structure that releases the spores by the aid of the long hygroscopic elaters (Fig. 16–12D). The capsule wall has unique thickenings consisting of branching bands on the radial walls of the cells (Fig. 16–12F).

This order is primitive, showing some relationships to the Marchantiales but still others to the Calobryales and Metzgeriales. If only the gametophyte were known, this genus would undoubtedly be placed in the Marchantiales; but several features, including the sporophyte's dehiscence and sporangial wall, serve to separate this genus into a distinct evolutionary line.

ORDER SPHAEROCARPALES. The order Sphaerocarpales contains three genera and approximately 20 species included in two families (Fig. 16–13). They are found primarily in warm temperate to tropical countries, where they are locally abundant. Both *Sphaerocarpos* and *Geothallus* are found on damp soil, whereas *Riella* is strictly a submerged aquatic growing on mud in shallow quiet pools or lakes. All genera of this order appear to be winter annuals. They are found primarily in regions of wet winters and dry summers.

In many respects the thallus of the Sphaerocarpales resembles that of the Metzgeriales, but a number of significant differences exist. Among the similarities is the thallose nature of the gametophyte—although the gametophyte of *Geothallus* is leafy in a manner similar to *Fossombronia* of the Metzgeriales. The thallus is either unistratose or multistratose and is undifferentiated throughout its thickness; it is also **anacrogynous.** Rhizoids are smooth-walled. The basic differences include the presence of a unistratose "bottle" around each sex organ (Fig. 16–13B–E). These bottles are on the dorsal surface of the thallus or, as in *Riella,* are lateral. Most species produce unisexual gametophytes. Within the sporophyte, the sterile cells are not elaters but starch-rich nutritive cells that break down and supply nutritive materials for the developing spores. The seta is essentially absent. The sporangium remains within the bottle, even when mature, and dehiscence of the capsule is by decay of the capsule wall. The jacket walls of the capsule lack special thickenings.

The genus *Sphaerocarpos* has been used in some important genetical studies. In this organism sex-correlated chromosomes were first discovered in plants. Since the spore-sculpturing characteristic can be used to separate species, and since tetrads are often enclosed in a single membrane when released, this genus is a convenient organism for genetical studies. Furthermore, in each tetrad two of the spores germinate to produce male gametophytes while the other two give rise to female gametophytes. The degree of lobing and ruffling and the general thallus shape are also phenotypic charac-

teristics that can be used. The presence of the sex-correlated chromosome controls spore sculpturing. Thus, in a female thallus, the sculpturing of spores resulting from an interspecific hybrid is characteristic of the spore that produced the maternal, not the paternal, thallus.

Riella is the only strictly submerged aquatic liverwort now extant, although the fossil liverwort *Naiadita* (of the Triassic) was presumably also a submerged aquatic and is considered to be related to *Riella* (Fig. 16–29E–H). The thallus of *Riella* is unique among the bryophytes. In many respects it is more specialized (by reduction) than the thallus of *Sphaerocarpos*. Two advanced features are the restriction of the rhizoids to the base of the stem and the fusion of the laminate part of the gametophyte. The various distinctive phases in growth of *Riella* also demonstrate specialization. The remarkable unistratose ruffle of the thallus is unknown elsewhere in the plant kingdom, and the restriction of the antheridia to chambers at the margin of the thallus is unknown in any other bryophyte.

ORDER MARCHANTIALES. This order, generally considered the most highly evolved order of the Hepaticae, contains 12 families with approximately 450 species in 33 genera (Fig. 16–14, 15). Members of this order are world-wide in distribution—for example, the genus *Marchantia*. Most species grow on moist earth or mud; a few are found most commonly in water. The popular idea of a liverwort is exemplified by members of this order, probably a result of the relatively large size of the gametophytes and the abundance of some of the species.

The gametophyte is always a prostrate thallus, generally differentiated internally into several distinct tissues. The uppermost layer of cells forms the epidermis, the outer walls of which are often cutinized. These cells generally possess little or no chlorophyll. In most genera the epidermis is interrupted by special pores that lead into air chambers. These pores are surrounded by several cells and are often elaborate in structure (Fig. 16–15B, G). In most

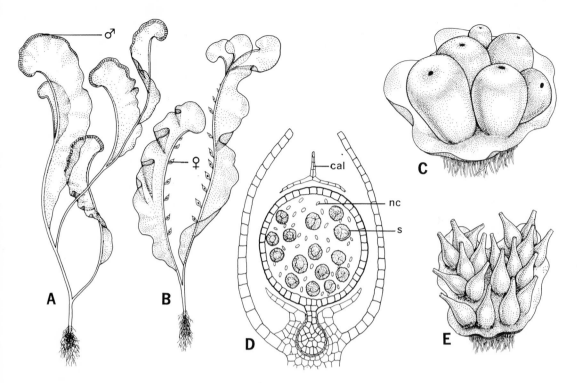

FIGURE 16–13   Sphaerocarpales. A, habit of *Riella americana* thallus with antheridia on margin, ×3; B, *R. americana* thallus with sporophytes on stem, ×3; C, *Sphaerocarpos cristatus* archegoniate plant, showing bottles containing sporangia, ×20; D, longitudinal section through *Sphaerocarpos* sporangium and bottle, ×35. E, *S. cristatus* antheridial plant, showing antheridium-containing bottles, ×20. *cal,* calyptra; *nc,* nurse cell; *s,* spores. (A, B, after Studhalter from *The Scientific Monthly,* Vol. 35, p. 307, fig. 2, with permission of *Science;* C, after Howe with permission of *Torrey Botanical Club Memoirs.*)

instances the pores remain open at all times, but in *Preissia* they partially close when the surrounding cells lose excessive water and open again with renewal of turgor. The air chambers contain filaments of cells rich in chloroplasts; or the chamber walls are strongly chlorophyllose while the chambers contain no filaments; or both walls and filaments contain chloroplasts. The pattern of the air chambers gives many of the genera a distinctive appearance that immediately separates members of this order from other thallose liverworts. Below the photosynthetic region lies a multistratose region of parenchymatous tissue, mainly nonchlorophyllose and functioning as storage tissue; occasional mucilage cells and cells containing large oil bodies are often scattered among the parenchymatous cells. A ventral epidermis encloses this layer.

From some of the lower epidermal cells, colorless rhizoids of two types generally emerge—some with smooth walls and others with regular peg-like ingrowths of the wall. Rhizoids are oriented both at right angles to the thallus surface and parallel to it. The rhizoids parallel to the thallus surface are important only in capillary conduction, whereas those perpendicular, besides performing this function, also anchor the thallus to the substrate. On the ventral surface of the thallus, multicellular ventral scales may also be present. Branching of the thallus is generally dichotomous. In some instances the thallus is ornamented by marginal hairs.

Within the order several types of tissue organization occur. In many species of *Riccia* the chlorophyllose tissue is composed of vertical columns of cells interspersed with vertical

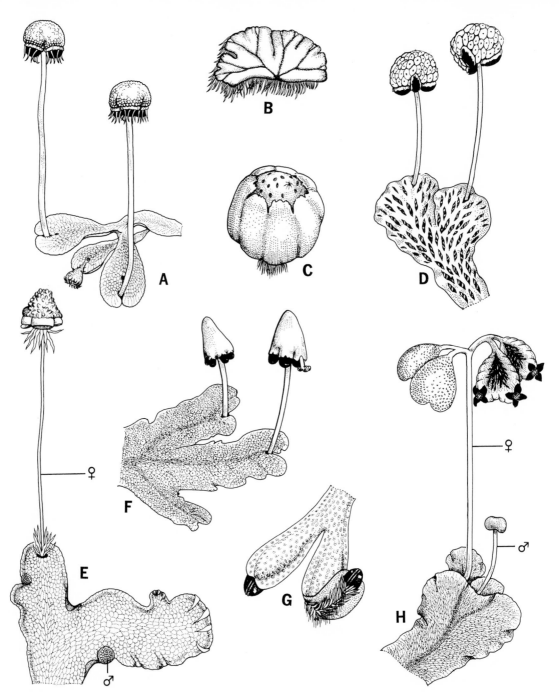

FIGURE 16–14   Marchantiales, showing variation in morphology. A, *Asterella ludwigii*, habit of portion of thallus bearing carpocephala with sporangia, ×3; B, *Ricciocarpus natans,* habit of aquatic thallus, ×6; C, *Carrpos monocarpus* thallus surrounding carpocephalum containing sporangium, ×15; D, *Mannia rupestris:* portion of thallus with carpocephala (note slits forming openings into air chambers of thallus), ×6; E, *M. siberica,* unisexual thallus with single carpocephalum (note operculum on sporangium), ×5; F, *Conocephalum conicum* thallus fragment with carpocephala bearing sporangia, ×2; G, *Targionia hypophylla,* portion of thallus with ventral sporangia, ×3; H, *Neohodgsonia mirabilis,* unisexual thallus with carpocephalum (left) and antheridiophore (right), ×4. (A, after Hattori and Schimizu with permission of *Hattori Botanical Laboratory Journal;* C, after Carr with permission of *Australian Journal of Botany;* D, E, after Schuster with permission of *American Midland Naturalist;* H, after E. O. Campbell with permission of the Royal Society of New Zealand.)

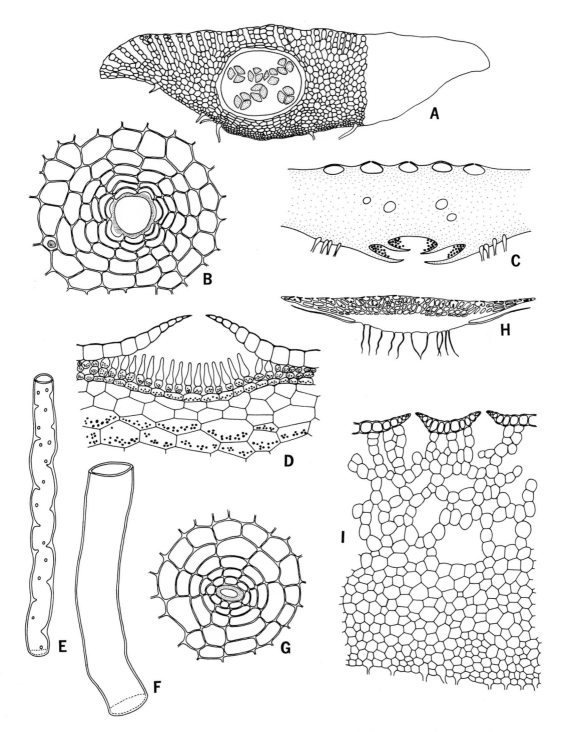

FIGURE 16–15   Anatomy of Marchantiales (cross sections through thalli). A, *Riccia beyrichiana,* show-ing sporangium containing spores, ×20; B, surface view of air-chamber pore of *Conocephalum conicum,* ×180; C, cross section of *C. conocium,* ×20; D, air chamber of *C. conocium,* showing chlorophyllose fila-ments, ×180; E, F, rhizoids of *C. conicum,* ×360; G, surface view of air-chamber pore of *Reboulia hemi-sphaerica,* ×180; H, thallus of *R. hemisphaerica,* ×7.5; I, detail of thallus and air chambers of *R. hemi-sphaerica,* ×180. (A, B, G–I, after Schuster with permission of *American Midland Naturalist;* C, D, after Cavers with permission of Trustees of *New Phytologist* and Messrs. Dawsons of Pall Mall, who reprinted F. Cavers' *The Inter-Relationships of the Bryophyta* in 1964.)

air chambers that open to the upper surface of the thallus (Fig. 16–15A). Also in *Riccia,* and in other genera, are many air chambers with unistratose chlorophyllose walls (Fig. 16–15H, I). In some genera the uppermost chambers open to the surface by an epidermal pore (Fig. 16–15D, I); in others there is no such opening. As in many of the Metzgeriales, the upper cells of the thallus in *Dumortiera* are chlorophyllose whereas the ventral ones are nonchlorophyllose. In *Conocephalum* and related genera the chlorophyllose layer is composed of air chambers with chlorophyll-rich multicellular filaments (Fig. 16–15D). These chambers generally open to the epidermis by an elaborate pore (Fig. 16–15B).

Thalli may be unisexual or bisexual, depending on the species. Archegonia and antheridia do not differ significantly in structure from those of other bryophytes. Their position on the thallus is variable throughout the order. In some genera the antheridial branch is ventral. In many genera the antheridia are borne dorsally on an elaborate, specialized, radially symmetrical branch—the **antheridiophore.** The antheridia are often embedded in a flattened receptacle that surmounts the perpendicular stalk of the antheridiophore (Fig. 16–14H). In others without a branch, the receptacle is simply a pad on the dorsal surface of the thallus borne near its apex (Fig. 16–14E). In still other genera the antheridia are in scattered pockets near the thickened central portion of the thallus. In most instances a single antheridium is in each pocket.

The archegonia are similarly placed on the thallus. When present, the **archegoniophore** is often elaborately papillose, hairy, or sculptured. The number of lobes in the receptacle varies; frequently there are four lobes, but there may be none, one, or more than nine. The archegonia are first borne dorsally, but growth of the receptacle ultimately inverts them so that they eventually hang neck down.

The location of the sporophytes depends on the location of the archegonia. When mature, the sporophyte usually possesses a short seta. The capsule wall is unistratose and with or without spiral thickenings. Elaters are present in most genera but are absent in others. As in most other hepatics, the spores are released by four valves or by irregular rupturing of the apex of the capsule. In some genera, spores are released only upon decay of the capsule wall; in others (*Mannia fragrans*) a differentiated lid, or operculum, breaks off and releases the spores. *Cyathodium* has a peristome-like opening with six to eight distinct teeth, but no operculum covers the "peristome" as in the Musci.

Spores are smooth or variously sculptured with elaborate papillae, reticula, or mamillae. Spore sculpturing is an important feature separating species of some genera, such as *Riccia.* Elaters are morphologically similar to those in the Jungermanniales.

Special asexual reproductive structures are uncommon in the order, but a few genera —such as *Marchantia*—bear gemma cups on the dorsal surface. These cups contain stalked multicellular gemmae that are released when the stalks break (Fig. 16–5H). On germination the gemma produces a new gametophyte.

Buds formed at the apices of the thallus branches can survive unfavorable seasons. After the rest of the thallus disintegrates, the buds may be carried by water or organisms to another locality.

Evolution in hepatic gametophytes shows the following general pattern, beginning with the primitive and proceeding to highly evolved characteristics:

1. Leaves radially arranged, all similar, barely differing from the stem; rhizoids absent.
2. Leaves radially arranged, all similar, differing from the stem, and actually leaf-like; rhizoids absent.
3. Leaves radially arranged, one rank slightly smaller and leaf-like; rhizoids absent.
4. Leaves bilaterally arranged with an additional rank forming amphigastria; rhizoids rare.
5. Leaves as in 4, but the location of rhizoids specialized: scattered over the under surface of the stem, restricted to amphigastria, or restricted to pads

that replace the amphigastria.

6. Gametophyte with leaves irregular in shape and arranged bilaterally, so that the gametophyte suggests a thallus.
7. Thallose gametophyte with leafy sexual branches.
8. Thallose gametophyte with no tissue differentiation; rhizoids thin-walled.
9. Thallose gametophyte with thallus much differentiated into tissues; rhizoids of two types.

Similar evolution exists in other aspects of gametophytic structure, developmental morphology of the sex organs, and general structure of the sporophyte. However, evolutionary trends in the sporophyte are not so apparent in the Hepaticae as in the Musci.

CLASS ANTHOCEROTAE
(Hornworts)

Superficially the hornworts resemble the thallose liverworts, but a number of significant features separate this class from other bryophytes. The class contains approximately 100 species in a single order, the Anthocerotales, which is generally treated as possessing a single family, the Anthocerotaceae, with five genera.

Hornworts are found throughout the world, although they are uncommon in Arctic regions. Generally they grow on damp, shaded earth, but some are epiphytic.

All members of the order have a thallose gametophyte that normally forms a rosette in which the dichotomous branching is often not apparent. In some instances the thallus is distinctly costate; in others, it has a variably multistratose band near the center. In some instances the thallus possesses dorsal lamellae or hairlike outgrowths. In several species multicellular marginal gemmae occur. The thallus of parenchymatous cells is not differentiated into tissues, although cavities commonly filled with mucilaginous material (Fig. 16–16H) appear in the thallus. These cavities frequently open to the ventral surface by stomate-like pores (Fig.

16–16B) and may be invaded by the blue-green alga *Nostoc*. There are no specialized mucilage cells similar to those in hepatics. Each cell of the thallus generally contains a single chloroplast surrounding a central pyrenoid, as in some of the green algae. The unistratose thallus margin is often variously lobed or crenulate (Fig. 16–16A). Many species in this family have perennating **tubers,** which in many instances arise near the edge of the thallus. These tubers are enclosed in an envelope of corky cells, and the inner cells are rich in oil and protein. Similar tubers are also present in some thallose hepatics. Ventral rhizoids, which are unicellular and smooth-walled, are present.

Sex organs are sunk deeply in the upper layers of the generally bisexual thallus (Fig. 16–16H). One or several antheridia are produced in each chamber. Each antheridium is structurally similar to that of the liverworts, although the antheridial jacket is less distinct and the stalk is generally short. Details of antheridial origin in the hornworts also differ from those of the hepatics; rupturing of the overlying thallus cells exposes the antheridia, which shed their sperm by regular or irregular splitting of the antheridial wall.

Although flask-shaped in inner contour, archegonia are not clearly differentiated from the other thallus cells. The egg is thus at the bottom of a flask-shaped depression that opens to the dorsal surface of the thallus.

The sporophyte is an elongated spindle attached to the gametophyte by its swollen haustorium-like base, the foot (Fig. 16–16A, D, E). There is no seta. Growth of the sporophyte is by a basal **intercalary meristem;** thus, the sporophyte can continue to grow as long as external conditions favor it. Until mature, the sporophyte is chlorophyllose. In the epidermis of most species are stomata with characteristic guard cells (Fig. 16–16C). These stomata lead to a system of intercellular spaces.

The sporangium ruptures along two preformed lines of weakness, which run the length of the maturing sporangium (Fig. 16–16A). Maturation is from the apex downward, and the valves split back from the **columella**—a central cylinder of sterile cells—to expose the spores.

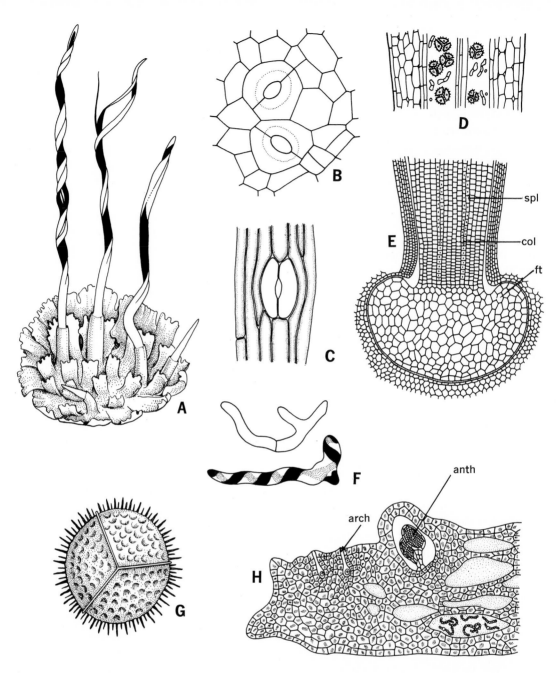

FIGURE 16–16   Morphology and anatomy of Anthocerotales. A, habit of *Anthoceros laevis*, with mature sporangia, ×5; B, pores of gametophytic thallus of *Anthoceros*, ×350; C, stoma with guard cells of *Anthoceros* sporangium wall, ×350; D, longitudinal section through mature sporangium (note pseudo-elaters among spore tetrads), ×80; E, base of *Anthoceros* sporangium, ×160. F, pseudoelaters of Anthocerotales (upper, *A. punctatus;* lower, *Megaceros endivaefolius*), ×500; G, papillose spore of *A. punctatus,* ×750; H, cross section through fertile thallus showing mucilage chambers, one filled with *Nostoc* filaments (note single chloroplast in each cell), ×80. *anth,* antheridium; *arch,* archegonium; *col,* columella; *ft,* foot; *spl,* sporogenous layer. (A, F, after Proskauer with permission of *Annals of Botany* and *Torrey Botanical Club Bulletin;* B, after Goebel with permission of G. Fischer; D, E, after Smith with permission of McGraw-Hill Book Co.; G, after Schuster with permission of *American Midland Naturalist;* H, after Howe with permission of *Torrey Botanical Club Memoirs.*)

In some species the outer elongated cells of the columella have weak spiral thickenings. The valves often coil and uncoil in response to moisture changes, thus assisting in spore removal. While spores are released from the apex of the sporophyte, new growth at the base continues to differentiate new sporangial tissue, as long as the sporophyte survives. The spores are usually separated when liberated, but sometimes they are released as tetrads. Spore wall sculpturing varies among species, and to a certain degree within a species (Fig. 16–16G). The wall is brown, yellow, or black, also depending upon the species. Among the spores are elongate, somewhat branched **pseudoelaters,** which are probably not effective in aiding spore release. Both unicellular and multicellular pseudo-elaters are present. The multicellular ones are made of a uniseriate filament of several cells. Pseudoelaters generally are thin-walled but sometimes possess irregularly thickened walls or have spiral thickenings (Fig. 16–16F).

The evolutionary significance of Anthocerotales is frequently emphasized because of the superficial resemblance of *Anthoceros* to some fossil vascular plants, the psilophytes. It is generally agreed that the psilophytes and Anthocerotae both had their origin from the same ancestral group of plants, and many botanists feel that the hornworts were derived from primitive psilophytes. Others feel that types similar to the hornworts were ancestral to the psilophytes! Spores of some species of *Anthoceros* closely resemble those of a fossil psilophyte, *Psilophyton princeps*.

CLASS MUSCI
(Mosses)

The mosses are readily distinguished from the hepatics and hornworts by a number of distinctive features.

1. All mosses have a leafy gametophyte, and in most the leaves are in three to five ranks. In a few genera there are lateral leaves and under leaves similar to amphigastria in the liverworts.

2. In many genera the leaf cells are elongate and the cells never bear trigones.

3. The leaves are often costate but otherwise generally unistratose; they are rarely notched or lobed.

4. The leafy gametophyte generally arises from a filamentous protonema. It produces uniseriate, multicellular protonema-like rhizoids that are often chlorophyllose when young. As they mature, the cell walls of the protonema and rhizoid are generally oblique.

5. The sporophyte is of firm tissue and may persist for several years. However, spores are produced in the capsule from sporogenous tissue that matures at the same time; hence, spore production in a sporophyte is restricted to a short period.

6. The young sporophyte is highly photosynthetic; but when mature, both capsule and seta are generally brown.

7. The seta elongates well before differentiation of the capsule, which is covered by a cap (calyptra) formed from the ruptured archegonium. The capsule wall lacks transverse thickenings, and stomata are often present.

8. Early differentiation in the capsule produces an endothecium (inner layer of cells) enclosed by an amphithecium (outer layer of cells). The spore jacket is derived from the amphithecium, but the spore mother cells may be derived from either amphithecial or endothecial layers.

9. The parenchymatous central sterile cells, the columella, generally form a central dome or cylinder continuous with the seta. The sporogenous layer forms an inverted cup around the columella or a cylinder that surrounds it. In a few genera a columella is lacking.

10. In most genera the capsule opens by means of a small cap (operculum) that breaks off the top of the capsule. Beneath this cap the mouth **(peristome)** of the capsule is generally ringed by teeth **(peristome teeth).**

In the mosses, the structure of the sporophyte has often evolved more rapidly than that of the gametophyte. Consequently, some genera possess a very highly evolved sporophyte and a relatively primitive gametophyte. The sporophyte, primarily the peristome, provides the basis for separating the main orders of mosses. In general, related genera possessing similar gametophytes produce sporophytes that resemble each other. When it has a conspicuously reduced sporophyte, a plant is placed in the order containing plants with similar gametophytes. In genera with a very reduced gametophyte, naturally the sporophyte characteristics are paramount. In the mosses, several parallel lines of evolution have occurred. Thus, for example, in the order Pottiales some species are at the same level of evolution as those in other genera in other orders. To place orders and families in an absolute linear order that directly reflects phylogeny is not possible. This impossibility plus different interpretations of the available information have led to varying opinions concerning the phylogenetic sequence of orders.

In the mosses a great array of morphological variation exists both in the gametophyte and in the sporophyte. This is in marked contrast to the liverworts and hornworts where, within the class, no great variation occurs in sporophyte structure.

GAMETOPHYTE

Individual gametophytes branch in a number of common patterns. In most species with erect gametophytes, each gametophyte that arises from the protonema is essentially unbranched, or the branches are parallel to the main axis. In a few gametophytes, a main erect shoot is tipped by a cluster of branches, so that the gametophyte resembles a small tree. Mosses with a reclining gametophyte possess pinnate, irregularly pinnate, or simply irregular branches. In the genus *Sphagnum* the branching is different from that of all other mosses and will be described in detail later.

Most moss leaves have a simple outline. The shape varies, but leaf shape is relatively constant for each species. Throughout some large genera—for example, *Bryum*—the leaf shape is relatively uniform. As shown in Figure 16–23, leaf apices, margins, and bases show a wide degree of diversity. Many leaves possess outgrowths from the midrib, the blade, or the margin. Much of the photosynthetic surface of *Polytrichum,* for example, is confined to the

parallel flap-like **lamellae** on the upper surface of the leaves (Fig. 16–20F).

The leaf cells exhibit a similar variation in shape. Although cell walls may vary in thickness and regularity, trigones are never present. In many mosses the cell surface bears papillae that vary in number and elaborateness. These papillae are wart-like thickenings of the cell wall and are most conspicuous over the cell protoplast. Oil bodies are simpler than those in the liverworts. The arrangement of differently shaped cells within the leaf, the nature of the papillosity, the leaf shape, the structure of the leaf margin, base, and apex—all these are important features that distinguish one moss from another.

The leaf costa, too, exhibits considerable variability among genera. The costa may have elongate or quadrate cells on its surface; in cross section the cells may be all alike, or some thick-walled and others thin-walled. The costa is single, double, or absent; it may be short or it may run the whole length of the leaf. It may be papillose while the remainder of the leaf is smooth; occasionally it bears flanges or teeth. These features are genetically determined and are valuable in distinguishing moss species.

The leaves are generally borne in more than three ranks and are usually arranged spirally on the stem. In some genera they are in two ranks, but this is not common. In most mosses all leaves of a plant are similar. In erect mosses, the leaves of the oldest portion of the stem tend to be smaller than those of the upper portion of the shoot. The leaves surrounding the sex organs often differ from the other leaves; those surrounding the antheridia are termed perigonial leaves, and those surrounding the archegonia are called perichaetial leaves.

The arrangement of the sex organs is generally constant in a species. Gametophytes are unisexual or bisexual, and in bisexual gametophytes the different sex organs are on the same branch or on different branches. The gametophyte is erect and attached to the substrate at the base, or the stem reclines and rhizoids emerge from the ventral surface to attach it to the substrate. In some genera a persistent, often extensive protonema attaches the reduced leafy gametophyte to the substrate.

Rhizoids are of relatively constant morphology throughout the mosses. The rhizoids are brownish, uniseriate, much-branched filaments. The cell walls are smooth or papillose. End walls of the cells vary from transverse to irregularly oblique. Rhizoids are found predominantly on the stem, but in some mosses—expecially those of aquatic environments—they are occasionally on the leaves. Some mosses have no rhizoids in the mature gametophyte (e.g., *Sphagnum*), whereas the stem of others (e.g., *Anacolia*) is heavily clothed with rhizoids. Rhizoids attach most mosses to their substrate. In humid environments the tips of branches of creeping mosses often produce rhizoids that attach to the substrate. In some mosses (e.g., *Funaria hygrometrica*) the principal function of the rhizoids appears to be to serve as a capillary network for water conduction.

Anatomically the stem of mosses is far more complex than that of the leafy liverworts. It reaches highest complexity in the largest erect mosses, the Polytrichidae (Fig. 16–20G).

SPOROPHYTE

The moss sporophyte shows equal diversity. Since the features are presumably genetically controlled, they are of considerable taxonomic value. The seta varies from long, exserting the capsule high above the perichaetial leaves, to short, or essentially absent, with the capsule immersed among the perichaetial leaves. In the Andreaeidae and Sphagnidae, growth of leafless gametophytic tissue (called **pseudopodium**) below the developing capsule raises the capsule above the leafy gametophyte. The seta is papillose or smooth and varies greatly in color; it possesses chlorophyll when young, although in some genera chlorophyll is very scant. In most mosses both seta and capsule are brown when the sporophyte is mature.

The capsule shows considerable variation in shape, but the wall is generally smooth (Fig. 16–25). The lower part of the capsule, just below the sporogenous layer, is the **apophysis.** This apophysis is occasionally specialized, as in many genera of the *Splachnaceae* (Fig. 16–25D). In many mosses, stomata most frequently lead into intercellular spaces in the apophysis (Fig. 16–27). The stomata may be important in gaseous exchange, but they are probably vestigial structures; their true function, if any, is not understood. They characteristically possess two guard cells, but rarely there are more. Sometimes the stomata consist of a single cell with a slit down the middle; sometimes the stomatal pore itself is plugged. The stomata are on the surface of the capsule, or each is nearly concealed by the extension of cell walls almost over the pore so that it lies at the bottom of an invagination. Although aquatic mosses normally lack stomata in the capsule, *Sphagnum* possesses many rudimentary stomata.

Most mosses have a peristome. The teeth of the peristome exhibit a remarkable diversity both within orders and within genera (Fig. 16–27) but are constant within a species. Some mosses have massive and cellular peristome teeth, as in the subclass Tetraphidae (Fig. 16–19E). In others, such as the order Dicranales, there is a single ring of peristome teeth, each sculptured and formed from remnants of cell walls (Fig. 16–27F). Still other mosses have a peristome of two series of teeth; the outer peristome is generally rather similar to that of the Dicranales, but the inner peristome is often colorless and rather delicate (Fig. 16–27A, C, D, H). In a number of mosses the peristome is rudimentary, consisting of tiny fragments of teeth. Although they have an operculum, many mosses lack a peristome; others lack an operculum, and the capsule opens irregularly.

The calyptra also varies in morphology and orientation. It is quite smooth or papillose or closely invested with filaments (Fig. 16–20B, 25A, C, G).

APOSPORY IN MOSSES

Because any young cell of either sporophyte or gametophyte is potentially capable of producing a protonema, it is possible to carry out a number of remarkable genetic experiments with many mosses. If a gametophyte is used for such a purpose, it is possible to produce another with genetic constitution identical to the parent. However, if the cells of the sporophyte give rise to a gametophyte, then this gametophyte is genetically different from that which bore the sporophyte. The sporophyte-produced protonema is diploid ($2n$), whereas that of the parental gametophyte is haploid ($1n$).

The $2n$ protonema and the haploid protonema can give rise to a normal leafy gametophyte in the same fashion. However, the potential of this diploid protonema to produce a normal sporophyte is particularly remarkable, as demonstrated for the genus *Tetraphis* of the Tetraphidae. In the genus *Physcomitrium,* a diploid gametophyte was induced to produce normal sporangia on the tips of developing leaves! This phenomenon is termed apospory.

By hybridizing diploid with haploid gametophytes of the same species much has been learned about the sexuality of mosses. It has been suggested that hybridization and apospory have possibly been important in the development of various races of mosses, and may have aided in production of some species.

SUBCLASSES OF MOSSES

The class Musci contains at least 15 orders of more than 80 families, which can be conveniently divided into six subclasses: Sphagnidae, Andreaeidae, Tetraphidae, Polytrichidae, Buxbaumiidae, and Bryidae. Each of these subclasses represents a distinct evolutionary line, and relationships among the subclasses are not clear either in the scanty fossil material or in extant species. The subclasses may be distinguished by the dichotomous key in Table 16–1.

SUBCLASS SPHAGNIDAE

The genus *Sphagnum* (the peat mosses) is the sole representative of the subclass Sphag-

TABLE 16–1

KEY TO MOSS SUBCLASSES

A. Peristome teeth massive, multicellular, without sculpturing or transverse bands, of a single series; if absent, an **epiphragm** generally present . . . **B**

A. Peristome teeth fine, formed of parts of two adjacent cell walls in a linear series, usually sculptured and with transverse bands, often of two or more series; if absent, epiphragm absent . . . . . **C**

  B. Peristome of four teeth, epiphragm absent; seta present; leaves without lamellae; protonema often producing **frondiform** leaves . . . . . .
. . . . **Tetraphidae**

  B. Peristome of 32 or 64 or more teeth or none; epiphragm generally present; leaves with lamellae; protonema never producing frondiform leaves
. . . . **Polytrichidae**

    C. Peristome teeth absent; seta nearly absent; capsule emergent from the perichaetial leaves by a pseudopodium . . . . . **D**

    C. Peristome teeth usually present; seta usually present; capsule never emergent on a pseudopodium . . . . **E**

      D. Capsule opening by an operculum; gametophyte bearing leaves containing dead porose hyaline cells, with spirally thickened walls, surrounded by several elongate chlorophyllose cells; protonema thallose
. . . . . . **Sphagnidae**

      D. Capsule generally opening by four preformed longitudinal slits; gametophyte bearing leaves with very thick-walled tiny cells; protonema a much-branched laminate structure . . . **Andreaeidae**

      E. Sporangium obliquely ovoid and somewhat flattened on upper surface, the narrow end pointed; inner peristome formed of a pleated hyaline sleeve; outer peristome generally of several rows of irregular thread-like teeth, or rudimentary . . . . **Buxbaumiidae**

      E. Sporangium various but never obliquely ovoid as above (E); inner peristome absent, or if present never with a pleated sleeve; outer peristome, if present, of a single row of teeth
. . . . . . **Bryidae**

nidae. About 100 species can be distinguished, although more than 300 have been described. Species are found throughout the world, but form extensive bogs only in the Northern Hemisphere.

GAMETOPHYTE. The protonema of *Sphagnum* is an irregularly lobed unistratose thallus bearing a number of filamentous multi-cellular rhizoids (Fig. 16–17J). It generally produces a single leafy gametophyte that lacks rhizoids. In some species the protonema arising directly from the spore produces rhizoid-like shoots from which develop secondary protonemata, each of which can produce a leafy gametophyte. Gametophytes are often quite large. Some reach lengths of nearly 3 meters, although the living portion is normally less than 0.2 m long; in compact forms the living portion is often only a few centimeters long. The gametophyte is unique, both in its detailed and gross morphology. The main stem bears widely separated leaves that generally differ from those on the branches. Branches are normally in fascicles of three to eight; the fascicles occur above every fourth stem leaf. If the species is submerged, all of the branches are essentially alike; but in emergent gametophytes, divergent branches usually grow outward from the stem and pendent branches lie close to the stem (Fig. 16–17A). The pendent branches normally are more slender and bear smaller leaves than the divergent branches. At the apex of the shoot all branches form a dense tuft, or **capitulum.**

The leaves are closely imbricated on all branches. All leaves are unistratose and lack a costa. Mature leaves are made up of a network of elongate chlorophyllose cells surrounding large dead hyaline cells (Fig. 16–17D). The hyaline cells generally possess transverse thickenings and pores and are normally swollen and broadly circular to elliptical in cross section; they are five to ten times as wide as the chlorophyllose cells. The chlorophyllose cells vary in cross-sectional shape and position in reference to the surfaces of the leaf (see Fig. 16–17E–G). The leaf margin is entire and bordered or unbordered by linear cells, or it is tattered, indicating that a number of the marginal cells were resorbed.

The stem is often brittle and is supported by floating in water or by other stems that compact many gametophytes into a cushion or mat. The cortical cells of the stem are hyaline and one to five cells thick. These cells are frequently porose and bear spiral thickenings like those of the hyaline leaf cells, or they are porose with no spiral thickenings (Fig. 16–17H, I, M, N).

The cortex of the branches is always a single cell thick. In some species the porose cells specialize to form scattered elongate **retort cells,** which are shaped like flasks with an apical pore, and occur among smaller nonporose hyaline cells (Fig. 16–17M, N). Because of the presence of large dead hyaline porose cells, *Sphagnum* gametophytes absorb great quantities of liquid, in some cases more than 20 times their own weight. The central axis beneath the cortex is generally differentiated into a multistratose outer region of thicker-walled (usually colored) cells and an inner cylinder of thin-walled hyaline parenchymatous cells (Fig. 16–17H).

The sexual branches are generally near the apex of the plant, most often in the outer part of the capitulum. The archegonia are on a short perichaetial branch and are surrounded by perichaetial leaves generally larger than other leaves and slightly different in cellular detail. The antheridia occur on separate divergent branches that are somewhat swollen near the tip, giving the branch a catkin-like appearance. The thickened portion of the branch possesses a single antheridium at the axil of each leaf. Antheridia are globose, as in the hepatics, and each is borne on an elongate stalk. Branched twisted filaments of cells (the paraphyses) surround each antheridium. These filaments probably retain moisture vital in the release and transport of the sperm.

SPOROPHYTE. The species of *Sphagnum* are distinguished entirely on the basis of gametophytic characteristics. The sporophyte is ephemeral, and in some cases infrequently produced; thus *Sphagnum* is often found without it. When it occurs, the sporophyte consists essentially of only the capsule (Fig. 16–17L). The foot is somewhat expanded in the apex of the pseudopodium, which elongates to extend the capsule beyond the perichaetial leaves. Normally a single capsule emerges from a perichaetium.

A thin colorless calyptra, which protects the developing sporophyte, is torn irregularly as

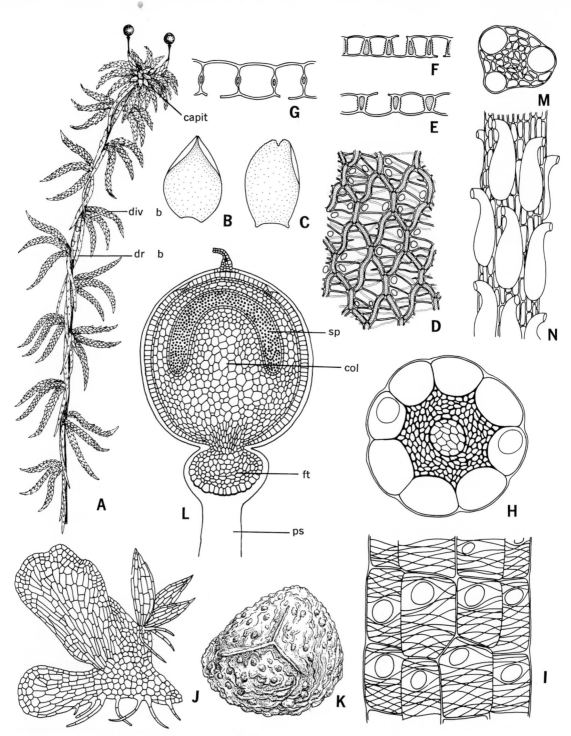

FIGURE 16–17   Morphology and anatomy of subclass Sphagnidae. A, habit of sporophyte-bearing shoot of *Sphagnum papillosum*, ×1; B, branch leaf of *S. papillosum*, ×12; C, stem-leaf of *S. papillosum*, ×12; D, leaf cells of *S. papillosum* (note network of chlorophyllose cells surrounding porose hyaline cells; also the fibril thickenings of walls of hyaline cells), ×165; E, cross section of *S. papillosum* leaf, showing relationship of hyaline and chlorophyllose cells, ×165; F, same for *S. squarrosum*, ×215; G, same for *S. magellanicum* ×235; H, cross section of branch-stem of *S. papillosum* (note hyaline outer cells and dark-

the capsule differentiates, and shreds usually remain at the base of the mature capsule. The ripe capsule is essentially spherical, and the operculum may be somewhat flattened or convex. The capsule wall bears numerous nonfunctional stomata on the surface.

The capsule jacket has two well-differentiated regions. The unistratose epidermis contains the rudimentary stomata; when mature, the cells of the epidermis have thicker walls. A multistratose region of parenchymatous cells beneath the epidermis is continuous with the dome-shaped columella (see Fig. 16–17L). The cells of the jacket are chlorophyllose while the capsule is developing, but the chloroplasts disappear when it is mature. A dome-shaped mass of spores overarches the columella, and the jacket closely invests the sporogenous layer. As in the Anthocerotae, the sporogenous cells and jacket are derived from the amphithecium. In this way *Sphagnum* differs from all other mosses.

Sculpturing of spores varies among *Sphagnum* species, but it has not been studied in any detail (Fig. 16–17K). Spore dispersal is remarkable. As the sporangium matures, the columella shrinks, leaving a gas-filled space. The capsule contracts in diameter as it dries, changing from a spherical to a cylindrical shape. This change causes compression of the trapped gas below the spores. When the compressed gas reaches a pressure of about five atmospheres, the operculum can no longer confine it. The operculum is then explosively thrown off, and the escaping gas carries the spores into the air.

ECOLOGY. *Sphagnum* is a significant constituent of the vegetation in much of the glaciated portion of the Northern Hemisphere. Aquatic species growing in lake and pool margins add to the acidity of these water bodies. As a result of this acidity, as well as antiseptic substances produced by *Sphagnum,* the aquatic environment becomes relatively free of decay organisms; organic material added to the water decays slowly and accumulates in the lake. The aquatic species of *Sphagnum,* at first restricted to the lake margin, form a floating mat of organic material, which expands over the lake. This quaking mat is a habitat suitable for other plants, including other *Sphagnum* species. Consequently, organic accumulation occurs both in the lake depths and on its margin. The bottom sediments are fine organic muds, but the *Sphagnum* deposits are more fibrous. In time the entire water body is completely overgrown by peat-forming vegetation, and in some areas the peat may be overgrown by forest.

These lake peat deposits are important in reconstructing the vegetational history of an area. Some pollen and spores that annually fall into such a lake ultimately sink to the bottom and are preserved from decay. Year after year new deposits are added, each layer recording the spores of many of the plants that grow near the lake. If water circulation does not disturb these deposits, careful analysis of the numbers and kinds of spores found in a peat boring will reveal the succession of vegetation.

Although *Sphagnum* decreases the wetness of some environments, it increases wetness in others. An expanding *Sphagnum* colony moving into a forest can, by its great water retention and absorption, make the soil so saturated that the forest trees are killed. Thus, a boggy environment can extend up slopes and greatly affect the structure and productivity of a forest.

RELATIONSHIPS. *Sphagnum* is often considered to belong to its own class, Sphagna.

walled cells of central axis), ×295; I, external view of stem of *S. papillosum,* showing hyaline porose outer cells with their fibril thickenings, ×225; J, prothallial protonema of *Sphagnum* bearing young leafy shoot, ×75; K, spore of *S. papillosum,* showing spore-wall sculpturing and trilete pore, ×1,100; L, longitudinal section through *Sphagnum* capsule, showing anatomy, ×95; M, cross section of branch-stem of *S. tenellum,* ×120; N, external view of branch-stem of *S. tenellum,* showing the hyaline retort cells, ×120. *col,* columella; *ft,* foot; *ps,* pseudopodium; *spl,* sporogenous layer. (L, after Cavers with permission of Trustees of *New Phytologist* and Messrs. Dawsons of Pall Mall, who reprinted F. Cavers' *The Inter-Relationships of the Bryophyta* in 1964).

However, the discoveries of Neuberg demonstrate the presence of Permian moss genera that resemble Sphagnidae in some respects and Bryidae in others. For example, in its shape and general form the leaf of the fossil genus *Intia* resembles that of some Bryidae. However, the leaf cells occasionally show a strong resemblance to the arrangement in *Sphagnum* leaves. In *Vorcutannularia* the resemblance is even stronger; and in *Protosphagnum* chlorophyllose and hyaline cells are clearly differentiated, much as in *Sphagnum* (Fig. 16–29A–D). Apparently *Sphagnum* is in the same general evolutionary line as other Musci, although it is clearly isolated from them. Within the genus, those species considered the most primitive are predominantly aquatic, whereas the more highly evolved species are found in somewhat drier situations.

ECONOMIC IMPORTANCE. In gardening *Sphagnum* peat is added in part to increase the moisture-holding capacity of the soil. *Sphagnum* peat has a number of other uses. For example, in Ireland, peat has long been used for fuel. During the First World War, *Sphagnum* was widely used in making surgical dressings. Its great absorptive capacity and antiseptic nature make it superior to cotton in some respects.

SUBCLASS ANDREAEIDAE

This subclass has a single order, *Andreaeales,* with one family, Andreaeaceae. Three genera make up the family: *Andreaea, Acroschisma,* and *Neuroloma. Andreaea* is found throughout the world, but is most frequent in cool temperate climates. The other genera are known only from the Southern Hemisphere, where they are rare and probably restricted to temperate South America. All genera form dark brown to blackish tufts on bare siliceous rock. A few species grow in wet sites, but most species are found on exposed outcrops and boulders. They occur from near sea level to high alpine localities and are sometimes conspicuous in late snow-patch areas.

Andreaea is represented by more than 100 described species, but careful study probably would reduce the clear-cut species to fewer than 50. *Acroschisma* and *Neuroloma* each possess a single species (Fig. 16–18).

GAMETOPHYTE. In *Andreaea* the spore germinates within the wall, becoming a globular multicellular mass. When the spore wall is broken, the chlorophyllose protonema emerges to form a much-branched thallose protonema (Fig. 16–18G). This often gives rise to elliptic unistratose flaps that increase the photosynthetic surface (Fig. 16–18F). These flaps produce a thallose protonema which may in turn produce buds that differentiate into leafy gametophytes (Fig. 16–18G). The gametophytes are attached to the substrate by characteristic moss rhizoids.

When mature, the leafy gametophyte is either unisexual or bisexual. It is freely branched, and only the younger portions are chlorophyllose; the remainder of the gametophyte is reddish or brownish. The leaves, spirally arranged and crowded (Fig. 16–18A, C) may or may not be costate, depending on the species. The bulk of the leaf is unistratose. Leaf cells are small, mainly isodiametric and thick-walled, and often papillose. The perichaetial leaves generally differ from those of the rest of the gametophyte; in bisexual species the perigonial leaves are also different. The stem of thick-walled cells is not differentiated into any recognizable layers (Fig. 16–18E). Similar to those of most mosses, the antheridia are somewhat elongate and borne on a stalk, and the archegonium is flask-shaped. Filamentous paraphyses are scattered among the sex organs.

SPOROPHYTE. As in the Sphagnidae, the sporophyte is borne on a pseudopodium. In general the capsule structure is similar to that of *Sphagnum*. The jacket is multicellular (but lacks stomata), the columella is elongate and dome-shaped, and the sporogenous cells overarch the columella (Fig. 16–18H). The calyptra is irregularly torn as in *Sphagnum,* or a portion of it is carried upward as a small cap on

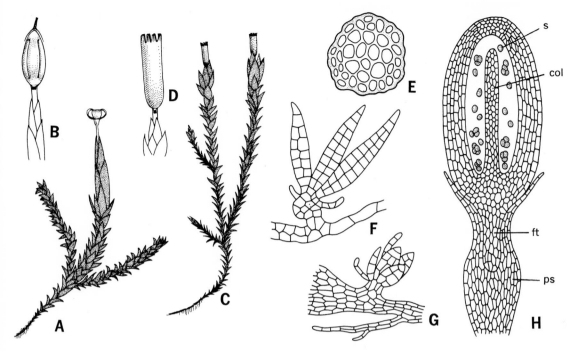

FIGURE 16–18.   Morphology and anatomy of subclass Andreaeidae. A, habit sketch of *Andreaea rupestris* bearing dehiscing sporangium, ×8; B, sporangium of *A. rupestris* when moist, ×15; C, habit of *Acroschisma wilsoni* bearing dehiscing sporangia, ×3; D, detail of sporangium of *A. wilsoni* showing peristome-toothlike splits around capsule mouth, ×8; E, cross section of stem of *Andreaea rupesiris*, showing undifferentiated cell structure, ×135; F, portion of straplike protonema of *Andreaea* with frondiform flaps, ×130; G, portion of protonema of *Andreaea* bearing a single young leafy shoot, ×130; H, longitudinal section through sporangium of *Andreaea*, ×130. *col,* columella; *ft,* foot; *ps,* pseudopodium; *s,* spore. (C, D, after Brotherus; F, G, after Ruhland in Engler, *Die natürlichen Pflanzenfamilien,* Vol. 10, p. 16, Fig. 10O, 11A, 108A, D, 1924.)

the developing capsule. There is no series of air spaces between the jacket and the sporogenous layer. As in all mosses, the sporangium is chlorophyllose while developing.

Andreaea is unique among the mosses in the dehiscence of the capsule (Fig. 16–18A, B). When the capsule dries, the inner thin-walled cells of the jacket shrink and the outer thicker-walled cells do not; the capsule contracts in length, opening the four (or rarely eight) vertical slits and releasing the spores. Wetting closes the capsule. In the genus *Acroschisma* the capsule opens by four to eight irregular teeth at the apex of the capsule. An operculum is absent in all Andreaeidae (Fig. 16–18D).

RELATIONSHIPS.   Although it appears to be an independent evolutionary line showing no clear relationship to any other group of mosses, the subclass Andreaeidae stands in many respects between the Sphagnidae and other classes of Musci. The thallose protonema and the presence of a pseudopodium are shared with the Sphagnidae, but the closest affinity of Andreaeidae in morphology and development is with other classes. In the Andreaeidae the sporogenous layer is derived from the outer layers of the endothecium as in all mosses other than *Sphagnum*. Additional features shared with other mosses but not with *Sphagnum* are: shape of antheridia, persistence of rhizoids, and general structure of the stem.

SUBCLASS TETRAPHIDAE

This subclass contains two genera, *Tetraphis* and *Tetrodontium*—both of which are essentially north temperate in distribution.

Tetrodontium also occurs in New Zealand. *Tetraphis,* represented by two species, grows mainly in coniferous forests, where it is particularly luxuriant on moist rotting logs. *Tetrodontium* is confined to siliceous rock, mainly on humid shaded overhangs (Fig. 16–19).

GAMETOPHYTE. The spore germinates to produce a normal protonema, which gives rise to frondiform unistratose flaps in much the same manner as in *Andreaea* (Fig. 16–19D). These thalloid structures often bud off a branch near the base, producing a normal leafy gametophyte. In *Tetraphis,* the frondiform flaps usually disappear after the leafy gametophyte appears. In *Tetrodontium,* the leafy gametophyte is greatly reduced and the frondiform flaps persist and provide the bulk of the photosynthetic surface. The erect leafy gametophytes form densely packed carpets in *Tetraphis* whereas in *Tetrodontium* they occur scattered over the rock surface. Gametophytes are attached to the substrate by rhizoids.

The ovate to lanceolate leaves are spirally arranged in three to five ranks (Fig. 16–19A). The leaves are unistratose except at the costa, which extends to near the leaf apex. Leaf cells are parenchymatous, hexagonal, and smooth.

The plants are bisexual, and sex organs are typical for mosses. Among the sexual shoots there are also gemmiferous shoots (Fig. 16–19A), which resemble the others except that several larger leaves at the apex of the gemmiferous shoot form a cup with stalked gemmae (Fig. 16–19B). The gemmae are, in essence, rather specialized paraphyses with lenticular tips. The gemmae break off readily and germinate to produce new protonemata that ultimately give rise to frondiform flaps and leafy gametophytes.

Stems are somewhat differentiated internally (Fig. 16–19C). The outer cells are thick-walled, and an inner layer of parenchymatous cells forms a central axis. A central strand of thick-walled cells is frequently present.

SPOROPHYTE. The short cylindrical sporangium is borne on an elongate seta, which may be papillose or smooth. In *Tetraphis pel-*lucida and *Tetrodontium* the seta is erect, but the seta of *Tetraphis geniculata* has a conspicuous angular bend—a feature rare in mosses. In all species the calyptra is pleated, and bell-shaped, and it covers most of the capsule (Fig. 16–19A). The operculum is conic and unistratose, resembling the outer wall of the jacket, from which it is derived. The jacket directly surrounding the sporogenous region is three to four cells thick, and the outer cells are thicker than the inner. No stomata are present. As in *Andreaea,* there is no air space between the jacket and the sporogenous layer (Fig. 16–19F).

The peristome is of four multicellular persistent teeth (Fig. 16–19E), which arise from the inner cell layers of the amphithecium and are attached below the mouth of the capsule. The teeth are not hygroscopic, and spores are released by shaking of the capsule, which is generally raised high above the leafy gametophyte. The columella of the Tetraphidae extends up to the base of the massive peristome teeth so that the sporogenous layer forms a cylinder around the columella.

RELATIONSHIPS. The Tetraphidae show relationships with the Andreaeidae through *Acroschisma* on the basis of superficial similarity of the peristome. The frondiform protonemal flaps are also reminiscent of the Andreaeidae. Other mosses with such flaps are *Diphyscium* in the Buxbaumiidae and *Oedipodium* in the Bryidae. In all subclasses other than Andreaeidae and Sphagnidae, the following are common features: the typical calyptra, the operculum, the well-differentiated stem, the erect leafy gametophyte, and the general nature of development of the peristome teeth.

It has been suggested that the Southern Hemisphere genus *Calomnion* is related to the Tetraphidae. The leaf arrangement and structure, production of frondiform protonemal flaps, and general appearance of the sporophyte are all very similar to *Tetraphis,* but *Calomnion* lacks a peristome, and its true relationship is uncertain; it has been placed in the Bryidae.

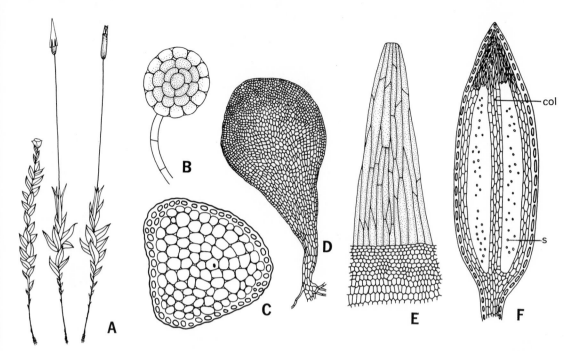

FIGURE 16–19   Morphology and anatomy of subclass Tetraphidae: *Tetraphis pellucida*. A, habit (gemma-bearing plant at far left), ×4; B, lenticular gemma, ×225; C, cross section of stem, showing slight differentiation in cells, ×35; D, frondiform protonemal flap, ×35; E, multicellular peristome tooth, ×150; F, longitudinal section through sporangium, ×10. *col*, columella; *s*, spore. (D, after Ruhland in Engler, *Die natürlichen Pflanzenfamilien*, Vol. 10, p. 19, Fig. 14, 1924.)

SUBCLASS POLYTRICHIDAE

This subclass, represented throughout the world, is relatively small, possessing a single order with two families. Eighteen genera containing nearly 370 species are recognized. It is a very natural group with both gametophytic and sporophytic morphology and anatomy showing a very strong uniformity throughout. Most species grow on soil. Some species are found in bogs and swamps and others are restricted to stream margins or rock faces.

GAMETOPHYTE.   Gametophytes of all Polytrichidae begin as a typical chlorophyllose, much-branched protonema. In a few species the protonema persists and provides the photosynthetic surface for the growing sporophyte; in such species the gametophyte is much reduced. Most members of the subclass are unisexual.

All Polytrichidae have erect gametophytes, and the sporophytes terminate the main branch or branches. Leaves are arranged spirally and are generally in five ranks, although in *Bartramiopsis* a three-ranked arrangement is apparent. Leaves are usually lanceolate and always costate. Normally the upper surface of the costa is covered by many longitudinal parallel lamellae (Fig. 16–20F). These are several cells high, and each is unistratose. The distal cells often differ structurally from others in the lamella. In many genera the lamellae are chlorophyllose, whereas the rest of the leaf possesses opaque or translucent cells without chlorophyll. In some species the lamina margin curves in over the lamellae during dry periods, thus reducing water loss in the leaf. The leaf margin is toothed or entire; it is generally unistratose and not strongly differentiated from other leaf cells, but in a few instances it is bistratose and the cells differ from those in the rest of the leaf. The basal cells of the leaf are frequently colorless and rectangular, whereas the upper cells are colored and quadrate. The lower portion of the leaf is often expanded and clasps the stem, whereas the remaining narrow

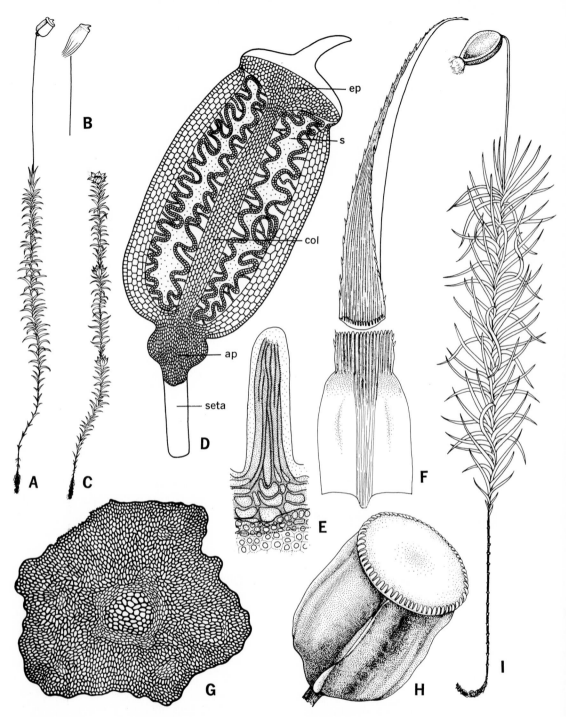

FIGURE 16–20   Morphology and anatomy of subclass Polytrichidae. A–H, *Polytrichum commune*. A, sporophyte-bearing plant after calyptra has fallen, ×1; B, sporangium with calyptra in place, ×1; C, antheridial plant, showing three successive years' crops of perigonia, ×1; D, longitudinal section through sporangium (idealized), ×25; E, multicellular peristome tooth, ×75; F, leaf, showing lamellae on upper surface, ×12; G, cross section of stem, showing differentiation into tissue-like areas, ×140; H, sporangium, showing peristome teeth and epiphragm, ×8. I, habit of *Dawsonia superba,* ×1. *ap,* apophysis; *col,* columella; *ep,* epiphragm; *seta,* seta; *s,* spore.

portion stands out at an angle to the stem. These overlapping leaf bases appear to be effective in providing a capillary transport for water utilized in the growth of the moss.

Gametophytes vary considerably in size. For example, in the genus *Dawsonia* some are nearly 60 cm tall (Fig. 16–20I), and some species of *Polytrichum* and *Pogonatum* are almost as tall. Yet in other genera the gametophyte may be less than 0.5 cm tall. In most genera the gametophyte is unbranched, but in some (as *Dendoligotrichum*) it possesses several branches and resembles a seedling spruce tree.

The stem is always wiry, indicating the large number of thick-walled cells in both the cortex and the central axis. Stem tissue is sometimes considerably differentiated. Cells that superficially resemble xylem and phloem (Fig. 16–20G) appear to be primarily supportive, although in some instances the central strand is important in transport of water and nutrients. Thickwalled cells of the leaf costa are joined with the cortical cells of the stem, which is often heavily clothed with rhizoids, particularly toward the base.

SPOROPHYTE. Most gametophytes produce a single sporophyte each year, but some produce several annually. The seta is erect, wiry, and structurally similar to the stem. The cylindrical or angled capsule is either erect or slightly inclined, and is usually covered by a large hairy calyptra (Fig. 16–20A, B, H). The capsule wall is multistratose and often bears some stomata. A cylindrical series of air spaces always lies between the jacket wall and the cylindrical sporogenous layer. The sporogenous layer surrounds the columella, and sometimes another series of air spaces separates the sporogenous layer from the columella (Fig. 16–20D). In most genera the apex of the columella is expanded to form a closure to the mouth of the capsule, the epiphragm. Spaces are present only between the peristome teeth, through which the minute spores escape. The spores in this subclass, among the smallest in the mosses, are generally less than 15 microns in diameter and very numerous—thousands of spores being produced by each capsule.

In the capsule of most Polytrichidae there is a single row of short, multicellular peristome teeth (Fig. 16–20E, H)—usually 32, 64, or rarely 16, depending on the genus. However, in *Dawsonia* there are several irregular rows of very long intertwisted peristome teeth. The epiphragm is absent in this genus. *Lyellia* and *Bartramiopsis* have no peristome teeth, but they do have an epiphragm.

RELATIONSHIPS. In spite of the rather complex gametophyte, the Polytrichidae exhibit a number of very primitive, mostly microscopic features. Also, the massive peristome teeth, the mode of leaf arrangement, and the vast numbers of spores produced are all considered primitive characteristics.

The Polytrichidae are possibly related to Buxbaumiidae, through the genus *Dawsonia*. In this genus the nature of the capsule and the complex peristome suggest some features of Buxbaumiidae. The subclass has been in existence at least since the Eocene Epoch, and its present wide distribution through a diversity of habitats and climates suggests that it is likely to persist for some millenia.

ECONOMIC IMPORTANCE. The genus *Polytrichum* has been used for stuffing mattresses and pillows. Linnaeus recommended it on the basis that mattresses stuffed with it harbored neither fleas nor infectious disease! *Polytrichum* has also been used to make brooms, and in Roman ruins in Great Britain an unfinished basket woven from *Polytrichum* stems was discovered.

SUBCLASS BUXBAUMIIDAE

This subclass, a small one of tiny plants, consists of predominantly Northern Hemisphere genera. Three genera and approximately 25 species have been recognized. Species grow on soil, rotten wood, humus, or acidic rock.

GAMETOPHYTE. The gametophyte of *Buxbaumia* is the simplest known among the mosses. Antheridial plants consist of a limited filamentous protonema that bears several microscopic antheridial buds. Each antheridium is surrounded by a photosynthetic clamshell-like expansion of a protonemal branch (Fig. 16–21C, D). The antheridium is globose, as is that of the Sphagnidae, and each is borne on a stalk. The archegonial plants have a more extensive protonema. Each plant bears several colorless leaves, which may be ciliate on the margins (Fig. 16–21B). One or two archegonia are borne by such a plant. No paraphyses are present with the sex organs. In *Diphyscium* and *Theriotia* the gametophyte is leafy and small (Fig. 16–21F). The leaves are usually costate and dark green, often multistratose and papillose. Perichaetial leaves often are tipped by an extension of the costa. In *Theriotia* there is a specialization of cells in the leaves, most cells being hyaline and the remainder forming definite rows of chlorophyllose cells. In *Diphyscium,* the protonema bears peltate protonemal flaps in a manner resembling Andreaeidae and Tetraphidae (Fig. 16–21H).

SPOROPHYTE. The capsule of *Buxbaumia* terminates a papillose seta (Fig. 16–21A). The whole sporophyte may be about 3 cm tall. In both *Diphyscium* and *Theriotia* the capsule has virtually no seta and is surrounded by elongate perichaetial leaves (Fig. 16–21F). The capsule of all genera is oblique, flattened on the upper side, and tapered to the short conical operculum. A small calyptra covers the operculum. When young, the sporophyte is photosynthetic. Indeed, in *Buxbaumia* the sporophyte must synthesize most of its food. In this genus the protonema produces a protein- and oil-rich tuber that presumably nourishes the young embryo until it develops sufficiently to support itself.

The capsule has a jacket three cells thick, and stomata are present at the base of the capsule. The stomata may be superficial or immersed. Beneath the jacket, chlorophyllose filaments traverse an extensive area of air spaces. The spore sac forms a cylinder surrounding the columella. As in most mosses, the columella is of parenchymatous cells and ends below the operculum (Fig. 16–21E).

The peristome is formed from several cell layers, as in the *Tetraphidae,* but there are a number of distinct rows of teeth—each row formed of fragmentary, thickened cell walls, as in the Bryidae. The inner peristome is a hyaline pleated cone, open at the tip (Fig. 16–21G). Outer peristome teeth occur in several rows or they are absent or very rudimentary. When present, the teeth are opaque and obscurely articulate, resembling those of the Bryidae. If all teeth are present in a rank, there are 16—a feature also reminiscent of most Bryidae.

RELATIONSHIPS. In peristomial development, the Buxbaumiidae resemble both Tetraphidae and Polytrichidae, but the actual structure of the peristome teeth conspicuously resembles that of the Bryidae. The Buxbaumiidae has a relatively highly developed sporophyte and considerable variation in gametophytic structure—suggesting a reduced remnant of an evolutionary line.

SUBCLASS BRYIDAE

This subclass contains the bulk of the mosses. There are 12 orders, at least 75 families, 650 genera, and approximately 13,700 species. Most families are poorly studied, and few genera are well understood. Even general evolutionary lines are unclear, and inadequate information has produced a certain lack of uniformity in general classification. Although general knowledge of temperate Bryidae is reasonably complete, that of tropical taxa is incomplete. Detailed morphological study has been confined to very few species.

Because of their great diversity, species of Bryidae are found nearly everywhere a plant will grow. Some species can tolerate extended periods of desiccation and others are aquatic, but most species flourish in environments of high humidity. Many species have strict substrate requirements; some are found only on lime, dung, tree bark of a certain texture, or even on leaves of tropical trees.

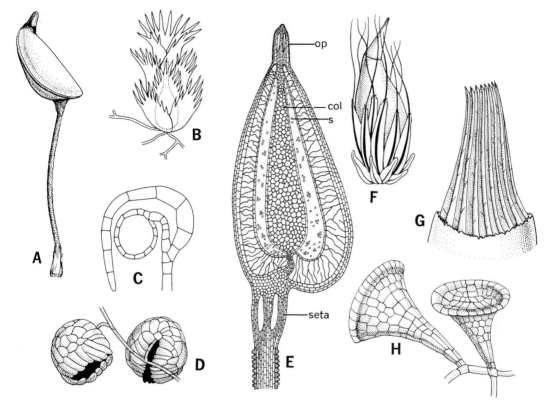

FIGURE 16–21   Morphology and anatomy of subclass Buxbaumiidae. A–E, *Buxbaumia aphylla*. A, habit, ×7; B, gametophyte with single archegonium, ×45; C, longitudinal section through antheridial "branch," ×400; D, antheridial "branches," external view, ×225; E, longitudinal section through sporangium, ×15. F–H, *Diphyscium foliosum*. F, habit of sporangium-bearing gametophyte, ×8; G, peristome (note pleated cone), ×40; H, protonemal flaps, ×25. *col*, columella; *op*, operculum; *seta*, seta; *s*, spores. (C, D, after Goebel with permission of G. Fischer; H, after Ruhland in Engler, *Die natürlichen Pflanzenfamilien*, Vol. 10, p. 21, Fig. 18A, 1924.)

GAMETOPHYTE. The morphological variety of Bryidae gametophytes is closely correlated with patterns of sporophytic variety (Fig. 16–22). Consequently, gametophytic features can be used to distinguish kinds of Bryidae. In most Bryidae the gametophyte begins as a much-branched filamentous green protonema that produces buds; the buds, in turn, differentiate to produce leafy gametophytes. Members of the Southern Hemisphere family Dicnemonaceae have spores that germinate precociously in the capsule; the multicellular "spore" produces both rhizoids and an apical bud that ultimately forms the basis of the leafy gametophyte (Fig. 16–28I). The protonema of a few Bryidae produces gemmae of characteristic morphology for the species (Fig.

16–4). Frondiform protonemal flaps are rarely formed (e.g., *Oedipodium griffithsianum*). In *Schistostega* and *Mittenia,* both genera of deeply shaded habitats, the protonema possesses branches with highly refractive lens-like cells. This protonema produces a yellow-green glow by reflected light.

A number of Bryidae have a very reduced leafy gametophyte. Such is the case for *Discelium,* where the protonema forms a green algalike web over moist earth. This moss, like others with a prominent protonema, retains the protonema until the sporophyte is mature. The protonema is frequently perennial, but in most mosses it disappears soon after the leafy gametophytes arise. Under moist conditions almost any actively dividing cell of a leafy gameto-

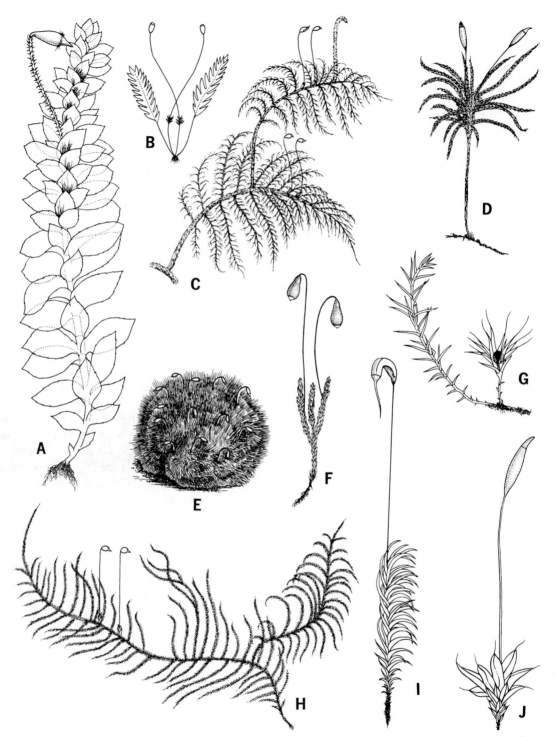

FIGURE 16–22   Variety in gametophytes and sporophytes of subclass Bryidae. A, *Eriopus remotifolius* (note amphigastria-like underleaves), ×4; B, *Schistostega pennata*, ×6; C, *Hylocomium splendens*, ×1; D, *Climacium dendroides,* ×1; E, *Grimmia pulvinata,* ×1; F, *Bryum* sp., ×1; G, *Archidium alternifolium,* ×6; H, *Eurhynchium oreganum,* ×2; I, *Dicranum scoparium,* ×1; J, *Tortula muralis,* ×2. (A, after Goebel with permission of G. Fischer.)

phyte is capable of forming a protomena which, in turn, differentiates buds in the same manner as a spore-produced protonema.

Bryidae are either **acrocarpous** or **pleurocarpous** in general growth form. The most primitive Bryidae are conceded to be acrocarpous; the more advanced are highly elaborate, much branched, and pleurocarpous. Acrocarpous mosses have the leafy gametophyte erect, and the current year's sporophyte terminates the main shoot or a main branch (Fig. 16–22I, J). Acrocarpous mosses generally form mats or cushions of erect shoots. Pleurocarpous mosses are much branched and creeping (Fig. 16–22A, C, H); the sporophyte of the current year is borne on a special short lateral branch. Basal rhizoids attach acrocarpous mosses to the substrate, and rhizoids often attach much of the reclining stem of pleurocarpous mosses to the substrate.

Leaves of most acrocarpous mosses are morphologically alike. The leaf arrangement is generally radial, but in a number of cases the gametophyte is bilaterally symmetrical as in some leafy hepaticae. In most Bryidae the perichaetical leaves differ somewhat from the other leaves.

In many pleurocarpous mosses the leaves of the main stem differ from those of the branches. Several pleurocarpous mosses (as in the Hypopterygiaceae) have lateral leaves and amphigastria-like leaves resembling those of many leafy hepatics (Fig. 16–22A). But general leaf structure, as well as sporophyte features, readily distinguish these mosses from the hepatics.

The leaf cells in the Bryidae show considerable variation in shape and structure. The basal cells often differ from those near the apex and may be larger or smaller than those of the rest of the leaf. Cells may be restricted to the basal corners (**alar region**) of the leaf; these cells are often swollen and pigmented. The marginal cells often clearly differ in shape from those of the rest of the leaf. The margins vary from elaborately toothed to entire. Although most Bryidae have elongate cells, quadrate cells are not uncommon. Cell walls may be with or without pits; they may be nodular, or wavy, but generally they are without these features. Sometimes the cell corners have thickened walls, but trigones are never present.

Most Bryidae have unistratose leaves. If the leaf is costate—and most are—the costal region is multistratose and cells of the costa often show a distinctive distribution of larger thin-walled and smaller thick-walled cells. The costa is probably supportive; it may be single and prominent or multiple and short. The costa and the rest of the leaf are connected to the outer cortex of the stem. In a few instances the leaf possesses lamellae (e.g., *Pterigoneurum* in Fig. 16–23E) or a great mass of chlorophyllose filaments (e.g., *Aloina*). In a number of Bryidae (e.g., Leucobryaceae) the leaf cells are dimorphic in a manner resembling *Sphagnum*. In such Bryidae the large hyaline cells are porose and surround an inner layer of smaller chlorophyllose cells. Papillosity of leaf cells is often elaborate, and these papillae may be restricted in their distribution. In some species the ends of the cells project on the face of the lamina as teeth. Leaf margins are bistratose or even multistratose, whereas most of the remainder of the leaf is unistratose. The margin is **revolute** (curled under, Fig. 16–23C, G), **involute** (curled up, Fig. 16–23E), or plane (Fig. 16–23A, B, D, F, H, J, N). The leaf itself may be undulate (Fig. 16–23M) or **plicate** (pleated, Fig. 16–23B). In some genera the leaves produce gemmae, which occasionally form in clusters at the leaf apex or on the costa or on cells of the blade (Fig. 16–4C, E, F). In several species the leaves are brittle and each fragment serves as a vegetative propagant (Fig. 16–4D).

Stem anatomy in the Bryidae is equally variable. Differentiation of cells is never as elaborate as in the Polytrichidae, but cortical and central axis cells generally are different. The cortical cells are of one or several layers and are thick-walled and small, or thin-walled and large. In some instances the cortical cells are papillose, but generally they are smooth. The central axis is usually composed of parenchymatous cells, but in many genera there is a central strand of thicker-walled cells. When the stem is young the central strand seems to func-

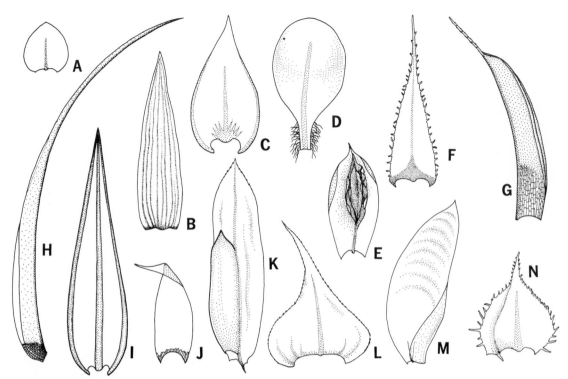

FIGURE 16–23   Variety in leaves of subclass Bryidae. A, *Hygrohypnum smithii*, ×15; B, *Orthothecium rufescens*, ×25; C, *Antitrichia californica*, ×20; D, *Oedipodium griffithianum*, ×15; E, *Pterigoneurum ovatum*, ×30; F, *Leucolepis menziesii*, stem-leaf, ×25; G, *Tortula ruralis*, ×13; H, *Dicranum scoparium*, ×15; I, *Sciaromium fryei*, ×20; J, *Brotherella roellii*, ×25; K, *Fissidens adianthoides*, ×15; L, *Eurhynchium oreganum*, ×15; M, *Neckera douglasii*, ×25; N, *Thelia hirtella*, ×30.

tion in conduction; when the stem is old the central strand aids in support and, in a few Bryidae, also in conduction. Young stems are chlorophyllose, but as the stem ages the chlorophyll is lost. Some oil and starch is stored in the stem cells. Rhizoids, present in nearly all Bryidae, are occasionally very abundant on the stem. The rhizoid walls are generally smooth, but they may be highly papillose.

The stem sometimes bears **paraphyllia** (Fig. 16–24). These are filamentous or leaf-like outgrowths that clothe the stem between the leaves or are restricted near leaf bases. Paraphyllia are chlorophyllose, often elaborate in outline and determinate in growth. Paraphyllia, found only on pleurocarpous mosses, are probably helpful in capillary water conduction.

The antheridia of the Bryidae are generally banana-shaped and borne on a multicellular stalk (Fig. 16–1A). They are surrounded by filamentous chlorophyllose paraphyses.

The archegonia are typically bryophytic, often with an extremely long neck (Fig. 16–1B, C), and surrounded by paraphyses. In bisexual species sex organs are distributed on separate branches, in the same cluster, or some mixed and others on separate branches. Many Bryidae are unisexual.

SPOROPHYTE.   In the Bryidae the sporophytic diversity parallels gametophytic variety (Fig. 16–25). However, in some genera, there is great variation in peristome structure. For example, in *Encalypta* some species have a double peristome, others have a single peristome, and still others have no peristome; other morphological features are relatively constant in this genus. In some large orders, such as Hypnobryales, the peristomes of all genera are almost identical.

In most Bryidae the sporophyte is borne on a seta. Seta color and structure are fairly

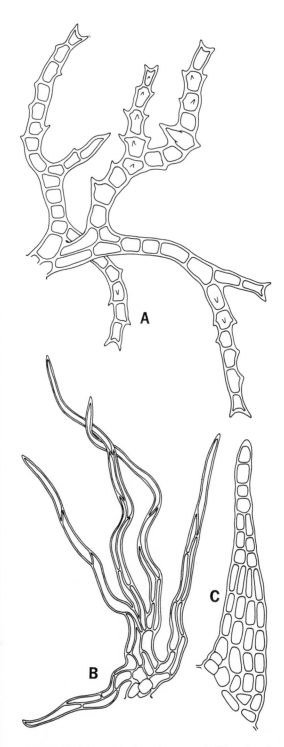

FIGURE 16–24   Variety in paraphyllia of sub-class Bryidae. A, *Thuidium delicatulum*, ×685; B, *Hylocomium splendens,* ×685; C, *Lescuraea incurvata,* ×685.

constant in the subclass. The seta is generally reddish brown, but it may be yellow, red, or colorless. One seta usually emerges from each perichaetium, but in some genera many sporophytes emerge. In bizarre and rare instances, multiple setae emerge from a single archegonium, and the tips are all crowded under a single calyptra. All setae are chlorophyllose when young. Anatomically the seta is very like the stem, except that the cortical cells are generally thick-walled. In most genera the seta is straight, but in some it is much curved so that the capsule is buried among the leaves. The orientation of the capsule is diversified but is reasonably constant in a genus.

In most Bryidae the capsule jacket is multistratose and has stomata (Fig. 16–26), which are generally restricted to the base of the capsule near the apophysis. Most capsules have air spaces similar to those of the Polytrichidae, but in some genera—especially aquatic ones—such spaces are absent.

The calyptra of Bryidae is generally smooth, but may be papillose or hairy. The lower edges of some calyptras are fringed by tattered or entire edges. The orientation of the calyptra is characteristic for the genus; in some genera it is possible to name the genus from the calyptra alone (Fig. 16–25).

Nearly all Bryidae have a columella of parenchymatous cells, with a surrounding sporogenous sleeve. Often a barrel-shaped series of air spaces occurs between the columella and the spore layer, and another between the spore layer and the jacket.

Most Bryidae possess an operculum. Often a specialized ring of hygroscopic elastic cells—the **annulus**—is found between the mouth of the capsule and the operculum. When the capsule is mature, this annulus aids in the release of the operculum. The operculum is generally concave and often has a central hump; or this hump often extends as a long snout (Fig. 16–25I); or the whole operculum is conical. Usually the operculum falls freely, but in some Bryidae it is fused with the columella and persists until the capsule decays (Fig. 16–25B, D). In the few Bryidae that have no operculum, the spores are shed by decay or by

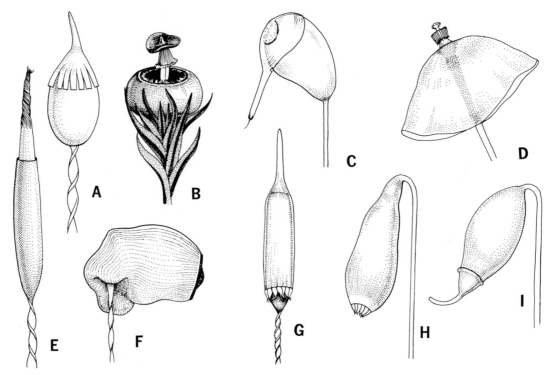

FIGURE 16–25   Variety in sporangia and calyptras of subclass Bryidae. A, *Rhacomitrium lanuginosum,* with calyptra, ×20; B, *Scouleria aquatica,* dehiscing, ×10; C, *Funaria hygrometrica,* with calyptra, ×15; D, *Splachnum luteum,* showing extensive hypophysis (sporangium dehiscing), ×6; E, *Tortula princeps,* dehiscing, ×7; F, *Philonotis fontana,* with operculum in place, ×8; G, *Encalypta ciliata,* with calyptra, ×10; H, *Leucolepis menziesii,* dehiscing, ×6; I, *Eurhynchium oreganum,* with operculum in place, ×10.

irregular rupturing of the capsule (Fig. 16–22G).

Most Bryidae that possess an operculum also have a peristome (Fig. 16–27). In the more primitive Bryidae the peristome is single and generally composed of 16 or 32 teeth formed from fragments of adjacent cell walls and derived from two cell layers of the amphithecium. Thus, the peristome teeth consist of fragments of cell walls. The teeth are variously sculptured and are generally brownish and opaque. In some genera the teeth are linear; in others, each tooth is forked; still others have the teeth much perforated. In nearly all Bryidae the teeth are composed of transverse plates. The teeth are hygroscopic and curl inward when slightly moist and flick outward when dry, or reverse the process in some instances. The irregular surfaces catch spores and aid in discharging them from the capsule. In some genera the peristome teeth emerge from a much-sculptured basal sleeve, or the teeth are rudimentary or even absent. In many genera the teeth break off gradually as the capsule ages.

Many Bryidae, including most pleurocarpous genera, have a double peristome. The outer peristome is similar to that just described. The function of the inner peristome is not clear. It is generally translucent and often possesses a continuous basal cylinder. The teeth of the inner peristome are not hygroscopic. They tend to alternate with those of the outer peristome, and between the teeth of the inner peristome there are often several filaments termed cilia. The inner peristome occasionally forms a perforated dome, with the teeth supporting the dome (Fig. 16–27H). In a few genera (e.g., *Fontinalis*) the inner peristome is a lacy lattice of interjoined teeth (Fig. 16–27C).

The spores are derived from the outer layers of the endothecium, as for all mosses other than the Sphagnidae. The spores are gen-

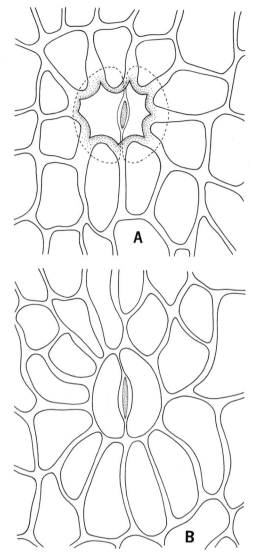

FIGURE 16–26   Stomata of sporangia in subclass Bryidae. A, immersed stoma of *Orthotrichum ohioense,* ×540; B, superficial stoma of *Funaria hygrometrica,* ×675.

ciously and are consequently multicellular when shed (Fig. 16–28I). Spores contain chlorophyll, oil, and generally starch.

ECONOMIC IMPORTANCE.   Capsules are eaten by birds and small mammals. No Bryidae are know to be poisonous, but their food value is rather low, since most of the tissue is indigestible cellulose. Bryidae and other mosses are infected by few disease-causing fungi and destructive invertebrates; consequently, mosses may contain antibiotic substances. Some antibiotic substances have been demonstrated, but it is uncertain whether these are produced by the moss or by contaminating bacteria and fungi. Minor uses for Bryidae are as packing material, decorative wreaths, hat decorations, and even mattress material. A number of Bryidae are troublesome as lawn and rockgarden weeds; others are useful as cover plants in gardens (especially in Japan). The ancient Greeks believed that some mosses induced sleep, and thus the genus *Hypnum* derives its name from the same root word as hypnotism.

RELATIONSHIPS.   The Bryidae are probably most closely allied to the Buxbaumiidae, with which they share the general structure of the peristome. Gametophytic similarity exists as well. Whether these similarities are a result of parallel evolution of two distinct lines is far from clear.

Within the Bryidae, evolutionary lines are just as vague. It seems probable that acrocarpous species with 16-toothed single peristomes are the most primitive, and pleurocarpous species with double peristomes are the most advanced. In the acrocarpous group the simplest gametophytic structure is present. With increase of teeth from 16 to 32, the structure and sculpturing of the teeth is elaborated and the pattern and sculpturing of the leaf cells is diversified. However, within these acrocarpous genera, some members are greatly reduced in structure. For example, in *Archidium* the gametophyte and sporophyte are nearly microscopic. The leaves are simple, and all cells are almost alike. The capsule lacks both an operculum and a columella; the spore size is

erally all alike **(homosporous),** but in a few genera they are of two distinct sizes **(heterosporous).** In the tropical genus *Macromitrium,* the large spores produce female gametophytes and the smaller spores produce male gametophytes (Fig. 16–28C). The spores are intermixed in the same capsule. Spore size and sculpturing varies (Fig. 16–28). Most spores are spherical with smooth walls, but some are kidney-shaped (*Ephemerum*—Fig. 16–28D). In some genera the spores germinate preco-

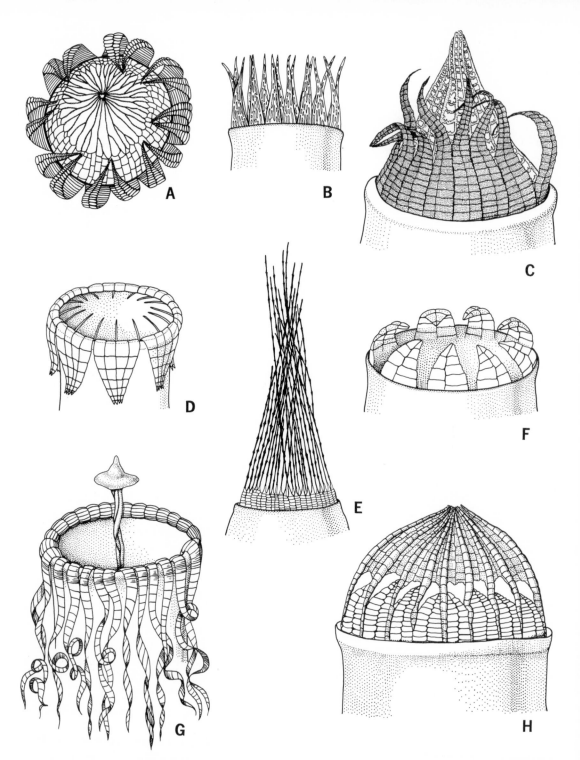

FIGURE 16–27   Variety in peristomes of subclass Bryidae. A, *Timmia bavarica*, showing endostome and exostome, ×35; B, *Coscinodon cribrosus*, ×50; C, *Fontinalis antipyretica*, ×30; D, *Ulota megalospora*, showing endostome and exostome, ×50; E, *Rhacomitrium canescens*, ×35; F, *Octoblepharum albidum*, ×50; G, *Tayloria splachnoides*, ×50; H, *Cinclidium stygium*, ×50. (A, after Lazarenko with permission of *The Bryologist;* G, H, after Schimper.)

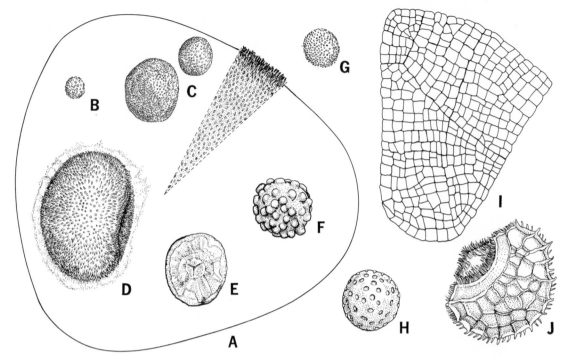

FIGURE 16–28   Variation in size and morphology of spores of subclass Bryidae, ×350. A, *Archidium alternifolium*, showing outline of spore to indicate size and a wedge to show sculpturing; B, *Ulota megalospora*; C, *Macromitrium comatum*, showing heterospory; D, *Ephemerum minutissimum*; E, *Encalypta ciliata*; F, *Encalypta rhabdocarpa*; G, *Octoblepharum albidum*; H, *Bruchia brevifolia*; I, *Dicnemon calycinum*, multicellular spore; J, *Bruchia drummondii*.

large (for mosses) and the spore number is low (Fig. 16–28A). In some acrocarpous families, such as Bryaceae, the sporophyte is rather complex with a double peristome and elaborately sculptured teeth. In this same family the gametophytes are remarkably simple in structure.

Similar evolutionary lines exist in pleurocarpous Bryidae, although the greatest diversity here is in the structure of the gametophyte. Among such Bryidae it is difficult to separate some genera and even some families. Consequently, understanding of the evolutionary lines is very tenuous.

FOSSIL BRYOPHYTA

Bryophytes have made poor fossils because they are simple, delicate, and small. For a competent determination, the palaeobryologist requires well-preserved material, including details of gametophyte cells and a fairly complete sporophyte. These conditions are rarely found in the fossil record. However, until recently even the small surviving fragments have often been neglected, but the work of Neuberg shows what can be done when the record is carefully studied.

Spores attributed to terrestrial plants have been found in Pre-Cambrian and Cambrian rocks in the Baltic. Whether some of these are from bryophytes is uncertain. From the same geographic area presumed bryophyte spores have been noted. The first unquestionable bryophyte fossil, from the Upper Devonian, was the gametophyte of a thallose liverwort probably related to the Metzgeriales. In the Upper Carboniferous further hepatics have been noted. Again these appear to be of metzgerialean affinities. However, some are superficially leafy, in a manner resembling *Fossombronia* and *Treubia* of modern floras. One fossil apparently is similar to the modern marchantialean genus *Riccardia*. A fossil ascribed to the Musci, with

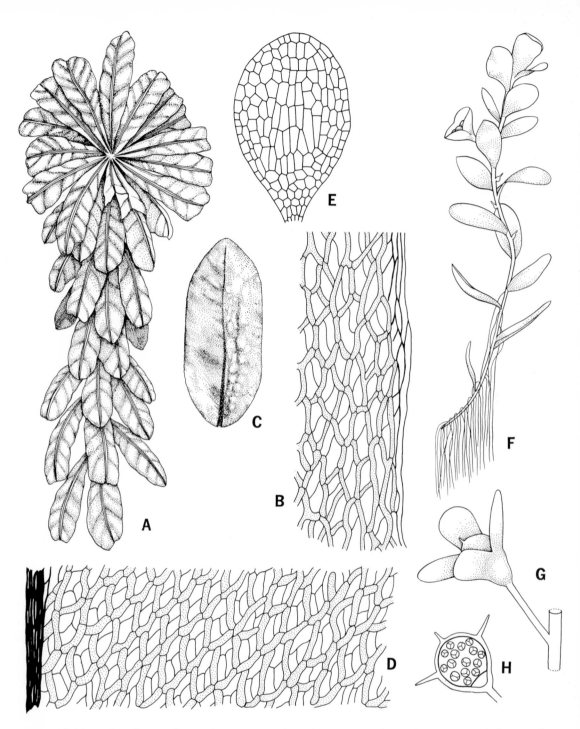

FIGURE 16–29   Fossil Bryophytes. A, reconstruction of *Vorcutannularia plicata,* moss of the Permian, ×2; B, cellular detail of leaf of *V. plicata,* showing hyaline and chlorophyllose cells as well as leaf margin, ×100; C, leaf of *Protosphagnum nervatum,* a Permian moss, ×8; D, cellular detail of leaf of *P. nervatum,* showing chlorophyllose and hyaline cells, ×100; E, leaf of *Naiadita lanceolata,* a Triassic liverwort, ×50; F, reconstruction of *N. lanceolata,* ×6; G, sporangium of *N. lanceolata,* ×10; H, longitudinal section through sporangium of *N. lanceolata,* showing tetrads of spores, ×8. (A–D, after Neuberg; E–H, after Harris with permission of the British Museum (Natural History) and *Annales Bryologici.*)

possible Polytrichidae relationships, is disputed.

Neuberg's remarkable discovery of mosses from Permian rocks marks milestone in fossil botany. She reported 13 species of mosses clearly of Bryidae affinities; but some representatives imply clear relationships with the Sphagnidae (Fig. 16–29A–D). None can be ascribed to modern genera, but their phylogenetic implications, especially in respect to the Sphagnidae, are especially significant, since an hepatic of marchantialean affinity is known from the Permian.

Mesozoic bryophyte fossils are equally limited in number. Among rare specimens of hepatics, one is presumed to be related to the Marchantiales; another is apparently of the Metzgeriales; a third evidently of the Jungermanniales. Some other hepatic fossils are thallose, but the structure is too vague to suggest relationships.

The most significant Triassic hepatic, carefully studied by Harris, is *Naiadita,* whose relationships appear to be with the genus *Riella* in the Sphaerocarpales (Fig. 16–29E–H). It is the only fossil hepatic discovered so far with attached sporangia. The presence of gemmae, rhizoids, archegonia, and well-preserved leaves enabled Harris to reconstruct this bryophyte (Fig. 16–29F). It appears to have been aquatic, as is *Riella*—a factor that presumably favored its fossilization. There are few reports of mosses from the Triassic except for a single species, presumably of the Bryidae.

In the Jurassic the record of thallose hepatics improves, with fossils attributed to the Metzgeriales as well as to other thallose species of unknown affinity. *Sphagnum,* known also from this period especially as spores, continues to be represented frequently up to the present. Cretaceous bryophyte fossils are few. A tiny moss fragment of uncertain relationships and a few scraps of thallose and leafy liverworts make up the record. Fragmentary material indicates the presence of *Sphagnum.* There is a great increase in fossils of the Cenozoic, and many can be compared with modern genera or families. A few of these fossils are of epiphytic species preserved in Baltic amber. Of the Quaternary fossils, the best represented genera are those presently common to aquatic environments. From the Quaternary moss fossils it has been possible to reconstruct the floristic history of some regions, especially in Europe, but there is a low representation of hepatics in the Quaternary record.

The fragmentary nature of both the fossils and the fossil record makes it impossible to utilize them in interpreting phylogeny. The most significant discoveries have been the Permian mosses and the Triassic *Naiadita.* These were sufficiently complete to make reasonably confident interpretations about their phylogenetic position.

REFERENCES

Allen, C. E., "The Genetics of Bryophytes, II." *Bot. Rev.,* 11: 260–287 (1945).

Bauer, L., "On the Physiology of Sporogonium Differentiation in Mosses." *J. Linn. Soc. Bot.,* 58: 343–351 (1962).

Blomquist, H. L., "Peat Mosses of the Southeastern States." *J. Elisha Mitchell Sci. Soc.,* 54: 1–21 (1938).

Bopp, M., "Morphogenese der Laubmoose." *Biol. Rev.,* 36: 237–280 (1961).

Bopp, M., "Development of the Protonema and Bud Formation in Mosses." *J. Linn. Soc. Bot.,* 58: 305–309 (1962).

Bowen, E. J., "The Mechanism of Water Conduction in the Musci Considered in Relation to Habitat." *Ann. Bot.,* 47: 401–422; 635–661; 889–912 (1933).

Bower, F. O., *Primitive Land Plants.* London: Macmillan & Co. Ltd. (1935).

Braithwaite, R., *The Sphagnaceae or Peat Mosses of Europe and North America.* London: David Bogue (1880).

Brotherus, V. F., *Musci (Laubmoose).* In Engler, A., and Prantl, K., *Die Natürlichen Pflanzenfamilien,* 2nd Ed. Vols. 10 and 11. Leipzig: W. Engelmann (1924–1925).

Campbell, D. H., *The Structure and Development of Mosses and Ferns.* London: Macmillan & Co. Ltd. (1895).

Cavers, F., "The Inter-relationships of the Bryophyta." *New Phytologist,* 9: 81–112; 158–186; 193–234; 269–304; 341–353 (1910); 10: 1–46 (1911).

Conard, H. S., *How to Know the Mosses and Liverworts.* Mt. Pleasant, Iowa: H. E. Jacques (1956).

Dixon, H. N., and Jameson, H. G., *The Student's Handbook of British Mosses,* 3rd Ed. Eastbourne: V. V. Sumfield (1924).

Fleischer, M., "Natürlichen System der Laubmoose." *Hedwigia,* 61: 390–400 (1920).

Frye, T. C., and Clark, L., *Hepaticae of North America.* Seattle, Wash.: University of Washington Press (1937–1947).

Fulford, M., "Recent Interpretations of the Relationships of the Hepaticae." *Bot. Rev.,* 14: 127–173 (1948).

Gimingham, C. H., and Robinson, E. T., "Preliminary Investigations on the Structure of Bryophytic Communities." *Trans. Brit. Bryol. Soc.,* 1: 330–334 (1950).

Goebel, K., *Organographie der Pflanzen.* Part 2: *Bryophyten-Pteridophyten.* Jena: G. Fischer (1930).

Grout, A. J., *Mosses with a Hand-lens and Microscope.* New York: Mt. Pleasant Press (1903–1908).

Grout, A. J., *Moss Flora of North America, North of Mexico.* 3 vols. Newfane, Vt.: Published by the Author (1928–1940).

Grout, A. J., *Mosses with a Hand-lens,* 4th Ed. Newfane, Vt.: Published by the Author (1947).

Harris, T. M., *"Naiadita,* a Fossil Bryophyte with Reproductive Organs." *Ann. Bryol.,* 12: 57–70 (1939).

Haskell, G., "Some Evolutionary Problems Concerning the Bryophyta." *Bryologist,* 52: 49–57 (1949).

Hattori, S., and Mizutani, M., "What Is *Takakia lepidozioides?" J. Hattori Bot. Lab.,* 20: 295–303 (1958).

Herzog, T., *Geographie der Moose.* Jena: G. Fischer (1926).

Keever, C.; Oosting, H. J.; and Anderson, L. E., "Plant Succession on Exposed Granite of Rocky Face Mountain, Alexander County, North Carolina." *Bull. Torr. Bot. Cl.,* 78: 402–421 (1951).

Lewis, K. R., "The Genetics of Bryophytes." *Trans. British Bryol. Soc.,* 4: 111–130 (1961).

Lorch, W., *Anatomie der Laubmoose.* In Linsbauer, *Handbuch der Pflanzenanatomie,* 7 (Lieferung 28) Berlin: Gebrüder Borntraeger (1931).

Marchal, L., and Marchal, M., "Aposporie et Sexualitie chez les Mousses." *Bull. Acad. Roy. Belgique, Cl. Sci.,* 750–776 (1911).

Neuberg, M. F., "Permian True Mosses of Angaraland." *J. Palaeontol. Soc. India.,* 3: 22–29 (1958).

Parihar, N. S., *An Introduction to the Embryophyta, I: Bryophyta,* 3rd Ed. Allahabad, India: Central Book Depot (1961).

Proskauer, J., "Studies in the Anthocerotales, VI." *Phytomorphology,* 10: 1–19 (1960).

Reimers, H., *Bryophyta: Moose.* In Engler, A., *Syllabus der Pflanzenfamilien,* 12th Ed. Vol. 1. Berlin: Gebrüder Borntraeger (1954).

Richards, P. W., *A Book of Mosses.* London: Penguin Books Ltd. (1950).

Richards, P. W., "Bryophyta." In Turrill, W. B. (Ed.), *Vistas in Botany.* London: Pergamon Press Ltd. (1959). Pp. 387–420.

Savicz-Ljubitzkaja, L. I., and Abramov, I. I., "The Geological Annals of Bryophyta." *Rev. Bryol. Lichen.,* 28: 330–342 (1959).

Schuster, R. M., "Boreal Hepaticae, a Manual of Liverworts of Minnesota and Adjacent Regions." *Amer. Midl. Nat.,* 49: 257–684 (1953).

Schuster, R. M., "Annotated Key to the Orders, Families and Genera of Hepaticae of America North of Mexico. *Bryologist,* 61: 1–66 (1958).

Smith, G. M., *Cryptogamic Botany.* Vol. 2: *Bryophytes and Pteridophytes,* 2nd Ed. New York: McGraw-Hill Book Co., Inc. (1955). Pp. 1–130.

Steere, W. C., "Cenozoic and Mesozoic Bryophytes of North America." *Amer. Midl. Nat.,* 36: 298–324 (1946).

Steere, W. C., "A Consideration of the Concept of Genus in Musci." *Bryologist,* 50: 247–258 (1947).

Steere, W. C., "Bryology." In *A Century of Progress in the Natural Sciences, 1853–1953.* San Francisco: California Academy of Sciences (1955). Pp. 267–299.

Thieret, J. W., "Bryophytes as Economic Plants." *Econ. Bot.,* 10: 75–91 (1955).

Verdoorn, F. (Ed.), *Manual of Bryology.* The Hague: Maritinus Nijhoff (1932).

Watson, E. V., *The Structure and Life of Bryophytes.* London: Hutchinson University Library (1964).

VASCULAR

PLANTS

17 / VASCULAR

PLANTS

The remaining chapters describe ten groups of vascular plants. Until recently, vascular plants were usually classified in the division Tracheophyta, because **xylem** and **phloem** conducting elements were believed to indicate close relationship. But in the last decade other morphological and anatomical differences that suggest more remote relationships have been recognized among some groups of vascular plants. Paleobotanical investigations indicate that many of the modern groups have been distinct lines as far back in geologic time as there is a clear record of vascular plants. Thus, a system of classification like Bold's (1957), which places grossly unrelated groups of vascular plants in separate divisions, appears warranted.

ORIGIN AND TIME SPAN

Recent discoveries of fossil spores have been cited as indicating that vascular plants existed in Cambrian times, some 550,-000,000 years ago (see Fig. 28–2 for geologic time scale), and several reports have been made of spores from the Pre-Cambrian of Russia. However, since spores of some bryophytes are similar to those of vascular plants, it has not been shown conclusively that these early spores came exclusively from vascular plants. Nevertheless, such findings suggest the presence in very ancient times of plants ancestral to either the bryophytic or vascular plant lineages.

The earliest fossil evidence of gross plant structure is a fragment of a stem-like axis with spirally arranged leaf-like appendages. This fossil, *Aldanophyton,* was found in Middle Cambrian strata from Russia. Although it resembles the stem of a lycopod (see Chapter 19), no internal or reproductive structures have been recovered, and its exact relationships to modern or fossil groups are not known. In fact, it has been suggested that *Aldanophyton* may be the remains of some organism other than a vascular plant.

In early Devonian rocks vascular plants are well documented by remains of stems, roots, and reproductive structures. During these times, the lycopod, arthrophyte, and psilophyte lineages were definitely established. By later Devonian times ancestors of the ferns and gymnosperms had evolved, and ancestors of all modern groups of vascular plants except the Anthophyta had appeared. (The anthophytes are recorded from the early Cretaceous but may have had a long prior evolution.) Throughout the long interval from Devonian to the present many taxa became extinct, whereas others were ancestral to new evolutionary avenues. Thus, the vascular plants of today are the net result of a very long period of evolution from at least Silurian times to the present—a span of over 400,000,000 years.

Many paleobotanists are actively pursuing the complex and exciting problem of the origin of the first vascular plants. However, at present no fossil evidence even suggests the likely ancestors of vascular plants; much speculation has occurred on the groups of living plants that could have been the ancestors to early vascular plants.

According to the two main theories, vascular plants evolved (1) from algae, most probably from ancestors of the Ulotrichales of the Chlorophyta (see Chapter 15); or (2) from bryophytic ancestors, most likely from *Anthoceros* or closely allied plants (see Chapter 16). Both theories are based on the premise that, with evolution, differentiation of xylem and phloem took place in the cells of the central region of the axis. In the case of the algae, it has been suggested that, with evolution, algal ancestors to the vascular plants were able to withstand increasingly longer periods of desiccation, and that they eventually evolved into forms that could survive on dry land throughout their life history. With *Anthoceros,* the main development appears to have been the evolution of xylem and phloem from central conducting cells. The other characteristic features of vascular plants—namely stomata, cuticle, and sporangia—are present on the sporophyte of modern *Anthoceros.* The generally accepted view is that both the bryophytes and vascular plants evolved from algal precursors. However, the detailed steps in the progression are lacking, and the problem continues to be highly speculative.

CHARACTERISTIC FEATURES OF VASCULAR PLANTS

The only characteristics unique to vascular plants are xylem and phloem tissues, but other characteristics are common to almost all vascular plants: an external waxy covering, the cuticle (also present in some bryophytes); differentiation into true stem, leaves, and almost always roots; a distinct alternation of generations, with the sporophyte independent and structurally more complex than the gametophyte; and a high ratio of volume to surface area of the plant.

The cuticle, vascular tissue, and a high volume/surface-area ratio favor survival upon land, particularly in habitats devoid of free surface water. The development of a cuticle allows for conservation of water in an aerial medium, as does a high ratio of volume to surface area. The specialized xylem cells provide adequate conduction of water from the soil to aerial portions of the plant, and are particularly necessary in perennial shrubs, and in trees that extend tens of meters into the air.

In general, the fossil record supports the hypothesis that evolution in the early vascular plants progressed from herbaceous aquatic forms to woody terrestrial plants. Almost all of the vascular plants in the early Devonian were small and apparently nonwoody. In Middle and Upper Devonian times larger and woody forms became common, and by Pennsylvanian times plants of tree stature were numerous. It is likely that during this same period the vascular plants were encroaching on more upland regions of the earth, becoming farther removed from aquatic habitats as more elaborate structures were evolved for acquiring and conserving water.

RANGE OF MORPHOLOGY AND DISTRIBUTION

Almost all vascular plants possess roots, stems, and leaves. The only major exceptions are found in the Psilophyta. In *Psilotum* and *Tmesipteris,* rhizoids are borne on a **rhizome,** and *Psilotum* has scale-like emergences that some interpret as true leaves. In other vascular plants, one or more of the basic organ systems is sometimes greatly reduced. For example, the leaves of *Equisetum* are scale-like and those of most cacti are reduced to spines. The stems of *Welwitschia* and the dandelion are also very short, barely distinguishable as narrow regions between the roots and leaves.

Vascular plants range from the tiny *Wolffia* (water-meal), with a size range of 0.7 to 1.5 mm, to *Sequoiadendron* (big tree of California), which grows to over 90 meters in height and over 10 meters in diameter at the base. Vascular plants include aquatics such as *Elodea,* terrestrial herbs such as the grasses and composites, woody shrubs, and trees that are predominantly woody. In general, the structure is related to the ratio of **secondary** to **primary tissues** developed in the plant. The greater the amount of secondary tissue, the woodier the plant. Most of the supporting strength in the plant is provided by the impregnated walls of **secondary xylem, sclerenchyma,** and **periderm**—all secondary tissues particularly well developed in shrubs and trees.

Vascular plants have a wide geographic distribution. Their greatest numbers in both species and individuals is in the tropics, gradually diminishing at higher latitudes. In the Northern Hemisphere vascular plants are known to occur in Greenland at 83° N. and in the Himalaya Mountains at altitudes of 6,000 meters. Vascular plants exist in virtually every type of habitat except extreme deserts and regions with permanent snow and ice. Most are essentially terrestrial, although some inhabit fresh water, and still fewer grow in brackish or marine conditions. Some species have wide ecological tolerances, whereas others are limited to very specialized conditions.

ECONOMIC IMPORTANCE

Vascular plants play an extremely important part in our economy, especially as sources of food for man and other animals and in providing building materials. Indirectly, vascular plants are important also in conservation and wild life management. Other more minor uses include: textiles industry (cotton); pharmaceuticals (atropine, digitalis, and others); and horticulture (landscaping, floral arrangements, botanical gardens). The conifers supply most of the timber, pulp, paper, and naval stores; several species are being widely cultivated where they are not indigenous to provide sources for these materials. The flowering plants are the main sources for food, pharmaceuticals, and horticultural plants, and are undoubtedly the most important group of plants for man.

REFERENCES

Andrews, H. N., Jr., *Studies in Paleobotany.* New York: John Wiley & Sons, Inc. (1961).

Bold, H. C., *Morphology of Plants.* New York: Harper & Row, Publishers (1957). Pp. 319–602.

Chamberlain, C. J., *Gymnosperms: Structure and Evolution.* Chicago: University of Chicago Press (1935).

Delevoryas, T., *Morphology and Evolution of Fossil Plants.* New York: Holt, Rinehart and Winston, Inc. (1962).

Eames, A. J., *Morphology of Vascular Plants.* New York: McGraw-Hill Book Co., Inc. (1936).

Emberger, L., *Les Végétaux Vasculaires.* In Chadefaud, M., and Emberger, L., *Traité de Botanique (Systématique).* Vol. II. Paris: Masson et Cie (1960).

Foster, A. S., and Gifford, E. M., *Comparative Morphology of Vascular Plants.* San Francisco: W. H. Freeman and Co. (1959).

Kräusel, R., *Versunkene Floren: Eine Einführung in die Paläobotanik.* Frankfurt: W. Kramer (1950).

Manton, I., *Problems of Cytology and Evolution in the Pteridophyta.* Cambridge: Cambridge University Press (1950).

Sporne, K. R., *The Morphology of Pteridophytes.* London: Hutchinson & Co. (Publishers) Ltd. (1962).

Zimmermann, W., *Die Phylogenie der Pflanzen,* 2nd Ed. Stuttgart: G. Fischer (1959).

18 / DIVISION

PSILOPHYTA

Included in the *psilopsid* division are the Psilotales, represented only by living plants, and the Psilophytales, known only
from the fossil record. Approximately 400,000,000 years separate
the occurrences of the two orders, and on this basis some botanists
argue that they can hardly be closely related. However, some very
close morphological and anatomical similarities exist among the
plants of the two orders. Thus, the orders can conveniently be
classified within the same division, with the reservation that plants
of the two taxa may not be phylogenetically related.

ORDER PSILOPHYTALES. The plants of this order are known
only from the Devonian Period. They are important components
of Lower and Middle Devonian floras on several continents—
particularly North America, Europe, and Northern Asia. As far
as is known, the psilophytes became extinct either in the late
Middle or early Upper Devonian. Until recent years, the psilophytes were considered to be the simplest and most primitive of all
vascular plants, and to have been the ancestral stock from which
the other groups of vascular plants evolved. However, at present
growing evidence indicates that early representatives of the other
groups existed along with the psilophytes, and that the psilophytes
represent a closed evolutionary avenue. But there is no doubt that
psilophytes are both simple and early vascular plants.

The most completely known psilophytes are three genera of
plants discovered from the Rhynie chert in Aberdeenshire, Scot-

land, and reported by Kidston and Lang from 1917 to 1921. The plants were petrified in the chert and show very complete external and internal detail.

The best known of these early vascular plants is *Rhynia,* two species of which have been described (Fig. 18–1A). As reconstructed, the plant consists of a rhizome with rhizoids, and aerial stems that attain 50 cm in height and up to 6 mm in diameter. The stem branches dichotomously and is leafless. The sporangia are borne terminally on some of the dichotomies.

The aerial stem consists of an epidermis with stomata, a cortex divided into a wide inner region containing **lacunae,** and a narrow outer zone with larger cells (Fig. 18–1B). The **stele** is central, consisting of a solid cylinder of **tracheids** with **annular thickenings** and surrounded by elongate cells that probably functioned as phloem, although sieve areas have not been observed (Fig. 18–1C). Neither an endodermis nor a pericycle has been identified. Because the shoots are leafless, it has been postulated that if photosynthesis occurred it was carried on in the stem.

The sporangia, cylindrical and separated from the stem by a narrow constriction, range up to 12 mm in length and 4 mm in diameter. The sporangial wall consists of a cutinized epidermal layer and several inner layers of thin-walled cells. There is no structure for dehiscence. The spores vary from 35 to 65 microns in diameter and have a thick wall with a coarsely granular to papillate ornamentation (Fig. 18–1D).

The two genera associated with *Rhynia* are *Horneophyton* and *Asteroxylon.* *Horneophyton* is essentially like *Rhynia,* but is smaller, more slender, contains thick tuberous segments on the rhizome, and possesses a columella in the sporangium.

Asteroxylon shows considerably more structural complexity than *Rhynia* and *Horneophyton.* The aerial stem is **monopodial** and densely covered with spirally arranged leaves about 5 mm long (Fig. 18–2A). The stem reaches 50 cm in height and 1 cm in diameter and arises from a branching, leafless rhizome.

The aerial stem is similar to that of *Rhynia,* with an epidermis containing stomata, an inner and outer cortex, and a prominent and relatively large five-armed **protostele** (Fig. 18–2B). The stele is **exarch,** and the thickenings of the tracheids vary from annular to **scalariform. Leaf traces** depart obliquely upward from the xylem arms and enter the bases of the leaves.

The sporangia assigned to *Asteroxylon* are terminal on leafless branch tips and average 1 mm in length. They have not been found attached but are intimately associated in the chert with the stems and have been assigned with some confidence to the leafy axes.

Until recently, the classical genus *Psilophyton* was also included in the order Psilophytales. This plant was originally described in 1859 by Sir J. W. Dawson from early Devonian rocks in the Gaspé Peninsula of Quebec. As reconstructed by Dawson, *Psilophyton* consists of smooth rhizomes from which spiny aerial branches arise. The aerial stem, up to 1.5 meters high, branches dichotomously and contains a solid cylinder of xylem with annular tracheids. Dawson declared that some of the branch tips bore terminal sporangia, and that others did not. Although he indicated that sporangia were attached to the stem tips, later collectors were not able to find them attached. Recent studies have shown that in some of the branches assigned to *Psilophyton,* sporangia are attached laterally rather than terminally. Thus, *Psilophyton* no longer appears related to the *Rhynia–Horneophyton–Asteroxylon* group with terminal sporangia, but appears to represent a separate avenue of early vascular-plant evolution.

The discovery and reconstruction of these early plants has prompted botanists to conclude that the psilophyte, as exemplified by *Rhynia,* is indeed the simplest type of vascular plant. Such features as protostelic rhizomes with rhizoids, dichotomous branching, absence of true leaves, and terminal sporangia have generally been regarded as what should be expected of simple vascular plants that evolved from aquatic ancestors. As a result, many have accepted *Rhynia* and other psilophytes as the most primitive vascular plants, and as the stock or group

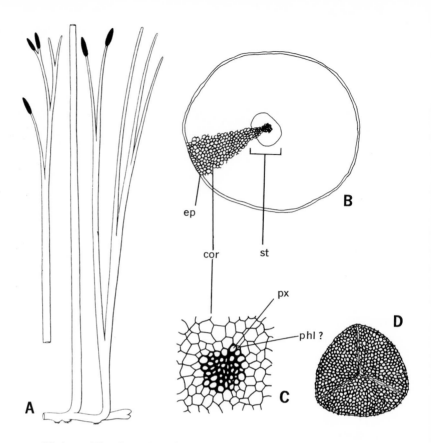

FIGURE 18–1   *Rhynia major.* A, reconstruction of habit, showing rhizome, dichotomous branching, and terminal sporangia, ×0.2; B, transverse section of stem, showing stele, cortex, and epidermis, ×9; C, transverse section of stele, showing exarch protoxylem, ×40; D, single spore with reticulate ornamentation and trilete tetrad scar, ×400. *cor,* cortex; *ep,* epidermis; *phl,* questionable phloem; *px,* protoxylem; *st,* stele. (After Kidston and Lang with permission of *Transactions of the Royal Society of Edinburgh.*)

from which all other vascular plants evolved. This concept has dominated evolutionary thinking on vascular plants for over 40 years, and is largely responsible for several of the proposed natural classifications. The discovery of spores and the re-evaluation of early fossils have suggested that representatives of the other major groups of vascular plants are at least as old as and probably older than the psilophytes. As a result, some students of Devonian floras emphasize that while the psilophytes are admittedly simple, they are not necessarily or even probably primitive. Thus, the psilophytes probably represent a group of vascular plants that evolved independently of other groups and became extinct during Devonian times.

ORDER PSILOTALES.   This order comprises two genera of plants, *Psilotum* and *Tmesipteris.* Both genera are known only as extant plants, but they have some morphological and anatomical features similar to the psilophytes.

Morphology.   The plant body consists of underground stems covered with rhizoids (Fig. 18–3). The rhizomes extend above ground into aerial stems that are green and dichotomously branched. In *Psilotum,* aerial stems range in length to 25 cm or more with numerous dichotomies. Scale-like emergences are scattered in a spiral arrangement around the stem. Since these are without veins some botanists do not consider them true leaves. In *Tmesipteris* (Fig. 18–4), the stem is usually unbranched,

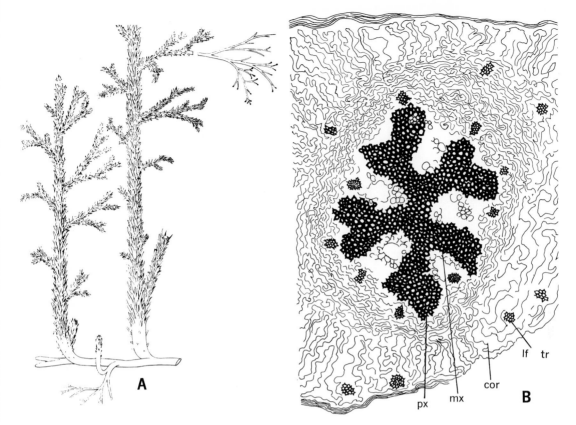

FIGURE 18–2   *Asteroxylon mackiei.* A, reconstruction of habit, ×0.5; B, transverse section of stem, showing five-armed actinostele with exarch protoxylem, and leaf traces, ×20. *cor,* cortex; *lf tr,* leaf trace; *mx,* metaxylem; *px,* protoxylem. (After Kidston and Lang with permission of *Transactions of the Royal Society of Edinburgh.*)

although some stems have a single dichotomy. True leaves are present, arranged spirally. Each leaf is long and narrow, bears stomata, and has a single vein. Both genera have a well-defined cuticle on stem and leaves.

A transverse section of the stem of both *Psilotum* and *Tmesipteris* reveals a central stele surrounded by cortex and epidermis (Fig. 18–5). The xylem of the rhizome in both genera comprises a solid core of scalariform tracheids, surrounded by elongated cells with thickened corners which apparently function as phloem. In aerial stems, the xylem occurs as separate bundles around a central pith consisting mainly of thick-walled sclerenchymatous cells. The bundles in *Psilotum* are exarch, whereas those of *Tmesipteris* are **mesarch**—i.e., the protoxylem is completely surrounded by **metaxylem.** In both genera, the **protoxylem**

consists of annular and helical tracheids, whereas all the metaxylem tracheids are scalariform.

Spore-bearing Organs. In *Psilotum,* some of the leaf-like emergences in upper regions of the stem are replaced by sporangia-bearing appendages (Fig. 18–6A). Although the exact nature of the fertile appendage is in doubt, some consider it to be a very short axis bearing two leaf-like emergences and three fused sporangia at the tip. In *Tmesipteris* the spore-bearing appendage is similar, usually consisting of only two fused sporangia at the tip of a short lateral branch with two leaves (Fig. 18–6B).

At maturity each sporangium consists of an outer wall of several layers of cells (Fig. 18–6C). The central region contains spore mother cells interspersed with parenchyma cells

FIGURE 18–3   Stems and branches of *Psilotum,* showing dichotomous venation, ×0.5.

FIGURE 18–4   Branch of *Tmesipteris,* showing spirally arranged leaves and several sporangia, ×1.5.

that act as a nutrient source for the developing spores and are completely used up by the time the sporangia split open.

Since the meiospores of *Psilotum* and *Tmesipteris* are of only one size, the plants are said to be **homosporous.** In both genera the spores are kidney-shaped and vary in length from about 50 to 80 microns (Fig. 18–6D). The thick spore wall is faintly reticulate and has a single longitudinal **suture** on the concave surface where the spore attaches to the other three in the tetrad. Single-suture spores are said to be **monolete** (literally, "one arm"). Spores of other vascular plants—e.g., the lycopods and some ferns—have a three-armed suture, or Y mark. Such **trilete** spores are more prevalent in primitive vascular plants than are monolete spores.

Prothallus.   Spores germinate directly into **prothallia** if conditions are suitable. The young prothallus begins to grow inside the spore wall but soon emerges, usually through the monolete suture. When mature, the prothallus is cylindrical, several millimeters long, and brown or yellow (Fig. 18–7A). The prothallus is subterranean and completely infested with mycorrhizal fungal hyphae. The sex organs, scattered randomly, are antheridia and archegonia (Fig. 18–7B) that develop from superficial cells of the prothallus. Both sex organs can be observed with a hand lens, but internal detail can be noted only in microscopic section. Antheridia are globular, consisting of an outer layer of sterile jacket cells and a central mass of spermatogenous cells that eventually develop into sperm. Each sperm is coiled and covered with many flagella. Upon maturation, a single opercular cell of the antheridium splits open, and the flagellated sperm escape to swim to the archegonia.

The archegonia of both *Psilotum* and *Tmesipteris* are generally below the surface of the prothallus. They consist of four to six tiers of neck cells that protrude slightly from the surface. Two neck canal cells fill the neck and overlie a large egg cell contained in the venter that is imbedded in the prothallus.

Psilotum has a chromosome count of $n = 52$–54; *Tmesipteris* has counts of $n = ca.$ 100 and $n = ca.$ 200. Most species are believed to be tetraploids.

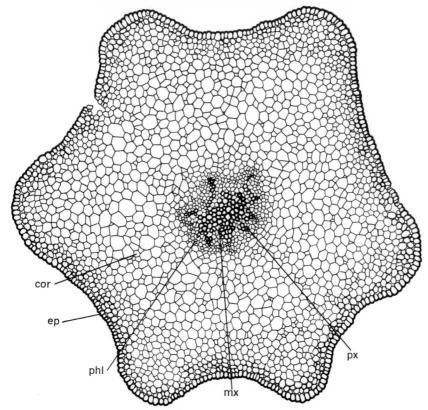

FIGURE 18–5   Transverse section of stem of *Psilotum*, showing stele, cortex,
and epidermis, ×55. *cor,* cortex; *ep,* epidermis; *mx,* metaxylem; *phl,* phloem;
px, protoxylem.

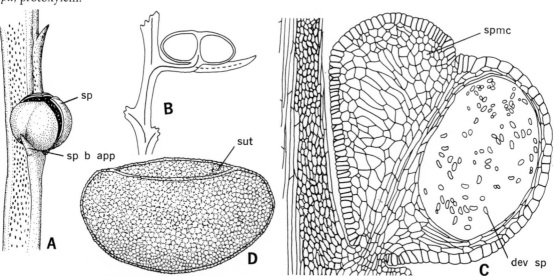

FIGURE 18–6   Reproductive organs of Psilotales. A, single sporangium of *Psilotum* subtended by sporangia-bearing appendage, ×2; B, vertical section through sporangium and appendage of *Tmesipteris,*
showing vascular bundle entering sporangium, ×2; C, vertical section through sporangium of *Psilotum,*
showing developing spores in one locule, ×20; D, single spore of *Psilotum,* showing a single longitudinal
suture and the faint reticulate ornamentation, ×500. *dev sp,* developing spores; *sp b app,* spore-bearing appendage; *spmc,* spore mother cell; *sp,* sporangia; *sut,* suture. (B, after Eames with permission of
McGraw-Hill Book Co.)

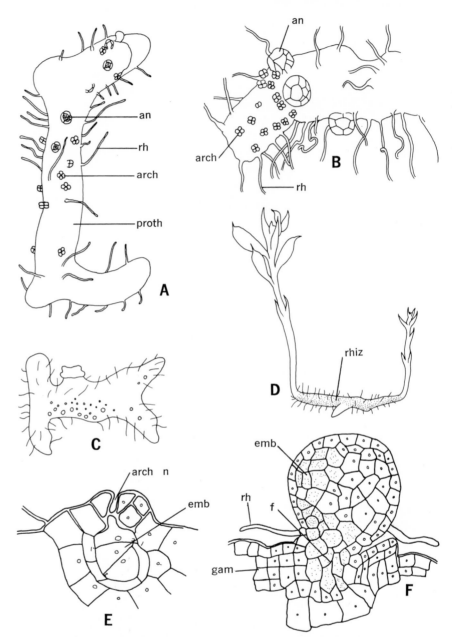

FIGURE 18–7   Gametophytes of Psilotales. A, prothallus of *Psilotum,* showing
irregular shape, rhizoids, antheridia, and archegonia, ×10; B, part of prothallus
of *Tmesipteris,* showing rhizoids, archegonia, and antheridia, ×12; C, complete
prothallus of *Tmesipteris,* ×5; D, young sporophyte of *Tmesipteris,* showing
two aerial shoots and lateral bud emanating from rhizome, ×5; E, young
embryo of *Tmesipteris,* showing planes of cell divisions at 1–1 and 2–2, and
archegonial neck, ×80; F, embryo of *Tmesipteris,* showing foot (*f*) extending
into gametophyte, and several rhizoids, ×50. *an,* antheridia; *arch,* archegonia;
arch n, archegonial neck; *emb,* embryo; *gam,* gametophyte; *proth,* prothallus;
rh, rhizoid; *rhiz,* rhizome. (A, B, after Lawson with permission of *Transactions
of the Royal Society of Edinburgh;* C–F, after Holloway with permission of
Transactions of Royal Society of New Zealand.)

Embryo. The zygote divides first at right angles to the long axis of the archegonium (Fig. 18–7E). The upper daughter cell subsequently divides to form the **primordium** of the stem, whereas the lower gives rise to a mass of parenchyma called the foot (Fig. 18–7F). As in the bryophytes, the foot absorbs food material from the prothallus and supplies it to the developing embryonic shoot. The first-formed branches usually develop directly into rhizomes, while later branches mature into aerial parts of the stem. When the young sporophyte becomes nutritionally independent of the gametophyte, the foot degenerates.

Distribution and Ecology. The two species of *Psilotum* occur in tropical and subtropical regions of both hemispheres. One species ranges as far north as South Carolina in North America and Japan in Asia, and as far south as Australia and New Zealand. *Psilotum* normally grows on humus-rich soil in moist shaded habitats, but sometimes it is epiphytic on shrubs and trees. The common species (*P. nudum*) is relatively easy to grow in a greenhouse if kept in a moist atmosphere.

Tmesipteris, with a single species, is limited to southern and eastern Australia, New Zealand, the Philippines, and some islands of Polynesia. It also thrives in damp and shaded habitats, and is mainly epiphytic on shrubs and tree ferns.

RELATIONSHIPS

Prior to the discovery of the psilophytes in the Rhynie beds in Scotland, *Psilotum* and *Tmesipteris* were often allied with the lycopods; they still are by some botanists, largely because of similarities in growth, branching, reduction in leaves, and anatomy of stems. Today, however, almost all students of morphology and taxonomy have grouped the psilophytes and Psilotales together in a separate taxon, variously termed Psilopsida, Psilophytinae, and Psilophyta.

There has been much controversy over the exact relations of the strictly fossil psilophytes and the two living genera of Psilotales. Evidence for considering the two groups closely related is chiefly morphological and anatomical, and includes the following characteristics shared by both living and fossil members: rhizomes with rhizoids, dichotomous branching, true leaves rudimentary or absent, sporangia terminal on branches, and protostelic vascular strands in the stem. On the basis of these similarities it has been argued that the modern Psilotales are primitive, and related to the fossil psilophytes. If so, the descendants of the Devonian psilophytes have persisted through some 400,000,000 years without a fossil trace.

Another interpretation suggests that *Psilotum* and *Tmesipteris* actually represent evolutionary reductions from other, more structurally complex groups, such as the lycopods. According to this hypothesis, ancestors of the two modern genera would have possessed more advanced structures—such as large leaves with veins, primary roots, and axillary sporangia; as a result of mutations and selection, these structures have been reduced. Although such reduction series have occurred in the plant kingdom, there is still no direct evidence for this in the Psilotales.

REFERENCES

Andrews, H. N., Jr., "Evolutionary Trends in Early Vascular Plants." *Cold. Spr. Harb. Symp. Quant. Biol.,* 24: 217–234 (1960).

Bierhorst, D. W., "Structure and Development of the Gametophyte of *Psilotum nudum." Am. J. Bot.,* 40: 649–658 (1953).

Bierhorst, D. W., "The Gametangia and Embryo of *Psilotum nudum*." *Am. J. Bot.,* 41: 274–281 (1954).

Bierhorst, D. W., "The Subterranean Sporophytic Axes of *Psilotum nudum*." *Am. J. Bot.,* 41: 732–739 (1954).

Bierhorst, D. W., "Observations on the Aerial Appendages in the Psilotaceae." *Phytomorphology,* 6: 176–184 (1956).

Dawson, J. W., *The Fossil Plants of the Devonian and Upper Silurian Formations of Canada.* Ottawa: Geological Survey of Canada (1871).

Holloway, J. E., "The Prothallus and Young Plant of *Tmesipteris*." *Trans. Proc. N. Z. Inst.,* 50: 1–44 (1918).

Holloway, J. E., "Further Notes on the Prothallus, Embryo, and Young Sporophyte of *Tmesipteris*." *Trans. Proc. N. Z. Inst.,* 54: 386–422 (1921).

Kidston, R., and Lang, W. H., "On Old Red Sandstone Plants Showing Structure, from the Rhynie Chert Bed, Aberdeenshire." Pts. 1–5. *Trans. Roy. Soc. Edinburgh,* 51: 761; 52: 603, 643, 831, 855 (1917–1921).

Leclercq, S., "Are the Psilophytales a Starting or a Resulting Point?" *Svensk. Bot. Tidsskr.,* 48(2): 301–315 (1954).

Sahni, B., "On *Tmesipteris vieillardi* Dangeard, an Erect Terrestrial Species from New Caledonia." *Phil. Trans. Roy. Soc. London,* 213B: 143–170 (1925).

19 / DIVISION

LYCOPODOPHYTA

Plants in this division are usually referred to as *lycopods*. They have one of the oldest histories among vascular plants, dating certainly from the early Devonian and possibly as far back as the Cambrian. The fossil record indicates that several evolutionary lines existed within the group, and that in the Carboniferous the lycopods were among the largest and most numerous plants. After the Carboniferous, the large tree-like lycopods disappeared, and the group as a whole declined in relative importance among vascular plants.

With the exception of the early members of Devonian times, the lycopods can be classified in five orders. Three of these have living representatives—Lycopodiales, Selaginellales, and Isoetales. The other two, Lepidodendrales and Pleuromeiales, are known only from the fossil record.

The divisional name Lycopodophyta is used here in preference to the Microphyllophyta of Bold. This follows a proposal by Andrews that the name Lycopodophyta is more appropriate because some lycopods have large leaves, and because the name lycopod has been so widely used in botanical literature.

GENERAL MORPHOLOGY

All of the plants in this division have true roots, stems, and leaves. Many have rhizomes with adventitious roots. Aerial portions of the stem show branching ranging from dichotomous to monopodial. Some have creeping stems.

In most lycopods, the leaves are arranged spirally and are very small. Each leaf contains a single vein that does not form a **leaf gap** at the point of emergence from the stele within the stem. Such leaves are **microphyllous.**

Sporangia are borne either in the axils of or on the **adaxial** surfaces of more or less specialized leaves, the **sporophylls.** Sporophylls and sporangia of some lycopods are localized in terminal **strobili** or cones, whereas sporophylls of others are spaced, resembling ordinary leaves. The meiospores are **trilete.** Some lycopods are **homosporous,** whereas others have spores of two sizes and are **heterosporous.** In the heterosporous plants, the **megaspores** (large) germinate **endosporally** to form female gametophytes, while the **microspores** also develop endosporally but into male gametophytes.

The best-known members of this group are three extant genera—*Lycopodium, Selaginella,* and *Isoetes.* Much of our knowledge of the lycopods has come from a detailed study of these. The fossil genera are less well known but do provide a glimpse of the probable evolutionary developments in the lycopod line. However, we still have a lot to learn, and future research will certainly broaden our concept of evolution within the division.

EARLY LYCOPODS

The possibility that *Aldanophyton* from the Cambrian of Siberia represents an early lycopod has already been mentioned (see Chapter 17). *Aldanophyton* consists of an axis with spirally arranged appendages that resemble leaves. Unfortunately, sporangia are absent, so a final decision about whether it is a lycopod must await further discoveries.

The earliest plant that exhibits undoubted lycopod characteristics is *Baragwanathia longifolia,* discovered in rocks of early Devonian Age in Australia (Fig. 19–1A, B). The plant consists of dichotomously branching stems closely covered by spirally arranged leaves. The leaves measure 0.5 to 1 mm in width and up to 4 cm in length. Each has a single vascular trace. On some regions of the stems, kidney-shaped sporangia are found in the axils of apparently unmodified leaves. It has not yet been determined whether the sporangia are attached to the stem or to the upper leaf surface. The vascular tissue consists of an exarch protostele, having 12 arms of primary xylem with annular tracheids.

Another genus that possesses lycopod characteristics has been found in rocks of Lower Devonian age. This is *Drepanophycus* (Fig. 19–2A). As reconstructed, it exhibits dichotomous branches arising from a rhizome. Short flattened leaves are arranged spirally around the stem. Each leaf contains a single vein. Some of the leaves bear sporangia on the upper surface, generally midway between the base and tip of the leaf. Thus, in general structure *Drepanophycus* is very similar to *Baragwanathia.*

Finally, a third plant with lycopod characteristics, *Protolepidodendron,* has been found in rocks of the Lower and Middle Devonian (Fig. 19–2B). It is similar to *Drepanophycus* but bears closely spaced leaves spirally arranged on the dichotomous stem. Each leaf is forked at the tip. Some of the leaves bear sporangia on the upper surface, as in *Drepanophycus.* The xylem core consists of a three-armed protostele composed of scalariform tracheids.

The characteristics possessed by the three early plants just described are remarkably like those of some species of the modern genus *Lycopodium.* This has led some investigators to suggest that ancestors of *Lycopodium* were in existence very early in the history of vascular plants, and that there has been virtually no structural modification in this line since that time.

ORDER LEPIDODENDRALES. During the Carboniferous, some of the lycopods reached tree stature. They were among the dominant elements of the forests that formed the vegetation of widespread coal swamps. These large lycopods are classified in the Lepidodendrales,

FIGURE 19–1   *Baragwanathia.* A, photograph of fragment of stem, showing crowded strap-shaped leaves, ×0.4; B, closer view of stem and leaves with several sporangia in axils, ×0.7 (After Lang and Cookson with permission of the Royal Society of London.)

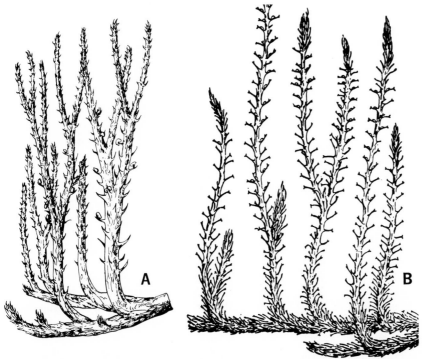

FIGURE 19–2   Early lycopods of the Devonian. A, *Drepanophycus* with dichotomous branching, flattened leaves with sharp tips, and sporangia on sporophylls in upper reaches of stem, ×1.6; B, *Protolepidodendron,* showing prostrate and upright dichotomous stems, forked leaves, and sporangia on adaxial surface of sporophylls, ×0.5. (After Kräusel and Weyland with permission of *Palaeontographica,* and *Senckenbergiana.*)

an order known only from fossils of late Devonian to early Permian.

The best-known plant of this group is *Lepidodendron* (literally, scale tree). *Lepidodendron* consists of a columnar trunk with a crown of branches at the top (Fig. 19–3). In some specimens, the trunk exceeds 35 meters in length and 1 meter in diameter. The branches of the crown are formed by dichotomous division, but the dichotomies are not always equal. Leaves are long, grass-like, and confined to the outer regions of the end branches. Left behind on older regions of the stem, **leaf cushions** form a very characteristic pattern on the outside of the trunk and branches. Reproductive organs consist of sporangia in cones borne on outer branches among the leaves.

Stems. Internal details of the stem can be observed very well in transverse section (Fig. 19–4A). The vascular cylinders of many of the older branches have a central parenchymatous pith, surrounded by a narrow ring of primary xylem containing scalariform tracheids. The protoxylem is exarch, with centripetal development of metaxylem (Fig. 19–4B). In many of the older branches, a ring of secondary wood immediately outside the primary xylem consists of thin-walled scalariform tracheids and **rays** one cell in width. The **cambium** and secondary phloem are also immediately outside but rarely preserved. In even the largest trunks of *Lepidodendron,* the entire vascular cylinder rarely exceeds 10 cm in diameter; probably very little structural support was derived from the vascular tissue.

Outside the secondary xylem is a relatively wide cortex, usually of two zones: an inner region with thin-walled parenchyma cells, and an outer region also containing parenchyma but often including strands of sclerenchyma fibers. The weak parenchymatous cells of both zones are often squashed and destroyed, producing a cavity outside the vascular tissue.

The tissue outside the cortex is periderm. In most species it consists of radial rows of elongated thick-walled cells resembling sclerenchyma fibers. In some species, the periderm is interspersed with lenticular areas that contain thin-walled cells. These cells probably secreted

FIGURE 19–3   Reconstruction of tree of *Lepidodendron*, showing roots, columnar stem, unequally dichotomous branching, and leafy twigs. (After Hirmer with permission of R. Oldenbourg.)

wax that covered the outside of the stem and helped to preserve them in rock. The periderm, up to 40 cm thick, is credited with supplying most of the support for the stem.

In most genera of the Lepidodendrales, the cambium of the periderm (**phellogen**) is located at the extreme outside of the stem among the bases of the leaves. As a result, most periderm development was toward the inside, or centripetal, preserving the leaf cushions where the leaves were attached to the stem. These

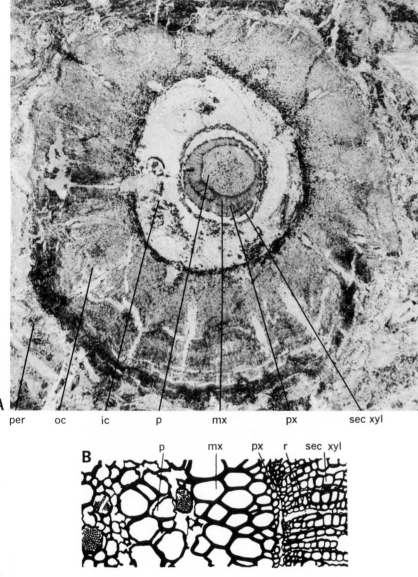

per   oc   ic   p   mx   px   sec xyl

p   mx   px   r   sec xyl

FIGURE 19–4   Transverse sections of stem of *Lepidodendron*. A, showing stele, cortex, and periderm, ×3.9; B, part of stele, showing pith, primary xylem, and secondary xylem, ×20. *ic,* inner cortex; *mx,* metaxylem; *oc,* outer cortex; *p,* pith; *per,* periderm; *px,* protoxylem; *r,* ray; *sec xyl,* secondary xylem.

cushions are rhomboidal in outline and form spiral rows around the stem (Fig. 19–5). Each cushion contains the scars of the single vein flanked by two **parichnos** (Fig. 19–6). The parichnos, which may have served in aeration, are channels of parenchyma cells which connected the leaf with the stem.

Leaves. Each leaf contains a single vein down the center of the blade (Fig. 19–7). The vein is continuous with the **leaf trace** of the stem and departs from the primary xylem without leaving a leaf gap. In the blade, the vein consists of a central core of xylem surrounded by cells that probably functioned as phloem. Outside the phloem is a region of tracheid-like cells, called **transfusion tissue,** which probably acted in transferring water and dissolved nutrients from the central vein to the outer tissues.

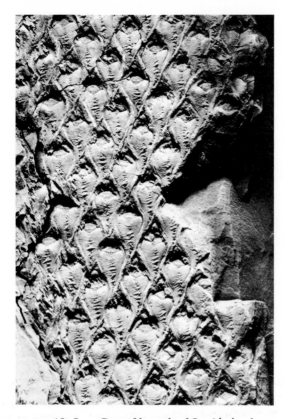

FIGURE 19–5   Part of branch of *Lepidodendron*, showing rhomboidal leaf cushions in oblique rows, ×2.

Cones. The Lepidodendrales have sporangia and sporophylls aggregated into cones. The form-genus name given to most cones is *Lepidostrobus* (from Greek *lepido,* "scale," plus *strobilos*). Although usually detached, enough cones have been found attached to stems to verify a relationship to *Lepidodendron*. The cones are usually slender and cylindrical (Fig. 19–8). Some are attached by a short stalk to the stem, others are sessile. Some specimens have a length of over 30 cm and a width exceeding 45 mm but most are much smaller. The cone consists of a central axis, bearing sporophylls in either a spiral or whorled arrangement. Each sporophyll is shield-shaped, turning upward at the tip. A single sporangium is attached to the upper surface of the sporophyll, and a small **enation** called the **ligule** is attached to the sporophyll a short distance distally from the sporangium. The ligule, also present on the leaves, is apparently re-

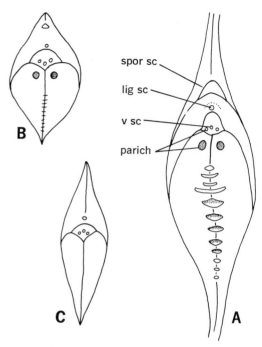

FIGURE 19–6   A–C, leaf cushions of three different species of *Lepidodendron*, showing details of structure. *lig sc*, ligule scar; *parich*, parichnos; *spor sc*, sporangial scar; *v sc*, vascular bundle scar. (After Zeiller.)

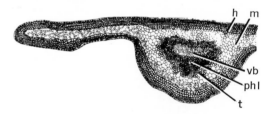

FIGURE 19–7   Transverse section of leaf of *Lepidodendron*, showing vein, transfusion tissue, and mesophyll. *h*, hypodermal tissue; *m*, mesophyll; *phl*, phloem; *t*, transfusion cells; *vb*, tracheids of vein. (After Andrews with permission of John Wiley & Sons, Inc.)

stricted to most of the heterosporous lycopods.

Most species of *Lepidostrobus* are heterosporous, bearing microspores and megaspores in different sporangia in the same cone. In general, microsporangia are concentrated on sporophylls toward the top of the cone, and the megasporangia toward the base. The microspores are trilete and subtriangular, with a narrow flange encircling a central body (Fig. 19–9A). They range in size from about 20 to 40 microns and were produced in large num-

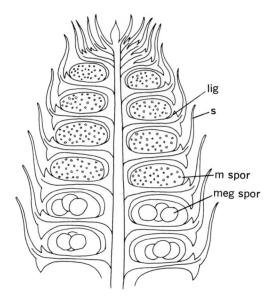

FIGURE 19–8   Vertical section through cone of *Lepidostrobus,* showing segregation of micro- and megasporangia on different sporophylls. *lig,* ligule; *m spor,* microsporangium; *meg spor,* megasporangium; *s,* sporophyll. (After R. Zeiller, "Études sur le *Lepidostrobus brownii* (Unger) Schimper," *Mém. Acad. Sci.,* Tome 52, 2ème sér., 1914.)

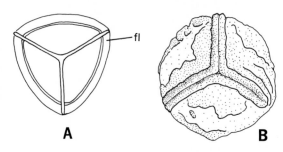

A   **B**

FIGURE 19–9   Spores of *Lepidodendron.* A, microspore showing trilete scar, and narrow flange (*fl*) encircling spore body, ×500; B, megaspore showing trilete scar and roughened spore wall, ×40. (After Potonié, "Synopsis der Sporae *in situ,*" *Beihefte zum Geologische Jahrbuch,* Vol. 52, pl. 3, fig. 73, 75, 1962.)

bers. The megaspores are also trilete and sub-triangular or circular (Fig. 19–9B). They are much larger than the microspores, ranging from 300 microns to over 2 mm in diameter. Some species produced 16 megaspores, others only four, and still others only one per sporangium; this has been cited as an evolutionary series of reduction in number of parts.

In a related cone genus, *Lepidocarpon,* specialized structures have been compared with those of a seed (Fig. 19–10). In the cone, the sporophyll encloses the sporangium except for a narrow **micropyle**-like slit at one end. A single megaspore developed within the sporangium. The envelopment of the megasporangium by the sporophyll is similar to the enclosure of a female sporangium by an integument in those plants producing true seeds—e.g., the gymnosperms. However, the two organs are not truly homologous, since the enveloping sporophyll would be comparable with a fruit or carpel rather than with an ovule. The reproductive unit of *Lepidocarpon* probably functioned as a seed in the following manner: the sporophyll protected the megasporangium and megaspore; the megaspore had a supply of stored food; and the sporophyll provided a receptacle for the microspores, thus assisting in fertilization.

Another genus of tree-sized lycopods abundant during the Carboniferous is *Sigillaria.* In general habit, it is very similar to *Lepidodendron.* The main distinguishing characteristic is the pattern of leaf cushions. In *Sigillaria,* the oval or round cushions are spirally arranged around the stem but are aligned in vertical rows.

Phylogeny.   The Lepidodendrales apparently arose during the latter half of the Devonian and increased in abundance and complexity during the Carboniferous. They appear to have reached a peak during the Upper Carboniferous (Pennsylvanian) and then declined very noticeably during the Permian. By the end of Permian times, the lepidodendrids were virtually extinct. It is believed that a prime factor in this dramatic decline was the change in world climate toward cool and dry conditions. Although it is generally held that the lepidodendrids represent the end of a line of lycopod evolution which culminated in an arborescent habit, a link is sometimes suggested between the Carboniferous *Sigillaria* mentioned above and a Triassic plant, *Pleuromeia,* described under the next order.

ORDER PLEUROMEIALES.   This order is best represented by the genus *Pleuromeia* from

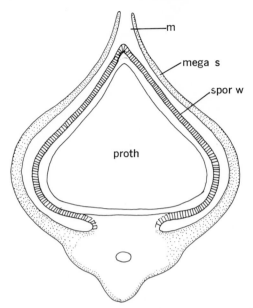

FIGURE 19–10   Vertical section through "seed" of *Lepidocarpon*, showing spore wall (*spor w*) surrounding prothallus (*proth*), megasporophyll (*mega s*), and micropyle (*m*), ×4. (After D. H. Scott, *Studies in Fossil Botany*, Adam & Charles Black, Ltd., London.)

Triassic rocks of Germany. *Pleuromeia* consists of a columnar and unbranched stem that reaches at least 2 meters in height and 9 cm in diameter (Fig. 19–11). The base of the stem expands into four or more lobes that support numerous rootlets. Leaves are attached spirally around the stem, and reach 11 cm in length and 1.5 cm in width. Each leaf bears a ligule and has two veins running full length. As in the lepidodendrids, the leaves were apparently shed from older regions as the stem grew in height.

The reproductive structures are borne in a cone at the tip of the stem. The plant is heterosporous, with the sporangia interpreted to be on the **abaxial** surface of the sporophylls. This is opposite to all other lycopods, and has been explained as representing a reduction from earlier plants that had both adaxial and abaxial sporangia. The megasporangia are large and contain trilete megaspores ranging from 500 to 700 microns. The microsporangia are relatively small and carry many trilete microspores measuring between 15 and 25 microns.

Another genus, *Nathorstiana*, is often placed in this order. It has been found only in

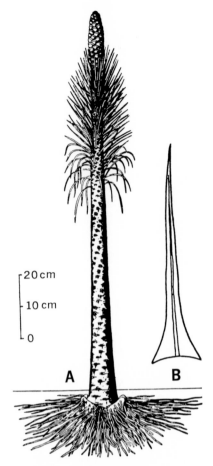

FIGURE 19–11   A, reconstruction of *Pleuromeia*, showing rootstock and roots, columnar stem, and leaves and cone toward top; B, single leaf. (A, after Hirmer with permission of *Palaeontographica*; B, after Mägdefrau, "Zur Morphologie und Phylogenetischen Bedeutung der Fossilen Pflanzengattung *Pleuromeia*," *Beihefte Botanisches Centralblatt*, Vol. 48, 1931.)

the Lower Cretaceous, and hence is younger than *Pleuromeia*. *Nathorstiana* is small and consists of an erect and unbranched stem up to 20 cm in length (Fig. 19–12). Roots occur at the bottom and emerge from ridges on the axis. No reproductive structures have been found. In size and structure *Nathorstiana* has been compared with the living *Isoetes*, and is believed by some to be a direct ancestor of the modern genus.

ORDER ISOETALES.   This order of lycopods contains two living genera, *Isoetes* and *Stylites*.

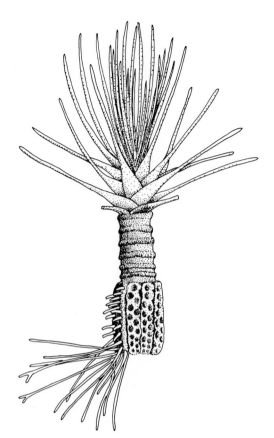

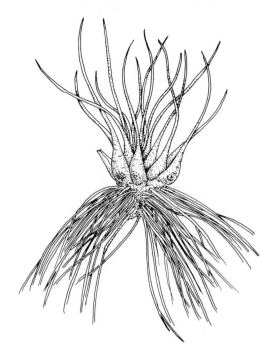

FIGURE 19–13   Habit sketch of plan of *Isoetes*, showing leaves, stem, and roots, ×1.

FIGURE 19–12   Reconstruction of *Nathorstiana*, showing rootstock, very short stem, and spiral collar of leaves, ×0.5. (After Mägdefrau, "Über *Nathorstiana*, eine Isoetacee aus dem Neokom von Quedinburg a. Harz," *Beihefte Botanisches Centralblatt*, Vol. 49, 1932.)

The history of *Isoetes* goes back to the Lower Cretaceous, and extends through Upper Cretaceous and Tertiary times to the present. *Stylites*, known only from existing plants, was first described in 1957 from specimens found growing around lake margins high in mountains of Peru. Both genera are structurally reduced when compared with other lycopods, and are believed to represent stages of reduction in a series *Pleuromeia–Nathorstiana–Stylites–Isoetes*.

Isoetes.   One of the most distinctive vascular plants, *Isoetes*, consists of a thick mass of tubular to strap-shaped leaves borne in a rosette on a very short stem (Fig. 19–13). In this habit it resembles a small onion. It grows submerged in shallow water, on the margins of

ponds or lakes, on muddy river banks, or in wet meadows. Over 50 species have been described. The genus, widely distributed in temperate latitudes, is rare in the tropics.

A closer examination of *Isoetes* reveals a stem with either two to four lobes (Fig. 19–15A). The stem is very short, bears dichotomously branching roots between the lobes, and grows from both an apical and a basal meristem.

The arrangement of tissues within the stem is unique (Fig. 19–14A). A core of primary xylem in the central region consists of tracheids interspersed with parenchyma. This core is surrounded by a very thin layer of primary phloem. As in other lycopods, leaf traces depart from the vascular cylinder and leave no leaf gaps.

In *Isoetes*, a cambium forms outside the primary phloem (Fig. 19–14B). The cambium produces a small amount of secondary tissue each year. The cells formed toward the inside consist of **sieve cells,** parenchyma, and what has been reported to be an occasional tracheid. The cells derived from the cambium toward the

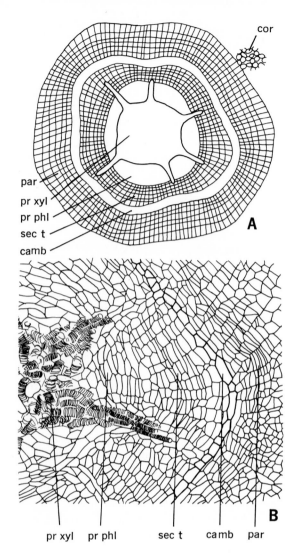

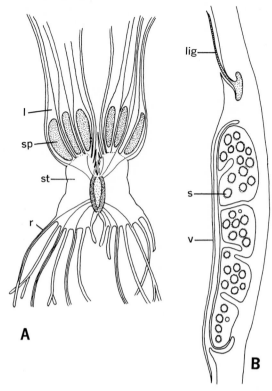

FIGURE 19–15 *Isoetes*. A, vertical section through sporophylls and stem (*st*), showing leaves (*l*), sporangia (*sp*), vascular core in stem, and attachment of roots (*r*), ×2; B, vertical section through single sporophyll, showing ligule (*lig*), velum (*v*), and spores (*s*), ×15. (A, after Eames; B, after Haupt with permission of McGraw-Hill Book Co.)

FIGURE 19–14 *Isoetes*. A, transverse section of stem of *Isoetes,* showing inner core of primary xylem (*pr xyl*) surrounded by primary phloem (*pr phl*); cambium (*camb*)—the clear area—with secondary tissue (*sec t*) on inside, secondary parenchyma (*par*) and cortex (*cor*) on outside, ×5; B, enlarged section of A, showing tracheids of primary xylem (*pr xyl*); primary phloem (*pr phl*); secondary tissue (*sec t*) inside cambium (*camb*) and secondary parenchyma on outside (*par*), ×15.

outside are all parenchymatous and act as a food storage tissue. Each year as new parenchyma is formed, outer tissues are sloughed off together with the leaf bases. Cambium outside the primary phloem, with production of phloem cells inside and parenchyma outside, is unique for vascular plants.

The leaves are borne in a spiral arrangement around the top of the stem (Fig. 19–15A). Each leaf is attached by a broad base and tapers toward a point. A ligule is attached on the adaxial surface (Fig. 19–15B), as in *Lepidodendron, Pleuromeia,* and most other heterosporous lycopods. A central vein runs the length of the leaf and is flanked on either side by parenchymatous canals. These have been compared with the parichnos canals of the *Lepidodendron* leaf. Four air chambers characteristic of submerged aquatic plants are located in the mesophyll. These appear to function in both gas exchange and flotation.

A mature plant of *Isoetes* usually possesses three sets of leaf-like organs around the top of the stem. The outer layers of leaves normally bear megasporangia and are hence

megasporophylls. These in turn enclose whorls of **microsporophylls.** The central appendages are usually immature leaves but often bear abortive sporangia.

The sporangia are single and relatively large, some reaching 10 mm in length (Fig. 19–15B). They occur at the base of the sporophyll just below the ligule and are partly or completely covered by a flap of the sporophyll, the **velum.** Outgrowths of the sporangial wall, called **trabeculae,** extend into the locule of the sporangium. The trabeculae and sporangial wall both possess a nutritive tissue, the **tapetum,** on the inner surface. The central cells, all potentially spore mother cells, form either microspores or megaspores in tetrads.

The number of microspores formed in a microsporangium of *Isoetes* is reported to exceed 1,000,000 in some species. Most of the microspores are bilateral and monolete, and range between 20 and 45 microns in length (Fig. 19–16C, D). Megaspores are produced in much smaller numbers, varying between 50 and 300 per sporangium. They range in diameter from 250 to 900 microns, and are trilete (Fig. 19–16A, B). The ornamentation of the spore wall, distinctive for each species, varies from granular to spiny to warty. Both microspores and megaspores germinate normally during the beginning of a growing season, and both produce relatively small multicellular gametophytes that mature inside the spore wall.

The male gametophyte starts with a uninucleate cell (Fig. 19–17A). This divides to produce a single **prothallial cell** at one end, and a central **antheridial initial.** The antheridial initial then divides to form an outer layer of wall cells and an inner core of four spermatogenous cells. Each spermatogenous cell produces a spirally twisted multiflagellate sperm. The flagellated sperms are more like those of ferns and *Equisetum* than those of other lycopods. This has led some investigators to suggest a closer alliance of *Isoetes* with the former two groups than with the lycopods.

The female gametophyte is entirely endosporal in development (Fig. 19–18). The large nucleus of the spore divides several times to form many free nuclei. Cell walls then begin to

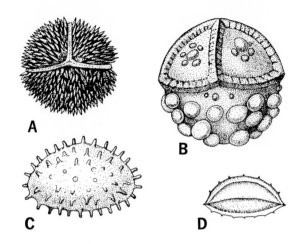

FIGURE 19–16   *Isoetes.* A, B, megaspores, ×5; C, D, microspores of two different species, ×500. (After Motelay and Vendryès.)

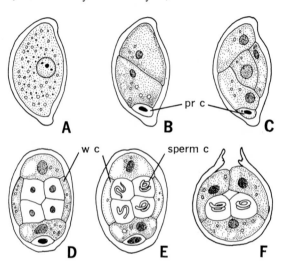

FIGURE 19–17   Development of male gametophyte of *Isoetes,* ×800. A, uninucleate cell; B, single prothallial cell (*pr c*) has formed at one end; C, antheridial initial in center surrounded by three wall cells (*w c*); D–F, stages in formation of sperm from spermatogenous cells (*sperm c*). (After Liebig with permission of *Flora.*)

form at one side and eventually encompass all the nuclei. Several archegonia develop on the surface of the gametophyte just beneath the trilete scar of the megaspore wall. Each archegonium consists of four tiers of neck cells, one neck canal cell, one ventral canal cell, and one large egg cell. At maturity, the neck canal cell disintegrates, and the neck cells spread apart to form a narrow canal. Fertilization is effected

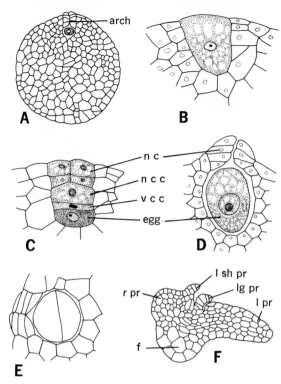

FIGURE 19–18 Development of female gametophyte and archegonia of *Isoetes*. A, single archegonium on periphery of mature gametophyte, ×100; B–D, development of archegonium, ×400; E, two-cell stage of embryo development, ×400; F, a late embryo, ×300. *arch,* archegonium; *f,* foot; *l pr,* leaf primordium; *l sh pr,* leaf sheath primordium; *lg pr,* ligule primordium; *n c,* neck cell; *n c c,* neck canal cell; *r pr,* root primordium; *v c c,* ventral canal cell. (A–E, after Campbell; F, after Liebig with permission of *Flora.*)

when a flagellated sperm swims through the neck and penetrates the egg.

The first division of the fertilized egg is oblique to the long axis of the archegonium. A second division occurs at right angles to the first, giving four cells in one plane. Each cell divides several times to produce quadrants that serve as primordia for the organs (Fig. 19–18F). One quadrant, lying toward the venter, differentiates into a massive tissue, the foot, that is embedded in the gametophytic tissue. The second quadrant, directed toward the venter, develops into the primary leaf. The quadrant lying closest to the archegonial neck differentiates slowly into the stem, and the fourth

quadrant gives rise to the primary root. Root hairs arise from outer cells of the embryonic root, which eventually protrudes from the megaspore and anchors the young **sporeling** in the soil.

Throughout the maturation of the embryo from the zygote, the long axis of the embryo is at right angles to the polar axis of the megaspore. This is the same orientation as in other extant lycopods, but it differs from that of the marattiaceous ferns (see Chapter 21) and the seed plants (see Chapter 23). In the latter two groups, the longitudinal axis of the embryo parallels the long axis of the archegonium. This is an important point in any discussion of the origin of the seed habit in plants and will be elaborated later.

Stylites. This genus, with two species, closely resembles *Isoetes* (Fig. 19–19). It consists of a cylindrical stem that branches dichotomously at least three times, resembling a candelabra. Rosettes of strap-shaped leaves girdle the apex of each branch of the stem. The roots are formed around the lower end of the stem, and have trace connections with the central stele. A most remarkable feature is the attachment of the sporangia far above the base of the sporophyll. The sporangia have trabeculae similar to those of *Isoetes.* The microspores are usually elliptical, monolete, and measure 10 to 20 microns in diameter. The megaspores are subtriangular, trilete, and measure about 500 microns.

Phylogeny. The two genera of the Isoetales are among the most distinctive of all vascular plants. Typical lycopods, they are microphyllous and have adaxial sporangia on sporophylls. The very small stems are usually interpreted as examples of extreme reduction, most likely from ancestors such as *Pleuromeia* and *Nathorstiana.* In showing some axillary extension and dichotomy, *Stylites* appears to be less reduced than *Isoetes.*

ORDER SELAGINELLALES. This order of lycopods has both fossil and living representatives, and dates from the Carboniferous. The extant plants are all included in the genus *Selaginella.* The fossil genus is *Selaginellites,* a

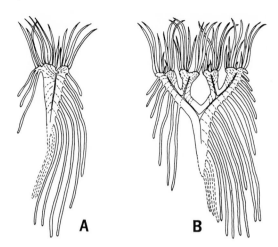

FIGURE 19–19   *Stylites.* A, side view showing disposition of roots and leaves on stem, ×1.3; B, front view showing double dichotomy of stem, ×1.3. (After Rauh and Falk, "*Stylites* Amstutz, eine neue Isoetaceae aus den Hochlanden Perus," *Sitzungsberichte der Heidelberger Akademie der Wissenschaften Mathematisch-Naturwissenschaftliche Klasse, 1,* Abhandlung 1959, p. 27, fig. 13.)

name that reflects the close relationship generally believed to exist between fossil and living plants. Indeed, apparently little evolutionary change has occurred in the *Selaginella* line from the very beginning. The ancestors to *Selaginellites* are unknown, but the line can be taken back some 300,000,000 years to the Carboniferous.

Selaginellites. This genus is represented by remains of both vegetative parts and cones. The stem is very slender, and branching ranges from monopodial to dichotomous (Fig. 19–20A). The leaves, small and pointed, are closely packed in a spiral around the stem. In some species the leaves are two-ranked, with two rows of long leaves (1 to 2 mm) attached on one side and two rows of shorter leaves on the other. This dimorphism of leaves is identical to that in some species of *Selaginella,* in which the long leaves are attached to the lower side and the short ones to the upper side of the stem.

Selaginellites is best known from investigations of cones (Fig. 19–20B). These small cylindrical structures, up to 7 mm in diameter and 12 mm long, consist of spirally arranged sporophylls. Both megasporangia and micro-

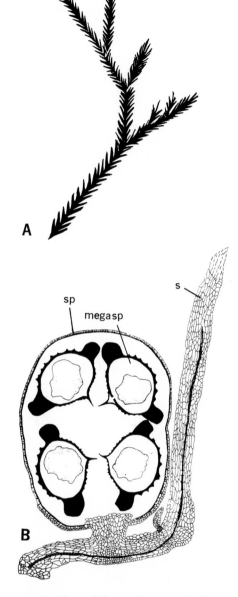

FIGURE 19–20   *Selaginellites.* A, habit sketch of branching stem; B, vertical section through sporophyll (*s*) and sporangium (*sp*) containing four megaspores (*megasp*). (A, after Halle; B, after Hoskins and Abbott with permission of *American Journal of Botany.*)

sporangia are borne on the adaxial surfaces of sporophylls and close to the stem; in some species, the megasporangia are concentrated in the lower sporophylls; in others they are mixed with microsporangia in the upper region. This zoning of sporangia also occurs in some species of the extant *Selaginella*.

Usually only four megaspores are found in a megasporangium. These are subtriangular, trilete, possess an equatorial flange, and vary from about 400 to 800 microns. The microspores occur in large numbers, are also trilete and flanged, and range in size from 40 to 80 microns. In most features, the microspores and megaspores are very similar to those of *Selaginella* and reflect the very close relationship between fossil and extant members of the group.

Selaginella. This genus, with some 700 species, is widely distributed over the earth. Most species live in the wetter tropics, but some exist in temperate regions, and a few are found in extreme climates such as the desert or the subarctic. In general they thrive in wet and shaded sites, but some will tolerate exposed habitats such as rocky cliffs. Some species are cultivated in greenhouses and florist shops, where they are valued for their feathery appearance.

In general, *Selaginella* plants are small and delicate (Fig. 19–21). In most plants, the stems are trailing, although some species grow as erect tufts, and a few are climbers. Branching is usually dichotomous, but may be **pseudomonopodial.** Some stems reach several meters in length, but most range from several centimeters to several decimeters. The stems, herbaceous and thin, are densely clothed with small and spiny leaves. Thus, most *Selaginella* plants resemble mosses, with which they may be confused in the field.

The small and simple leaves vary in outline from round to lanceolate to thread-like (Fig. 19–22A–C). They are arranged spirally, in **decussate** pairs, or in four longitudinal rows. Most species have two rows of large leaves on the lower surface, and two rows of smaller leaves attached to the upper side. This appears to be a modification of a spiral arrangement, allowing for more efficient interception of light. As mentioned earlier, this same condition is found in some fossil members.

Each leaf contains a single midrib vein, consisting of an upper band of xylem with annular and helical tracheids, and a lower column of phloem with sieve cells. The leaf trace departs from the stele of the stem without forming a leaf gap. There is a distinct epidermis, with stomata on both surfaces or sometimes restricted to only one. The mesophyll contains chloroplasts and has large intercellular spaces. In some species, a palisade layer develops beneath the upper surface.

The leaves of *Selaginella* are similar to those of the Lepidodendrales, Pleuromeiales, and Isoetales in possessing a ligule. This is a tongue-shaped projection formed by the adaxial epidermis near the base of the leaf. Its function is completely unknown, although it may be secretory or help to keep the stem apex and leaf primordia from drying out during early growth.

The mature stem of *Selaginella* has a well-defined epidermis, cortex, and stele (Fig. 19–23B) which develop from either a single apical cell or a group of initials, depending on the species. The epidermis is one cell thick and does not have stomata. The cortex is composed of large parenchyma cells, and the outer layers often have thickened walls. *Selaginella* differs from most other vascular plants in having a system of air spaces traversed by elongated endodermal cells called trabeculae. These have **Casparian strips** on the radial wall and link the cortex and vascular tissue across the spaces.

The arrangement of the vascular tissue ranges from protostelic to **siphonostelic.** Some species have more than one stele and hence are **polystelic** (Fig. 19–23B). The polysteles extend through the central space, each being attached to the inner cortical wall by trabeculae (Fig. 19–24). Each stele has exarch protoxylem, with metaxylem formed centripetally. **Vessels** have been reported in some species of *Selaginella*. The xylem is surrounded by several layers of parenchyma, which in turn is surrounded by sieve cells of the phloem. The stele is ensheathed by a single layer of parenchyma, from which trabeculae radiate. Both branch and leaf traces depart obliquely from the stele and pass outward through the cortex.

The primary root of the sporeling soon shrivels and dies. The functional roots are all adventitious. Some roots emanate from the un-

FIGURE 19–21   Stems, leaves, and strobili of *Selaginella*, ×1. A, *Selaginella krausiana*; B, *S. wallacei*; C, *S. willdenovii*.

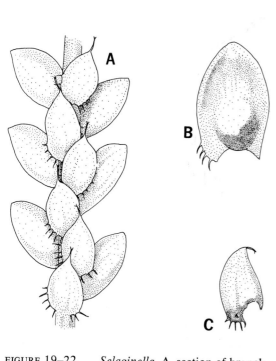

FIGURE 19–22   *Selaginella*. A, section of branch with leaves flattened into four longitudinal rows, ×100; B, single leaf from lateral row, showing broad blade with clawlike emergences, ×15; C, single leaf from upper row with narrow forked appendage at distal end of relatively narrow blade, ×15.

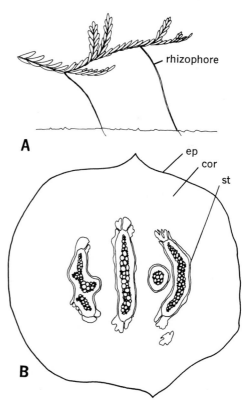

FIGURE 19–23   *Selaginella*. A, branch showing two rhizophores extending to soil, ×1; B, diagram of transverse section of stem showing epidermis (*ep*), cortex (*cor*), and stele (*st*), ×40.

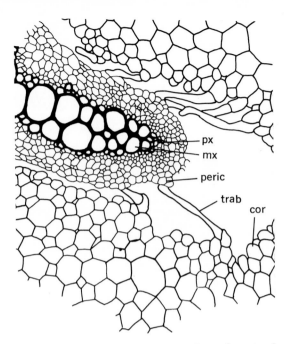

FIGURE 19–24   Transverse section of part of stele and cortex of stem of *Selaginella,* showing exarch protoxylem (*px*), metaxylem (*mx*), pericycle (*peric*), trabeculae (*trab*), and cortex (*cor*), ×150.

derside of the stem, whereas others are formed at the tips of structures called **rhizophores** —prop-like appendages that grow downward from the branch forks of ascending stems to the surface of the ground (Fig. 19–23A). The adventitious roots then emerge from the tip of the rhizophore and penetrate the soil. Rhizophores are generally interpreted as specialized stems, since they bear both leaves and cones.

Selaginella is heterosporous, and the sporophylls bearing megasporangia and microsporangia are aggregated into strobili (Fig. 19–25A). In some, the sporophylls are compact, in others very loose. Many species have sporophylls almost identical to sterile leaves, distinguished only by sporangia. Others have sporophylls smaller than sterile leaves, often devoid of chlorophyll. Each sporophyll has a ligule identical to that of the leaf. The sporangia develop from initials that are either on the stem or on the adaxial surface of the sporophyll very near the axil (Fig. 19–25B, C). In some species, lower sporophylls bear mainly megaspo-

rangia, whereas upper ones support microsporangia. In others, each type of sporangium occurs in two vertical rows, and in still others, distribution is random.

Several hundred microspores are produced in the microsporangia (Fig. 19–25C). The microspores, subtriangular and trilete, are variously ornamented with granules, spines, and flanges (Fig. 19–25D). They range in size from 30 to 80 microns. The number of megaspores produced per megasporangium is usually four, but as few as one and as many as 40 have been reported (Fig. 19–25B). The megaspores, also subtriangular and trilete, have thick walls, various sculpturing, and range from 150 to 600 microns (Fig. 19–25E).

The gametophytes of both spores develop endosporally. In addition, the gametophytes often mature while the spores are still in their respective sporangia. In the megaspores, endosporal prothallial development and retention have been cited as main stages in the evolutionary development of the seed habit in plants.

The development of both male and female gametophytes is similar to that already noted for *Isoetes*. In the microspore, the meiospore nucleus divides to form a central antheridial initial and a peripheral prothallial cell (Fig. 19–26B). The antheridial initial divides many times, ultimately producing a one-cell-layer jacket that surrounds central spermatogenous cells (Fig. 19–26D). Each of the latter produces a sperm, which is disc-shaped with two anterior flagella. The jacket cells break down at maturity, and the sperm then become free-swimming inside the spore wall (Fig. 19–26E). The sperm escape by the splitting of the spores along the **commissures** of the trilete mark.

The female gametophyte also develops endosporally while the megaspores are within the megasporangium (Fig. 19–27A). As in *Isoetes,* the single nucleus divides many times to produce a free nuclear stage. Wall formation around the nuclei begins just beneath the trilete mark and continues until the cavity is filled with cells. Archegonia then develop on the outer regions, usually just beneath the trilete mark (Fig. 19–27B, C). At this time, the megaspore wall has usually split along the trilete mark, and

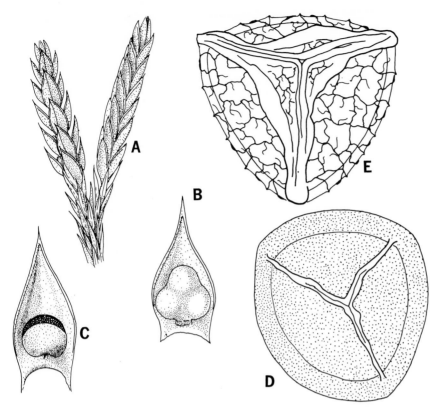

FIGURE 19–25   Reproductive organs of *Selaginella*. A, four-sided strobili at tips of two branches, ×4; B, adaxial surface of single megasporophyll, showing megasporangium with three lobes reflecting three of enclosed megaspores, ×20; C, single microsporophyll with microsporangium split open to show mass of microspores, ×20; D, microspore showing well-defined trilete mark and outer flange on wall, ×100; E, megaspore showing thick wall and thickenings along trilete tetrad scar, ×200.

the prothallus of the gametophyte has protruded. Each archegonium is embedded in the prothallus and consists of four rows of neck cells, one neck canal cell, one ventral canal cell, and one egg. At maturity, the neck canal cells disintegrate, forming a canal through which the flagellated sperm have free access to the egg.

The fertilized egg divides transversely to form an upper and a lower cell. After repeated divisions, the upper cell develops into a **suspensor.** This is a cylindrical structure that pushes the embryo deeply into the prothallus. The lower daughter cell matures into the embryo proper. This is oriented transversely, and consists of shoot, foot, and root, just as in *Isoetes* (Fig. 19–27D). The young sporophyte becomes independent when the developing root eventually is established in the soil, and the

stems and leaves become photosynthetically active.

Selaginella is apparently related to the other heterosporous lycopods through the following features: microphyllous leaves; stems with dichotomous or pseudomonopodial branching; adventitious roots; sporangia borne adaxially on sporophylls; heterospory; and ligules on both leaves and sporophylls. *Selaginella* is directly linked with the fossil *Selaginellites* by a very close similarity of structure. There appears to be no direct phylogenetic relationship to the *Lepidodendron – Isoetes* line; rather the herbaceous and heterosporous condition in *Selaginellites* appears to have persisted with little modification since at least the Carboniferous. Any ancestors to the *Selaginellites–Selaginella* line should be sought in herbaceous

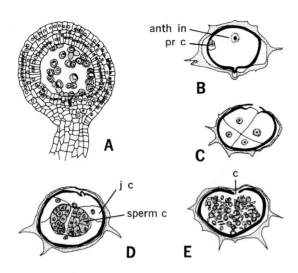

FIGURE 19–26 Male gametophyte development in *Selaginella*. A, vertical section through mature microsporangium, showing wall and developing microspores in tapetal fluid, ×50; B–E, stages in development of microspores, ×500. *anth in,* antheridial initial; *c,* commissure; *j c,* jacket cell; *pr c,* prothallial cell; *sperm c,* spermatogenous cell. (After Slagg with permission of *American Journal of Botany.*)

lycopods of the early Carboniferous or perhaps Devonian Periods. It is often assumed that the heterosporous lycopods evolved from homosporous ancestors through changes in the size of spores and segregation of the sexes. If this assumption is true—and there is no direct fossil evidence to support it—the ancestors to both of the heterosporous lycopod lines could be found in some of the herbaceous and apparently homosporous Devonian plants such as *Drepanophycus* or *Baragwanathia*.

ORDER LYCOPODIALES. This order is represented by three genera: *Lycopodium* and *Phylloglossum* are present in extant floras, whereas *Lycopodites* is reserved for fossil members. The plants of this order differ from the other lycopods mainly in being homosporous. In most other respects they are very similar to the Selaginellales, and in many of the fossil specimens, homospory and heterospory are the only criteria that can validly distinguish plants of the Lycopodiales from the Selaginellales.

Lycopodites. This genus comprises remains of stems, leaves, and cones which resemble in general form those of the extant *Lycopodium* (Fig. 19–28). The thin herbaceous stems have small, spirally arranged leaves. The strobili are cylindrical and small. It is generally accepted that these are homosporous plants, although few if any *Lycopodites* contain only one size of spore. *Lycopodites* has been found from the Carboniferous to the present. As with *Selaginella,* apparently little evolutionary change has occurred from the early representatives to the modern *Lycopodium.*

Lycopodium. The common names for species of this genus are "club moss" and "ground pine," because of superficial resemblances to mosses and pines. *Lycopodium* is world-wide in distribution, but most species are found in the tropics. All are relatively small and herbaceous plants; some are erect and shrubby, whereas others are prostrate and creeping and in some cases subterranean (Fig. 19–29). All species are densely covered with small, scale-like leaves. Both epiphytic and terrestrial species are known.

The stem is usually branched dichotomously, although **sympodial** and pseudomonopodial branching occur in some species. Those with prostrate stems usually have a main branch with smaller side branches, and grow to several meters in length. All stems have a massive apical meristem that differentiates into a well-defined epidermis, cortex, and stele.

The epidermis of the stem is one cell thick and bears stomata similar to those of the leaves. The cortex is moderately thick, with sclerenchyma bands in some species. An endodermis is usually developed on the inner face of the cortex, with Casparian strips on the radial walls (Fig. 19–30). The pericycle, located inside the endodermis, varies from three to six layers of parenchyma; this is the usual site for the origin of adventitious roots.

The vascular tissue is quite variable in organization, but the different patterns are generally regarded as variations of a protostele. Furrowing of the vascular cylinder produces several patterns; the most common are the **actinostele,** with several radiating arms inter-

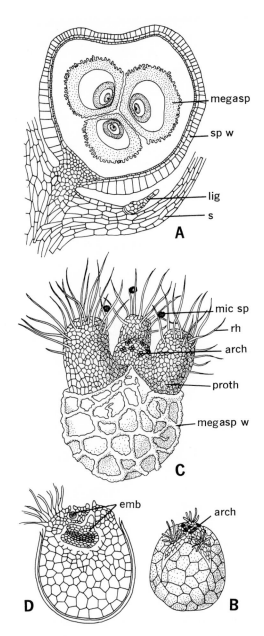

FIGURE 19–28 Two fragments of *Lycopodites* showing leaves and strobili at tips, ×1. (After Geinitz.)

spersed with parenchyma (Fig. 19–30A), and the **plectostele,** with xylem and phloem split into several to many plates (Fig. 19–30B). All species have xylem and phloem arranged initially as an actinostele, which in some species modifies, with maturation, into variations of a plectostele.

The xylem is all primary, and the arrangement is exarch. The protoxylem tracheids have annular and helical thickenings; those of the metaxylem are scalariform, or with circular and **bordered** pits. The phloem consists of sieve cells with oblique end walls and scattered sieve areas interspersed with parenchyma cells.

Leaf traces depart from the protoxylem points of the stele, without leaving a leaf gap, and pass obliquely through the pericycle and

FIGURE 19–27 Development of female gametophyte of *Selaginella*. A, vertical section through megasporangium and three megaspores, ×250; B, single megaspore showing archegonia on slightly protruding gametophyte, ×500; C, prothallus with archegonia protruding from megaspore, showing several microspores trapped on rhizoidal appendages, ×500; D, two embryos developing in archegonia (one on left is in two-celled stage; one on right has developed primordia and foot), ×500. *arch,* archegonia; *emb,* embryo; *lig,* ligule; *megasp,* megaspore; *megasp w,* megaspore wall; *mic sp,* microspores; *proth,* prothallus; *rh,* rhizoids; *s,* sporophyll.(A,after Haupt with permission of McGraw-Hill Book Co.; B–D, after Bruchmann.)

A

B

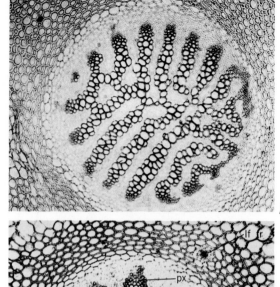

A

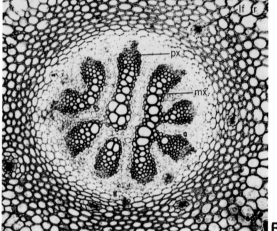

B

FIGURE 19–30 *Lycopodium.* Transverse sections of two species (note actinostelic arrangement of xylem and phloem in A, and plectostele in B, ×50). *lf tr,* leaf trace; *mx,* metaxylem; *px,* protoxylem.

FIGURE 19–29 *Lycopodium.* A and B, part of stem and leaves of two different species, ×0.8.(B, courtesy Chicago Natural History Museum.)

cortex into the bases of the leaves. Each leaf has only one trace, which forms the midvein. A transverse section of the stem will usually show many such leaf traces, reflecting the large number of leaves clothing the stem.

The leaves of most species are small, usually lanceolate in outline, and broadly attached to the stem. The most common arrangement is spiral, but in some species they are whorled, and in a few they are of two sizes and decussate, as noted in *Selaginella.* The single vein has endarch xylem with spiral tracheids and a small amount of phloem (Fig. 19–31A). The whole vein is often ensheathed by an endodermis. The mesophyll contains spongy parenchyma with chloroplasts and generally intercellular spaces. Stomata normally occur on the epidermis of both leaf surfaces, but in some species they are restricted to one side. Epidermal and guard cells usually contain chloroplasts and are covered by a cuticle.

Adventitious roots are common in *Lycopodium.* These roots arise from the pericycle and angle somewhat through the cortex before emerging. In some species, adventitious roots occur regularly on the underside of the stem—in others only in terminal regions of the stem.

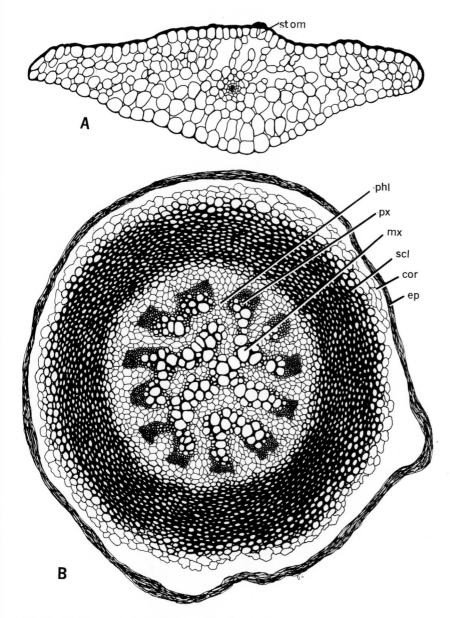

FIGURE 19–31   *Lycopodium,* ×20. A, vertical section of leaf, showing
stoma (*stom*), mesophyll, and central vein; B, transverse section of root, showing plectostelic arrangement of vascular tissue. *cor,* cortex; *ep,* epidermis; *mx,*
metaxylem; *phl,* phloem; *px,* protoxylem; *scl,* sclerenchyma.

Each root has several to many dichotomous
branches. Root hairs are abundant and grouped
in pairs as a result of a split in the epidermal
root-hair primordium just before the evagination of the cell wall.

The root consists of the cortex and stele
(Fig. 19–31B). The vascular tissue is an ex-

arch protostele, and most commonly is **diarch.**
Some roots, however, are **monarch, triarch,** or
tetrarch, and in some species the stele will
grade from one of these into another.

All species of *Lycopodium* are homosporous. The relatively large and reniform sporangia are borne on the adaxial surface of sporo-

phylls, usually close to the axil as in the other extant lycopods. In some species, the sporophylls are green and identical to vegetative leaves (Fig. 19–32B). In others, the sporophylls are pale, reduced to small scales, and aggregated into strobili. The strobili occur at the end of the main stem or on lateral branches and are either sessile or stalked (Fig. 19–32A). Each sporangium is borne on a very short stalk and opens at maturity by a narrow transverse slit (Fig. 19–33).

The structure of the spores of *Lycopodium* is quite diagnostic for the genus (Fig. 19–34). They are subtriangular in outline and trilete. The ornamentation on the wall usually consists of reticulate thickenings with upright projections where ridges of the reticulum coalesce. Spores of some species have a pitted or rugulate (wormy) ornamentation. The area comprising the three contact faces lying between the arms of the trilete mark is almost always bare of ornamentation. The spores range in diameter from about 25 to 50 microns.

The spores germinate either on or in the soil after remaining dormant for periods ranging from several days to several years. The developing prothallus breaks through the spore along the arms of the trilete mark and becomes established in the soil. The mature gametophyte varies widely with the species but is always small and inconspicuous (Fig. 19–35). The gametophyte varies from irregularly ovoid to carrot-shaped. Those on the surface of the soil are green and usually mature in one season, whereas subterranean prothalli are colorless and infected with mycorrhizal fungus. Maturation of prothalli takes as long as one year in some species.

The antheridia and archegonia are borne on the same prothallus, either on the upper surface or at the base of lobes (Fig. 19–35). Antheridia and archegonia are intermingled on the prothalli of some species but segregated into different areas on the same prothallus in others. The antheridia are globose, either completely sunken in the prothallus or slightly protruding (Fig. 19–36A). Each consists of a jacket one cell thick and a central mass of gamete mother cells that mature to produce

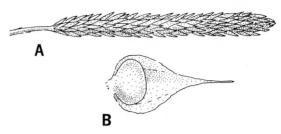

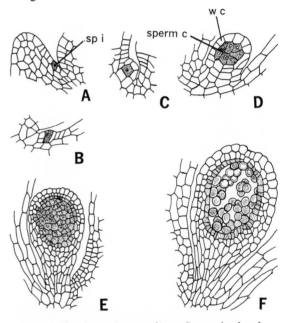

A

B

FIGURE 19–32   *Lycopodium*. A, single strobilus showing spirally arranged sporophylls, ×2; B, adaxial surface of single sporophyll showing sporangium, ×10.

FIGURE 19–33   *Lycopodium*. Stages in development of sporangium, from single-cell initial in A to mature stage with spores in F, ×50. *sp i,* sporangial initial; *sperm c,* spermatogenous cells; *w c,* wall cells. (After Bower.)

sperm. Each sperm is fusiform or droplet-shaped and has two or sometimes three flagella at the anterior end (Fig. 19–36B). Sperm escape from the antheridium after the dissolution of a single cell of the jacket.

The archegonia are also sunken, with only the neck protruding. Each consists of three or four rows of neck cells, surrounding one to 13 neck canal cells, and a single ventral canal cell overlying a large egg (Fig. 19–36C). At maturity, the neck cells separate and the canal cells dissolve, allowing passage of the sperm directly to the egg in the venter (Fig. 19–36D).

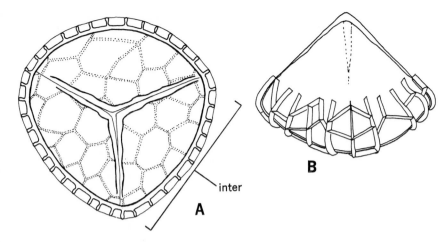

FIGURE 19–34   *Lycopodium* spores, ×500. A, proximal view showing trilete mark, and reticulations on distal surface; B, lateral view showing un-ornamented contact faces, and reticulation on distal surface. *inter,* interradial.

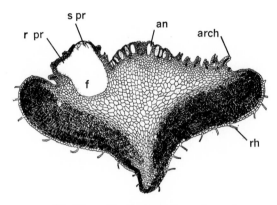

FIGURE 19–35   Vertical section through pro-thallus of *Lycopodium,* showing rhizoids (*rh*), antheridia (*an*), archegonia (*arch*), and a single embryo with foot (*f*), root primordium (*r pr*), and stem primordium (*s pr*), ×8. (After Bruchmann.)

The fertilized egg divides transversely to the long axis of the oriented archegonium, as in *Selaginella* (Fig. 19–37A). The daughter cell oriented toward the neck divides to form a several-celled suspensor, while the lower daughter cell divides to form the foot and the stem and root primordia (Fig. 19–37B). During development, the young embryo is not pushed very far into the prothallus by the suspensor. Prior to emergence, the embryo has a large foot. The root primordium is on one side; and the stem primordium, with one to several leaf primordia, arises at the opposite pole (Fig. 19–37C). Even after the young sporophyte

becomes rooted in the soil, the prothallus often persists for some time before disintegrating.

Lycopodium reproduces vegetatively in several ways. In some species, bulbils or gemmae form annually on new stem tips. These appear to be flattened branch tips with enlarged lateral leaves. They fall to the ground and grow directly into new plants. In other species, the older part of the stem dies off annually, leaving the tips; these act as resting buds and take root the next growing season. In a plant with many branch endings, many new plants are established each year.

In most features, *Lycopodium* is similar to *Selaginella.* Both genera have herbaceous and essentially dichotomous stems, exarch xylem, microphyllous leaves, and adaxial sporangia. The fundamental differences are the homosporous condition and **exosporal** prothallial development exhibited by *Lycopodium.* As far as can be determined, *Lycopodium* has descended directly from *Lycopodites,* which in turn was possibly derived from some of the earliest lycopods such as *Baragwanathia* or *Drepanophycus.* There appears to have been little structural modification in this line of evolution.

Phylloglossum. This genus has a single species confined to parts of southern and western Australia, Tasmania, and New Zealand. Although closely related to *Lycopodium,* it shows several important structural differences.

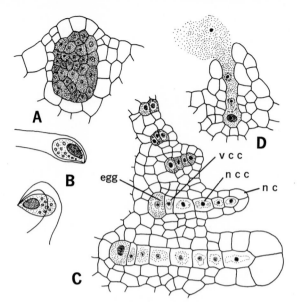

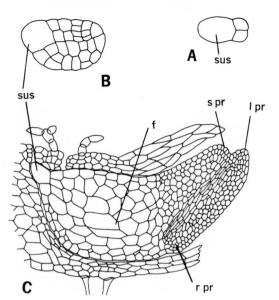

FIGURE 19–36   *Lycopodium*. A, immature antheridium showing central spermatogenous cells surrounded by jacket cells, ×50; B, mature sperm cells showing two flagella, ×1,000; C, stages of archegonial maturation with neck cells (*n c*), neck canal cells (*n c c*), ventral canal cells (*v c c*), and egg, ×50; D, mature archegonium which has disrupted prior to fertilization, ×50. (After Bruchmann with permission of *Flora*.)

FIGURE 19–37   A–C, stages in development of embryo of *Lycopodium*, ×30. *f*, foot; *l pr*, leaf primordium; *r pr*, root primordium; *s pr*, stem primordium; *sus*, suspensor. (After Bruchmann with permission of *Flora*.)

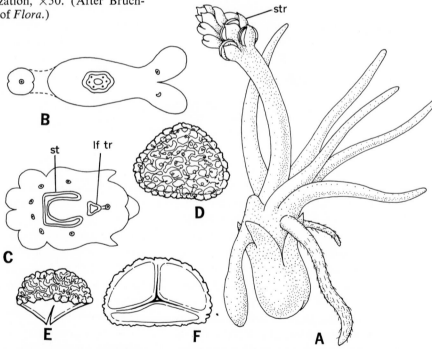

FIGURE 19–38   *Phylloglossum*. A, habit sketch, showing strobilus (*str*), ×2; B, tranverse section of base of strobilar axis with trace of petiole at left, ×4; C, transverse section toward base of stem showing stele (*st*) and single leaf trace (*lf tr*), ×4. D–F, three views of spores, ×500. D, distal surface showing rugulate ornamentation; E, lateral view, and F, proximal view, both showing the unornamented contact faces. (After Bertrand.)

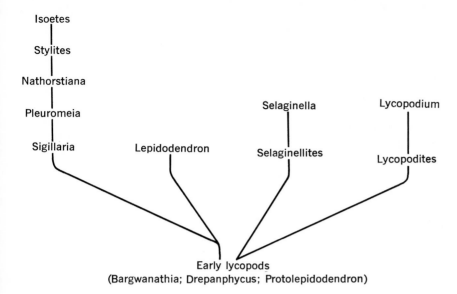

FIGURE 19–39   Graphic representation of probable evolution of three lines of descent in Lycopodophyta.

The fossil history of the genus is unknown.

Phylloglossum, a small plant that grows several centimeters high, consists of a fleshy tuber supporting a short stalk at the upper end (Fig. 19–38A). Several leaves emanate in a tight spiral from the top of the stalk. A short root and a branch of the stalk, called a young tuber, are often found extending laterally from the stalk. The young tuber, the only part that lives from one growing season to the next, is a vegetative reproductive structure. It has been described as structurally homologous to the apical branch buds of some species of *Lycopodium,* and it functions in the same way.

The vascular tissue of the *Phylloglossum* tuber and short stalk is a siphonostele and thus differs from the vascular tissue of *Lycopodium* (Fig. 19–38B). In the leaves, the stele divides into scattered vascular bundles with mesarch protoxylem (Fig. 19–38C).

A strobilus is produced on a stalk or **peduncle** from the tip of the stem. It consists of sporophylls with adaxial sporangia that are homosporous. The spores are similar to those of *Lycopodium,* with heavy rugulate ornamentation (Fig. 19–38D). They germinate into green cylindrical prothalli, 2 to 6 mm long, which are similar to the green surface prothalli

of *Lycopodium.* Antheridia and archegonia, produced on the upper surface, closely resemble those of *Lycopodium.* The development of the embryo is also essentially the same as in *Lycopodium,* except in *Phylloglossum* the stem and root primordia are much reduced.

Phylloglossum appears to be very closely related to *Lycopodium,* differing mainly in the structure of the stele, the position of leaves, and the absence of branching. *Phylloglossum* is probably a reduced lycopod, as evidenced by the siphonostele, the mesarch xylem, and the reduced tuberous stem.

PHYLOGENY OF LYCOPODS

The evidence accumulated suggests that three main lines of evolutionary development have occurred in the lycopod division, as shown in Figure 19–39. No attempt is made here to select any particular early lycopod as a stock for one of the probable lines of descent, since evidence for relationships is very meager. However, in spite of this the three lines of evolution are fairly well documented from the fossil record. No doubt future research, particularly on the early lycopods, will shed much light on initial developments of the main lines in the group.

The earliest lycopods all appear to be homosporous. Heterospory probably did not evolve until sometime in the latter part of the Devonian, where megaspores are found dispersed in some plant-bearing rocks. The heterosporous condition appears to have been established independently in both the lepidodendrid–*Isoetes* and the *Selaginellites–Selaginella* lines of descent. Homospory, on the other hand, was probably maintained in the *Lycopodites–Lycopodium* line from early lycopods.

Two structural modifications would be requisite for establishing heterospory from homospory: the development of two distinct sizes of spore; and the segregation of the sex cells—with the antheridia limited to the prothallus of the microspore and the archegonia restricted to the prothallus of the megaspore. It is not known how this transformation was accomplished, or how complex or lengthy it may have been. But heterospory became established in several other groups of vascular plants during their early evolution, indicating that the transformation was not unique to lycopods.

REFERENCES

Amstutz, E., *"Stylites,* a New Genus of Isoetaceae." *Ann. Missouri Bot. Gar.,* 44: 121–123 (1957).

Andrews, H. N., Jr., *Studies in Paleobotany.* New York: John Wiley & Sons, Inc. (1961). Pp. 214–255.

Banks, H. P., "Notes on Devonian Lycopods." *Senckenbergiana,* 41: 59–88 (1960).

Barclay, B. D., "Origin and Development of Tissues in the Stem of *Selaginella wildenovii." Bot. Gaz.,* 91: 452–461 (1931).

Bertrand, C. E., "On the Development and Morphology of *Phylloglossum drummondii." Phil. Trans. Roy. Soc. London,* 176 (II): 665–678 (1885).

Bower, F. O., "Studies in the Morphology of Spore-Producing Members: Equisetineae and Lycopodineae." *Phil. Trans. Roy. Soc. London,* 185B: 473–572 (1894).

Chaloner, W. G., "On the Megaspores of Four Species of *Lepidostrobus." Ann. Bot.,* N.S., 17: 263–293 (1953).

Chaloner, W. G., "A Carboniferous *Selaginellites* with *Densosporites* Microspores." *Palaeontology,* 1: 245–253 (1958).

Dunlop, D. W., "Notes on the Cytology of Some Lycopsids." *Bull. Torrey Bot. Club,* 76: 266–277 (1949).

Eggert, D. A., "The Ontogeny of Carboniferous Arborescent Lycopsida." *Palaeontographica,* 108B: 43–92 (1961).

Foster, A. S., and Gifford, E. M., *Comparative Morphology of Vascular Plants*. San Francisco: W. H. Freeman and Co. (1959). Pp. 130–190.

Graham, R., "An Anatomical Study of the Leaves of the Carboniferous Arborescent Lycopods." *Ann. Bot.,* 49: 587–608 (1935).

Harvey-Gibson, J., "Contributions Toward a Knowledge of the Anatomy of the Genus *Selaginella* Spr." *Ann. Bot.,* 8: 133–206 (1894); 10: 77–88 (1896); 11: 123–155 (1897); 16: 449–466 (1902).

Hirmer, M., *Handbuch der Paläobotanik*. Vol. 1: *Thallophyta, Bryophyta, Pteridophyta*. Munich and Berlin: R. Oldenburg (1927).

Hirmer, M., "Rekonstruction von *Pleuromeia sternbergi* Corda, Nebst Bemerkungen zur Morphologie der Lycopodiales." *Palaeontographica,* 78B: 47–56 (1933).

Hsü, J., "Anatomy, Development, and Life History of *Selaginella sinensis,* I: Anatomy and Development of the Shoot." *Bull. Chinese Bot. Soc.,* 3: 75–95 (1937).

Krishtofovich, A. N., "Discovery of Lycopodiaceous Plants in the East Siberian Cambrian." *Doklady Akad. Nauk. S.S.S.R.,* 91: 1377–1379 (1953).

Lang, W. H., "Studies in the Morphology of *Isoetes.*" *Mem. Proc. Manchester Lit. Phil. Soc.,* 59: 1–57 (1915).

Lang, W. H., and Cookson, I. C., "On a Flora, Including Vascular Land Plants Associated with *Monograptus,* in Rocks of Silurian Age, from Victoria, Australia." *Phil. Trans. Roy. Soc. London,* 224B: 421–449 (1935).

Mägdefrau, K., "Über *Nathorstiana,* Eine Isoëtacee aus dem Neokom von Quendlinburg A. Harz." *Beih. Bot. Centralbl.,* 49: 706–718 (1932).

Paolillo, D. J., Jr., "The Developmental Anatomy of *Isoetes.*" *Illinois Biol. Monogr.,* 31: 1–130 (1963).

Pfeiffer, N. E., "Monograph of the Isoetaceae." *Ann. Missouri Bot. Gard.,* 9: 79–232 (1922).

Potonié, R., "Synopsis der Sporae in Situ." *Beih. Geologisches Jahrb.,* 52: 1–204 (1962).

Rauh, W., and Falk, H., *"Stylites* E. Amstutz, Eine Neue Isoëtacee aus den Hochanden Perus." *Sitz. Heidelberger Akad. Wiss. Jahrb.,* 1959: 1–83 (1959).

Sporne, K. R., *The Morphology of Pteridophytes*. London: Hutchinson & Co. (Publishers) Ltd. (1962). Pp. 50–93.

Stewart, W. N., "More about the Origin of Vascular Plants." *Plant Sci. Bull.,* 6(5): 1–5 (1960).

20/DIVISION

ARTHROPHYTA

The plants classified in this division are variously called arthrophytes, sphenopsids, or *articulates*. The last name seems to be most appropriate, because the most striking feature of these plants is the regular jointing of the stem. Together with the whorled arrangement of leaves and branches at the nodes, this jointing makes the group distinctive among vascular plants.

Arthrophyta is an ancient division of plants, with the first record in the early Devonian. As with the lycopods, the articulates were more diversified and numerous during the late Paleozoic than in later times. The division is usually subdivided into five orders—the Hyeniales, Pseudoborniales, Sphenophyllales, Calamitales, and Equisetales. Except for the Equisetales, all of the plants are known only from the fossil record. Again like the lycopods, several well-defined lines of evolution can be traced from the early Devonian representatives through the Carboniferous, where they reached a peak. This was followed by a general decline to the present time, when the genus *Equisetum* is the sole representative.

GENERAL MORPHOLOGY

With the exception of the earliest genera, plants of the Arthrophyta have true roots, stems, and leaves. As far as is known, the stem is herbaceous in all but the Calamitales of the late Devonian and Carboniferous; plants of this order have a decidedly woody habit due to the formation of secondary tissue. Again in all but the earliest genera, the stem is characterized by joints or nodes which occur at regular intervals throughout the length. The branches and leaves are arranged in whorls at the nodes. The leaves of the articulates vary from extremely small scale-like emergences to moderately large flat blades; roots are known only in a few instances and appear to be adventitious in most genera.

Reproductive organs in the early members consist of sporangia situated terminally on short lateral branches. In the later groups, the sporangia are produced on special structures called **sporangiophores;** these are always compacted into **cones,** with or without interspersed sterile bracts. Both homospory and heterospory are known in the division, but heterospory is apparently most common.

Much of our information on anatomy, gametophytes, and embryos has come from detailed investigations of the extant *Equisetum.* However, some excellent anatomical detail has also been discovered in fossil members, particularly of some genera of the Calamitales and Sphenophyllales. Together, the information obtained has given some insight into the relationships of various genera, and we have a relatively good picture of the phylogeny of the articulates.

ORDER HYENIALES. The oldest genus is *Protohyenia,* found in early Devonian rocks of western Siberia. As reconstructed, the plant probably consisted of a cylindrical prostrate stem (which has not been observed) with upright branches emerging from the upper surface (Fig. 20–1B). The upright branches, themselves unbranched, bear lateral appendages that fork toward the tips. Some lateral branches are sterile and probably represent the photosynthetic organs, whereas others bear oval sporangia about 3 mm long. The sporangia are terminal on slender branches, and occur in twos, threes, or fours.

The stem and branches of *Protohyenia* are without joints, and the branching is only weakly whorled, if at all. Hence, the distinctive features of the later articulates are lacking, and some investigators consider the inclusion of this genus in the Arthrophyta tentative. Mainly the similarity of *Protohyenia* to two other Middle Devonian genera, *Hyenia* and *Calamophyton,* has prompted the classification of *Protohyenia* with the articulates.

Hyenia. In many respects this plant is similar to *Protohyenia,* but it is somewhat more complicated (Fig. 20–1A). *Hyenia* has a definite rhizome, and numerous upright branches extend from the upper surface. Roots extend downward on the opposite side in at least one species. The upright shoots bear lateral branches, both sterile and fertile. The sterile branches fork dichotomously several times and terminate in narrow tips that point outward. The fertile appendages are also branched dichotomously and bear sporangia on tips bent in toward the axis. *Hyenia* lacks a jointed stem but shows a closer affiliation with other articulates in having whorled leaves and sporangia.

Calamophyton. Some extremely fine compressions of this plant have been discovered and have yielded excellent reconstructions (Fig. 20–2). The stem consists of a main axis with lower branches forming at one point in a digitate manner. Successive branchings occur dichotomously or monopodially. Some parts of the main stem bear transverse bands. Although these bands superficially resemble joints or nodes, they do not bear whorls of branches or leaves as do the joints of other orders of articulates, and hence they are not generally credited as being true nodes.

Both sterile and fertile appendages are borne laterally on the stem. The sterile appendages reach up to 10 mm in length and branch two to four times dichotomously. Each branch terminates in notched, somewhat flattened lobes; these are generally believed to be homologous with leaves (Fig. 20–3). Each fertile branch is divided into an upper and a lower branch (Fig. 20–4). In turn, each of these bears three side branches, and each side branch terminates in two sporangia. Thus, 12 sporangia could occur on every fertile appendage that has a full complement.

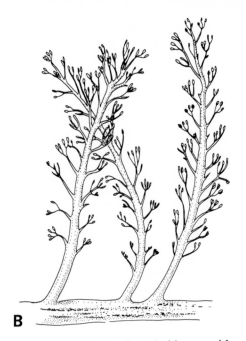

A   B

FIGURE 20–1   Early articulates. A, *Hyenia,* showing section of rhizome with three aerial branches bearing fertile appendages, ×0.5; note rhizoids, rhizome, and aerial stems bearing (at right) sterile and (at left) fertile appendages. B, *Protohyenia* from early Devonian of Russia, ×0.4. (A, photograph courtesy S. Leclercq, after Leclercq with permission of Royal Belgium Academy; B, after Ananiev.)

Except for a different arrangement of the stem and branching, *Calamophyton* is very similar to *Hyenia.* Both plants have sterile and fertile appendages in whorls and possess terminal sporangia. Although there is no clear-cut jointing of the stems, these two genera and *Protohyenia* are generally believed to be among the earliest and most primitive of the articulates. Just how they may have evolved into the later representatives is not known, but continued searching in Devonian and early Carboniferous rocks will undoubtedly enhance our knowledge of the origins of the remaining four orders.

ORDER PSEUDOBORNIALES.   This order is represented by a single genus and species, *Pseudobornia ursina.* It was discovered in Upper Devonian rocks of Bear Island in the Greenland Sea south of Spitzbergen.

Pseudobornia consists of a stem that ranges in diameter up to 10 cm and has distinct nodes at regular intervals (Fig. 20–5). The leaves, usually four in number, are arranged in whorls at the nodes. Each leaf branches dichotomously near the point of attachment and bears a number of small pinnate appendages and thus resembles a feather. Sporangia are borne on the lower surfaces of sporangiophores which resemble reduced leaves and which are grouped in a loose spike or strobilus. The sporangiophores are reported to contain spores. Nothing is known of the internal structure, and *Pseudobornia* is linked with the other articulates on the basis of the jointed stem and whorled appendages. It is not generally affiliated with any other order of the division, and probably represents a specialized offshoot that ended in late Devonian or early Carboniferous times.

ORDER SPHENOPHYLLALES.   This group of small herbaceous plants lived from the late Devonian to the early Triassic. The sphenophylls probably formed a considerable part of the undergrowth of forests during the Carboniferous, since they are found abundantly in rocks associated with some coal seams. From the

FIGURE 20–2   *Calamophyton* showing digitate branching of first order, dichotomous or monopodial branching of higher orders, and sterile and fertile appendages, ×1. (Photograph courtesy S. Leclercq, after Leclercq and Andrews with permission of Missouri Botanical Garden.)

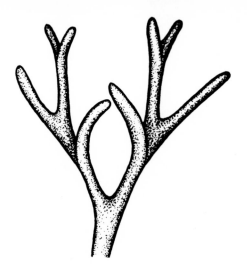

FIGURE 20–3   Sterile appendage of *Calamophyton* showing first dichotomy, and three secondary branches that develop on each primary, ×10. (After Leclercq and Andrews with permission of Missouri Botanical Garden.)

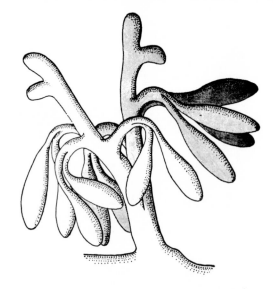

FIGURE 20–4   Fertile appendage of *Calamophyton* showing two orders of branching and six sporangia on each secondary branch. (After Leclercq and Andrews with permission of Missouri Botanical Garden.)

general habit, several paleobotanists have suggested that the sphenophylls were vine plants or trailers.

Sphenophyllum is the best-known genus of the group (Fig. 20–6). The stem is slender, with regularly spaced nodes and adventitious roots arising at intervals. The leaves vary in number from six to nine per whorl, and usually are not more than 2 cm in length. They are attached in whorls at the nodes. Each leaf is wedge-shaped, flat, and variously notched along the outer edge. Several veins arise from a single vein at the base of the leaf, then diverge and branch toward the outer edge of the leaf.

Young stems have a cortex and epidermis. Older stems have one to many layers of periderm which develop with the cortex. Internally, the stem presents an interesting and unique structure. The primary vascular tissue is an exarch protostele in the shape of a triangle, with three points of protoxylem (Fig. 20–7A). In older stems, secondary xylem is formed as a cylindrical zone surrounding the triangular primary xylem. In the secondary xylem, the tracheids opposite the protoxylem poles are smaller than the others. Both primary and secondary tracheids have several rows of bordered pits. Rays are conspicuous in the secondary xylem.

FIGURE   20–5   *Pseudobornia*, showing two nodes on stem, and radially disposed feather-like leaves, ×0.6. (After Nathorst.)

FIGURE 20–6   Several branches of *Sphenophyllum*, showing whorls of leaves at nodes, and two terminal strobili on branches to left, ×0.2. (After Smith with permission of McGraw-Hill Book Co.)

The reproductive units of *Sphenophyllum* are cones (Fig. 20–7C, D). They are thin, cylindrical, and borne at the tips of the stem. The cone consists of whorls of bracts fused to each other around the central stalk. Just above the bracts, whorls of sporangiophores emanate from the axis, and each bears a terminal sporangium. Both homosporous and heterosporous cones have been reported. The spores of homosporous species range from 75 to 125 microns, and consist of a central body surrounded by a wrinkled outer jacket, the **perispore.**

The jointed stems and whorled arrangement of leaves and cone bracts indicate that the sphenophylls belong to the arthrophyte division. However, they are distinct from the other orders of articulates in the structure of stem, leaf, and cone. The Sphenophyllales appear to have had a separate line of descent from their first appearance in the late Devonian, and probably arose from one of the early articulates in the Silurian or early Devonian. Following their maximum development during the Upper Carboniferous and Permian, they appear to have become extinct during the Triassic.

ORDER CALAMITALES.   The order Calamitales contains several genera of plants, ranging in geologic time from the late Devonian to the Triassic. The group reached a zenith in terms of size of plants and complexity of structure in the Upper Carboniferous. *Calamites,* the best-known genus, reached tree stature and represents in size in the Arthrophyta what *Lepidodendron* does in the *Lycopodophyta.*

As reconstructed from fossil remains of the different organs, *Calamites* consists of a large articulated stem that reaches up to 10 meters in length and 25 cm in diameter (Fig. 20–8A). Apparently the aerial parts were borne on rhizomes, much as in *Equisetum.* Characteristic features of the stem include well-defined nodes and vertical ribs that run the length of the internodes. Most of the fossilized stems are casts of the relatively large pith, and hence the ribs are actually imprints of the grooves of pith which lie between the protoxylem poles. However, a few specimens of petrified stems show remarkably well-preserved anatomical detail.

Both leaves and branches are borne at the nodes in whorls. The leaves, found mostly on smaller branches, vary from eight to 13 in a whorl and appear to be aligned more or less parallel to the long axis of the stem. The leaves vary from oval to lanceolate in shape and have a single vein. Because they are often found detached from the stem, the leaves are usually classified in separate genera—namely, *Annularia, Asterophyllites,* and *Lobatannularia* which differ from each other in details of morphology (Fig. 20–8B, C).

The anatomy of the stem of *Calamites* is distinctive. The vascular tissue consists of a cylinder of xylem surrounding a large central pith (Fig. 20–9A). The primary xylem occurs as regular bundles around the outside of the pith. Each bundle contains a hollow canal left behind by the disintegration of the **endarch** protoxylem (Fig. 20–9B). Secondary xylem, consisting of well-defined wood rays and tra-

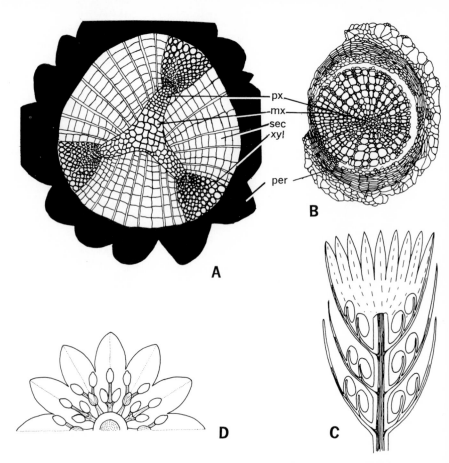

FIGURE 20–7   *Sphenophyllum*. A, transverse section of stem, showing three-armed exarch protostele, radial rows of secondary xylem and rays, and periderm, ×50; B, transverse section of root with primary xylem and periderm, ×40; C, median longitudinal section through cone, showing fused bracts and sporangiophores, ×10; D, plan view of one half of bract-whorl, showing position of sporangia on sporangiophores, ×10. *mx,* metaxylem; *per,* periderm; *px,* protoxylem; *sec xyl,* secondary xylem. (C, after D. H. Scott, *Studies in Fossil Botany,* Adam & Charles Black, Ltd., London; D, after Hirmer with permission of R. Oldenbourg.)

cheids with bordered pits, forms a cylinder outside the primary bundles.

Roots have been found attached to the stems and appear to be adventitious. They have no nodes and contain exarch protoxylem. Some appear to have arisen from lower nodes of the upright stem, and hence acted as prop roots.

The sporangia are grouped in cones. One of the most common genera of cones belonging to *Calamites* is *Calamostachys* (Fig. 20–10). The cones are elongate and cylindrical, measuring several centimeters in length and up to 1 cm in diameter. Each cone has whorls of sterile

bracts alternating with whorls of sporangiophores. The peltate sporangiophores are attached at right angles to the axis halfway between the whorls of bracts; each bears sporangia directed toward the axis.

The earliest genus of the Calamitales is *Asterocalamites,* known from the late Devonian and early Carboniferous. This was similar to *Calamites,* except that the ribs on the internodes did not alternate from one node to the next, and the cones generally lacked sterile bracts. Although *Asterocalamites* existed earlier than *Calamites,* it is not known whether

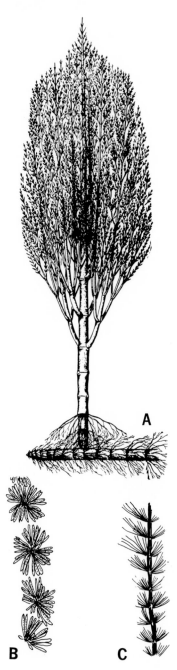

it was ancestral to *Calamites* or split off from the same stock during the early evolution of the Calamitales.

Good evidence relates *Calamites* fairly closely to the extant *Equisetum,* which will be described in the following paragraphs. The main features in common are: (1) jointed stems with whorls of leaves at the nodes, (2) canals in the protoxylem, and (3) the formation of sporangia on peltate sporangiophores. Points of difference include: large leaves, secondary xylem, and whorls of sterile bracts in the cones—all of which are present in *Calamites* but absent in *Equisetum*. Although the two genera are usually considered to be related, it is not known whether they arose from a common ancestral stock, or whether *Equisetum* is a direct and reduced descendant from *Calamites*.

ORDER EQUISETALES. This order is represented by the single extant genus *Equisetum*. The history of the order goes back to the late Carboniferous where plants very similar to the extant species are called *Equisetites*. This fossil genus, recorded through the Mesozoic and Cenozoic Eras, shows that little evolutionary change occurred during the long interval leading to the modern *Equisetum*.

In habit, a plant of *Equisetum* looks remarkably like a miniature *Calamites* of the Carboniferous. The sporophyte of *Equisetum* consists of deeply sunken rhizomes with aerial shoots (Fig. 20–11). Each upright stem consists of a central axis, with or without branches, depending on the species. If present, branches are arranged in whorls at regularly spaced nodes. Parallel ridges on the rhizomes, aerial shoots, and branches extend between the nodes; the ridges are formed by ribs of sclerenchyma underlying the epidermis.

The leaves, small and scale-like, are formed in whorls at the nodes (Fig. 20–12). The bases of the leaves are fused into a collar and completely encircle the stem just above the node. Each leaf has a single vein forming a midrib and bears stomata on the lower epidermis. The leaves are usually green when young, but become bleached and withered with

FIGURE 20–8   *Calamites.* A, reconstruction of plant showing rhizome, roots, jointed aerial stem, and side branches bearing leaves; B, leaf whorls of *Annularia,* foliage of *Calamites,* ×0.5; C, leaf whorls of *Asterophyllites* (also foliage of some species of *Calamites*), ×0.5. (A, after Hirmer with permission of R. Oldenbourg; B, C, after Andrews, copyright 1947 by Comstock Publishing Company, Inc., used by permission of Cornell University Press.)

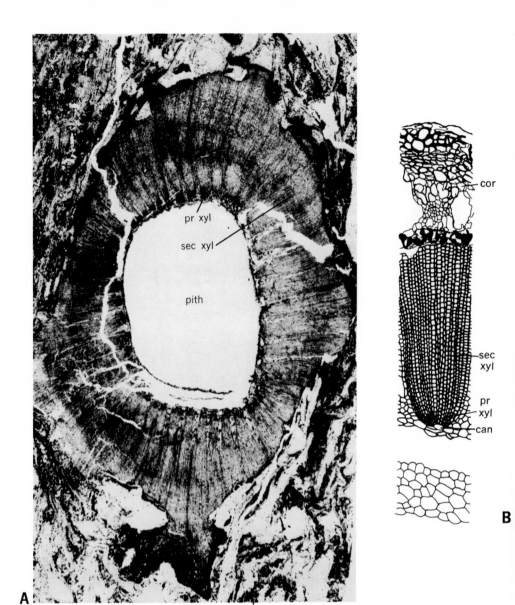

FIGURE 20–9   *Calamites*. A, photograph of transverse section of stem, showing pith, primary xylem (*pr xyl*), and secondary xylem (*sec xyl*),×1.6;B, part of stele showing pith, canal (*can*) in the protoxylem, radiating rows of secondary xylem, and cortex (*cor*), ×10.

age. Most of the photosynthetic function is performed in the stem.

The number of branches at a node is usually equal to the number of leaves. *Equisetum* is peculiar among vascular plants in having branches that break through the leaf sheath. The branches arise from branch primordia hidden by the base of the sheath that is fused to the stem.

Roots are produced at nodes on the rhizome. They are adventitious and arise from the lower surfaces of branch primordia. The root primordia show active development, but the branch primordia of rhizomes are relatively

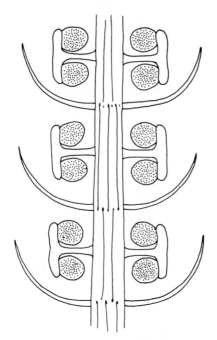

FIGURE 20–10 Longitudinal median section through *Calamostachys,* a cone of *Calamites,* showing sterile bracts alternating with sporangiophores, ×5. (After Arnold with permission of McGraw-Hill Book Co.)

The vascular tissue consists of bundles of primary xylem and phloem arranged in a ring on the periphery of the pith (Fig. 20–13B). Each bundle has protoxylem innermost with centrifugal metaxylem, and is hence endarch. Characteristically, most of the protoxylem cells break down to form a narrow longitudinal channel, the **carinal canal** (Fig. 20–14A). Usually, a few annular and helical tracheids of protoxylem remain intact on the periphery of the carinal canal. The metaxylem, with scalariform tracheids and reticulate and simple vessels, forms outside the carinal canal, usually in two lateral patches. Bounded by the carinal canal on the inside, and the two lateral islands of metaxylem on the outside, the phloem contains both sieve cells and phloem parenchyma. There is no development of secondary tissues. The individual vascular bundles fan out at the nodes to form a continuous ring of xylem and phloem called the **nodal ring.** The stele at the node has been variously interpreted as an **ectophloic siphonostele,** a **dictyostele** (see p. 410), or a medullated **protostele.**

A pericycle one cell thick lies immediately outside the phloem and is continuous around the stem. In some species an endodermis forms a band immediately outside of the pericycle. However, in others there are two endoderms —one inside and one outside the bundles. And in still other species, an endodermis surrounds each bundle.

Immediately outside the endodermis (Fig. 20–13B) is the cortex, composed of large thinwalled parenchyma with chloroplasts in the outermost layers. Throughout the cortical parenchyma are columns of sclerenchyma that provide most of the support for the stem. The columns opposite the vascular bundles are usually larger and form the prominent ridges on the outside of the stem. Smaller columns of sclerenchyma subtend the grooves between the ridges.

A distinctive feature of the cortex is the large and regularly spaced **vallecular canals** that contain air and alternate with the vascular bundles. Together with the carinal and central canals, they form air channels of the type found most commonly in aquatic plants.

dormant and only occasionally develop into aerial shoots. As the rhizome grows in length, new roots and aerial shoots form, and the colony grows. Because rhizomes are often a meter or more down in the soil and fragment easily, *Equisetum* is difficult to eradicate from gardens.

The sporangia are borne in cones at the tips of stems. In some species, cones are produced on vegetative shoots; in others, on separate fertile shoots. Although structurally similar to the vegetative axes, the fertile shoots are usually without branches or chlorophyll, and they wither soon after spore maturation.

The axis of *Equisetum* comprises epidermis, cortex, and stele (Fig. 20–13A). The cortex forms a moderately narrow cylinder, as do the vascular bundles of the stele. In most species of *Equisetum,* much of the diameter of rhizomes and aerial stems consists of a relatively large pith in the center of the axis. In larger parts of aerial stems, the pith breaks down to form a cavity called the **central canal.**

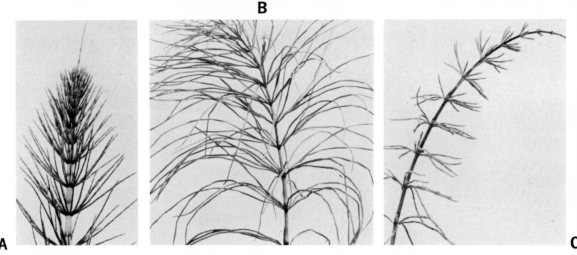

FIGURE 20–11　　Habit of *Equisetum,* ×0.5. A, *E. sylvaticum;* B, *E. telmateia;* C, *E. arvense.*

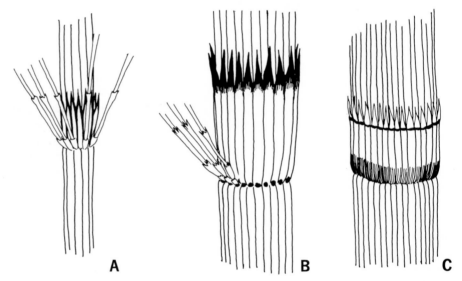

FIGURE 20–12　　Sections of stems of three species of *Equisetum,* showing leaf-whorls and branches, ×2. A, *E. telmateia;* B, *E. arvense;* C, *E. hiemale.*

The epidermis is one cell thick with the wall thickened noticeably on the outer tangential surface. Silicon heavily deposited on the wall surface gives a rough texture to the stem, and stomata are numerous in the grooves. Immediately above the guard cells lie subsidiary cells that apparently help reduce the stomatal opening during extremely dry conditions.

The leaf trace departs from a vascular bundle just below the nodal ring (Fig. 20–14B, C). It does not leave a leaf gap, and angles obliquely upward through the cortex and epidermis to form the midrib of the leaf. Each leaf trace consists of a very narrow strand of mes-

arch xylem and accompanying phloem. The branch traces alternate with leaf bases, and connect directly with the metaxylem of the nodal ring.

The cones consist of peltate sporangiophores arranged in whorls (Fig. 20–15A). The ends of the sporangiophores are flattened into five- or six-sided plates, and the stalk is attached to the center of the plate (Fig. 20–15B, C). The sporangia, arranged peripherally, are directed in toward the axis; they vary in number from five to ten per sporangiophore. The mature wall of the sporangium, only one cell thick, ruptures along a longitudinal slit to disperse the

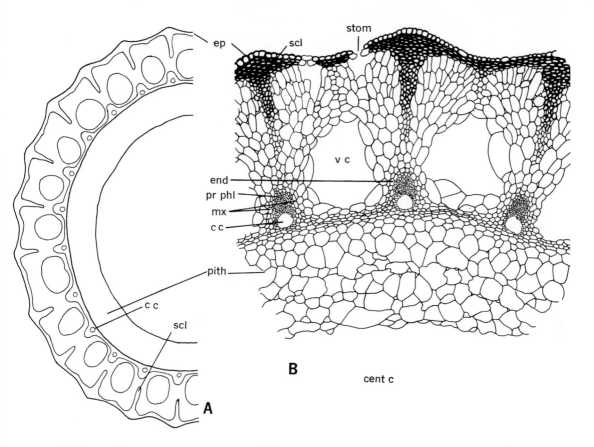

FIGURE 20–13   *Equisetum.* A, diagram of half a transverse section of stem, showing large central canal, carinal canals, vallecular canals, and bands of sclerenchyma, ×10; B, part of transverse section of
Equisetum stem showing details of tissues, ×80. *c c,* carinal canal; *cent c,* central canal; *end,* endodermis;
ep, epidermis; *mx,* metaxylem; *pr phl,* primary phloem; *scl,* sclerenchyma; *stom,* stoma; *v c,* vallecular
canal.

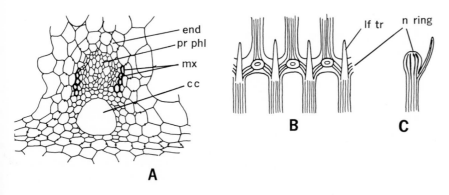

FIGURE 20–14   *Equisetum.* A, part of transverse section of stem in area immediately surrounding vascular bundle, showing endodermis (*end*), carinal canal
(*c c*), metaxylem (*mx*), and primary phloem (*pr phl*), ×250; B, C, drawings of
part of decorticated node, showing nodal ring of xylem (*n ring*) and leaf traces
(*lf tr*), ×30. (B, C, from *Anatomy of Woody Plants* by E. C. Jeffrey by permission of The University of Chicago Press, copyright 1917.)

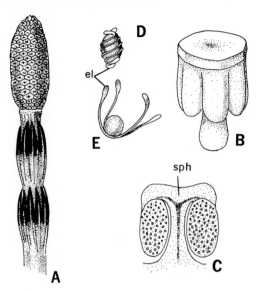

FIGURE 20–15 Reproductive organs of *Equisetum*. A, cone at tip of reproductive branch of *E. temateia*, ×1; B, single sporangiophore, showing axis, peltate disc, and recurrent sporangia, ×12; C, vertical section through single sporangiophore (*sph*), showing masses of spores inside two sporangia, ×15; D, E, views of spores with elaters (*el*) tightly curled about endospore in D, and elaters expanded in E, ×120. (After Haupt with permission of McGraw-Hill Book Co.)

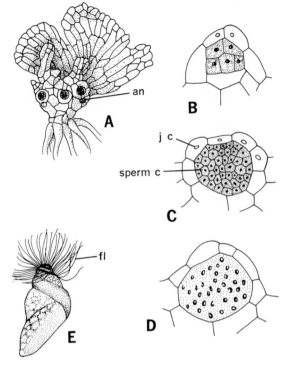

FIGURE 20–16 *Equisetum*. A, lateral view of prothallus, showing antheridia (*an*) toward base of lobes, ×25; B–D, stages of maturation of antheridia, showing jacket cells (*j c*) and spermatogenous cells (*sperm c*), ×200; E, single sperm with flagella (*fl*), ×1,250. (A, after Walker with permission of *Botanical Gazette;* B–D, after Smith with permission of McGraw-Hill Book Co.; E, after Sharp with permission of *Botanical Gazette*.)

spores. The unique spores of *Equisetum* are spherical, varying in diameter from about 30 to 45 microns. The mature spores also contain numerous chloroplasts. They consist of an inner layer, the **endospore,** and an outer **perispore** (Fig. 20–15D, E). The elaborate perispore comprises four strap-shaped bands, called **elaters,** which are **hygroscopic** and attached at one spot. When wet, the elaters are tightly coiled in a spiral around the endospore; on drying, they expand and straighten out, assisting in the separation and dispersal of spores from the sporangium.

Measurements of spores have shown the size to be bimodal, suggesting that *Equisetum* is heterosporous, although the size distinction is not as great as in heterosporous lycopods and ferns. Also, some spores yield unisexual prothalli bearing only antheridia, whereas others are bisexual; it is not known whether this represents early stages in the evolution of heterospory, or late stages in an evolutionary reversion to homospory from heterospory.

Spores are short-lived and germinate under suitable conditions to form prothalli that are small, green, and lobed (Fig. 20–16A). Rhizoids grow from cells on the lower (ventral) surface; sex organs are formed on the upper surface about one month following germination.

In bisexual prothalli, the archegonia form mainly on the upper surface of the cushion-like prothallus, which remains meristematic and produces upright lobes that are dark green and photosynthetic. The archegonia are similar to those of *Lycopodium* and *Selaginella*. The neck protrudes above the thallus and consists of four tiers of cells with usually three cells per tier (Fig. 20–17A). The neck contains one or two neck canal cells, and a ventral canal cell overlying a large egg in the venter.

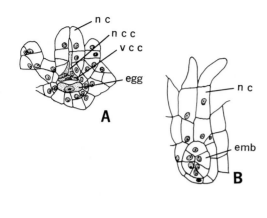

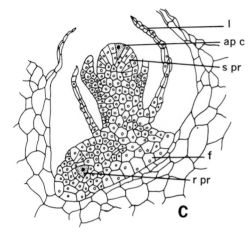

In most species, antheridia usually form later than the archegonia on the upper surface of bisexual prothalli. Antherida are similar to those of *Lycopodium,* with a jacket layer one cell thick and a central mass of spermatogenous cells (Fig. 20–16B–D). The latter develop into large, spirally twisted sperm that bear many flagella toward one end (Fig. 20–16E).

Following fertilization, the zygote divides to form four cells in a quadrant. The upper two cells develop into the stem and first leaves, the lower two into the foot and root (Fig. 20–17B, C). As in the lycopods, the embryonic root grows directly down through the prothallial tissue and into the soil. After the young stem emerges through the neck of the archegonium, secondary branches of the stem form, and one or several of these grow below the soil to become the rhizome.

Equisetum contains some 25 species. The genus is cosmopolitan except for Australia, with the most luxuriant species in the tropics. The plants grow well on acid soil, and are often prolific on railroad embankments, gravel bars, and sand dunes; other suitable habitats are swamps, lake margins, and moist woodlands. Although generally favored by moist climates and soils, *Equisetum* does tolerate somewhat xeric conditions, probably because of sunken stomata and a relatively deep growth of rhizomes and adventitious roots, often found 2 meters below the surface of the soil.

In earlier times, *Equisetum* was used for cleaning pots and pans, and assumed the name of "scouring rush." The abrasive action was derived from the deposits of silicon in the epidermis. These have also been known to cause intestinal inflammation and death in horses that browse large quantities in the spring.

FIGURE 20–17   *Equisetum.* A, vertical section through archegonium, showing neck cells (*n c*), neck canal cells (*n c c*), ventral canal cell (*v c c*), and egg, ×210; B, vertical section through archegonium, showing early stage of embryo (*emb*) in venter, ×210; C, late embryo showing stem primordium (*s pr*) with juvenile leaves (*l*) and large apical cell (*ap c*), foot (*f*), and root primordium (*r pr*), ×120. (A, after Jeffrey; B, after Sadebeck; C, after Smith with permission of McGraw-Hill Book Co.)

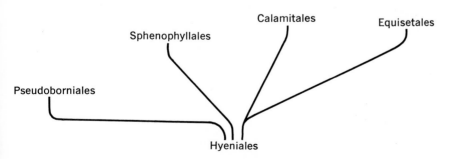

FIGURE 20–18   Probable phylogenetic relationships of orders of articulates.

PHYLOGENY OF ARTHROPHYTA

The most probable picture of relationships in the Arthrophyta is presented in Figure 20–18. Noteworthy are the separate lines leading to the Pseudoborniales and Sphenophyllales. These obviously special lines of evolutionary development ended without leaving recognizable descendants. The other line indicates a relationship between the Calamitales and Equisetales. However, there are no intermediate connecting links between any of the later orders and the early and primitive Hyeniales.

REFERENCES

Ananiev, A. R., "New Lower Devonian Fossil Plants from the Southeast of Western Siberia." *Akad. Nauk S.S.S.R.* (Botany), 42: 691–702 (1957).

Andrews, H. N., Jr., *Studies in Paleobotany.* New York: John Wiley & Sons, Inc. (1961). Pp. 256–288.

Arnold, C. A., "Petrified Cones of the Genus *Calamostachys* from the Carboniferous of Illinois." *Univ. Michigan Contrib. Mus. Paleont.,* 14: 149–165 (1958).

Barratt, K., "A Contribution to Our Knowledge of the Vascular System of the Genus *Equisetum.*" *Ann. Bot.,* 34: 201–235 (1920).

Bierhorst, D. W., "Vessels in *Equisetum.*" *Am. J. Bot.,* 45: 534–537 (1958).

Bierhorst, D. W., "Symmetry in *Equisetum.*" *Am. J. Bot.,* 46: 170–179 (1959).

Bold, H. C., *Morphology of Plants.* Harper & Row, Publishers (1957). Pp. 367–380.

Browne, I. M. P., "Anatomy of the Aerial Axes of *Equisetum kansanum.*" *Bot. Gaz.,* 101: 35–50 (1939).

Foster, A. S., and Gifford, E. M., *Comparative Morphology of Vascular Plants.* San Francisco: W. H. Freeman and Co. (1959). Pp. 191–219.

Golub, S. J., and Wetmore, R. H., "Studies of Development in the Vegetative Shoot of *Equisetum arvense* L., II: The Mature Shoot." *Am. J. Bot.,* 35: 767–781 (1948).

Hirmer, M., *Handbuch der Paläobotanik.* Munich and Berlin: R. Oldenburg (1927). Pp. 343–474.

Kräusel, R., and Weyland, H., "Pflanzenreste aus dem Devon, III: Über *Hyenia* Nath." *Seckenbergiana,* 14: 274–280 (1932).

Leclercq, S., and Andrews, H. N., Jr., "*Calamophyton bicephalum,* a New Species from the Middle Devonian of Belgium." *Ann. Missouri Bot. Gard.,* 47: 1–23 (1960).

Sporne, K. R., *The Morphology of Pteridophytes.* London: Hutchinson & Co. (Publishers) Ltd. (1962). Pp. 91–113.

21/DIVISION

PTEROPHYTA

This division of vascular plants encompasses the *ferns* and several plants of the Devonian referred to as *preferns*. The ferns are distinguished from most other plants by large, feathery leaves that in most cases unroll from the tip during growth, and the possession of sporangia on the undersurface of the leaf or occasionally on special fronds.

As a group, the *pterophytes* extend in time from the mid-Devonian to the present. They have formed conspicuous elements of all major floras from the Carboniferous to modern times, but they do not appear to have been predominant plants at any one time. Because of this, it has often been suggested that the pterophytes have not been very successful as a group. However, it appears that in terms of both numbers of species and numbers of individuals, they have remained relatively constant, and so have held their own from the early Mesozoic to the present.

The pterophytes are usually classified in eight orders. The preferns are Protopteridiales, Cladoxylales, and Coenopteridales. The ferns are Marattiales, Ophioglossales, Filicales, Marsileales, and Salviniales. Only the last five of these have extant genera and species. The Filicales contain by far the largest number of existing ferns, with 12 families, about 170 genera, and nearly 9,000 species.

GENERAL MORPHOLOGY
AND ANATOMY

All ferns consist of stems, roots, and leaves. In many, the stem is much reduced (Fig. 21–1A) or exists as a creeping rhizome;

409

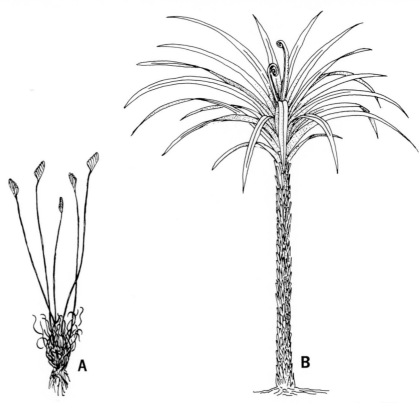

FIGURE 21–1   A, habit view of *Schizaea,* small fern showing fine filiform leaves and sporangia-bearing stalks, ×1; B, habit view of *Cyathea,* tree fern showing leaf bases attached to trunk, and crown of leaves at top, ×0.01. (B, after Hooker.)

in some tropical forms, it becomes columnar—the so-called "tree ferns" (Fig. 21–1B). The girth of tree ferns is due to a massive development of sclerenchyma, often accompanied by closely packed adventitious roots. The stem may be either superficial and creeping, or subterranean as a rhizome. With the exception of two genera, *Botrychium* and *Angiopteris,* the ferns consist solely of primary tissues. Leaves and roots are produced from nodes, usually in clumps.

In almost all ferns the leaves are the conspicuous organs, and in some species they are large, flat, and dissected into several or many lobes. In many instances, special terms are applied to the different parts of the leaves. The whole leaf is called a **frond,** which includes a central stalk called the **rachis.** In a compound frond the subdivisions are called **pinnae** (singular, **pinna**), and the ultimate division of a pinna is usually referred to as a **pinnule** (Fig. 21–2).

The venation of the pinnules in ferns is either "open" or "closed" (Fig. 21–3). In the open type, the vein endings terminate very close to the margin of the pinnule or submarginally within the mesophyll, and do not link up together to form a network. This is considered to be a primitive type of venation because it is found in most of the early fossil plants. In closed venation, the smaller veins join one another to form a reticulate pattern. This is considered to be a derived condition and is possessed by most of the angiosperms as well as some ferns.

The ferns show considerable variety of internal structure (Fig. 21–4). The stele may be a protostele (*Lygodium*), a siphonostele (*Schizaea*), or a dictyostele (*Mohria*). A dictyostele is considered to be a modified siphonostele in which the ring of xylem and phloem is broken into distinct units or bundles termed **meristeles.** The three genera listed are all mem-

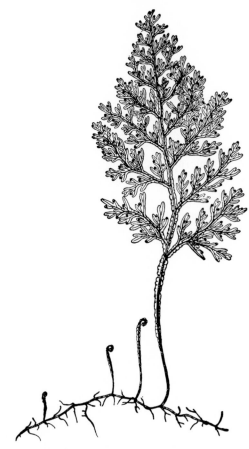

FIGURE 21–2   Habit view of filmy fern *Hymenophyllum*, showing roots on rhizome, circinate leaves, and mature frond with sporangia at tips of pinnules, ×0.5. (After Smith with permission of McGraw-Hill Book Co.)

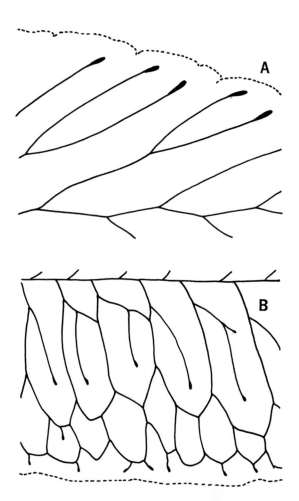

FIGURE 21–3   Fern venation. A, part of cleared pinnule of *Microlepia*, showing open venation, ×20; B, part of cleared pinna of *Polypodium*, showing net or reticulate venation, ×20.

bers of the family Schizaeaceae (Filicales), and illustrate how different types of stele occur in one group of closely related ferns.

The primary xylem is nearly always mesarch, but in a few genera it is either exarch or endarch. The xylem consists mainly of scalariform tracheids. In at least two genera (*Pteridium* and *Marsilea*), there are true vessels, with perforated end plates between the vessel members. The phloem usually forms a solid ring outside the xylem **(ectophloic),** but it is known to occur as a ring on both sides of the xylem **(amphiphloic).** In ferns with dictyosteles, the phloem forms either a solid cylinder around the outside of all the bundles, or forms a ring around the xylem of each bundle. Leaf traces are large and conspicuous, often forming shapes such as a C or a U. The traces leave large gaps in the vascular cylinder, except in species with protosteles.

In some ferns with larger stems, such as the tree ferns, the vascular supply is increased through the development of accessory bundles both outside and inside the vascular cylinder. In some ferns, this accessory development goes so far as to form another cylinder outside or inside the primary one. Thus, a cross section of a thick or columnar fern stem will show a ground mass of parenchyma and sclerenchyma surrounding vascular strands (Fig. 21–51, p. 447).

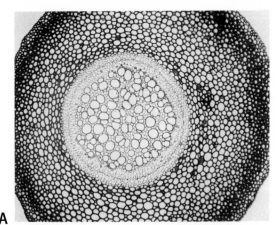

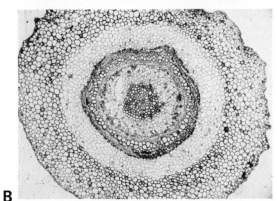

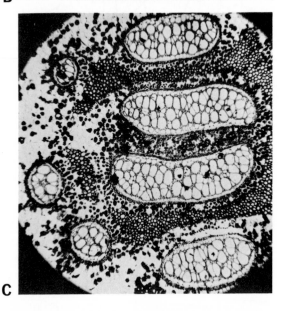

FIGURE 21–4   Fern steles. A, transverse section of *Gleichenia* stem, showing protostele, cortex, and epidermis, ×3; B, solenostele of stem of *Dicksonia,* ×3; C, dictyostele of rhizome of *Pteridium,* ×8.

Internally, the leaves of ferns contain mesophyll, which in some species is differentiated into palisade and spongy parenchyma (Fig. 21–5A). Intercellular air spaces are numerous, and vary in size with species. The veins are variously branched, with adaxial xylem and abaxial phloem, and are often surrounded by bands of sclerenchyma. The epidermis is lightly cutinized. Virtually all of the epidermal cells contain chloroplasts, including the guard cells. The stomata are usually confined to the lower surface.

REPRODUCTION

In extant ferns, the reproductive structures either consist of individual sporangia or **synangia** (fused sporangia). Sporangia may either occur singly or clustered into **sori** (singular, **sorus**). In some genera the sori are covered by an outgrowth of the leaf tissue, the **indusium,** or they may be naked (Fig. 21–5B–F). Sporangia and synangia usually occur on the abaxial surface of the pinnules, but they are marginal in some ferns, and in a few genera they are borne on specialized stalks believed to be much-reduced fronds. Sporangia are never on sporangiophores, as in the articulates, or on the adaxial surface as in lycopods.

Most ferns are homosporous, but some fossil representatives and the extant genera of the water ferns (Marsileales and Salviniales) are heterosporous. The spores of homosporous genera range in size from about 15 to 90 microns and have extremely varied patterns of ornamentation. Both trilete and monolete spores occur, with trilete predominating.

The two ontogenetic types of sporangial development in the ferns are **eusporangiate** and **leptosporangiate** (Fig. 21–6). In eusporangiate development, the sporangium arises from one or several superficial initials on the abaxial surface of the lamina. Following periclinal divisions of the initials, the inner derivatives form the sporogenous cells, and the outer cells form the sporangial wall. At maturity, the sporangium is relatively large, has a wall of several layers, and contains a large number of spores. In leptosporangiate development, the sporan-

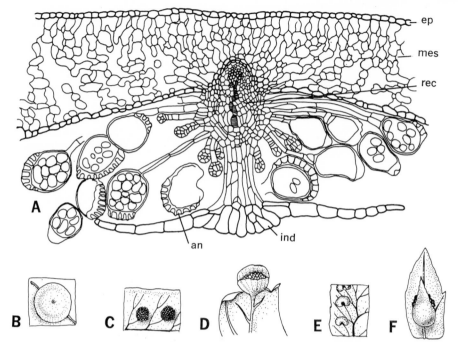

FIGURE 21–5   Fern sori. A, vertical section through fern sorus, showing receptacle (*rec*) containing scalariform tracheids, indusium (*ind*) emanating from receptacle, and stalked sporangia with annuli (*an*); mesophyll (*mes*) and epidermis (*ep*) of leaf are shown above, ×25. B–F, sori from different species, showing various shapes of indusia, ×10. C, exindusiate sori, ×10.

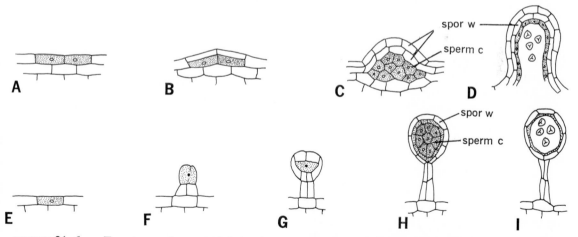

FIGURE 21–6   Two types of sporangial development. A–D, eusporangiate development, with several wall layers (*spor w*) surrounding spermatogenous cells (*sperm c*), ×120; E–I, leptosporangiate development in which outer initials form both wall and spermatogenous tissues on stalk, ×120.

gium originates from a single superficial initial on the lamina. This divides periclinally, but both the sporogenous and the wall cells are formed by the outer daughter cell. At maturity, the sporangium is small, has a single-layered wall, and contains a small number of spores. Ferns are often classified by the type of sporangial development: the Filicales, Marsileales, and Salviniales are leptosporangiate; the other orders are eusporangiate.

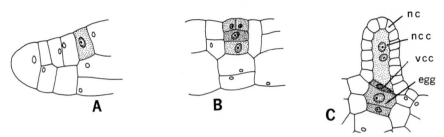

A   B   C

FIGURE 21–7   Archegonial development in ferns. A, single archegonial initial in wall of prothallus, ×250; B, several archegonial derivatives, ×250; C, mature archegonium with neck cells (*n c*), neck canal cells (*n c c*), ventral canal cell (*v c c*), and egg. (After Stokey with permission of *Botanical Gazette*.)

Fern gametophytes consist of a prothallus that produces gametangia and sex cells. Gametophyte development is exosporal. In some ferns, the prothallus is massive and several to many cells thick. In others, it may be heart-shaped and only one cell thick. Activity of one or more apical cells causes growth of prothalli.

The prothalli of homosporous ferns are generally bisexual, but as a rule the antheridia mature before the archegonia, reducing the likelihood of self-fertilization. The archegonia are flask-shaped, with the venter sunken in the tissue of the prothallus (Fig. 21–7). The protruding neck consists of several to many tiers of cells. As a rule there is one binucleate neck canal cell, a ventral canal cell, and a large egg in the venter. The archegonia are thus very similar to those of *Equisetum* and the extant lycopods.

Antheridia are globose structures either sunken into or projecting from the prothallus (Fig. 21–8). Recent investigations have shown that a substance called the antheridial factor seems to initiate antheridia in young prothalli by removing a factor inhibiting antheridial formation. Antheridia consist of an outside layer of sterile wall cells with a cap cell at the top that opens to release sperm. The sperm are large, spirally coiled, and multiflagellate. In many ferns, sperm apparently move toward an archegonium because they are chemically attracted by malic acid or other substances secreted from the archegonium.

As usual, fertilization results in the development of an embryo (Fig. 21–9A). At an advanced stage, the embryo consists of the primordia of root, stem, and a leaf, together with a

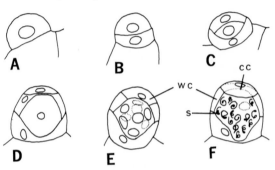

A   B   C

D   E   F

FIGURE 21–8   Antheridial development in ferns. Wall cells (*w c*) are beginning to form in C, and both cap cell (*c c*) and sperm (*s*) have differentiated in F, ×420. (After Davie with permission of *American Journal of Botany*.)

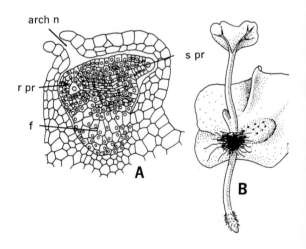

A   B

FIGURE 21–9   Embryo of ferns. A, embryo within confines of archegonial venter, showing foot (*f*), root primordium (*r pr*), stem primordium (*s pr*), and archegonial neck (*arch n*), ×100; B, young fern sporophyte with root, stem, and first leaf (still attached to prothallus), ×2. (A, after Haupt with permission of McGraw-Hill Book Co.; B, after Campbell.)

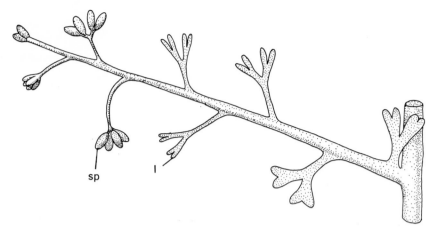

FIGURE 21-10   Side branch of *Protopteridium* with sterile leaflike appendages (*l*), and sporangia at tips of stalks (*sp*), ×3. (After Halle with permission
of *Paleontologica Sinica*.)

conspicuous foot that serves as an haustorial
organ transmitting food materials from the prothallus to the embryo. A suspensor develops in
only a few genera. Soon after the young sporophyte becomes established in the soil, the prothallus and primary root shrivel and die (Fig.
21-9B). The root function is taken over by the
development of adventitious roots that arise in
the pericycle of the young stem.

PREFERNS

ORDER PROTOPTERIDIALES.   The six genera of plants in this order may not be closely
interrelated, but they exhibit primitive fern-like
characteristics. The plants are from the Middle
and Upper Devonian. Some believe that the
genera of the Protopteridiales are stocks from
which later groups of ferns evolved, although
the exact relationships are obscure. Most of
these preferns possess characteristics similar or
identical to those of the psilophytes, and therefore some investigators believe the preferns are
more closely related to the Psilophyta than to
the Pterophyta.

The plants in Protopteridiales are generally fern-like in habit but show little differentiation into stems and leaves. In most plants, the
ends of the appendages are somewhat flattened
and expanded into pinnule-like laminae, but
they are not broad as in a true frond. The

sporangia are all terminal and usually grouped
in clusters. They lack a special dehiscent layer,
the **annulus,** and are all believed to have shed
their spores through an apical pore or fissure.

The classical genus *Protopteridium* has
been found in eastern North America, Europe,
and China (Fig. 21-10). The stem has a sympodial type of branching with terminal
branches divided dichotomously. The lateral
branches support flattened appendages that resemble a very simple frond. Some of the appendages, particularly toward the ends of the
branches, bear oval sporangia on their tips.
Nothing is known of the internal structure of
the axis or appendages.

Another genus of the Protopteridiales is
Svalbardia from the Devonian of Spitzbergen,
Germany, and Canada (Fig. 21-11). As reconstructed from numerous fragmentary specimens, it consists of a monopodial axis some
2 meters long. The side branches are almost
opposite each other. The sterile branches divide
dichotomously to form terminal appendages
that are either slightly expanded, or merely
unexpanded ends of the branches. These appendages, considered to be the leaf-laminae,
apparently have a single vein.

Some of the primary side branches have
lateral secondary branches that develop sporangia along the leading edge. The sporangia are
about 2 cm long, oval to circular, and are borne
on short stalks.

Another genus, *Aneurophyton,* is noteworthy because it has well-developed secondary wood, and apparently reached shrub or small tree dimensions (Fig. 21–12A, B). The branching is monopodial as in *Svalbardia,* with the side branches supporting rows of dichotomously divided structures interpreted as fronds. Sporangia borne in clusters on the tips of branches resemble modified leaves. In the stem, the solid protostele is three-rayed (triarch) and is completely surrounded by secondary xylem. Some of the smaller specimens have a cortex with scattered strands of sclerenchyma.

The remaining genera, which show similar development of very rudimentary pinnule-like structures and terminal sporangia, provide support for the general belief that the Protopteridiales represent the early ancestral stock of the ferns. Whether these preferns were actually derived from the Psilophyta or evolved from an earlier stock is an unsolved problem being actively pursued by paleobotanists who search for Silurian and Devonian fossils.

ORDER CLADOXYLALES. This order of preferns ranges from the Middle Devonian through the Carboniferous. Some plants of the order occur as early in geologic time as the Protopteridiales, but some noteworthy differences in the Cladoxylales suggest that they represent a specialized line of descent which ended during the late Carboniferous. In fact, some evidence suggests that the Cladoxylales may not be related to the pterophytes at all, but may represent a completely different evolutionary line.

The best known of several genera is *Pseudosporochnus* from the Middle Devonian (Fig. 21–13). As reconstructed, the plant appears to have the habit of a small tree with many branches. The main stem or trunk reaches a length of at least 25 cm and a diameter of 3 cm, bears roots at the bottom, and forms a crown of first-order branches at the top. The first branches rebranch into crowns of second-order branches, which in turn branch dichotomously into terminal branches (Fig. 21–13D). The last two orders of branches support delicate, spirally arranged fronds. Each frond consists of thin, flattened appendages that divide

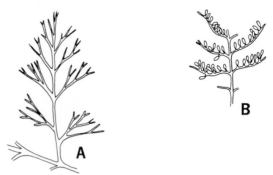

FIGURE 21–11   *Svalbardia.* A, sterile branch with dichotomizing appendages that probably functioned as leaves, ×0.5; B, fertile branch with sporangia attached to leading edge of appendages, ×0.5. (From Andrews with permission of John Wiley & Sons, Inc.)

dichotomously several times. Some fronds are entirely sterile, whereas others bear both sterile and fertile parts. In fertile segments, oval and sessile sporangia are borne in pairs at the tips of the appendages. Nothing is known about the spores.

The arrangement of vascular tissue is unique, but appears to be similar to that in other genera of Cladoxylales (Fig. 21–13B, C). The xylem of the branches consists of 16 to 21 columns, which are linear, U-, or V-shaped in cross section. The protoxylem is located slightly toward the outside of each column, and development is mesarch. Most tracheids have scalariform thickenings. Apparently, the columns of xylem anastomose to varying degrees throughout the length of the axis. Very similar patterns of xylem arrangement are found in *Cladoxylon,* another Devonian and Carboniferous genus.

The tissue surrounding the xylem columns is parenchyma, with circular to elliptical nests of **sclereids** forming a circle outside the arms of xylem. The cortex appears to be parenchymatous. Epidermal details are lacking.

The exact relationships of the Cladoxylales to other groups are problematical. Most investigators regard the order as a specialized line of ferns, but others consider it as a group ancestral to the seed plants through the pteridosperms (see Chapter 22). One view is that the Cladoxylales is an order of early fern-like plants distinct from the Protopteridiales. An important difference is that the Protopteri-

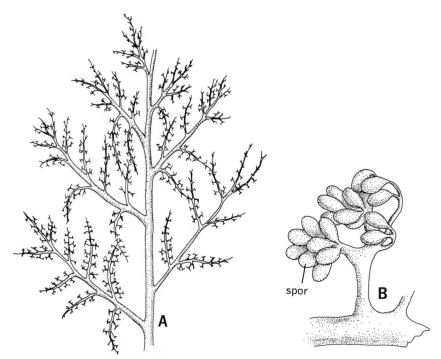

FIGURE 21–12   *Aneurophyton.* A, several branches on axis, each with terminal bifurcating appendages that probably served as leaves, ×0.5; B, single fertile stalk with sporangia (*spor*), ×20. (After Kräusel and Weyland with permission of *Senckenbergiana.*)

diales have sporangia in clusters on special appendages. Unfortunately, nothing is known of the internal structure of the genera of Protopteridiales, and so a direct comparison cannot be made with the Cladoxylales in this respect.

ORDER COENOPTERIDALES.   The plants of this order are known chiefly from investigations of petrified remains ranging from the late Devonian to the Permian. Many of the features of the coenopterids are primitive, and very likely many of the plants of this order are the same that are classified as Protopteridiales when found as compressions.

Four families are generally recognized. All have protostelic stems, frond-like appendages that branch in three dimensions, and sporangia borne terminally on fertile appendages.

Botryopteris, one of the best-known genera, is found from the early Carboniferous to the Permian—often petrified in coal balls (Fig. 21–14). The stem is slender, branched,

and only a few millimeters in diameter. It has a cylindrical mesarch protostele, in which phloem completely surrounds the xylem. No secondary tissues are known. The fronds are arranged spirally, and in one species at least have flattened pinnules on pinnae. The petioles of *Botryopteris* are quite characteristic, having the xylem in the shape of the Greek letter omega—ω (Fig. 21–15A–C). The sporangia are borne in clusters of several thousand on stalks having the same ω-shaped xylem trace. The homosporous sporangia are terminal on short **pedicels.**

In some of the genera in other families of the order, the much-modified vascular strands of petioles form shapes such as two opposed anchors, a cross, or a dumbbell.

The Coenopteridales are generally fernlike because they possess mesarch protosteles, fronds, and sporangia with annuli. Some students have suggested that this group is ancestral to more modern fern groups; others consider the Coenopteridales a specialized group that

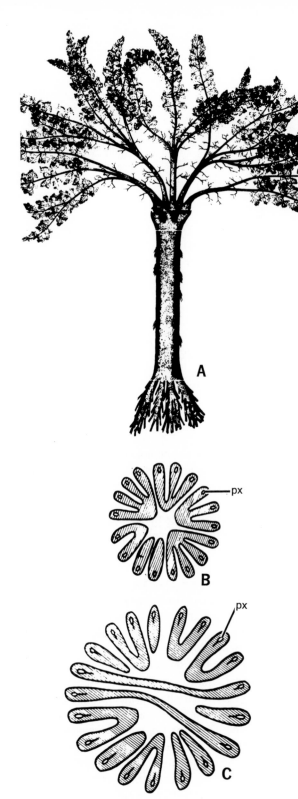

FIGURE 21–13 *Pseudosporochnus.* A, reconstruction of whole plant, showing roots, columnar stem, digitate first-order branches, and leafy appendages; B, C, two patterns of vascular bundles as found in a third-order branch B, and a first-order branch C, showing the location of protoxylem (*px*); D, stem and digitate branching, ×0.75. (Photograph courtesy S. Leclercq after Leclercq and Banks with permission of *Palaeontographica.*)

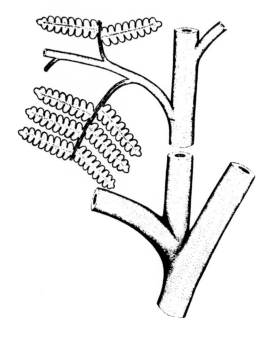

FIGURE 21–14   Reconstruction of petiole and pinnae of *Botryopteris* (note characteristic ω-shaped vascular bundle in petiole), ×4. (After Delevoryas and Morgan with permission of *American Midland Naturalist*.)

ended in the Permian. Although they are often suggested as descendants of the Psilophyta. The coenopterids had clearly evolved fern-like structures and hence appear to be more closely allied with the Pterophyta. Whether the coenopterids—and indeed the other primitive preferns—evolved directly from the psilophytes or from an earlier stock is presently unknown. However, the problem is exciting and important and awaits further discoveries.

TRUE FERNS

ORDER MARATTIALES.   This order, with both extant and fossil genera, extends from the middle Carboniferous to the present. As far as can be ascertained, the early representatives have structures very similar to some extant genera, indicating a direct line of descent since Carboniferous times.

In the seven extant genera only one genus, *Marattia,* is distributed in both hemispheres

TABLE 21–1

GEOGRAPHICAL DISTRIBUTION OF THE EXTANT GENERA OF MARATTIALES

GENUS	DISTRIBUTION
Angiopteris	Madagascar; Indo-Malaysia
Archangiopteris	Southwestern China; Formosa
Christensenia	Philippines
Danaea	Americas
Macroglossum	Borneo
Marattia	Widespread in tropics; New Zealand
Protomarattia	Tonquin

(Table 21–1). Most genera are found in the wetter tropics, particularly in the East Indian islands and adjacent mainland regions.

General Morphology and Anatomy.   The stems of most marattiaceous ferns are short, stout, and erect—although at least one fossil attained the stature of a tree fern, and one modern genus has a creeping stem (Fig. 21–16). Branching does not occur except in some species of a single modern genus, and leaf bases are persistent except in one fossil genus.

The fronds are usually very large, oval, and once or several times pinnate, except for one genus (*Christensenia*) with a frond palmately divided into five lobes. Venation is dichotomous and open in six of the genera, and reticulate in the other (*Christensenia*—Fig. 21–17). As in the Ophioglossales among the ferns, two fleshy stipules occur at the base of the frond petiole.

The root system generally consists of a series of adventitious roots, with one root emerging from the base of each frond. The roots, thick and fleshy, branch several times. The vascular tissue is usually an actinostele, with several to many protoxylem points.

Reproduction.   Sporangia are borne in sori on the abaxial surface of the pinnules. The sori are usually arranged in two rows on the pinnule, often superimposed over a vein. They

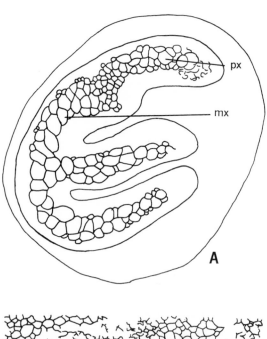

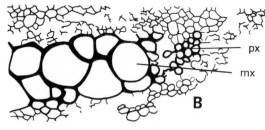

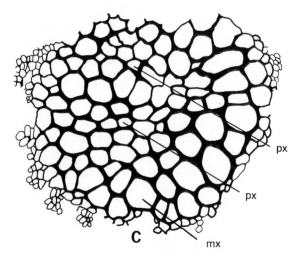

FIGURE 21–15   *Botryopteris*. A, transverse section of vascular bundle from petiole, showing positions of protoxylem (*px*) and metaxylem (*mx*), ×8; B, enlarged view of tip of one arm of vascular bundle, showing small cells of protoxylem and larger cells of metaxylem, ×15; C, vascular bundle of stem, showing mesarch protoxylem, ×7.

lack indusia. The sessile sporangia are large and eusporangiate in origin, and are either free or fused into synangia (Fig. 21–18). Dehiscence of sporangia occurs by a slit or a terminal pore. All of the Marattiales are homosporous and display a wide variety of spore shapes and ornamentation. Each sporangium produces from 1,500 to 7,000 spores.

The gametophytes of marattiaceous ferns are relatively large, consisting of a flat green prothallus often irregular in shape and containing an endophytic fungus. The prothalli grow on the surface of the soil and are anchored by rhizoids. The antheridia occur on both surfaces, are large and sunken (Fig. 21–19A), and produce up to several hundred coiled sperm with many flagella. Archegonia are also sunken, with two to three tiers of neck cells, one large neck canal cell, and (except in one genus) a large ventral canal cell overlying the egg (Fig. 21–19B).

The first division of the fertilized egg is transverse. Successive divisions form a massive embryo with a weakly developed foot but with no distinct primordia for leaf, shoot, and root. A suspensor forms only in certain genera, and even then not regularly in all individuals. The long axis of the embryo is parallel to the long axis of the archegonium, and the stem and leaf primordia grow through the prothallus before emerging (Fig. 21–19C).

The anatomy of the stem in Marattiales is very complex. The cortex is parenchymatous and contains numerous mucilaginous canals. In young stems the vascular tissue first develops as a protostele. Later it differentiates into an amphiphloic siphonostele, and in species with large stems it eventually develops into a dictyostele (Fig. 21–20A) made up of large overlapping leaf gaps and anastomosing vascular bundles. These bundles are often formed in concentric rings with **amphicribral** mesarch or endarch xylem (Fig. 21–20B). The tracheids have scalariform pitting as do those of the next order, the Filicales. The only report of secondary growth is a slight amount of secondary xylem in the extant genus *Angiopteris*.

Fossil Genera. Remains of plants believed to be marattiaceous have been found in

FIGURE 21–16   *Angiopteris*. Habit view (left) showing rootstock and fronds, and (right) detailed section of pinnule with venation. (After Bitter in Engler, *Die natürlichen Pflanzenfamilien*, Vol. 1, Pt. 4, p. 437, Fig. 240, 1902.)

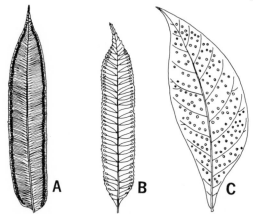

FIGURE 21–17   Pinnae of marattiaceous ferns showing outline, venation, and arrangement of sporangia. A, *Angiopteris*, ×0.5; B, *Marattia*, ×0.5; C, *Christensenia*, ×0.5. (After Bitter in Engler, *Die natürlichen Pflanzenfamilien*, Vol. 1, Pt. 4, p. 433, Fig. 238A, C, D, 1902.)

the Carboniferous, usually in rocks associated with coal seams. The fossils consist largely of petrified remains of stems, of petioles, and of fronds, and compressions of pinnules with sporangia and synangia attached.

The best-known genus showing vegetative structures is *Psaronius*. Judging from reconstructions based on petrified remains, this plant attained the stature of a tree fern, with a columnar tapering trunk and a crown of fronds at the top (Fig. 21–21). Close inspection has shown that the trunk consists of a central stem surrounded by a thick and compact region of adventitious roots. Toward the top, the true stem thickens and the cylinder of adventitious roots becomes thinner. It has been postulated that the main support for *Psaronius* was derived from this thick mantle of roots, as in many extant tree ferns such as *Cyathea*. Specimens of this latter genus reach a height approaching 20 meters, and the slender trunk is supported mainly by a thick layer of roots covering the lower portion of the stem (Fig. 21–1B, p. 410).

The vascular tissue of the stem of *Psaronius* consists of more or less concentric circles of amphiphloic xylem (Fig. 21–22). Only one or two circles develop in the base of the stem, but more appear at higher levels where the stem is wider. Similarly, there are only three rows of leaf traces in basal regions of the stem, but as many as 14 in upper regions (Fig. 21–22B).

The fronds believed to belong to *Psaronius* are large and twice-pinnate. The pinnules are usually attached by the whole width of the base, have parallel sides, and are rounded at the tips. Some fronds of this type have been found bearing sporangia and synangia very

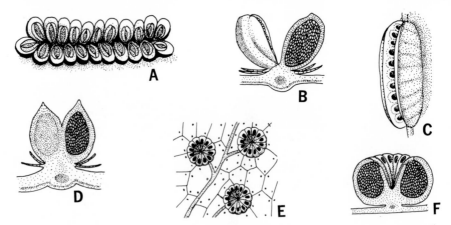

FIGURE 21–18   Different synangia and sporangia of marattiaceous ferns. A, B, *Angiopteris*, ×1; C, D, *Marattia*, ×1; E, F, *Christensenia*, ×1. (A–C, E, after Bitter in Engler, *Die natürlichen Pflanzenfamilien*, Vol. 1, Pt. 4, p. 434, Fig. 239A, B, E–H, 1902; D, F, after Hooker-Baker.)

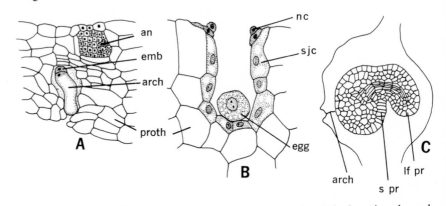

FIGURE 21–19   Sex organs in marattiaceous ferns. A, vertical section through prothallus (*proth*) showing immature antheridium (*an*) above, and two-celled embryo (*emb*) within archegonium (*arch*) below, ×250; B, vertical section through archegonium showing neck cells (*n c*), sterile jacket cells (*s j c*), and large egg, ×350; C, vertical section through embryo showing leaf (*lf pr*) and stem primordia (*s pr*), ×400. (A, after Land with permission of *Botanical Gazette;* B, after Haupt with permission of McGraw-Hill Book Co.; C, after Campbell with permission of Carnegie Institution of Washington.)

similar to those of the extant marratiaceous genera.

Phylogeny. On the basis of similarities in gross morphology, vascular anatomy, and reproductive structures, there are good grounds for referring Carboniferous and Mesozoic genera to the Marattiales. It appears that few structural changes have occurred in the order since the Carboniferous. Although nothing is known about the ancestors of the Marattiales, the fossil evidence suggests that marattiaceous ferns were relatively important and widespread elements of the flora of the Carboniferous. However, in more recent geological times the number of individuals may have declined—and possibly the number of species as well. This hypothesis finds support in the relatively narrow geographic and ecologic distribution of six of the seven existing genera, and the small number of species in three of the genera. Unfortunately, the fossil record of the Marattiales in the Mesozoic and Tertiary is meager, and it is not known when this apparent decline occurred or how extensive it may have been.

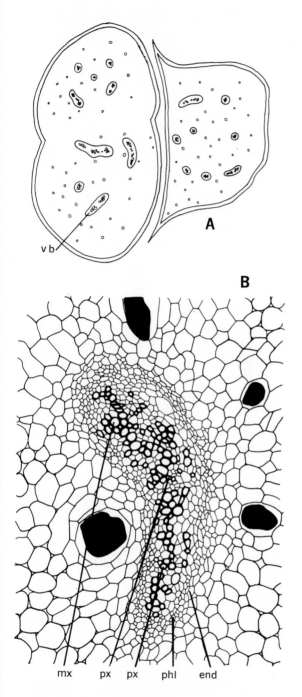

FIGURE 21–21 *Psaronius*. Reconstruction of plant showing tapering trunk and crown of fronds at top, ×0.02. (After Morgan with permission of the University of Illinois Press.)

FIGURE 21–20 *Marattia*. A, transverse section of stem and one frond showing dictyostelic arrangement of vascular bundles (*v b*), ×5; B, anatomy of one vascular bundle from stem in A, showing protoxylem (*px*) with small tracheids, metaxylem (*mx*), phloem (*phl*), and endodermis (*end*), ×40.

The extant genera of the Marattiales possess characteristics that have prompted some investigators to suggest a relationship with the Ophioglossales. The common characteristics include: eusporangiate development, presence of stipules, stomata on sporangial walls, similar antheridia and archegonia, and embryogeny.

An evolutionary series is sometimes erected for the reproductive structures of the Marattiales. The most generally accepted view is that the free-sporangial condition is more primitive than that of the synangium with fused sporangia. This concept is based on the fact that the early ferns and other early vascular plants all have free sporangia, and synangia could only have been derived through a fusion process from free-sporangial ancestors. However, both free and fused sporangia occur in the Carboniferous marattiaceous ferns, and there is no clue of evolutionary links with earlier ferns from the Devonian.

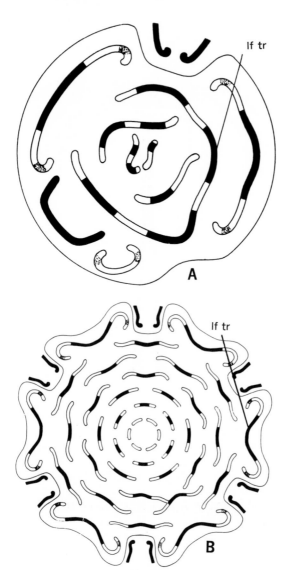

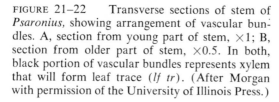

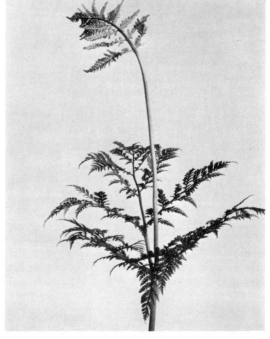

FIGURE 21–22   Transverse sections of stem of *Psaronius,* showing arrangement of vascular bundles. A, section from young part of stem, ×1; B, section from older part of stem, ×0.5. In both, black portion of vascular bundles represents xylem that will form leaf trace (*lf tr*). (After Morgan with permission of the University of Illinois Press.)

FIGURE 21–23   Habit photographs of ferns of the Ophioglossaceae. A, habit of *Ophioglossum,* showing leaf and fertile spike, ×0.8; B, *Botrychium* showing dissected pinnules and sporangial spike in center, ×0.3. (A, courtesy J. A. Herrick; B, courtesy Chicago Natural History Museum.)

ORDER OPHIOGLOSSALES. To date, there are no authentic records of fossil ferns of this group, and the order is represented entirely by three living genera. Two of these, *Botrychium* and *Ophioglossum,* are world-wide in distribution, and each comprises about 40 species. The third genus, *Helminthostachys,* has only a single species, and is restricted to parts of tropical Asia and Polynesia.

There is no early fossil history of the Ophioglossales, but the plants are usually considered primitive—based mainly on a comparison of the structures with those of other primitive groups, such as the Coenopteridales, the Marattiales, and some families of the Filicales. Some of the evidence for this will be presented following a survey of the three genera.

Habit and Morphology. The ferns of this order are all herbaceous perennials, and most —particularly in the tropics and subtropics— are evergreen. Both terrestrial and epiphytic species are known. The plants are small to moderately large—with several less than 8 cm in height, and others about 2 meters (Fig. 21–23).

The plants have short rhizomes that are either erect or creeping. Fronds, borne at intervals, may consist of a simple single blade or they may be variously divided. The three genera are distinct in the form of the frond: that of *Botrychium* is divided pinnately, that of *Helminthostachys* **ternately,** and that of *Ophioglossum* is a simple blade. Venation is reticulate in *Ophioglossum,* but dichotomous and open in the leaves of the other two genera. All the leaves have erect **vernation,** rather than the **circinate** type of other ferns.

The vascular tissue of the stem ranges from an ectophloic siphonostele in *Botrychium* and *Helminthostachys* to a dictyostele in *Ophioglossum* (Fig. 21–24, 25). The xylem is mesarch in *Helminthostachys,* and endarch in the other two genera. The pitting of the tracheids is reticulate in *Ophioglossum;* in the other two genera the pitting is bordered—the type characteristic of gymnosperm tracheids— not scalariform as in other ferns. Also of interest is the development in *Botrychium* of secondary xylem in radial tracheid rows inter-

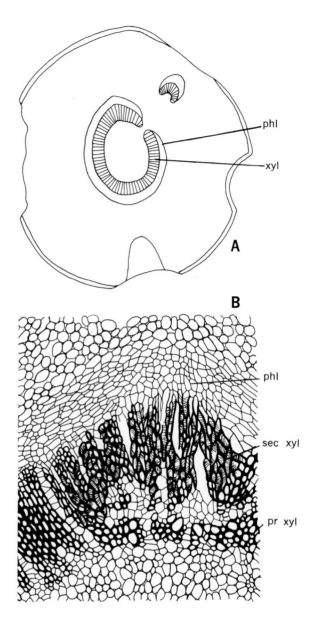

FIGURE 21–24   *Botrychium.* A, transverse section of stem showing xylem (*xyl*) surrounded by phloem (*phl*) in stele, and one leaf trace toward upper right, ×7; B, section of stele of *Botrychium* showing primary xylem (*pr xyl*), secondary xylem (*sec xyl*), and phloem, ×60.

spersed with rays one cell wide. The primary xylem occurs as small groups on the inner edge of the secondary xylem next to the pith (Fig. 21–24B). Leaf traces form large gaps in the stele. Each petiole usually receives one trace,

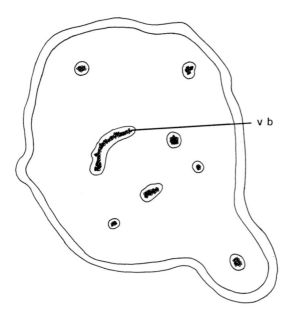

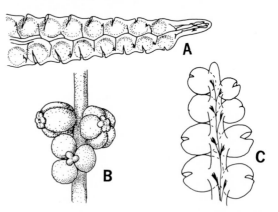

FIGURE 21-26   Sporangia of ophioglossaceous ferns. A, *Ophioglossum*, ×0.3; B, *Helmintho-stachys*, ×0.3; C, *Botrychium*, ×0.3. (A, after Goebel with permission of G. Fischer; C, after Eames with permission of McGraw-Hill Book Co.)

FIGURE 21-25   Transverse section of stem of *Ophioglossum*, showing dictyostelic arrangement of vascular bundles (*v b*), ×100. (Note bundle in lobe to lower right which would eventually emerge as trace either to leaf or to sporangial spike.)

but some species of *Ophioglossum* have two. The stems contain an endodermis just outside the vascular tissue, and in some species a second endodermal layer occurs on the inside as well. The cortex is thin-walled parenchyma without sclerenchyma strands or other supporting tissue.

Reproduction.   The sporangia in the three genera are borne on stalked spikes attached to the petiole near the base of the lamina. The spikes of *Botrychium* and *Helminthostachys* are branched, that of *Ophioglossum* unbranched. In the branched spikes, the sporangia are globular and arranged in two rows on the outside of the sterile tissue of the spike (Fig. 21-26B, C). In *Ophioglossum*, the sporangia are embedded in two lateral rows (Fig. 21-26A) and dehisce by a horizontal slit. These sporangia are thick-walled and eusporangiate, thus resembling those of the Marattiales, articulates, and lycopods.

The spores are trilete, variously ornamented, and all of one size. They are produced in large numbers (1,500–15,000). If conditions are suitable following dispersal, they germinate into prothalli. The prothalli are small, usually resembling a cylindrical tuber, but they may be flat or irregular in shape; they are usually pale yellow or brown, and bear varying numbers of rhizoids (Fig. 21-27A). Prothalli are subterranean or grow in the shelter of leaf bases of other plants; some are branched, and in some species the growth and branching continue for several years. All prothalli are infected with a mycorrhizal fungus that assists in supplying nutrient material from the humus.

The antheridia and archegonia are almost identical to those of the Marattiales, the articulates, and the lycopods (Fig. 21-27B, D). The sperm are coiled and multiflagellate as in the these groups (Fig. 21-27C).

The development of the embryo is similar to that in the marattiaceous ferns; some species have a suspensor, and others do not. Development of the embryo and the primordia of the main organs is slow, often taking a year or longer. The long axis of the embryo is parallel to the long axis of the archegonium, comparable to the Marattiales but different from the other orders of ferns.

Phylogeny and Structural Series.   The complete lack of fossil representatives prevents any conclusion about the origin or phylogenetic relationships of the Ophioglossales. Mainly because the sporangia are arranged laterally on a fertile spike, the suggestion has been made that the Ophioglossales could have been derived

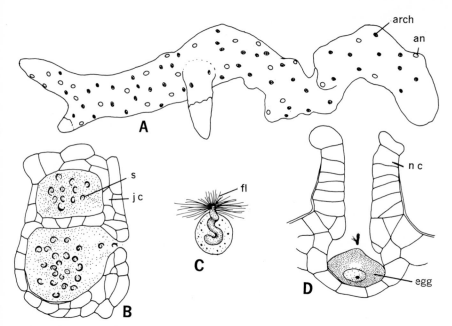

FIGURE 21–27   Sex organs of ophioglossaceous ferns. A, prothallus of *Ophioglossum,* showing positions of archegonia (*arch*) and antheridia (*an*), ×30; B, mature antheridia of *Botrychium* containing motile sperms (*s*) within jacket cells (*j c*), ×140; C, single sperm of *Ophioglossum* showing tuft of flagella (*fl*) at one end, ×1,000; D, vertical section through archegonium, showing neck cells (*n c*) and egg, ×300. (A, C, after Bruchmann; B, D, after Jeffrey.)

from an ancestral group of ferns such as the Coenopteridales. While this may well be true, the case for derivation is weak without fossil evidence.

When compared with other groups of vascular plants, it is evident that many of the structural features of the Ophioglossales are relatively primitive. The following are among the most significant features: eusporangiate development of sporangia (including large size), thick walls, large numbers of spores, and absence of any specialized structure for dehiscence; the stalked condition of sporangia in *Botrychium* and *Helminthostachys,* which indicates a terminal position; and vascular traces leading to the sporangia, a characteristic shared only with the Psilotales and the anthophytes.

There are two main explanations for the generally primitive condition of the Ophioglossales. Either they are truly primitive in the sense of having evolved very little from a primitive ancestral group, or they have experienced reduction from more complex ancestors. It is

also possible that some structural features are truly primitive, whereas others are derived. Thus, the large, thick-walled, and non-annulated sporangia are probably primitive. However, there is evidence that the fertile spike of *Botrychium* is the result of fusion of two adjacent frond-like appendages, which have presumably lost the leafy lamina through reduction. If this is so, the fertile spike of *Ophioglossum* also probably represents a more drastic reduction of fertile fronds, resulting in the two lateral rows of sporangia imbedded in sterile tissue.

ORDER FILICALES.   The ferns of this order are generally classified into some 14 or more families, with about 200 genera and some 8,000 species. They constitute the largest part of the total fern flora of the world, with their greatest development in the tropics.

The earliest record of the order is from the Carboniferous, where plants of two or three families have been discovered. All of the other families apparently evolved during the Mesozoic, and by mid-Mesozoic times, the Filicales constituted one of the major elements of the world's flora. Although several families are probably moving toward extinction, evolution of others is still progressing, and it appears probable that the order will retain a significant place among vascular plants for a considerable time.

The ferns of the Filicales differ from those of the other orders mainly in the structure and development of the sporangia. Whereas the Marattiales and Ophioglossales have large, thick-walled sporangia that develop in the eusporangiate manner, the sporangia of the Filicales and the Marsileales and Salviniales are small, thin-walled, and have leptosporangiate development. Some investigators consider that this distinction warrants dividing the Pterophyta into two classes: the Eusporangiopsida and the Leptosporangiopsida. However, a taxonomic distinction based only on this one characteristic tends to overshadow the other characteristics that distinguish the various orders of both eusporangiate and leptosporangiate ferns from each other. Furthermore, sporangial development in the Osmundaceae shows characteristics of both types, and hence this family cannot conveniently be grouped with either of the sporangial classes.

Habit. The habits of the ferns of this order are quite diverse. Some are very small with moss-like fronds; others are moderate in size and herbaceous; still others attain the stature of shrubs and trees. Both terrestrial and epiphytic habits are common. Some are climbers, others creepers, and many form relatively dense thickets or carpets on the forest floor or in fields.

Most ferns inhabit wet regions, but some are **mesophytic,** and a few exist in extremely dry sites. In the warmer latitudes most of the ferns are evergreen, whereas in colder regions the fronds die back in the winter months. However, most are perennial and the rhizome remains alive during adverse climatic conditions.

Stems. The stems of filicalean ferns are variable, but three main types are found. Some stems are quite short, and either erect or horizontal; this is usually called a **rootstock.** The most common ferns have long slender rhizomes, usually creeping, and branched or unbranched. The third type of stem, that of the tree fern, ranges from short and stocky to tall and columnar. Branching is weakly developed, but is usually dichotomous. Most rhizomes are covered by a thick mat of hairs or scales, that covers the growing points but often fall off from older regions. The scales are usually flat and elongated, and in many cases are diagnostic for species.

The stems of Filicales possess well-defined epidermis, cortex, and stele. The cortex almost always contains one or more bands of sclerenchyma interspersed in the cortical parenchyma. An endodermis is usually present on the inner surface of the cortex and also occurs on the inside of the vascular tissue in all species with an amphiphloic siphonostele. A pericycle of one to several layers of parenchyma lies between the endodermis and the vascular tissues. Four main types of stele are recognized in the Filicales: protostele; **ectophloic siphonostele; amphiphloic siphonostele (solenostele);** and **dictyostele.** The latter two types are found most commonly with the dictyostele predominating. Specific examples of each of the stelar types will be given in the descriptions of families.

The protoxylem, nearly always mesarch, has helical tracheids. Metaxylem is largely composed of scalariform tracheids. Secondary xylem has not been reported in any of the Filicales. Vessels have been reported in several genera.

The phloem comprises sieve cells and parenchyma. It forms a continuous layer outside the xylem in the ectophloic siphonostele, a layer on either side of the xylem in the amphiphloic siphonostele (solenostele), and usually completely surrounds the xylem (amphicribral) in the vascular bundles of the dictyostele.

Leaves. The leaves of the Filicales range in length from a few millimeters to large fronds of several meters. The fronds are usually divided pinnately once, twice, or three times, but some are palmate.

The lamina of the frond varies widely in shape and amount of dissection. Similarly, there is wide variation in the outline of ultimate divisions, or pinnules. Venation is open in most genera and species, with dichotomous branching of the terminal veins. However, reticulate venation is not uncommon. The fronds of all species exhibit circinate vernation, and uncoil from the base of the frond toward the tip and from the rachis to the margin. The coiled tips, known in some places as fiddleheads, are considered a culinary delicacy.

Sori and Sporangia. The sporangia of the Filicales are grouped into sori in all except one family, the Schizaeaceae. The sori vary in size, shape, and position. In most genera, the sori are circular, linear, or kidney-shaped; in a few, the sporangia are spread out in longitudinal rows, thus forming an extended sorus. In most families, the sori are covered by membranous indusia, although some families have naked sori **(exindusiate).** The indusium is attached in a variety of ways, and generally conforms in outline to the sorus.

Sori are either marginal or abaxial on the fronds. There is good evidence that during evolution from the preferns with terminal sporangia (e.g., Protopteridiales), the sporangia formed later along the margins (e.g., several Carboniferous ferns of uncertain alliance), and that in still later descendants, the sporangia shifted inward to an abaxial position (e.g., Filicales). This evolutionary trend is termed the **phyletic slide** (Fig. 21–28) and has led to a general acceptance of the hypothesis that genera of Filicales with marginal sporangia are primitive, whereas those with abaxial sporangia are derived.

The sori in most families lie at the vein endings or immediately under the veins. In some families, they are arranged in two rows, one on either side of the midrib. In others, the margin of the lamina curls over the sori, thus providing protection.

Three main types of sporangial development within sori have been recognized in the Filicales (Fig. 21–29). In the first, called **simple,** all the sporangia in a sorus mature at the same time. The second is **gradate,** in which the sporangia in the central region of the sorus mature before those toward the outside. In the third type, the **mixed,** the sporangia appear to mature in no particular sequence. This is generally accepted as an evolutionary series, with the simple type primitive, the mixed the most advanced, and the gradate intermediate.

The sporangial wall is one cell thick and has an annulus that functions in dehiscence. The annulus is quite variable in form and consists of specialized cells with all the walls but the outer thickened (Fig. 21–30). In several families, the annulus is composed of a group of cells at the apex of the sporangium. In other families, it forms as a row of cells obliquely across the wall, and in still others, as a vertical row. This series is also regarded as an evolutionary one, with the apical development primitive, the vertical advanced, and the oblique intermediate.

Both monolete and trilete spores are produced in the Filicales, with the trilete predominating in the geologically older families (Fig. 21–31). Perispores are present in some genera, particularly on the monolete spores of the Dennstaedtiaceae. The ornamentation of the spore wall is quite variable, ranging from granular to spiny, and from reticulate to coarsely striate. The number of spores produced in a sporangium varies from as low as 16 to as high as 512, the primitive families having larger numbers.

Gametophytes. In most Filicales, the spores develop into flat, heart-shaped prothalli that contain chlorophyll and grow on the surface of the soil or in moist vegetation or humus. The prothalli vary from 2 to 12 mm in length. Growth occurs first in the notch from an apical cell, and later from a group of meristematic cells. In several genera, the prothallus is filamentous, resembling an algal filament or moss protonema. Rhizoids develop from the lower surface, and help to anchor the prothallus to the substrate.

The antheridia and archegonia usually develop on the lower, or ventral, surface of the same prothallus. The antheridia are generally formed first, often in the central region among the rhizoids. Archegonia develop later, and usually occur in the thicker portion of the prothallus near the meristematic cells of the notch. The development of antheridia, archegonia, and the embryo is essentially the same as described for the other ferns on p. 414.

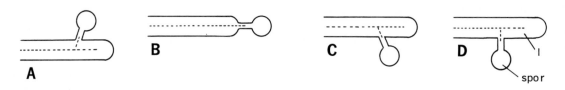

FIGURE 21–28   Sketches of "phyletic slide," depicting change in position of sporangia (*spor*) on leaf (*l*) which appears to have occurred during evolution of ferns.

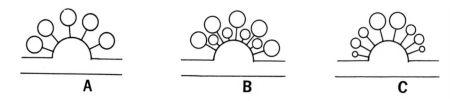

FIGURE 21–29   Three types of sporangial maturation on sori of ferns. A, simple; B, mixed; C, gradate.

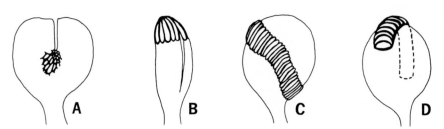

FIGURE 21–30   Four types of annulus in filicalean ferns. A, *Osmunda,* with small patch of annular cells, ×230; B, *Anemia* showing annular cap characteristic of Schizaeaceae, ×230; C, oblique annulus as found in Cyatheaceae, Dicksoniaceae, and Hymenophyllaceae, ×230; D, vertical annulus characteristic of Polypodiaceae and Dennstaedtiaceae, ×230. (After Bower with permission of Hafner Publishing Co., Inc.)

BRIEF OUTLINE OF FAMILIES OF FILICALES.   A good deal of revision is still taking place in the classification of the Filicales, with as few as 14 and as many as 44 families proposed by different specialists. We will adopt the system outlined by Holttum, restricting discussion to nine main families. The remaining five families are small, with rather problematical relationships and few or no fossil representatives.

The nine families to be described have fossil records back to various geological times. The earliest family recognized is the Schizaeaceae in the Carboniferous. Other families had their beginnings at various other times in the late Paleozoic and Mesozoic eras. Many of the earlier-evolved families appear to have passed their evolutionary zenith and to be headed to-ward extinction. Others appear to be actively and progressively evolving. The taxonomic difficulties encountered, as in the Dennstaedtiaceae, are probably a result of this present-day evolution; variations in structure and cytology have not become sufficiently distinctive to allow for a clear-cut classification.

Family Osmundaceae.   The earliest record of this family is from the Permian, in which four genera of fossils show structural details that link them with modern genera. Throughout the Mesozoic, leaf compressions (some with sporangia) and the occasional petrified stem indicate that the Osmundaceae was at least widespread, if not abundant, during these times. During the Tertiary, the family appears to have decreased, at least in the Northern Hemisphere. This was likely the result of a

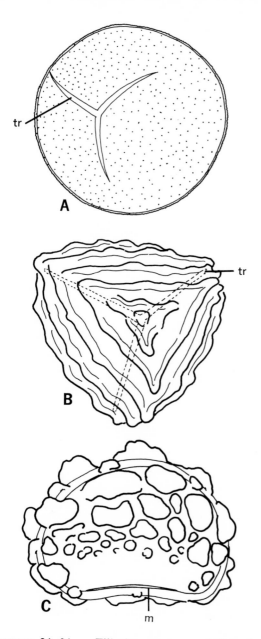

FIGURE 21–31   Filicalean spores, ×1,000. A, *Osmunda*, showing trilete mark (*tr*), thin wall, and granulose ornamentation; B, *Anemia*, with sinuate ridges on distal surface, and trilete mark (*tr*) of proximal surface indicated by broken lines; C, *Polypodium*, showing characteristic bean-shaped outline, monolete mark (*m*), and heavy razorback thickenings on wall.

progressively cooling climate, possibly combined with evolutionary senescence within the family.

The Osmundaceae comprises three extant genera. *Osmunda*, with about 12 species, is cosmopolitan in distribution. *Todea* and *Leptopteris*, restricted to regions of the Southern Hemisphere, are small tree ferns.

Osmunda has an erect, branching rootstock that bears a close rosette of fronds at the apex of each branch. The fronds are large, and either once- or twice-pinnate (Fig. 21–32A). Venation is open and pinnate with dichotomously branched vein endings (Fig. 21–32B). The vascular tissue of the petiole is C-shaped in cross section. Unlike most Filicales the base of the petiole has stipule-like appendages, resembling the Marattiales and Ophioglossales.

The vascular tissue of the stem is dictyostelic, with long narrow leaf gaps (Fig. 21–32D). The endodermis is not broken at the gaps, but forms a continuous cylinder surrounding each leaf trace as it extends obliquely outward through the cortex.

The sporangia are scattered or loosely grouped into sori on reduced pinnules (Fig. 21–32B, C). Each sporangium is stalked, with a cluster of thickened cells on one side forming a rudimentary annulus. Dehiscence occurs along a line of thin-walled cells running from the annular cluster across the top of the sporangium. The spores are subtriangular and trilete; the ornamentation is coarsely granular to baculate (Fig. 21–32E). In size, spores vary from 40 to 70 microns. The chromosome number of six species of *Osmunda*, one of *Todea*, and three of *Leptopteris* has been shown to be $n = 22$ in all cases.

The prothallus of *Osmunda*, which is representative of the genera, is flat with a central cushion area and two lateral wings. Rhizoids are numerous along the cushion. Antheridia occur on both the cushion and the margin before the archegonia form. The archegonia also develop on the cushion or along its margins, and are similar to those of the Ophioglossales. Following fertilization, the **proembryo** develops considerably before the primordia of the adult organs are discernible.

The Osmundaceae is usually considered to be among the most primitive families of the Filicales because its members have large spo-

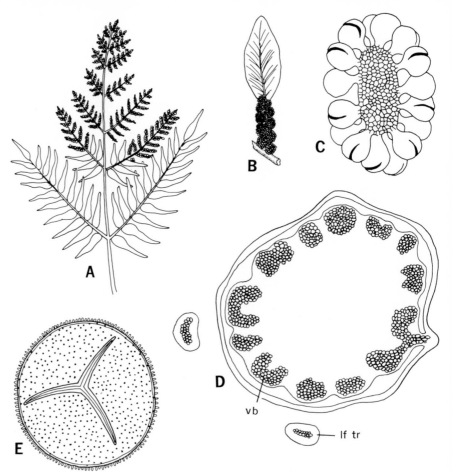

FIGURE 21–32   *Osmunda*. A, habit sketch of pinnae, showing outline of pinnules and sporangia clustered on some terminal pinnae, ×0.25; B, single pinnule
showing sporangia along basal part of rachis, and leaf blade above, ×0.5; C,
transverse section through sporangial cluster, ×4; D, transverse section of stem,
showing vascular bundles (*v b*) of dictyostele and two leaf traces (*lf tr*), ×6; E,
single spore showing trilete mark and regular bacula on wall, ×1,000. (B, C,
after Bauer.)

rangia that develop simultaneously, a weakly
developed annulus, numerous spores (128–
500+) and sperm, and a late-maturing embryo.
In their massive structure, weak annulus, and
simultaneous development, the sporangia are
similar to those of the eusporangiate ferns, the
Marattiales and Ophioglossales. Thus, the Osmundaceae represents a group transitional between the eusporangiate and leptosporangiate
ferns.

Family Schizaeaceae.   The schizaeaceous
ferns extend from the Carboniferous to the
present. The earliest fossils consist of fronds
that bear sporangia and spores resembling

those of extant genera. The early fossil sporangia have several rows of cells in the annulus
instead of the single row of modern genera,
suggesting that reduction of the annulus has
accompanied evolution of the sporangia. The
record of the family is also documented during
the Mesozoic with fronds, sporangia, and dispersed spores. Fossils assignable to modern
genera are found in rocks from the Cretaceous
to the present and indicate that the family is
today less widespread—probably as a result of
the cooling of the climate in the Tertiary.

Four genera of the Schizaeaceae are distributed mainly in the tropics. Two of these,

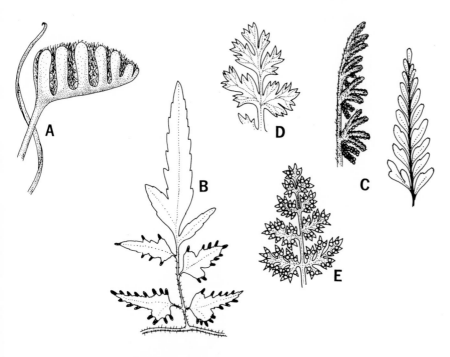

FIGURE 21–33   Leaves and sporangia of the Schizaeaceae. A, *Schizaea,* ×5;
B, *Lygodium,* ×1; C, *Anemia,* ×1; D, E, *Mohria,* ×1.

Schizaea and *Lygodium,* also extend north to eastern North America and south to Australia and New Zealand. The genus *Anemia* is widespread in tropical and subtropical America and also occurs in South Africa and Madagascar. Finally, the genus *Mohria* is restricted to South Africa, Madagascar, and other islands of the Indian Ocean.

The leaves of the four genera are very different (Fig. 21–33). The branching of the leaf is dichotomous in most species of *Schizaea,* either pinnate or palmate in *Lygodium,* and pinnate in *Anemia* and *Mohria.* Venation is pinnate and open in most species but reticulate in others. The leaves range in size from the small simple blade of *Schizaea* to the long fronds of some tropical tree-climbing species of *Lygodium* that grow to 3 meters in length.

The arrangements of the vascular tissues range from a protostele in *Lygodium,* a siphonostele in *Schizaea* and *Anemia,* to a dictyostele in *Mohria* (Fig. 21–34). A pericycle and endodermis are present in most species, and the cortex varies in thickness.

In all genera, the sporangia are usually arranged a short distance in from the margin in two rows on the pinnules. Large oval sporangia occur singly, rather than grouped into sori, and they are covered by flaps of leaf tissue. An annulus sits like a cap on the apex of each sporangium and consists normally of one row of thick-walled cells. Dehiscence occurs along a longitudinal suture in the sporangial wall.

The spores number either 128 or, more often, 256 per sporangium. They are oval and monolete in *Schizaea,* but subtriangular and trilete in other genera (Fig. 21–35). Unique ridges on the walls of some *Anemia* and *Mohria* spores run in different directions on the various faces of the spore, giving a microscopic appearance of crisscrossing ribs. The ornamentation in *Lygodium* spores varies from reticulate thickenings to a smooth wall.

The prothallia are flat and heart-shaped in three genera, but filamentous in *Schizaea.* The sex organs are similar to other Filicales, except that the archegonia of *Schizaea* are entirely superficial.

The Schizaeaceae, with representatives from the Lower Carboniferous, is the oldest family of Filicales. During the interval from the Jurassic to the Tertiary, Schizaeaceae were very widespread, at least over much of the Northern Hemisphere. The four modern genera apparently originated during the middle of the Mesozoic, since their remains are recorded from the Jurassic and Cretaceous.

There is reasonably good evidence of the sporangial evolution in the Schizaeaceae. The Carboniferous sporangia have several layers of annular cells, often forming an irregular patch over the tip. At least one Mesozoic species has a sporangium with an annulus of a single row of cells; in several other species, sporangia have a weakly developed second row. As mentioned earlier, the modern genera have a single row of cells, indicating that reduction in the annulus has occurred with evolution.

Several structural features of modern genera are generally considered primitive: large sporangia, with a high spore number and longitudinal dehiscence; annulus in the form of an apical cap, rather than as a transverse, oblique, or vertical row; a relatively complex antheridium, with a high sperm number; and the presence of a protostele (in the rhizome of *Lygodium*).

The Schizaeaceae do not appear to have been either ancestral to or descended from any of the other families of the Filicales. As seems to be the case with the Osmundaceae, the origins of Schizaeaceae were probably in the complex of the Protopteridiales–Coenopteridales.

Family Gleicheniaceae. Plants of this family are known from the Carboniferous to the present. As in the two previous families, plants of the Gleicheniaceae appear to have been most abundant and widespread during the Mesozoic, particularly in the Cretaceous Period. Today, there is one genus, *Gleichenia,* with four subgenera widely distributed throughout the tropics and subtropics, locally forming a very conspicuous feature of the vegetation.

The Carboniferous genus *Oligocarpia* (Fig. 21–36) shows affiliations with the Gleicheniaceae. Fronds of *Oligocarpia* are several times pinnate and bear sporangia in rings

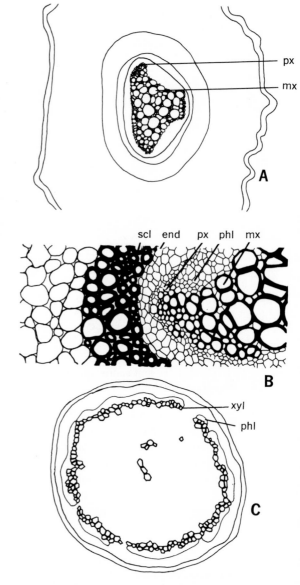

FIGURE 21–34   Vascular anatomy of schizaeaceous ferns. A, three-armed protostele of *Lygodium* with protoxylem (*px*) at poles and metaxylem (*mx*) forming core, ×30; B, transverse section of part of *Lygodium* stele showing sclerenchyma fibers (*scl*), endodermis (*end*), protoxylem (*px*), metaxylem (*mx*), and phloem (*phl*), ×170; C, siphonostele of *Anemia* in transverse section, showing xylem (*xyl*) and phloem (*phl*), ×15.

near the ends of the pinnule veins. Most sori have four or five sporangia but some have more. Each sporangium, stalked and globular, bears an annulus of a single row of cells around

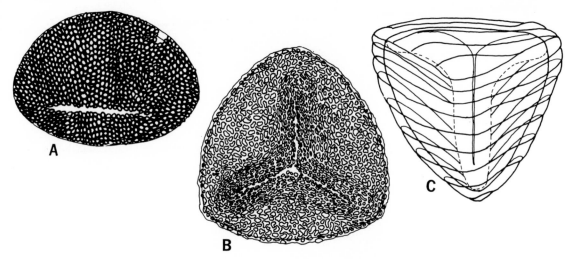

FIGURE 21–35   Spores of schizaeaceous ferns, ×1,000. A, *Schizaea* with thick reticulate ornamentation and monolete tetrad mark; B, *Lygodium,* showing irregular patchy bacula on wall and trilete mark; C, *Anemia,* showing parallel ridges and grooves that curve around spore wall, and trilete mark (*tr*) partly hidden at top.

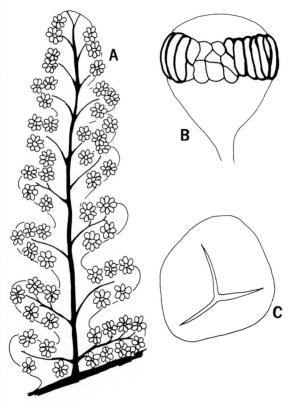

FIGURE 21–36   *Oligocarpia.* A, single fertile pinna showing outline of pinnules and clusters of sporangia, ×10; B, single sporangium showing annulus, ×165; C, single spore with smooth wall and trilete mark, ×1,000. (After Abbott with permission of *Palaeontographica.*)

the equator. This row is interrupted on one side by a longitudinal region of thin-walled cells that probably acted as a dehiscence slit. This arrangement is very similar to that of the extant *Gleichenia.*

A genus of Mesozoic fronds is called *Gleichenites*—a name that indicates close similarities to *Gleichenia.* During the Tertiary, fossils of this family are almost unknown in the medium to high latitudes of the Northern Hemisphere, probably because of the cooling climates of this era.

The large and widespread genus *Gleichenia* includes about 120 species. Although mainly tropical and subtropical, it is also found in temperate regions of the Southern Hemisphere, notably Australia. Many of the species are xerophytic, inhabiting open situations or the edges of the forests. In some places, species form impassable thickets that prevent the growth of other plants. Some species inhabit mountain slopes, others lowlands.

Gleichenia bears fronds at somewhat long intervals on a creeping rhizome. The fronds are usually long—some reaching a length of 6 meters or more (Fig. 21–37). The fronds are one-, two-, or sometimes three-pinnate, with very distinctive branching; the types of branching form the basis for the division of the genus

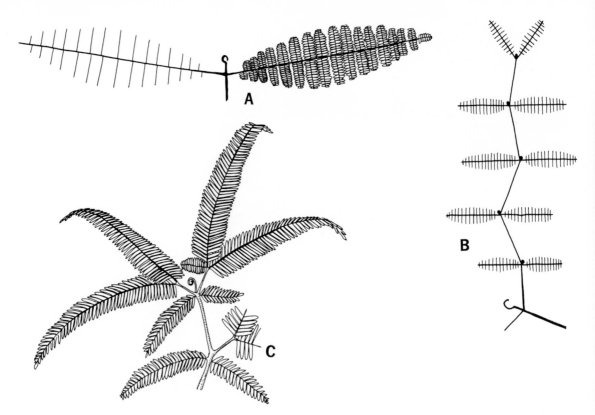

FIGURE 21–37   Types of branching in *Gleichenia*. A, twice-pinnate branching with pinnae at right angles to rachis, ×0.2; B, three-pinnate arrangement, with secondary pinnae at right angles to primary pinna, ×0.2; C, dichotomous branching of rachis and pinnae, ×0.2. (After Holttum with permission of Government Printing Office, Singapore.)

into subgenera. The frond usually has two lateral branches, with an apical bud at the junction. In some species, no further branching of the fronds takes place. However, in others the buds at the tips of the first lateral fronds produce two additional lateral branches, and the process is repeated until a much-branched frond is formed. Many species have indeterminate growth of fronds.

The pinnules are either short and rounded or long and narrow; they are completely separated from each other. Venation is open and more or less dichotomous (Fig. 21–38A). The vascular tissues are usually protostelic, but two species have siphonosteles. The xylem is mesarch and the tracheids scalariform. The xylem is completely surrounded by phloem, which in turn is enclosed by a pericycle and an endodermis. The cortex of most species has abundant sclerenchyma.

Sporangia are grouped into sori below the veins or sometimes at the vein tips. The sori contain from four to eight sporangia in a ring and are arranged in two rows—one on each side of the midrib. Each sporangium is large and has a single-row annulus that lies obliquely around the wall (Fig. 21–38B, C). Dehiscence occurs through an elongate slit.

The spores of *Gleichenia* are produced in numbers ranging from 128 to 1,024 per sporangia. They are triangular and trilete, and vary in size from 30 to 50 microns (Fig. 21–38D). The spores of most species are smooth-walled and characterized by a trilete mark elevated on a ridge. In another genus (or subgenus), *Sticherus*, the spores are bean-shaped and monolete with a thin smooth wall.

The prothallus is similar to that of *Osmunda*, with a central cushion area and two lateral wings. The sex organs, formed on the

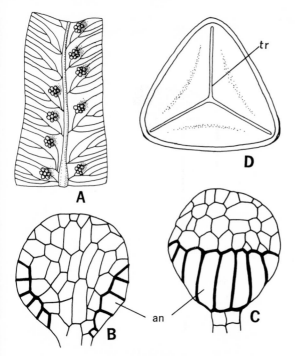

A

B

C

D

tr

an

FIGURE 21–38   Sporangia and spores of gleicheniaceous ferns. A, section of pinnule showing
venation and clusters of sporangia, ×3; B, C,
sporangia showing position of annulus (*an*),
×170; D, spore of *Dicranopteris* with smooth wall,
trilete mark , and slightly thickened ridges
indicated by stippled areas between arms of
trilete, ×1,000. (A–C, after Smith with permission of McGraw-Hill Book Co.; B, after Bower.)

under side of the prothallus, are very similar to
those of the Osmundaceae and other families of
Filicales. The embryo develops primordia as in
the other ferns—the first leaves and stem from
the upper cells, the root and foot from lower
cells of the proembryo.

For the family Gleicheniaceae, the fossil
evidence indicates a line of descent from the
Carboniferous to the present, proceeding from
Oligocarpia–Gleichenites–Gleichenia. As with
the Osmundaceae and Schizaeaceae, the Gleicheniaceae most likely descended from the
Protopteridiales–Coenopteridales complex, although a direct link is not apparent.

Most fern investigators relate the Gleicheniaceae closely to the Cyatheaceae, a family
of tree ferns to be discussed later. Both families
produce superficial (abaxial) sporangia that
have oblique annuli and lack true indusia. The

most likely suggestion is that the Cyatheaceae
evolved from some of the early Gleicheniaceae,
possibly in the late Carboniferous or early
Mesozoic. The earliest fossils definitely assignable to the Cyatheaceae are from the Jurassic,
which suggests a much later origin for this
family than for the Gleicheniaceae.

Some of the primitive features of the
Gleicheniaceae include the following: protostelic and dichotomous stems, presence of
hairs instead of scales on stems of some species,
large sporangia with oblique annuli, large numbers of spores, and simultaneous development
of sporangia (simple type).

Family Matoniaceae. The extant plants of
this family are classified in two genera, *Matonia*
and *Phanerosorus;* both are restricted to the
Indo-Malaysian region—a marked contrast
with their rather widespread distribution in the
Mesozoic, where they are found in Europe,
North America, and Asia. The Tertiary record
of the family is virtually unknown at higher
northern and southern latitudes, suggesting that
the family may have become restricted during
the Cretaceous or early Tertiary.

Both the fossil and extant plants of
Matonia are characterized by an apical division
of the frond into two equal lateral branches.
Each branch divides again into a series of pinnae that contain both open pinnate venation
and anastomosing veins, particularly near the
sori.

The best-known fossil genus is *Phlebopteris,* ranging from the late Triassic to early
Cretaceous (Fig. 21–39). The frond of this
genus also branches at the apex and bears strap-
shaped pinnae emerging at right angles to the
rachis. Each pinna has a central midvein and
anastomosing lateral veins. Sori of fertile pinnae are arranged in two rows, one on either side
of the midrib. Each sorus is circular, comprising five to 15 sporangia, each with an oblique
annulus.

Extant genera are very limited in geographical distribution. *Matonia* occurs on isolated mountains in Malaya and Borneo, and
Phanerosorus is found in similar sites in Borneo
and New Guinea. Both genera have a long
creeping rhizome that branches dichotomously.

FIGURE 21–39   *Phlebopteris* from the Triassic of southwestern United States, ×1. (Photograph courtesy C. A. Arnold with permission of McGraw-Hill Book Co.)

The rhizome is unique in that the vascular tissue consists of usually three concentric siphonosteles—a condition termed **polycyclic** (Fig. 21–40). Each siphonostele is amphiphloic, with mesarch xylem and scalariform tracheids. Leaf gaps occur in both the middle and outer siphonosteles but not in the central stele, which is sometimes protostelic, particularly in young rhizomes. Leaf traces departing from the nodes are C-shaped in cross section.

The fronds of this family are also unique. In *Matonia,* the petiole is long and forks into two lateral branches (Fig. 21–41A), which in turn branch again many times, resulting in a fan-shaped frond with pinnate branches radiating from the end of the petiole. In this type of branching *Matonia* closely resembles the fossil *Phlebopteris. Phanerosorus* has a different type of frond; it is slender and trailing, and distally unequally forked. The pinnules contain midribs, from which lateral veins arise and anastomose. The resulting weak network is better developed in fertile pinnules.

The sori are arranged in two rows, one on each side of the midrib, and are usually situated over the forking point of anastomosing veins (Fig. 21–41C). Each sorus consists of from six to nine sporangia. The sporangia are arranged in a ring and covered by an indusium, which is an overarching outgrowth of the tissue located within the sporangial ring. Each sporangium has a single-layered annulus aligned obliquely along the wall.

Both trilete and monolete spores occur in the family, apparently even in the same species. Many spores have a thin perispore that varies in ornamentation from smooth to scabrate (Fig. 21–41D). The prothalli are reported to be similar to those of *Gleichenia.*

The record of the Matoniaceae appears to be very clear from the Triassic to the present. Although no direct fossil connections are known, the closest alliance is with the Gleicheniaceae, on the basis of similarities of sporangia and abaxial sori. There is also an affiliation with the genus *Dipteris* of the Poly-

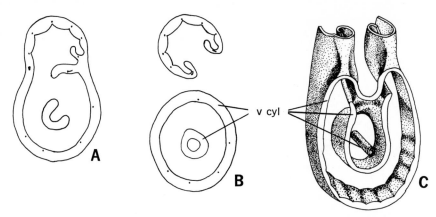

FIGURE 21–40   Vascular anatomy in *Matonia*. A, transverse section of younger stem, showing leaf trace beginning to form at tip, ×8; B, leaf trace has split completely from outer vascular cylinder (*v cyl*), ×8; C, tricyclic vascular arrangement of older rhizome, showing connections of leaf traces with both second and third cylinders of xylem and phloem, ×10. (After Tansley and Lulham.)

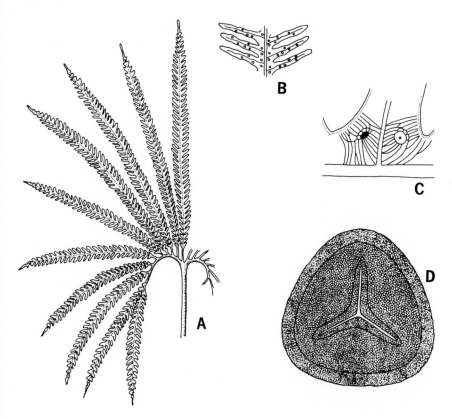

FIGURE 21–41   Matoniaceae. A, part of frond of *Matonia* showing two primary lateral branches, and petiolate pinnae arising from one lateral, ×0.2; B, several pinnules of *Matonia* showing position of sori, ×0.5; C, basal part of one pinnule of *Matonia* showing venation near two sporangia, ×2; D, spore of *Phanerosorus* showing dense scabrate ornamentation and thickened rim around trilete mark, ×800. (A–C, after Holttum with permission of Government Printing Office, Singapore.)

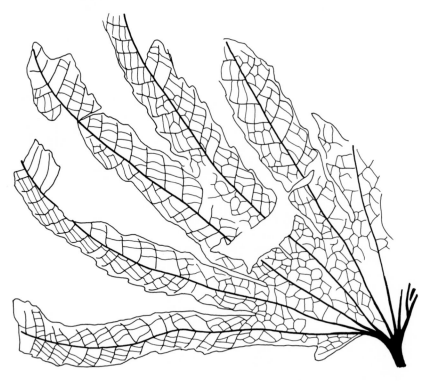

FIGURE 21–42   *Clathropteris* single leaf from late Triassic of Greenland, showing division of blade and venation, ×1. (After Harris with permission of *Meddelelser om Grønland.*)

podiaceae (*sensu* Holttum), which has a dichotomous branching of the frond, abaxial sori, and an oblique annulus. Again, the relationship is remote, since the Matoniaceae and Polypodiaceae are very distinct from as early as the Triassic.

Family Polypodiaceae (sensu *Holttum*). This family has been revised recently to include the genera *Dipteris, Polypodium,* and several others believed to represent a natural phylogenetic group. At the same time, many of the genera formerly allied with *Polypodium* are classified with the family Dennstaedtiaceae. Although it is too early to see how widely acceptable this new classification scheme will be, several workers on ferns have already adopted the system.

As in the Matoniaceae, the earliest fossils of Polypodiaceae are from the Triassic. Several genera, some with very large fronds, are recognized. One of the better-known genera is *Clathropteris,* which has been found fairly widely in Mesozoic rocks (Fig. 21–42). The

plant consists of a frond divided palmately into distinct lobes at the top of a petiole. Each lobe has a toothed margin, straight lateral veins, and a network of reticulate veins between the laterals. The sori are arranged in a row on each side of the main veins, as in the modern *Dipteris.* Several other closely related genera, with both fronds and sori, are also known from the Mesozoic. Interestingly, these genera have yielded spore counts ranging from 64 to 512 per sporangium. In the Northern Hemisphere, where *Polypodium* is the main representative, the family appears to have diminished markedly during the late Cretaceous and Tertiary.

Most of the extant genera, about 20 in number, are found in the tropics and subtropics, particularly in eastern Asia. In a few primitive genera, the vascular cylinder is a solid siphonostele; in most others, the cylinder is a dictyostele consisting of a ring of vascular strands (Fig. 21–43A, B). Most genera are epiphytes with a creeping rhizome. The fronds

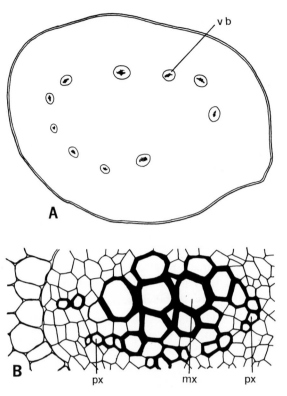

A

B
px   mx   px

FIGURE 21–43 *Polypodium.* A, transverse section of stem, showing dictyostelic arrangement of vascular bundles (*v b*), ×2; B, single vascular bundle of A, showing protoxylem (*px*) and metaxylem (*mx*), ×25.

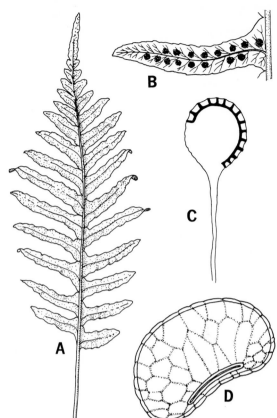

FIGURE 21–44 *Polypodium.* A, single frond showing shape of pinnules, ×0.5; B, pinnule showing venation and exindusiate sori, ×1; C, sporangium with vertical annulus, ×100; D, single monolete spore with polygonal or hexagonal verrucae, ×1,000.

arise in two rows from the rhizome and range from entire to lobed to pinnate (Fig. 21–44A, B). Almost all genera are characterized by a reticulate venation. The sori are quite variable but lack an indusium; some sori are round, whereas others are variously elongated along the veins or parallel to the margin. The sporangia are stalked and have a vertical annulus of one row of cells (Fig. 21–44C). Dehiscence is transverse. The spores of most species are bilateral and monolete, without a perispore, and in many cases with a verrucate or reticulate ornamentation (Fig. 21–44D).

The similarities of frond branching, venation, and soral structure indicate that the fossil genera of the Mesozoic are direct ancestors of the extant genera. Some investigators have tried to relate this family to the Matoniaceae, which has similar fronds. However, in the Matoniaceae indusia cover the sori, suggesting that the

affiliation with Polypodiaceae may be rather remote.

Family Hymenophyllaceae. The ferns of this family are often called "filmy ferns" because most have a delicate lamina one cell thick. The family is generally considered primitive, but undoubted fossils are very scarce. Fragments of fronds with sporangia have been described from the Carboniferous as *Hymenophyllites;* these sporangia have a transverse or oblique annulus similar to that of the extant *Hymenophyllum.* However, some investigators doubt that the fossils have been correctly interpreted and hesitate to accept them as evidence of Paleozoic members of the family. Spores from the Cretaceous and Tertiary are similar to those of *Hymenophyllum.*

The two main extant genera, *Hymenophyllum* and *Trichomanes,* are frequently divided into several genera, each containing one or more species. The plants thrive in very moist areas, especially tropical rain forests, where many are epiphytes in shaded habitats. Geographically, they are very widespread, ranging at least to latitudes 53° N. and 45° S.

The rhizomes are relatively thin and creeping, with hairs on young growth. When present, roots are adventitious. The fronds depart upward from the top of the rhizome, either singly or in small tufts. The laminae vary greatly in size and shape, ranging from entire to deeply lobed (Fig. 21–45A, B). As noted previously the lamina is only one cell thick, except at the veins. Venation is open and dichotomous. **False veins** have been identified in many species of *Trichomanes* as single rows of specialized cells that appear to support the margins of the delicate lamina.

The vascular tissue is protostelic, sometimes with considerable parenchyma in the xylem. The vascular cylinder is surrounded successively by bands of pericycle parenchyma and endodermis. The cortex of almost all species is thinner than in other Filicales (Fig. 21–45F, G).

The sori are arranged terminally along the leaf margins, usually at the end of one-veined lobes or at the vein endings (Fig. 21–45C). Each sorus is elevated on a receptacle, and is covered with an indusium that develops from two flaps of tissue—one flap from the abaxial surface, the other from the adaxial. The flaps cover the sorus until spores are shed. Development of sporangia is gradational, with the uppermost of the receptacle maturing first, those lower down maturing later. Each sporangium has an oblique annulus of one row of cells and dehisces transversely (Fig. 21–45D).

The spores are triangular and thin-walled, with a well-developed trilete mark, and ornamentation ranging from granulate to baculate (Fig. 21–45E). They range in size from 15 to 60 microns, and vary in number from about 128 to 512 per sporangium. Germination occurs readily, but prothalli grow slowly, *Hymenophyllum* has a ribbon-like thallus, with

irregular lobes and marginal rhizoids; *Trichomanes* has a much-branched filamentous prothallus. Both antheridia and archegonia are borne on some of the ultimate lobes. Antheridia are emergent, have a jacket of several cell layers, and produce a larger number of sperm than other Filicales. Archegonia are characterized by relatively long, curved necks.

The fossil record reveals little concerning the evolution of the Hymenophyllaceae, except that it possibly started in the Carboniferous. It was probably widespread during the later Mesozoic and Tertiary, at least in the Northern Hemisphere. One extant species recently found in the Queen Charlotte Islands off the west coast of Canada probably represents a remnant from Tertiary floras that persisted through the glaciations of the Pleistocene.

The Hymenophyllaceae are often referred to as a primitive group. However, some of the supposed primitive characteristics—such as small size, thin laminae, small amount of vascular tissue, and small gametophytes—are most likely the result of reduction accompanied by ecological specialization to wet conditions. Other characteristics, such as marginal sori, protostelic stem, dichotomous venation, and large spore and sperm output are probably truly primitive. However, the presence of an indusium and the gradate development of sporangia are considered advanced features, compared to those of primitive families such as the Osmundaceae and Gleicheniaceae. The Hymenophyllaceae probably are not related to other families of Filicales; they may have evolved from a separate stock of the Protopteridiales–Coenopteridiales complex.

Family Dicksoniaceae. The five genera of this family are mostly tree ferns, predominantly of the tropics but also widely distributed in warm temperate regions of the Southern Hemisphere, particularly Australasia.

The family appears to have had its beginnings in the Mesozoic; supposed dicksoniaceous ferns are found abundantly in some horizons of the Jurassic and Cretaceous. The family apparently began to retreat from the Northern Hemisphere during the later Cretaceous, since

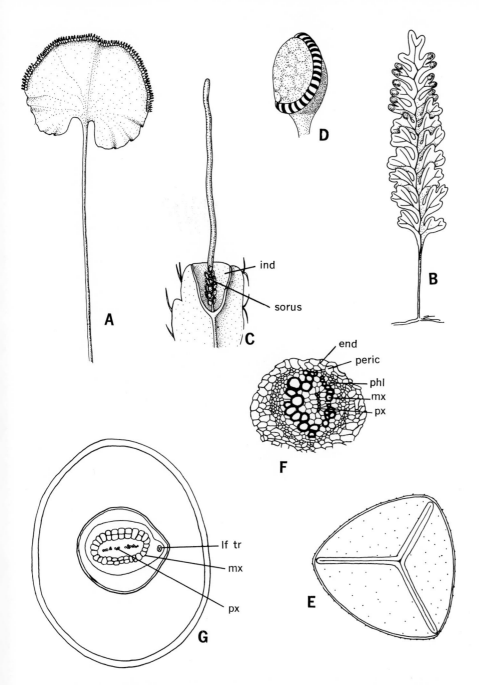

FIGURE 21–45   Hymenophyllaceae. A, leaf of *Cardiomanes* showing venation and marginal sori, ×0.5; B, frond of *Hymenophyllum* showing sporangia on distal pinnules, ×1; C, vertical section through sorus of *Trichomanes*, showing indusium (*ind*), ×100; D, sporangium with oblique annulus, ×120; E, spore of *Mecodium* showing thickened ridge along trilete mark, and light baculate ornamentation, ×1,000; F, single vascular bundle of *Hymenophyllum* showing protoxylem (*px*), metaxylem (*mx*), phloem (*phl*), pericycle (*peric*), and endodermis (*end*), ×25; G, transverse section of stem of *Hymenophyllum*, showing central vascular bundle and one leaf trace (*r tr*), ×60. (C, D, after Bauer; F, G, after Boodle.)

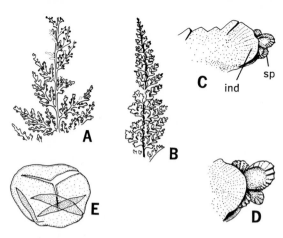

FIGURE 21–46 *Coniopteris*. A, B, sketches of fragments of pinnae, showing sporangia in A, ×1; C, D, sori with indusia (*ind*) covering sporangia (*sp*); C, ×20; D, ×40; E, single spore recovered from sporangium, ×400. (After Harris with permission of the British Museum—Natural History.)

fossil representatives from the Tertiary of North America are unknown.

The best-known fossil genus is *Coniopteris,* which is found widely in early Jurassic to sphere, and sporadically in the Southern Hemisphere (Fig. 21–46). Fronds are at least three-pinnate, with slender and several-lobed pinnules. The sori are situated on the margins of the lobes and covered by indusial flaps, thus closely resembling the sori of extant genera.

About 30 species are distributed among five genera, and *Dicksonia* and *Cibotium* have the largest numbers of species. Most species are tree ferns, with either short and stout trunks, or trunk-like prostrate rhizomes (Fig. 21–47, 48A). The top of the trunk is characterized by a thick coating of hairs, which have been used by some Pacific islanders for upholstery stuffing. The fronds are in most cases large, much-dissected, and three-pinnate; pinnules exhibit open and dichotomous venation (Fig. 21–49A, B). The sori are distinctly marginal, and usually situated at the tips of veins.

The sporangia are covered by two indusial flaps—one adaxial and the other abaxial, as in the Hymenophyllaceae. The sporangia are gradate in development on the receptacle, and have an oblique annulus of one row of cells. The spores are triangular and trilete, often

FIGURE 21–47 Tree fern from Costa Rica, ×0.02. (Photograph courtesy J. Kuijt.)

thick-walled, with ornamentation varying from finely granulate to verrucate (Fig. 21–49D). The spores germinate to form typical heart-shaped prothalli, with a prominent notch, cushion area, and wings. The spores are relatively slow to grow and mature.

The sex organs are of the general filicalean type. The antheridia are globose, with a jacket of five cells (including the cap cell), and produce many sperm. The archegonium has a long, curved neck that protrudes well above the surface of the prothallus, usually with two neck canal nuclei. The development of the embryo is not well known, but is apparently of the filicalean type.

In general evolutionary pattern and in many structural features, the Dicksoniaceae

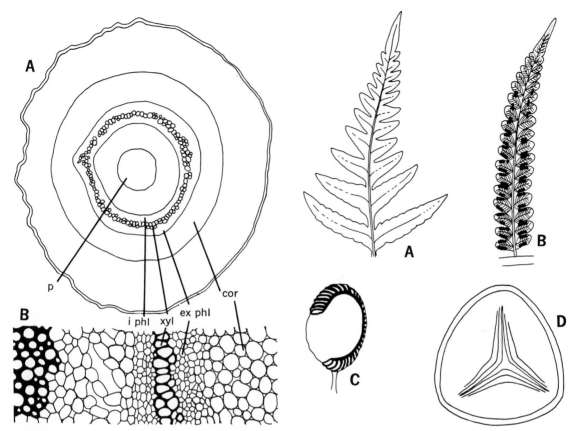

FIGURE 21-48   *Dicksonia*. Transverse section of stem of *Dicksonia*, showing amphiphloic siphonostele, cortex, and epidermis, ×25; B, part of stele in A, ×50. *ex phl*, external phloem; *cor*, cortex; *i phl*, internal phloem; *p*, pith; *xyl*, xylem.

FIGURE 21-49   Dicksoniaceae. A, part of frond of *Cibotium*, ×0.5; B, fertile frond of *Cibotium*, showing sporangia toward margins of pinnules, ×0.5; C, sporangium of *Cibotium* with vertical-oblique annulus, ×130; D, single spore of *Cibotium* showing thickened ridges flanking trilete mark, ×1,000.

parallels the Cyatheaceae. The main differences are the abaxial sporangia and scales on trunks and fronds exhibited by the Cyatheaceae, described below. In the marginal and terminal sori, however, the Dicksoniaceae are markedly different from the Cyatheaceae, and any relationship must be remote. Present evidence suggests a derivation of the Dicksoniaceae from ancestors with marginal sporangia. Whether this stock was also ancestral to the Cyatheaceae is presently unknown.

Family Cyatheaceae. This family is made up of a single extant genus, *Cyathea,* with about 700 species distributed widely in the tropics and extending locally into the subtropics. Optimum habitats are high, moist mountains. As with the Dicksoniaceae, most species are tree ferns, some attaining a height of 15 meters.

The history of the Cyatheaceae extends from the Jurassic to the present. However, fossil remains are relatively scarce, suggesting that the family may not have been abundant since the Jurassic. One of the best examples is *Protopteris,* a petrified tree-fern stem from the early Cretaceous (Fig. 21-50). The stem is studded with persistent leaf bases arranged spirally in closely packed rows. Internally, there is a siphonostele with leaf gaps. The leaf traces are horseshoe-shaped, with the open end down. The structure is very similar to that of some extant species of *Cyathea.*

Dispersed spores allied with the Cyatheaceae have been reported from the Jurassic, Tertiary, and Pleistocene in New Zealand,

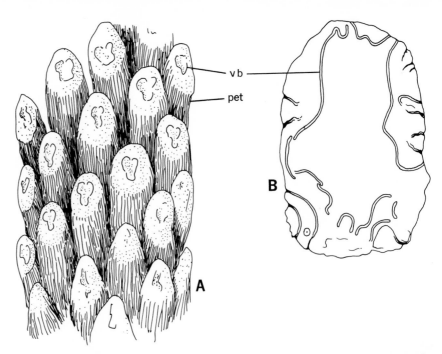

FIGURE 21–50   *Protopteris*. A, part of stem with petiole bases (*pet*) containing vascular bundle scars (*v b*), ×0.3; B, outline of vascular tissue in thin section of stem, ×4. (A, after Corda; B, after Seward with permission of Cambridge University Press.)

and from Jurassic and Cretaceous horizons in several countries of the Northern Hemisphere.

The extant genus of tree ferns, *Cyathea*, is widely dispersed in the Southern Hemisphere, ranging south to New Zealand, and north to Central America and the Indo-Malaysian region. It is relatively scarce in Africa.

The stem is usually massive and stout; in older specimens a thick mat of black adventitious roots forms the main anchorage and support for the stem (Fig. 21–1B). Most stems are shaped like an inverted cone (obconical); they widen for some distance toward the top but gradually assume a constant thickness. The vascular cylinder ranges from a slightly dissected siphonostele to a true dictyostele (Fig. 21–51). In species with dictyosteles, the individual meristeles are V-shaped, with the two arms facing toward the outside of the stem. Each meristele is surrounded by a pericycle and endodermis. Strands of xylem found in the pith and cortex of many species are interpreted as representing reduced internal steles, such as

those in the stems of *Matonia*. Leaf traces are formed from several strands of xylem and phloem originating from different gaps and from the central pith bundles. The cortex is usually narrow and often has well-developed bands of sclerenchyma.

The fronds are usually large and two-pinnate, with well-developed petioles (Fig. 21–52A,B). The pinnules are long, with a definite midrib and pinnately arranged lateral veins that are often branched and always open. A characteristic feature in *Cyathea* is the abundance of scales that cover the apex of the stem and the bases of the petioles.

The distinctly abaxial sori are often cup-shaped; they are arranged in two rows, one on each side of the midrib. Indusia are usually present, but may be absent in some species in which protection is afforded by hairs of the receptacle. The sporangia are stalked and attached to a raised receptacle. The oblique annulus forms a continuous row around the sporangial wall. The development of sporangia is gradate. Each sporangium usually produces 64

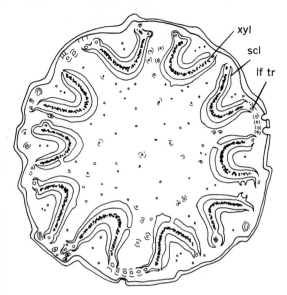

FIGURE 21–51   Transverse section of stem of
Cyathea showing V-shaped meristeles and numerous leaf traces (*lf tr*), ×0.5. *scl*, sclerenchyma,
xyl, xylem. (After Ogura.)

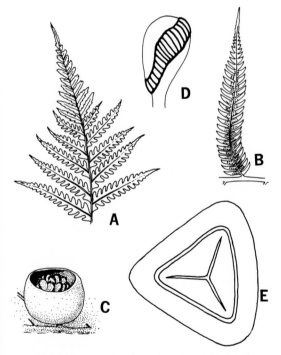

FIGURE 21–52   *Cyathea*. A, part of frond showing outline of pinnae and pinnules, ×0.5; B, fertile
pinnule with two rows of sporangia on pinnules,
×0.5; C, sorus with cup-shaped indusium, ×8;
D, sporangium with oblique annulus, ×120; E,
single spore showing trilete mark and thickened
region inside double line, ×500.

spores. They are all trilete, circular to triangular in shape, and vary from smooth to faintly
granulate in ornamentation (Fig. 21–52E).
They range in size from 30 to 70 microns.

The prothallia are heart-shaped, with intermingled rhizoids and gametangia on the underside. The globose antheridia usually have a
five-celled wall, with the upper cell functioning
as a cap cell. Archegonia have long and somewhat curved necks, with one to several neck
canal nuclei overlying a ventral canal cell. The
development of new sporophytes by **apogamy** is
frequently reported for *Cyathea*; new sporophytic outgrowths usually develop from one of
the cells in the neck primordia of the developing archegonium.

The closest affiliation of the Cyatheaceae
appears to be with the Gleicheniaceae, based
mainly on similarities of sori and sporangia. In
both families, the sori are located on veins on
the abaxial surface, and the sporangia have
oblique annuli. Evolution of the Cyatheaceae
presumably occurred sometime between the
origin of early gleicheniaceous ferns in the later
Carboniferous and the first appearance of
cyatheid fossils in the early Jurassic. At least
one investigator suggests that very active evolution is still taking place in the genus *Cyathea*.

Family Dennstaedtiaceae.   This family
was first described by Holttum and comprises
11 subfamilies of admittedly diverse structure,
many of which were formerly classified in the
Polypodiaceae. The justification for what may
appear to be an artificial grouping is that all
ferns of the subfamily seem to be linked to a
primitive type such as *Dennstaedtia*. Some genera of each subfamily appear to be more closely
related to *Dennstaedtia* than do others.

The greatest problem in classification of
the Filicales lies in this complex of subfamilies
of the Dennstaedtiaceae. The classification is in
a state of flux, with no two investigators in
agreement. For example, Pichi-Sermoli has elevated many of Holttum's subfamilies to the
rank of order or family, and arranged genera
into a total of 44 families. Copeland, in another
well-known treatise, has established several
families not recognized by Holttum, and referred to some of Holttum's subfamilies of

TABLE 21–2

SUBFAMILIES AND COMMON GENERA OF THE DENNSTAEDTIACEAE

SUBFAMILIES	GENERA
Dennstaedtioideae	*Dennstaedtia* or *Microlepia*
Lindsayoideae	*Lindsaya*
Davallioideae	*Davallia*
Oleandroideae	*Nephrolepis*
Pteridoideae	*Pteridium*
Asplenioideae	*Asplenium*
Blechnoideae	*Blechnum*
Lomariopsidoideae	*Elaphoglossum*
Dryopteridoideae	*Dryopteris*
Tectarioideae	*Ctenitis*
Athyricideae	*Athyrium*

Dennstaedtiaceae as families. As yet, it is impossible to say which of these is the most natural and hence the most desirable system; we might well have chosen either of these other two with justification.

The subfamilies of Dennstaedtiaceae, together with the corresponding genera that are most widespread geographically, are listed in Table 21–2. It should be emphasized that the genera listed have not been chosen to represent the subfamilies. To do so would be impossible in most instances, since the genera within one subfamily vary so widely in characteristics that no one can be taken as typical or representative.

The following paragraphs outline some of the main features of the family, emphasizing trends in structural characteristics. For more complete information on both subfamilies and genera, refer to the works of Holttum in the bibliography.

Dennstaedtia is regarded as the primitive genus; its characteristics are taken as the datum to which the modifications of the subfamilies are related. The stem of *Dennstaedtia* and related genera is a creeping rhizome with hairs. Most other subfamilies have either creeping or climbing rhizomes, or erect and columnar stems; both forms of stem have scales. The vascular system varies from a protostele to a siphonostele to a dictyostele; some members even have a polycyclic arrangement. The number of leaf traces varies from one to several and is usually characteristic for the genus. As in the

other ferns, the endodermis surrounds a pericycle; in some dictyosteles, the endodermis surrounds each bundle (e.g., *Pteridium*).

The fronds are quite variable—branched and finely divided in *Dennstaedtia* and some other genera, but reduced to a simple blade in others. Pinnules and venation are likewise variable; the entire reduced forms with reticulate venation have possibly been derived from the lobed types with open venation. Some examples of pinnules with venation and sori are illustrated in Figure 21–53.

Dennstaedtia has marginal sori situated at the ends of the veins and covered by indusia of abaxial and adaxial flaps that form a cup. According to Holttum. the sori of the family show a divergence into three main types (Fig. 21–54):

1. *Fusion sori*. These have apparently evolved through the lateral fusion of individual sori of the *Dennstaedtia* type; they form a line at or close to the margin of the lamina. A complete series of stages showing this fusion can be seen in species of the genus *Lindsaya*.

2. *Circular sori*. These more or less rounded sori are situated at the vein endings or just back from the ends, with various shapes of indusia or sometimes without indusia. Examples of this type are scattered among the subfamilies (e.g., the genera *Nephrolepis*, *Asplenium*, *Dryopteris*, and others).

3. *Elongate sori*. These are divided into three subtypes, depending on the position and origin of the sori and veins: along one side of a vein, as in *Asplenium*, and originating from a round sorus; along one or both sides of a vein, as in *Athyrium*, and also originating from a round sorus; or along fused veins close to the midrib, as in *Blechnum*, and possibly originating from a round sorus as in *Asplenium*.

The spores of the subfamilies also display a wide range in features (Fig. 21–55). Both monolete and trilete forms are common, sometimes even in the same genus, as in *Lindsaya*. Some spores have a well-developed perispore as an extra covering outside the spore wall. Ornamentation varies from smooth to strongly baculate to coarsely verrucate. In general, the morphology of spores supports the classification

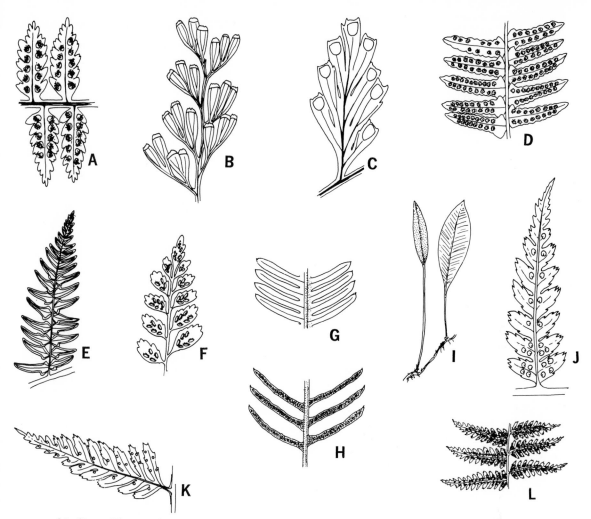

FIGURE 21–53   Pinnae of genera of Dennstaedtiaceae. A, *Dennstaedtia*, ×3; B, *Lindsaya*, ×2; C, *Davallia*, ×4; D, *Nephrolepis*, ×0.5; E, *Pteridium*, ×0.5; F, *Asplenium*, ×1; G, H, *Blechnum* (G, sterile; H, fertile), ×1; I, *Elaphoglossum*, ×0.5; J, *Dryopteris*, ×1; K, *Ctenitis*, ×4; L, *Athyrium*, ×0.5.

based on other structural features, but there are a few discrepancies.

The earliest fossils assignable to this family are from the early Jurassic Period and have been allied with the extant *Davallia*. In the early Cretaceous, leaf compressions of several genera are fairly common, attesting to an increase in representation of the family during this time. By late Cretaceous and early Tertiary times, many of the modern genera were widespread, some existing in far northern latitudes even to Greenland, Spitzbergen, and Siberia. As with ferns of other families, general cooling of climates leading to the Pleistocene ice advance is credited with restricting many genera

to subtropical and tropical regions. Today, the subfamilies are most abundant and widespread in the Southern Hemisphere, with relatively few genera reaching into cool temperate climates of the Northern Hemisphere.

With such a diverse assemblage of ferns and general lack of fossil evidence, it is very difficult to determine phylogenetic relationships with any confidence. Holttum postulates that *Dennstaedtia* was derived from the Dicksoniaceae on the basis of similarities of such features as marginal sori with indusial flaps, gradate sporangia, and oblique annulus. From *Dennstaedtia* and allied genera, he derives four main lines of development leading to the other

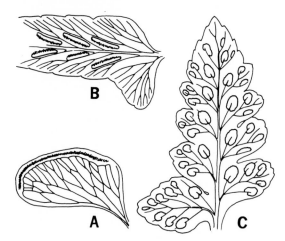

FIGURE 21–54   Three types of sori in Dennstaedtiaceae. A, fusion sori, ×1; B, elongate sori, ×1; C, circular sori, ×1. (After Holttum with permission of Government Printing Office, Singapore.)

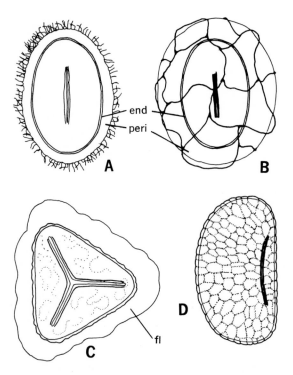

FIGURE 21–55   Four types of spores in Dennstaedtiaceae. A, *Elaphoglossum,* with thick hairy perispore (*peri*) enclosing endospore (*end*), ×1,-000; B, *Asplenium* also with distinct endospore and perispore, ×1,000; C, *Pteris,* which is trilete, with outer flange (*fl*) on wall, ×1,000; D, *Davallia,* with hexagonal verrucae giving pebbly appearance to spore wall, ×1,000.

450 / *VASCULAR PLANTS*

TABLE 21–3

PRIMITIVE AND ADVANCED CHARACTERIS-
TICS IN THE FILICALES *

	PRIMITIVE	DERIVED
stem	slender creeping rhizomes with two rows of fronds on upper surface; protostelic; covered with hairs	upright columnar trunk; polycyclic dictyostele; scales instead of hairs
fronds	large and much branched; dichotomous branching; venation open and dichotomous	small and unbranched; pinnate branching; venation closed and reticulate
sori	simple	gradate, leading to mixed
sporangia	terminal or marginal; large and thick-walled; stout stalk; annulus an unspecialized cluster of cells; large number of spores	superficial on abaxial surface; small and thin-walled; narrow stalk; single row of cells in annulus; small numbers of spores
gametophytes	large; flat dorsiventral thallus and thick cushion area; slow in growth and maturation	small; delicate with no cushion area; unbranched; rapid growth and maturation
antheridia	large; more than four wall cells; several hundred sperm	small; one to four wall cells; small numbers of sperm
archegonia	long and straight neck with several to many neck cells	short and recurved neck with small number of neck cells

* Compiled from Bower, Eames, Holttum, and Sporne.

subfamilies. This is a good example of phenetic series classification based on relative primitiveness and advancement of characteristics of extant plants.

There is good evidence that at least some of the subfamilies of the Dennstaedtiaceae are

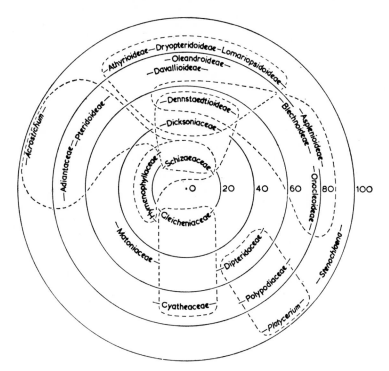

FIGURE 21–56   Classification of Filicales in which families are grouped together by broken lines according to their presumed phylogenetic relationships. Numbers represent successive grades of relative advancement expressed as percentage. (After Sporne with permission of Hutchinson & Co., Ltd.)

still evolving. The family as a whole seems relatively young, and much future evolutionary development is likely.

PHYLOGENY OF FILICALES.   In the descriptions of the various families of the Filicales, numerous references have been made to fossil representatives. As a result of a fairly good fossil record, we are able to trace the time of origin and in some cases the evolutionary development of most of the families. In addition, we can recognize truly primitive features in early fossil members. By applying the primitive criteria to families for which there is little or no fossil record, it is possible to draw up a phylogenetic classification for all the families, as in Figure 21–56. The more primitive families are in the center, and the more advanced range outward along a scale of 0 to 100. The broken lines indicate areas of affinity in which families or subfamilies are most likely closely related. This diagram does not indicate the fossil an-

cestry of the groups; to do this would require a third dimension going below the diagram (see Fig. 28–1).

Several of the primitive and advanced characteristics used to determine filicalean phylogeny appear in Table 21–3. The characteristics generally used for classification are the sori and sporangia, but the other criteria are often used as corroborating evidence.

ORDER MARSILEALES.   Until recently the plants of this order were usually combined with those of the Salviniales into a single order, Hydropteridales. This common classification was based on heterospory and the fact that the plants are usually aquatic. However, structural differences among the genera are sufficiently great to warrant splitting the complex into at least two orders.

The three genera in the Marsileales are *Pilularia*, *Regnellidium*, and *Marsilea*. The last two are more closely related, and are often

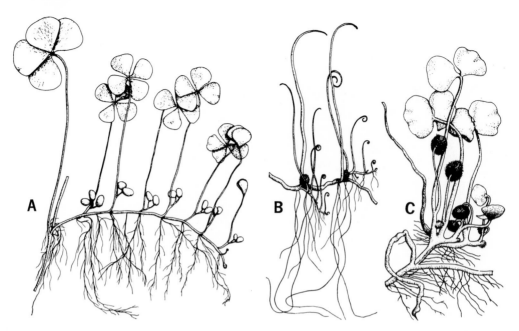

FIGURE 21–57   Marsileales. A, habit view of plant of *Marsilea* showing rhizome, roots, leaves, and sporocarps, ×1; B, habit view of *Pilularia* showing coiled leaves, sporocarps, and roots, ×1; C, habit view of *Regnellidium,* ×1. (A, after Eames, B, after Meunier in Eames, C, after Lindman in Eames, with permission of McGraw-Hill Book Co.)

placed in a separate family, Marsileaceae. The history of the order is meager. The only evidence is provided by the discovery of spores identical with *Pilularia* in Jurassic rocks from New Zealand. However, the vegetative remains are delicate, and the other two genera may have a fossil history as yet undiscovered.

Morphology.   All three genera are small and have creeping branched rhizomes (Fig. 21–57). Adventitious roots arise from the lower surface, usually at the nodes. The leaves are borne on the upper surface, in some instances in two rows. Those of *Marsilea* and *Regnellidium* have lobed leaflets, whereas the leaves of *Pilularia* are without laminae. The veins of *Marsilea* anastomose to form a network; those of *Regnellidium* are finely dichotomous. When the plants are aquatic, the leaflets float on the surface of the water; in terrestrial specimens, they are erect or somewhat spreading.

The rhizomes of all species have amphiphloic arrangements of the vascular tissue (Fig. 21–58). The xylem is exarch or mesarch, with scalariform tracheids. Leaf gaps are large, with

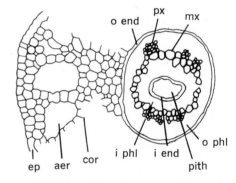

FIGURE 21–58   Transverse section of stem of *Marsilea* showing stele, and cortex with aerenchyma, ×100. *aer,* aerenchyma with large cavities; *cor,* cortex; *ep,* epidermis; *i end,* inner endodermis; *i phl,* inner phloem; *mx,* metaxylem; *o end,* outer endodermis; *o phl,* outer phloem; *px,* protoxylem. (After Smith with permission of McGraw-Hill Book Co.)

simple traces extending into the petioles. Both an internal and an external endodermis are usually present, although *Pilularia* often lacks the internal layer. The cortex contains air cavities within the parenchyma; such a tissue, termed **aerenchyma,** is very common in aquatic plants. Presumably, it functions in gas ex-

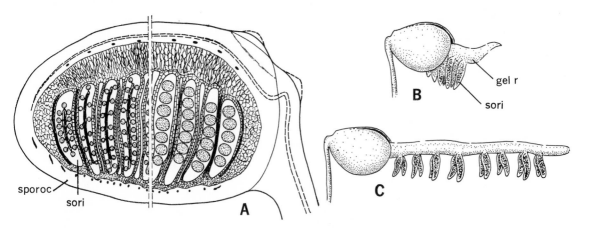

FIGURE 21–59   Sporocarp of *Marsilea*. A, vertical sections through sporocarp (*sporoc*), showing sori containing microsporangia on left, and sori with megasporangia on right, ×15; B, gelatinous ring with sori extended from split sporocarp, ×4; C, gelatinous ring (*gel r*) fully extended, and sporangia ready to dehisce, ×4. (After Eames with permission of McGraw-Hill Book Co.)

change and in providing buoyancy for submerged organs.

Sporangia.   The sporangia of the Marsileales are borne in a special structure called a sporocarp (Fig. 21–59). This is a hard, nut-like receptacle that varies from round to bean-shaped. It is usually interpreted as originating from a fertile pinnate leaf that has been folded inward and subsequently fused along the edges. The sporocarps are attached either in the axils of the leaves or directly to the petioles.

Within the sporocarp, the sporangia of *Marsilea* are borne on receptacles enclosed within sori. The sori are arranged in two lateral rows on the inner walls (Fig. 21–59A). Each sorus is elliptical, covered by an indusium, and has an elongated receptacle with a single vascular trace. The receptacle bears megasporangia along the apical ridge and microsporangia toward the base. The arrangement in *Pilularia* and *Regnellidium* is essentially the same as in *Marsilea*.

When submerged, the sporocarp splits open into two valves and the sori are extruded in a very unique manner (Fig. 21–59B, C). A gelatinous ring lying inside the sporocarp swells and emerges through the split in the wall, dragging the sori outside. The indusium of each sorus soon disintegrates, and the spores are either shed directly or germinate inside the sorus.

Both megasporangia and microsporangia produce 32 or 64 spores, but all except one of the megaspores degenerate. The microspores are about 50 microns in diameter, trilete, and in *Pilularia* invested with a perispore (Fig. 21–60A). The megaspores are several hundred microns in diameter, trilete, and usually ellipsoidal (Fig. 21–60B). In *Marsilea,* the trilete ridge of the megaspores is elevated into a papilla, and the outer cell layer becomes gelatinous when wet. If environmental conditions are right, both types of spore germinate almost immediately after shedding.

The male gametophyte, consisting of nine cells, develops inside the microspore wall (Fig. 21–60C, D). At maturity, there is a single prothallial cell, six jacket cells, and two central spermatogenous cells. The spermatogenous cells divide to form 16 sperm, which escape through the ruptured microspore wall. The sperm is tightly coiled with posterior flagella (Fig. 21–60E).

The female gametophyte also develops endosporally, with the first division occurring immediately below the trilete mark. At maturity the gametophyte consists of a single archegonium, a few encircling cells at the apex, and a single basal cell filled with reserve food materials (Fig. 21–61A). The archegonium and a limited amount of gametophyte tissue protrude through the papilla at maturity. The archego-

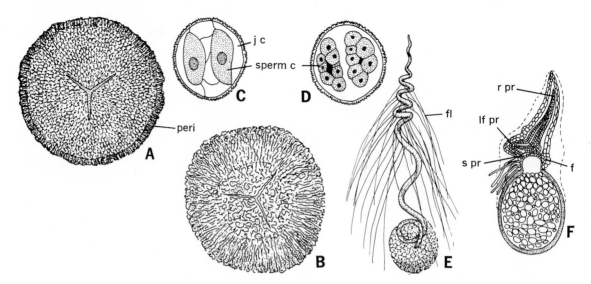

FIGURE 21–60 Marsileales. A, microspore of *Marsilea* showing perispore (*peri*), ×1,000; B, microspore of *Pilularia* showing trilete mark, and minutely folded outer spore wall, ×1,000; C, D, two stages in development of cells of male gametophyte inside microspore (*sperm c,* spermatogenous cells; *j c,* jacket cells), ×355; E, single sperm of *Marsilea* showing coiled body and long flagella (*fl*), ×1,200; F, embryo protruding from archegonium of megaspore, showing stem primordium (*s pr*), leaf primordium (*lf pr*), root primordium (*r pr*), and foot (*f*), ×30. (C–E, after Sharp with permission of *Botanical Gazette;* F, after Sachs.)

nium is thus advantageously placed to receive the sperm, which are trapped in the gelatinous sheath. Following fertilization, the zygote divides very quickly to form quadrants, each of which subsequently differentiates into an organ. The outer two develop into the leaf and root, the inner two into stem and foot. Cells of the gametophyte continue to invest the young embryo for some time before rupturing (Fig. 21–60F).

Phylogeny. Several specialists suggest that the Marsileales is related to the Filicales, particularly to the families Schizaeaceae, Hymenophyllaceae, and Cyatheaceae. This is based on similarities in structure—especially in sporangia, leaves, epidermal hairs, and anatomy. However, there are no direct links between the Marsileales and any other group, and so relationships, if any, must be remote. Although the spores of *Pilularia* from the Jurassic of New Zealand indicate a history at least from the Mesozoic, a clear picture of phylogeny must await future fossil discoveries.

ORDER SALVINIALES. The ferns of this order are small and aquatic, and occur free-floating in fresh-water ponds and lakes. There

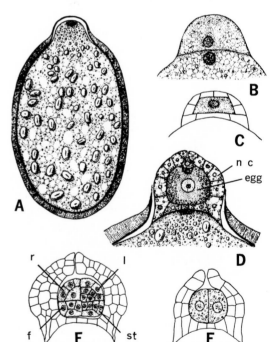

FIGURE 21–61 Female gametophyte and embryo of *Marsilea*. A, megaspore with archegonial initial at top, ×35; B–D, stages in development of archegonium, showing neck cells (*n c*) and egg in D, ×180; E, F, two early stages in embryonic development, showing primordia of root (*r*), leaf (*l*), stem (*st*), and foot (*f*). (After Haupt with permission of McGraw-Hill Book Co.)

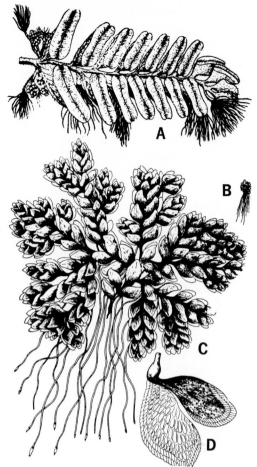

FIGURE 21–62 Habit views showing roots, leaves, and sporocarps. A, *Salvinia*, ×10; B–D, *Azolla;* B, C, ×10; D, sporocarp, ×25. (After Martius in Eames with permission of McGraw-Hill Book Co.)

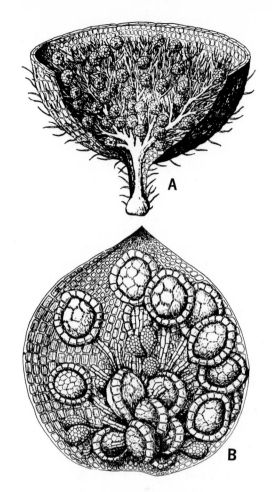

FIGURE 21–63 Sporocarps of Salviniales. A, *Salvinia*, ×80; B, *Azolla*, ×100. (After Martius in Eames with permission of McGraw-Hill Book Co.)

are only two genera: *Azolla* with some five species, and *Salvinia* with 13 (Fig. 21–62A, B). Both are heterosporous, and bear sporangia in sporocarps. The species of the two genera differ markedly in structural details, and are usually classified in two separate families.

The history of the Salviniales is relatively short. *Salvinia* has been reported from the Upper Cretaceous, and *Azolla* has been found in abundance in Tertiary rocks from some localities in North America, Europe, and Asia.

Morphology. Plants of both genera have very delicate branched stems that lie flat on the water. In *Salvinia,* there are whorls of three leaves, two occurring laterally, the third submerged and dissected into many hair-like filaments. These filaments are multicellular and rigid, and apparently function as roots. In *Azolla,* the leaves are spatulate, and arranged alternately in two rows. Each leaf is divided into two lobes. The upper is photosynthetic with stomata, and remains exposed to the air. The lower lobe is colorless, and probably functions in absorbing water. *Azolla* differs from *Salvinia* in having true roots extending into the water from the junctions of the branches. As well as deriving nutrient material, the roots probably help to maintain the orientation of the plant in moving water.

Unlike those of the Marsileales, a sporocarp of *Azolla* and *Salvinia* represents a single sorus, and the sporocarp wall is a modified indusium. Both genera normally produce megasporangia and microsporangia in separate sporocarps on the same plant. The sporocarps of *Azolla* are borne on the first leaf of a lateral branch (Fig. 21–63B). Those producing microsporangia are large and round, whereas those containing a single megasporangium are small and somewhat elongate. In both sporocarps, the sporangia develop on elongated receptacles. Although both micro- and megasporangia begin to differentiate on each receptacle, one type usually aborts, so that the mature sporangia are of a single kind.

The sporangia of *Azolla* develop a unique structure known as the **periplasmodium.** This is a multinucleate, mucilaginous mass that originates from the tapetum of the sporangial wall. In the megasporangia, the periplasmodium separates into four sectors known as **massulae.** One of these surrounds the single functional megaspore, while the remaining three sit as a cap on top. The megaspore germinates to form a small protruding prothallus that contains one to several archegonia. The periplasmodium of the microsporangium also breaks up into a variable number of massulae. Each has microspores embedded near the outer edge, which are trilete and range from 15 to 25 microns in diameter. In some species, the units of the massulae terminate in anchor-like filaments. These become readily enmeshed with the massulae of the megaspores, thus facilitating fertilization. The male gametophyte develops into a single antheridium that ultimately produces eight sperm.

The sporocarps of *Salvinia* are similar to those of *Azolla,* except that many megasporangia develop instead of only one, and a single massula is produced in the microsporangium (Fig. 21–63A). The megagametophyte develops essentially inside the megaspore, although it protrudes slightly at maturity and exposes several archegonia for fertilization.

Phylogeny. The relationships of the Salviniales to the other ferns are completely unknown, and the order is generally considered to be a specialized group among the ferns. Some investigators have suggested a connection to the Hymenophyllaceae, based on supposed similarities in sporangial structure. However, this link appears very tenuous, and any relationship in this direction is remote. If the first record of representatives of the group in the late Cretaceous is a true picture, the two genera of Salviniales may be reduced and specialized ancestors of some Mesozoic Filicales.

REFERENCES

Andrews, H. N., Jr., "Evolutionary Trends in Early Vascular Plants." *Cold Spring Harbor Symposia,* 24: 217–234 (1960).

Andrews, H. N., Jr., *Studies in Paleobotany.* New York: John Wiley & Sons, Inc. (1961). Pp. 59–128.

Bower, F. O., *The Ferns.* Vols. 1–3. London: Cambridge University Press (1923, 1926, 1928).

Copeland, E. B., *Genera Filicum.* Waltham, Mass.: Chronica Botanica Co. (1947).

Delevoryas, T., *Morphology and Evolution of Fossil Plants*. New York: Holt, Rinehart and Winston, Inc. (1962). Pp. 67–94.

Eames, A. J., *Morphology of Vascular Plants*. New York: McGraw-Hill Book Co., Inc. (1936). Pp. 117–304.

Erdtman, G., *Pollen Morphology and Plant Taxonomy: Gymnospermae, Pteridophyta, Bryophyta*. Waltham, Mass.: Chronica Botanica Co. (1957).

Evans, A. M., "Ameiotic Alternation of Generations: A New Life Cycle in the Ferns." *Science,* 143: 261–263 (1964).

Foster, A. S., and Gifford, E. M., *Comparative Morphology of Vascular Plants*. San Francisco: W. H. Freeman and Co. (1959). Pp. 240–319.

Harris, W. F., "A Manual of the Spores of New Zealand Pteridophyta." *New Zealand Dept. Sci. Ind. Res.,* Bull. 116 (1955).

Holttum, R. E., "A Revised Classification of Leptosporangiate Ferns." *J. Linn. Soc. (Bot.) London,* 53: 123–158 (1947).

Holttum, R. E., *Flora of Malaya*. Vol. 2: *Ferns of Malaya*. Singapore: Government Printing Office (1954).

Leclercq, S., and Banks, H. P., *"Pseudosporochnus nodosus* sp. nov., a Middle Devonian Plant with Cladoxylalean Affinities." *Palaeontographica,* 110 (B): 2–31 (1962).

Näf, U., "Antheridium Formation in Ferns—A Model for the Study of Developmental Change." *J. Linn. Soc. (Bot.) London,* 58: 321–332 (1963).

Pichi-Sermoli, R. E. G., "The Higher Taxa of the Pteridophyta and Their Classification." *Uppsala Univ. Årsskr.,* 6: 70–90 (1958).

Seward, A. C., "The Past and Present Distribution of Certain Ferns." *J. Linn. Soc. (Bot.) London,* 46: 219–240 (1922).

Sporne, K. R., *The Morphology of Pteridophytes*. London: Hutchinson & Co. (Publishers) Ltd. (1962). Pp. 114–174.

Verdoorn, F. (Ed.), *Manual of Pteridology*. The Hague: Martinus Nijhoff (1938).

Wagner, W. H., Jr., "Irregular Morphological Development in Hybrid Ferns." *Phytomorphology,* 12: 87–100 (1962).

Wagner, W. H., and Sharp, A. J., "A Remarkably Reduced Vascular Plant in the United States." *Science,* 142: 1483–1484 (1963).

White, R. A., "Tracheary Elements of the Ferns, I." *Am. J. Bot.,* 50: 447–454 (1963).

White, R. A., "Tracheary Elements of the Ferns, II." *Am. J. Bot.,* 50: 514–522 (1963).

22/DIVISION

PTERIDOSPERMOPHYTA

The plants of this division are known only as fossils. They range from the early Carboniferous to the Cretaceous, and appear to have reached maximum numbers and structural diversity in the late Carboniferous.

The *pteridosperms,* or seed ferns as they are often called, are characterized by fern-like fronds that bear both **seeds** and **pollen-**producing organs. The seeds show structural similarities to those of modern cycads, whereas many of the pollen organs are synangia consisting of sporangia without annuli. Other features include secondary xylem with bordered pits on the radial wall, a prominent cortex with fiber strands, and large leaf traces that consist of one to several vascular strands. Some of the pteridosperms were trees, whereas others were apparently smaller, somewhat sprawling plants.

Prior to 1903, many of the fronds in Carboniferous rocks were generally believed to be those of true ferns, and the Carboniferous had been referred to generally as the "Age of Ferns." In 1903, it was demonstrated that a seed belonged to the same plant as a genus with fern-like fronds. This initiated the concept of pteridosperms. Since that time, many seeds and pollen-organs have been discovered attached to fronds, and there is now a fairly good concept of the pteridosperms. However, there is little doubt that additional fossil discoveries will further enhance our knowledge.

The pteridosperms are usually classified into five families.

Two of these are limited to the Paleozoic, and the other three occur in the Mesozoic. Although all the families are generally considered to be true pteridosperms, they have a great diversity in structure, and the exact phylogenetic relationships are not well known.

PALEOZOIC PTERIDOSPERMS

Family Lyginopteridaceae. This Carboniferous family contains the classical *Lyginopteris oldhamia,* the first plant shown to bear both fern-like fronds and seeds (Fig. 22–1). The stem, which reaches a diameter of 3 cm, contains a central pith, surrounded by mesarch bundles of xylem and phloem (Fig. 22–2, 3). Secondary xylem and phloem form a narrow cylinder outside the primary bundle. The secondary xylem has large tracheids with bordered pits and numerous rays. Outside the secondary phloem is a parenchymatous inner cortex, and an outer cortex consisting of anastomosing fiber cells with interspersed parenchyma. Stalked glands with globular heads cover the outer surface of smaller stems. A periderm, found in larger stems, appears to have differentiated from cells of the inner cortex.

The leaves of *Lyginopteris* are up to half a meter long and fern-like with pinnate branching. The pinnules have several lobes and are constricted at the base. The seeds of *Lyginopteris* occur on the tips of fronds (Fig. 22–4A). Each seed, barrel-shaped and approximately 5 mm long, consists of an innermost gametophyte enclosed by the sporangial wall, or **nucellus.** This in turn is enclosed by a single **integument,** except for a narrow opening, the **micropyle,** at the tip of the seed. Here, the nucellus projects as a beak into a flask-shaped chamber, the **pollen chamber,** which is formed between the beak and the overarching integument. It has been surmised that **pollen grains** found in the pollen chamber produced sperm that fertilized the egg in the archegonium directly, as in extant cycads. The whole seed is enclosed in a **cupule,** consisting of segments

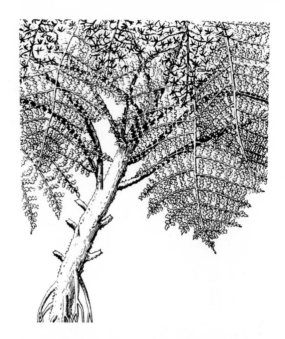

FIGURE 22–1   Reconstruction of part of *Lyginopteris oldhamia,* showing roots, trunk, and fronds, ×0.5. (After Emberger with permission of Masson et Cie.)

with globular glands that completely covered the seed at maturity. These glands, identical to those on the stems and frond petioles, provide important evidence for linking isolated fragments of seeds, leaves, and stems.

Although pollen-organs have never been found attached to *Lyginopteris,* they are believed to be similar to those named *Crossotheca* (Fig. 22–4B). Pollen-organs of *Crossotheca* consist of a central axis with lateral branches terminating in slightly flattened appendages. The sporangia hang from the margin of the lower surface of each appendage. In at least one species the spores are trilete, smooth-walled, and measure from 43 to 58 microns.

Other stems, leaves, and seeds found in Carboniferous rocks are very similar to *Lyginopteris,* and are classified in the same family.

Family Medullosaceae. This is another family of Carboniferous pteridosperms distinguished by polystelic stems. Most of the stems are classified in a single genus, *Medullosa,* of which *Medullosa noei* is a good representative.

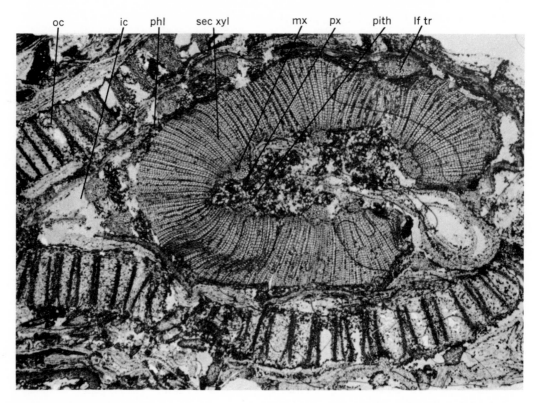

FIGURE 22–2   Transverse section of stem of *Lyginopteris*, showing stele and cortex, ×4. *ic*, inner cortex; *lf tr*, leaf trace; *mx*, metaxylem; *oc*, outer cortex; *phl*, phloem; *px*, protoxylem; *sec xyl*, secondary xylem.

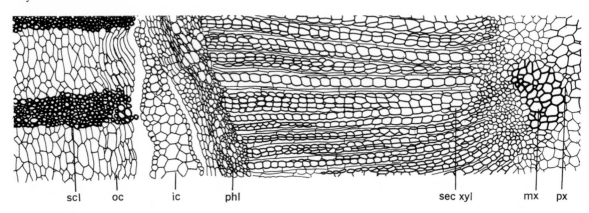

scl   oc   ic   phl   sec xyl   mx px

FIGURE 22–3   Strip from pith to outer cortex of transverse section of stem of *Lyginopteris* ×30. *ic*, inner cortex; *mx*, metaxylem; *oc*, outer cortex; *phl*, phloem; *px*, protoxylem; *scl*, sclerenchyma fibers; *sec xyl*, secondary xylem.

As reconstructed, *Medullosa noei* consists of a trunk about 5 meters in height, with prop roots around the base, and spirally arranged fronds toward the top (Fig. 22–5). Numerous leaf bases cover the central regions of the stem. The fronds are dichotomously branched and have a pinnate arrangement of both secondary pinnae and pinnules.

The anatomy of the stem is very characteristic (Fig. 22–6A). The vascular tissue is in the form of a polystele, and the number of steles varies from a few in young stems to many

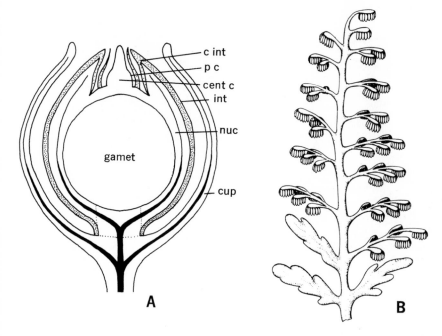

FIGURE 22–4   *Lyginopteris*. A, seed and cupule, showing vascular strands in black, ×1; B, *Crossotheca*, probable pollen organ of *Lyginopteris*, showing sporangia hanging from lower surfaces of flattened appendages, ×2. *cup*, cupule; *c int*, canopy of integument; *cent c*, central column; *int*, integument; *nuc*, nucellus; *p c*, pollen chamber. (A, after Oliver and Scott; B, from Andrews with permission of John Wiley & Sons, Inc.)

in older stems. Each stele contains a central core of primary xylem with mesarch protoxylem, and is surrounded by a cylinder of secondary xylem and phloem. The steles, embedded in parenchyma containing secretory cells, are bounded on the outside by a parenchymatous cortex. Periderm is found on the inner face of the cortex. In older stems, the cortex sloughs off during development, and the periderm forms the outer limits of the stem.

Numerous leaf traces occur at different levels in the cortex. Each trace departs from the outside of a stele, as a concentric bundle with secondary xylem. As it passes through the cortex it loses the secondary xylem and splits into several collateral bundles before entering the petiole of the frond.

Seeds named *Pachytesta* have been found closely associated with *Medullosa noei* (Fig. 22–6B). *Pachytesta* has a nucellus containing a vascular strand and possesses a somewhat flat-

tened pollen chamber at the distal end of the nucellus. The integument consists of several layers and, except at the base, is completely free from the nucellus; it arches over the pollen chamber, forming the micropyle. Seeds of the general form of *Pachytesta* have been found in place of a terminal or lateral pinnule on some fern-like fronds.

A pollen-bearing organ believed to belong to *Medullosa* is named *Dolerotheca* (Fig. 22–7). This shallow, cup-shaped organ consists of many elongate sporangia fused together. The pollen grains have a single furrow, or sulcus, thereby resembling the grains of cycads.

PTERIDOSPERM EVOLUTION

The pteridosperms of the early Carboniferous are among the first plants to have true **ovules** (unfertilized seeds). The ovule, which

FIGURE 22–5 Reconstruction of *Medullosa* showing roots, leaf bases, and fronds, ×0.03. (After Stewart and Delevoryas with permission of *The Botanical Review*.)

can be best defined as "an integumented female sporangium," is generally considered a major structural achievement in the evolution of vascular plants. The enclosure of the sporangial wall by an integument makes possible both better protection and a nutrient supply for the developing female gametophyte—features almost certainly giving seed plants an advantage over plants with uncoated sporangia. Thus, it is of great interest that plants with seeds had evolved as early as the early Carboniferous. It is even more significant that this marked the beginning of a long series of evolutionary developments among several major groups of vascular plants with seeds, including the various taxa of **gymnosperms** and **angiosperms** to be described in the following chapters.

The steps in evolution of the ovule offer an exciting and somewhat speculative problem, and several theories have been proposed to explain the probable derivation. One theory holds that the lobed integument surrounding

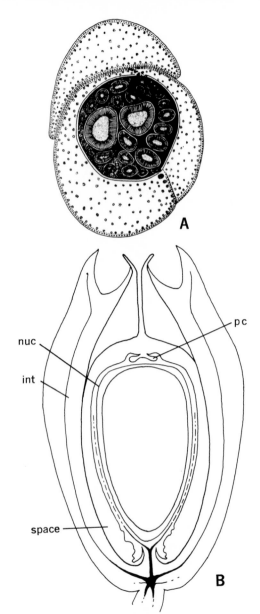

FIGURE 22–6 A, transverse section of *Medullosa* stem showing polystelic arrangement of vascular tissue, and secretory cells in outer parenchyma, ×1; B, vertical section through *Pachytesta* showing nucellus (*nuc*), integument (*int*), and pollen chamber (*p c*), ×1. (A, after Stewart and Delevoryas with permission of *The Botanical Review*; B, after Stewart with permission of *American Journal of Botany*.)

the female sporangium in an ovule such as that of *Lyginopteris* actually formed from the reduction and fusion of sterile or possibly fertile **telomes**—a telome being a single terminal seg-

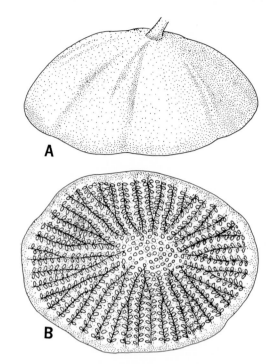

FIGURE 22–7   *Dolerotheca.* A, view of top of organ, ×2; B, view of underside showing numerous pollen sacs opening to outside, ×2. (After Schopf with permission of *Journal of Paleontology.*)

ment of a branching axis. Another theory suggests that, during the course of evolution, a female sporangium became modified by a separation and a differentiation of the sporangial wall into an outer integument and an inner nucellus, accompanied by a branching of the vascular strand.

In actual fact, we do not have any direct evidence for the evolutionary ancestry of the Paleozoic pteridosperms or of the seed habit. The early pteridosperms may have descended from such fern-like plants as *Cladoxylon,* species of which are polystelic and have secondary development of tissues. It has also been suggested that plants of the Upper Devonian progymnosperms, discussed in Chapter 25, were ancestral to the pteridosperms. According to this hypothesis, the pteridosperms probably evolved as one line from progymnosperms, and the coniferophytes along a separate line. However, the progymnosperms possess only a pteridophyte type of reproduction. There is no suggestion of an attainment of the seed habit, but they exhibit vegetative characteristics allied with both the pteridosperms and coniferophytes.

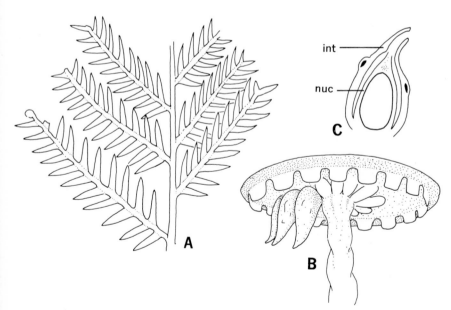

int

nuc

FIGURE 22–8   *Lepidopteris.* A, part of frond, ×0.3; B, peltate disc with seeds attached to underside, ×4; C, vertical section through seed, showing nucellus (*nuc*) and integument (*int*), ×15. (After Harris with permission of *Meddelelser om Grønland.*)

Before considering Mesozoic pteridosperms, we will digress briefly to consider the
origin of the seed habit, and to introduce some
terms that will be used throughout later chapters. These topics follow naturally from the
discussion of Paleozoic pteridosperms, and will
provide a common background for tracing the
evolution of the seed habit in other groups of
seed plants.

THE SEED HABIT

Botanists generally accept that the seed
evolved by the integumentation of a megaspore
of some ancestral heterosporous stock. However, a good case has been made by Thomson,
and more recently supported by Bold, that it is
entirely possible and even probable that a homosporous form was ancestral. As noted by
Thomson, the critical features in seed organiza-

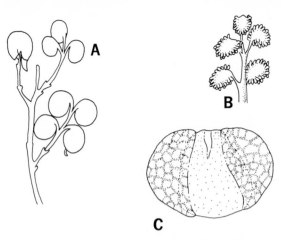

FIGURE 22–9   *Corystospermaceae.* A, seed-
bearing branches of *Umkomasia* showing typical
shield shape of seed in upper left, ×1; B,
Pteruchus, pollen-bearing organ, ×0.75; C, pollen
grain isolated from *Pteruchus,* ×500. (A, B, after
Thomas with permission of Royal Society of
London; C, after Townrow with permission of
Grana Palynologica.)

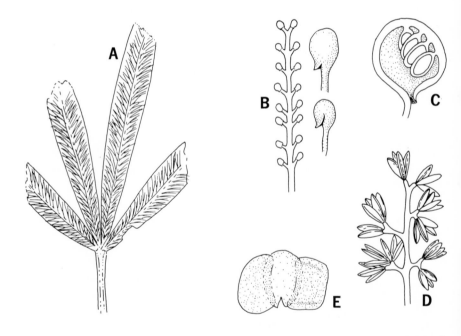

FIGURE 22–10   Caytoniaceae. A, *Sagenopteris,* leaf of plant bearing *Caytonia*
seeds, ×0.3; B, *Caytonia,* seed-bearing axis, with two helmet-shaped cupules,
×0.6; C, vertical section through cupule of *Caytonia* showing four seeds attached to inner wall, ×5; D, *Caytonanthus,* pollen-bearing organ, ×0.6; E,
pollen grain isolated from pollen sacs of *Caytonanthus,* ×1,000. (A, after
Seward with permission of Cambridge University Press; B–D, after Thomas
with permission of Royal Society of London; E, after Townrow with permission of *Grana Palynologica.*)

tion are **sex differentiation** and endosporal prothallial development. These features are accompanied by a food supply derived from a tapetal nucellus, instead of from stored food, as in free-sporing plants. Size difference, which is so significant in heterosporous free-sporing plants, is completely unimportant in seed development. In fact, as shown by Thomson, in a great many seed plants there is no significant difference in size between the uninucleate seed-spores and pollen-spores, and he cites several instances where the pollen spore is actually larger than the seed spore.

Botanists generally accept that a heterosporous and hence unisexual plant is obviously the most likely ancestor to the seed, because sex differentiation goes hand in hand with heterospory. This is, in fact, quite possible, and although we do not want to prejudice the case, we do feel that Thomson has presented a good argument for homospory. Ancestral heterospory for the origin of the seed habit should not be blindly accepted without good evidence—especially the suggestion that sex differentiation could not have occured in homosporous ancestors.

In view of this unsettled problem, we are employing special names for the spores, sporangia, and sporophylls in seed plants. These are **androspore, androsporangium,** and **androsporophyll** for the pollen units; **gynospore, gynosporangium,** and **gynosporophyll** for the seed units. By using such designations, we are emphasizing the importance of sex differentiation in seed plants, and also keeping the terms compatible with those used for angiosperm flowers—namely **androecium** and **gynoecium.** Thus, we have names that can be applied to the structures that lead to development of gametes in all seed plants—designations that emphasize sex differentiation and deemphasize differences in size of spore.

MESOZOIC
PTERIDOSPERMS

Plants believed to be affiliated with the seed ferns are known from Triassic and Jurassic

rocks of both the Northern and Southern Hemispheres. These plants are usually classified into three distinct families, which show no apparent relationship to each other except for the possession of seeds and fern-like foliage. The families are described fully in paleobotanical texts, but can only be mentioned briefly here.

Because of their possession of seeds and their position in time, the chief significance of these plants is the possibility that they offer clues to the origin of angiospermy. This is particularly true of the plants of the Caytoniaceae, which have characteristics so close to angiospermy that they were once considered to be actual forerunners of the angiosperms.

Family Peltaspermaceae. This family is represented by plants from the late Triassic of South Africa and Greenland. The best-known genus is *Lepidopteris,* which has twice-pinnate fern-like fronds with open venation in the pinnules (Fig. 22–8A). Seeds about 15 mm in diameter have been found attached to the lower surface of a peltate stalked disc (Fig. 22–8B). Each seed is oval, about 7 mm long, with a micropyle formed by a curved integument (Fig. 22–8C). The oval pollen grains are contained in pollen sacs produced in two rows on the lower surface of branches that resemble reduced pinnae.

Family Corystospermaceae. Several genera of detached seeds and pollen-bearing organs from early Mesozoic rocks in Africa and South America have been classified as a distinct family, the Corystospermaceae (literally, helmet seed). The plants appear to have been small with fern-like fronds. Reproductive organs are unisexual and arranged on branched axes. Seed-bearing branches arise from the stem in the axil of a bract and have recurved cupules on the branch tips (Fig. 22–9A). The helmet-shaped cupules contain seeds with micropyles that project beyond the lips of the cupule. Branches supporting pollen-bearing organs have no subtending bract, and the sporangia are clustered on the expanded tips of the branch endings (Fig. 22–9B). Bladdered pollen grains have been found in some of the sporangia (Fig. 22–9C).

Family Caytoniaceae. This family is represented by leaves, seed-bearing organs, and pollen-producing organs in rocks ranging in age from Triassic to Lower Cretaceous (Fig. 22–10). Although they were originally believed to be angiospermous, later investigations indicated that the plants were not truly angiosperms; they are now generally considered to be a specialized offshoot of the pteridosperms.

The most significant fossil is the seed-bearing organ called *Caytonia*. This consists of a central axis with two lateral rows of circular sacs (Fig. 22–10B). Each of these is a cupule that opens by a lip near the base (Fig. 22–10C). Seeds are attached inside the wall of the cupule and project into the cavity. The resemblance of this cupule to the **carpel** of an angiosperm prompted botanists to assign *Caytonia* originally to the angiosperms. Later work, however, disclosed pollen grains inside the cupule, indicating that pollination took place in each ovule rather than on the lip of the cupule—not a true angiospermous condition. However, *Caytonia* is an example of evolutionary development close to angiospermy, and suggests how the process may have occurred in other lines.

REFERENCES

Andrews, H. N., Jr., *Studies in Paleobotany*. New York: John Wiley & Sons, Inc. (1961). Pp. 129–166.

Andrews, H. N., Jr., "Early Seed Plants." *Science,* 142: 925–931 (1963).

Bold, H. C., *Morphology of Plants*. New York: Harper & Row, Publishers (1957). Pp. 451–471, 603–620.

Delevoryas, T., "The Medullosaceae—Structure and Relationships." *Palaeontographica,* 97(B): 113–167 (1955).

Delevoryas, T., *Morphology and Evolution of Fossil Plants*. New York: Holt, Rinehart and Winston, Inc. (1962). Pp. 103–128.

Thomson, R. B., "Evolution of the Seed Habit in Plants." *Trans. Roy. Soc. Canada,* Ser. 3, 21(5): 229–272 (1927).

Townrow, J. A., "The Peltaspermaceae, a Pteridosperm Family of Permian and Triassic Age." *Palaeontology,* 3: 333–361 (1960).

Walton, J., *An Introduction to the Study of Fossil Plants,* 2nd Ed. London: A. & C. Black Ltd. (1953).

23/DIVISION

CYCADOPHYTA

Plants of this division are classified into two distinct orders, the Bennettitales (sometimes called Cycadeoideales) and the Cycadales. The Bennettitales are known only from fossil remains, ranging from the early to late Mesozoic. The Cycadales are also recorded as fossils from the early Mesozoic, but persist to the present, with nine genera scattered in subtropical and tropical latitudes. Both groups reached maximum development in mid-Mesozoic times, when they formed a conspicuous and dominant part of the flora. It is almost certain that both lines had their origins in the Paleozoic pteridosperms.

The two groups, collectively called *cycadophytes,* are usually treated as distinct orders within one division (or subdivision). However, good evidence indicates that the two groups are not closely related. This concept may gain sufficient support from future research to warrant the creation of two distinct divisions. The two orders are similar in several respects, especially in plant habit and macroscopic leaf organization, and for the present they can probably best be treated as separate orders of the single division Cycadophyta.

ORDER BENNETTITALES (CYCADEOIDEALES). The plants of this order form one of the striking and dominant elements of Mesozoic floras, leading some investigators to call the Mesozoic Era the "Age of Cycads." The Bennettitales apparently evolved in the late Carboniferous or Permian, reached a zenith of development in the Jurassic, and declined dramatically to extinction in the late Cretaceous. Thus, in general evolutionary pattern, they appear to parallel the rise and fall of the dinosaurs. Quite logically, this has led to the suggestion that the Bennettitales and dinosaurs were to some degree interdependent, although no direct evidence for this has been found.

The Bennettitales comprise two families, the Cycadeoideaceae and Williamsoniaceae. Although obviously related, plants of the two families show distinct differences in habit, anatomy, and reproductive structures.

Cycadeoidea is the best-known genus of the Cyadeoideaceae (Fig. 23–1). It has been found in many parts of the world but especially in the Black Hills of South Dakota. The stems consist of short, often barrel-shaped trunks that superficially resemble pineapple fruits. Some species have branched trunks, but many are unbranched. A close examination reveals a dense covering of leaf bases arranged spirally around the stem. These bases are surrounded by a thick mat of long flat multicellular hairs or scales. No mature leaves have been found attached to the stems, but young leaves indicate a pinnate arrangement of leaflets. From this it is generally interpreted that mature leaves were pinnate fronds arranged in a crown at the top of the trunk.

The stems have a large pith and cortex, and a narrow cylinder of xylem. In this arrangement, they resemble the stems of the extant species of the Cycadales. The primary xylem is endarch, with tracheids and rays of secondary xylem arranged in radial rows. The tracheids have bordered pitting of a circular or scalariform pattern. Leaf traces are numerous, and they are usually conspicuously C-shaped with the concave side pointing inward.

The reproductive organs of *Cycadeoidea* are most interesting, and have received much critical attention. They are found embedded in the trunk among the leaf bases, often in large numbers. Each unit is a bisporangiate fructification, consisting of a central cone-shaped receptacle. This receptacle is subtended and surrounded by fleshy segments containing embedded pollen sacs (Fig. 23–2A, B). The seeds are embedded in **interseminal scales** on the same receptacle; each has a single integument, and so is similar to the seeds of extant cycads.

The bisporangiate structure has variously been called a strobilus, cone, and flower, but its exact nature is unknown. Recent studies of the vascular bundle arrangement have indicated that the reproductive stalk has connections with the leaf traces instead of directly with the stele as in normal axillary branches. Thus, the fructification appears to be a foliar rather than a **cauline** structure. Although similar in general arrangement to a flower such as that of *Magnolia* (see Chapter 27), the seeds are entirely without development of an ovary. Thus, there is no homology with the angiosperm flower, and the term "flower" should be abandoned or used with reservations in any group but the Anthophyta (see Chapter 27). The whole structure appears closer to a compound strobilus or cone, and such a designation avoids any suggestion of homology or relationship with anthophytes.

The well known genus *Williamsonia* is found in Jurassic rocks on several continents. The plants differ from *Cycadeoidea* in having elongated, branched, and somewhat columnar trunks with the characteristic spirally arranged leaf bases, and whorls of leaves at the branch endings (Fig. 23–3). The leaves are frond-like, with one row of pinnate leaflets arranged along each side of the rachis.

The reproductive structures are generally similar to those of *Cycadeoidea*, although most specimens appear to be unisexual. The seed-bearing organ has seeds embedded on a receptacle (Fig. 23–4C), whereas the pollen-bearing organ has either pollen sacs free on pinnate appendages, or fused into synangia on the inner surfaces of appendages (Fig. 24–4A, B). It is not known whether the plants were **monoecious** or **dioecious.**

Detached leaves of the Bennettitales are widespread in Mesozoic rocks, and are sometimes abundant. In morphology, the leaves cannot generally be distinguished from those of the Cycadales. However, critical investigations have shown that the stomatal and epidermal pattern of bennettite leaves is decidedly different from that of the Cycadales. The most critical feature is the origin and arrangement of the

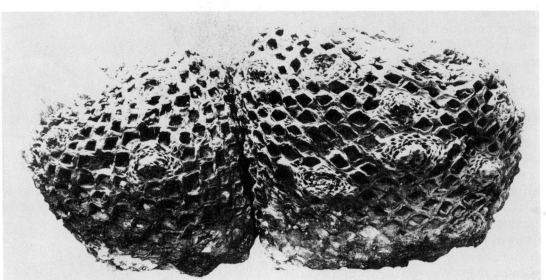

FIGURE 23–1   A, B, petrified trunks of *Cycadeoidea* showing rhomboidal leaf bases and embedded strobili, ×0.33. (After Wieland.)

guard and subsidiary cells of the stomata. In bennettite leaves, the development of the stomatal apparatus is called **syndetocheilic.** In this type, the subsidiary cells and guard cells originate from the same mother cell (Fig. 23–5A, B). Another noteworthy feature is the presence

of thick cuticle layers on the outer walls of the guard cells.

Another type of development of stomatal apparatus, found in the fossil and extant Cycadales, is called **haplocheilic.** In this type the two guard cells develop from a single initial,

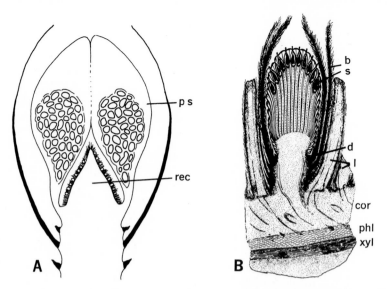

FIGURE 23–2   A, strobilus of *Cycadeoidea* in vertical section showing pollen sacs (*p s*) overarching seed-bearing receptacle (*rec*), ×1; B, vertical section through strobilus of *Cycadeoidea* showing numerous seeds embedded in receptacle, ×1. *b*, bract; *cor*, cortex; *l*, leaf base; *phl*, phloem; *s*, seed; *xyl*, xylem. (A, after Delevoryas with permission of *American Journal of Botany*; B, after Wieland.)

whereas the subsidiary cells originate as ordinary epidermal initials that subsequently become modified (Fig. 23–5C, D). The subsidiary cells usually form a ring around the guard cells, which have no appreciable cuticular thickenings on the walls.

Phylogeny of Bennettitales. The Bennettitales are generally believed to have originated from the pteridosperms. The structure of stem and leaf are evidence of such a derivation, but the relationships of the reproductive organs are obscure.

The most controversial organ is the bennettite fructification, which has often been compared to an angiosperm flower such as that of *Magnolia.* The bracts beneath the ring of pollen-bearing appendages have been compared to calyx and corolla of this genus; the pollen-bearing appendages have been equated to the stamens; and the ovules on the receptacle compared with the fruits of a magnolian receptacle. However, despite this similarity both paleobotanists and neobotanists have pointed out most emphatically that the bennettite seeds are without carpels, and so are strictly related to gymnosperm seeds. Thus, there appears to be no close relationship between the Bennettitales

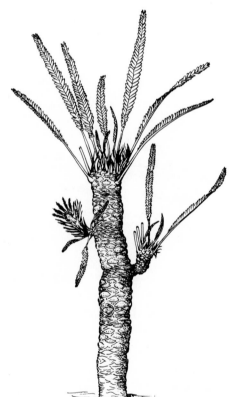

FIGURE 23–3   Reconstruction of *Williamsonia* showing branches, leaf bases, and leaves, ×0.03. (After Sahni with permission of Geological Survey of India.)

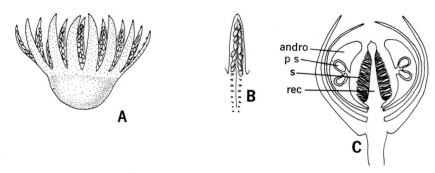

FIGURE 23–4   *Williamsonia*. A, pollen-bearing organ showing pollen sacs on inner surface, ×0.6; B, single lobe with pollen sacs, ×1; C, vertical section through seed-bearing organ, showing seeds (*s*) attached to receptacle (*rec*), pollen sacs (*p s*) embedded in androsporophylls (*andro*), ×1.5. (A, B, after Nathorst with permission of *Kungl. Svenska Vetenskapsacadamiens Handlingar;* C, after Harris with permission of Royal Society of London.)

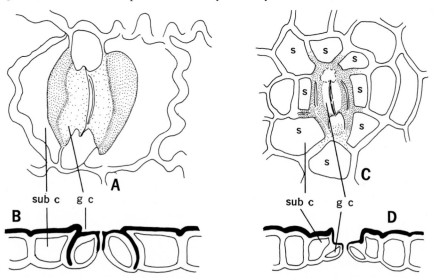

FIGURE 23–5   Stomatal patterns in cycadophytes. A, B, syndetocheilic stomata of leaves of *Pterophyllum,* a bennettite leaf, showing two subsidiary cells (*sub c*), guard cells (*g c*), and cuticle in black, ×600; C, D, haplocheilic stomata of *Pseudoctenis,* a cycadalean leaf, showing ring of subsidiary cells , guard cells, and cuticle in black, ×500. (After Harris with permission of *Meddelelser om Grønland.*)

and the angiosperms, but the general similarities of reproductive structures present notable examples of parallel evolutionary development. If there is any relationship, it is certainly remote in the Paleozoic pteridosperms.

The Bennettitales also apparently have a somewhat remote relationship to the Cycadales. Although they share general anatomical and morphological similarities, the Cycadales differ markedly from the bennettites in having unisexual cones and a haplocheilic development of stomata. It is generally believed that the Ben-

nettitales and Cycadales evolved from the pteridosperms, but along different paths from an early time. The bennettite avenue, which led to the development of a flowerlike organ, ended in extinction at almost the same time that the dinosaurs disappeared. In contrast, the cycads evolved unisexual cones and have persisted to the present as nine genera.

ORDER CYCADALES.   This order of cycadophytes forms one of the smallest, yet most interesting groups of living vascular plants. From

Mesozoic times, when they were widespread and relatively abundant, they declined in numbers of species and individuals during the Cretaceous and Tertiary periods. Today, the nine extant genera are found in relatively limited regions of the tropics and subtropics (Table 23–1). The restricted ranges suggest that the cycads are heading toward extinction.

Morphology. In general habit, the extant cycads most closely resemble palm trees and tree ferns (Fig. 23–6). The forms of stem range from very short and bulbous to tall and columnar. In nearly all, the leaves are large pinnate fronds borne in a crown at the apex of the stem. Cycads range from very small forms, with mainly subterranean stems (*Bowenia* and *Stangeria*), to arborescent plants at least 18 meters in height (*Macrozamia*). Most genera and species are arborescent and range in height between the extremes, but seldom reach over 2 meters.

The outside of the trunk in all arborescent species is covered by a conspicuous armor of leaf bases (Fig. 23–7). The leaves are cut off by an abscission layer that develops in the petiole several centimeters out from the stem. The number of leaf bases on a stem has been used to calculate the age in several genera. For example, in *Dioon,* where leaves are produced every other year, Chamberlain estimated that if the number of leaves of an adult plant is 20, theoretically ten leaves would be formed in one year. From this, it follows that a specimen with 10,000 leaf bases would be approximately 1,000 years old! Such specimens have been recorded in the genus *Dioon.*

The leaves resemble fern fronds, and are pinnate in all but *Bowenia,* which is bipinnate. The leaflets are aligned in two lateral rows, one on each side of the rachis. Leaflets are usually entire, tough, and xeromorphic with a thick cuticle and sunken stomata. Most species show well-marked palisade and spongy mesophyll (Fig. 23–8A, B). The venation appears at first glance to be parallel, but is definitely dichotomous; the branch veins depart obliquely and quickly assume a parallel orientation. Leaflets of *Cycas* have only one vein, which forms a prominent midrib.

TABLE 23–1

DISTRIBUTION OF EXTANT CYCADS

GENUS	DISTRIBUTION BY COUNTRIES	
Cycas	Australia; East Indian Islands; India; China; Southern Japan	EASTERN HEMISPHERE
Macrozamia *Bowenia*	Australia	
Encephalartos *Stangeria*	South Africa	
Zamia	Florida; West Indies; Mexico; Central America; northern South America; Andes Mountains south to Chile	WESTERN HEMISPHERE
Microcycas	Western Cuba	
Ceratozamia *Dioon*	Mexico	

Anatomy. The internal structure of the stem of cycads is similar to that of the Bennettitales (Fig. 23–9). The pith and cortex are relatively thick, and the dictyostelic vascular cylinder relatively thin. A small amount of secondary wood develops centrifugally in radial rows, but without forming well-defined growth rings (Fig. 23–10A). The pitting of the tracheids is generally bordered (Fig. 23–10B). Rays vary from one to several cells in width, and up to 20 cells in depth; they often contain starch grains or crystals of calcium oxalate. Both the pith and cortex contain prominent mucilaginous canals and large amounts of starch. The cortex is bounded on the outside by a well-marked but thin periderm.

One of the most interesting features of cycad anatomy is the arrangement of leaf traces. The number of traces varies with the species but always shows a pattern called **girdling** (Fig. 23–11). Individual traces arise from leaf gaps which are located some distance around the stele from the leaf insertion. Thus, in passing to the leaf base, the traces girdle the stele. Each trace passes upward slightly through the cortex, approaching closer to other traces before entering the leaf base. This process is also found in many angiosperms, particularly monocotyledons with parallel venation. How-

A

B

FIGURE 23-6   Habit views of extant cycads.
A, *Zamia*, ×0.1; B, *Cycas*, ×0.005. (B, after
Brown with permission of Blaisdell Publishing
Company.)

FIGURE 23-7   Trunk of *Dioon spinulosum*
showing thick covering of sharp leaf bases, ×0.3.
(Courtesy Chicago Natural History Museum.)

ever, it is not present in the bennettites, which
have traces passing directly from the stele to
the leaf base.

The primary root of cycads is large, especially in the seedling. Adult roots attain great
lengths; in one example, a *Dioon* root has a
diameter of 3 cm 12 meters from the stem. The
primary vascular tissue is an exarch protostele,
ranging from diarch to tetrarch. Secondary

growth is common. A noteworthy feature is the
negative geotropism exhibited widely in the
roots. On reaching the surface of the soil, many
roots develop clusters of nodules. At first these
contain bacteria, and later the blue-green alga
Anabaena. Whether the nodules function in
nitrogen fixation and assist in assimilation
has not been determined.

Reproduction.   In all extant cycads except *Cycas*, reproductive units are compacted
into either strobili or cones. The gynostrobili of
Cycas and *Dioon* are similar to true strobili,
whereas those of the other genera are compact
cones. All genera are completely dioecious.

Most of the cycads bear the strobili at the
apex of the stem, but in at least two genera they
are borne laterally and in the axils of the leaves.
Many of the strobili are extremely large and
heavy; seed cones (gynostrobili) exceeding 70
cm in length and weighing over 30 kg are typical for *Macrozamia denisonii*. In most cycads,
the seed cones are conspicuously larger than
the pollen cones (androstrobili).

The pollen cones are borne singly or in
small groups at the stem tip (Fig. 23-12).
Each cone consists of many androsporophylls
spirally arranged on a central axis. The sporo-

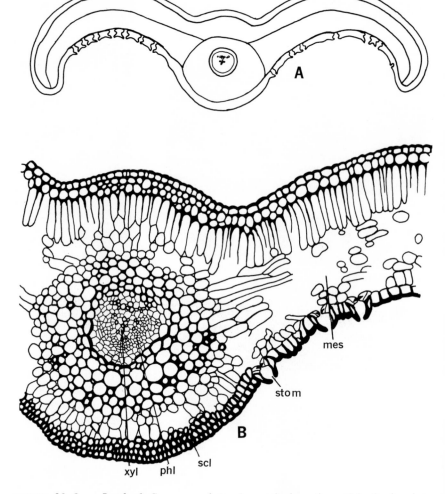

FIGURE 23–8   Leaf of *Cycas revoluta*. A, vertical section of leaf, showing vascular bundle and stomata, ×35; B, cellular details of part of vertical section of leaf, ×80. *mes,* mesophyll; *phl,* phloem; *scl,* sclerenchyma; *stom,* stoma; *xyl,* xylem.

phylls are narrow at the point of insertion and flare out distally; they are usually oriented in vertical rows (Fig. 23–12A). Each sporophyll has clusters of androsporangia congregated on both sides of a median keel. These clusters have been called sori and contain from one to five sporangia, depending on the genus. The total number of sporangia per sporophyll varies from 28 in *Zamia* to over 1,000 in *Cycas.*

Each androsporangium is borne on a short stalk and develops eusporangiately. After repeated divisions of initials, several layers of cells are produced. Inner cells become the

spore mother cells, whereas the outer layers develop into the tapetum and the sporangial wall. During development of the androspore mother cells, the tapetum and inner wall cells break down, forming a multinucleate protoplasm that serves as a source of food for the maturing androspores.

Following meiosis in the spore mother cells, the androspores differentiate endosporally into the gametophyte (Fig. 23–13). The androsporal cell divides into a small prothallial cell and the large central antheridial initial. The antheridial initial then divides to form a small

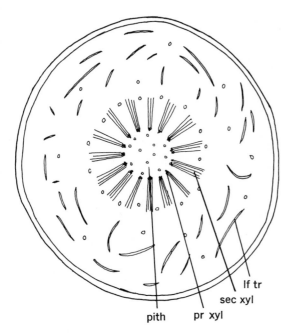

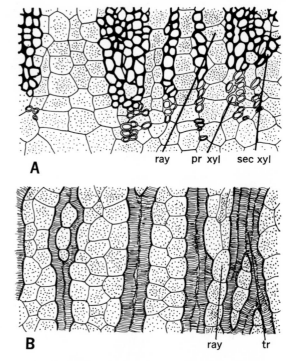

FIGURE 23-9 Transverse section of cycad stem showing pith, primary xylem (*pr xyl*), secondary xylem (*sec xyl*), and oblique leaf traces (*lf tr*) in cortex, ×1. (From *Morphology of Gymnosperms* by J. M. Coulter and C. J. Chamberlain by permission of The University of Chicago Press, copyright 1910 and 1917.)

FIGURE 23-10 Vascular tissue of cycad stem. A, part of transverse section showing primary xylem tracheids (*pr xyl,* white), secondary tracheids (*sec xyl*), and rays, ×70; B, part of longitudinal section showing pits and thickenings of tracheids (*tr*) and rays (*ray*), ×70.

generative cell that lies against the prothallial cell, and a larger tube cell that is centrally located.

At this stage of maturation, the immature **androgametophytes** are shed from the sporangia as pollen grains. The pollen grains of most cycads are circular or elliptical, with a single furrow on one surface (Fig. 23-13F). They are produced in large numbers and are generally dispersed by wind.

When a pollen grain lands on the **pollen drop** at the micropyle of an ovule, further elaboration of the gametophyte takes place. A pollen tube begins to evaginate from the furrow of the grain; it gradually grows into the nucellus of the ovule, serving an haustorial function. At the same time, the tube nucleus migrates out into the basal part of the pollen tube. The swollen base extends into the pollen chamber formed from the dissolution of nucellar cells. The generative cell also divides to form two cells—a sterile cell that develops next to the prothallial

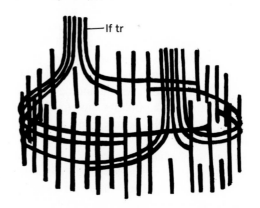

FIGURE 23-11 Vascular pattern of cycad stem, showing "girdling" of leaf traces (*lf tr*), ×0.3. (After Dorety with permission of *The Botanical Gazette*.)

cell, and an **androgenous cell** near the base of the pollen tube (Fig. 23-13C). Finally, the androgenous cell undergoes a single division to form two androgametes, or sperm cells (Fig. 23-13E).

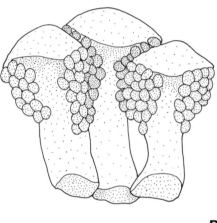

A   **B**

FIGURE 23–12   A, androstrobilus of *Dioon* showing vertical rows of androsporophylls and sporangia on the abaxial surfaces of the sporophylls, ×0.4; B, three androsporophylls of *Zamia,* showing closely packed pollen sacs on abaxial surfaces, ×5.

The development of the androgamete is interesting. Just prior to nuclear division, two dense bodies with radial arms form on opposite sides of the nucleus. These are the blepharoplasts (Fig. 23–13D). As the androgenous cell elongates, the blepharoplasts shift through 90° to lie at right angles to the long axis of the pollen tube. As the two androgamete nuclei separate, the blepharoplasts break up into granules that orient themselves spirally around the body of the nucleus. These differentiate into the spiral band of flagella of the gamete.

The androgametes begin to move while still enclosed within the body cell. At first, they are stuck together and tumble around as the flagella begin to move. The gametes pulsate and move in amoeboid fashion, recoiling suddenly when their apices strike the wall of the tube. After about an hour they separate, and after another half-hour they escape into the pollen tube. They move straight ahead by rotat-

ing on their long axis, and move up and down the tube. Eventually, the side wall of the pollen tube swells and bursts, discharging the two gametes and associated fluid cytoplasm.

All but two genera of cycads have compact seed cones consisting of spirally arranged gynosporophylls (Fig. 23–14). *Cycas* has a rosette of sporophylls that resembles reduced pinnate leaves. In *Dioon,* the gynostrobilus contains loosely compacted sporophylls that are entire. This lessening in complexity of gynosporophylls is accompanied by a reduction in ovule number from six to eight in *Cycas* to two in most other genera. This is generally considered to represent a reduction series that reflects an evolutionary trend.

The ovules are usually sessile, or are borne on very short stalks on the adaxial surface of the gynosporophylls. In most instances the ovules are oriented with the micropyle toward the central axis (Fig. 23–15A, D). Ovules vary

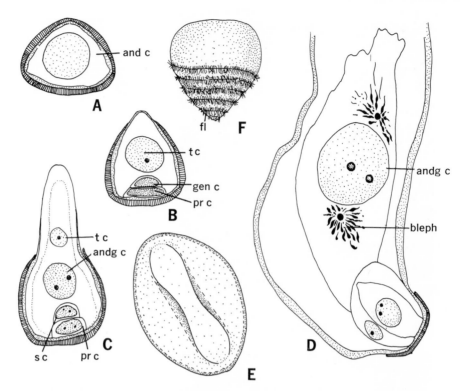

FIGURE 23–13   Androgametophyte of cycads. A, single-celled pollen grain with androsporal cell (*and c*), ×900; B, pollen grain with prothallial cell (*pr c*), generative cell (*gen c*) and tube cell (*t c*), and with pollen tube just beginning to form (top), ×900; C, late stage of maturation of androgametophyte with prothallial cell (*pr c*), sterile cell (*s c*), androgenous cell (*andg c*), and tube cell (*t c*), ×900; D, almost mature androgametophyte showing two androgametic nuclei in androgenous cell (*andg c*), and two blepharoplasts (*bleph*), ×350; E, external view of *Zamia* pollen grain, showing sulcus on distal surface, ×1,000; F, single androgamete showing spirally arranged flagella, ×1,000. (A–D, after Chamberlain with permission of *The Botanical Gazette;* F, after Webber.)

in size from 6 cm in some species of *Cycas* and *Macrozamia* to as small as 5 mm in *Zamia pygmaea.*

The essential structures of an ovule can best be observed in a median longitudinal section (Fig. 23–16). Initially, the white central mass is the nucellus (gynosporangium). This is surrounded by an integument that comprises three distinct layers—a middle stony layer with a fleshy layer on either side. The inner fleshy tissue is largely resorbed during development of the gametophyte, but part remains as a thin papery layer. Two vascular strands enter the base of the integument; each branches to give strands in both the outer and inner fleshy layers.

Within the central region of the gynosporangium, a gynospore mother cell undergoes meiosis to form four gynospores that initiate the gametophyte generation (Fig. 23–17A–C). The four gynospores are normally arranged in a linear tetrad within the gynosporangium. Usually only the basal gynospore remains functional and the other three degenerate. In their germination, the gynospores follow stages very similar to those in a free-sporing plant such as *Selaginella.* The functional gynospore enlarges markedly, undergoing many nuclear divisions (Fig. 23–17D, E). At the same time, the cells of the surrounding gynosporangium are digested, providing both space and nutrient for

A

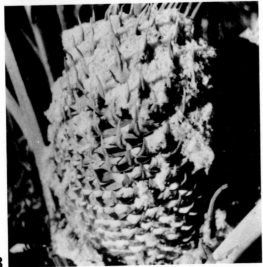

B

FIGURE 23–14 Gynostrobili of cycads. A, gynostrobilus of *Encephalartos* attached to top of stem, ×0.14; B, an erect gynostrobilus of *Macrozamia*, ×0.5.

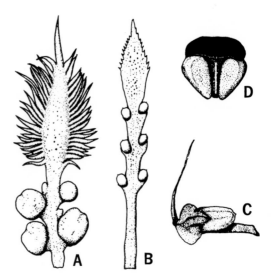

FIGURE 23–15 Gynosporophylls of cycads. A, seeds attached below leaflike blade of *Cycas revoluta* sporophyll, ×0.2; B, seeds and sporophyll of *Cycas circinalis*, ×0.2; C, single gynosporophyll of *Macrozamia* with short spikelike protuberance, ×0.2; D, sporophyll of *Zamia* showing nonelaborated peltate sporophyll, ×0.6. (After Haupt with permission of McGraw-Hill Book Co.)

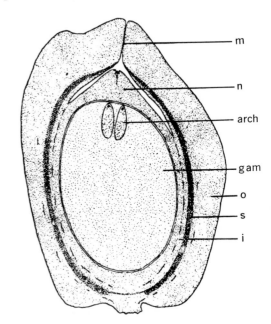

FIGURE 23–16 Longitudinal seed of *Zamia*, showing gametophyte (*gam*), archegonia (*arch*), nucellus (*n*), integument (*i*), middle stony layer of integument (*s*), outer fleshy integumentary layer (*o*), and micropyle (*m*), ×4. (After Haupt with permission of McGraw-Hill Book Co.)

the enlarging gynospore. At maximum development, the free-nucleate gametophyte fills most of the original gynosporangium. The many free nuclei are suspended in watery cytoplasm, and are congregated at the periphery of the gametophyte. The main difference between this and *Selaginella* is the retention of the gametophyte and the sporangium within the integument.

478 / *VASCULAR PLANTS*

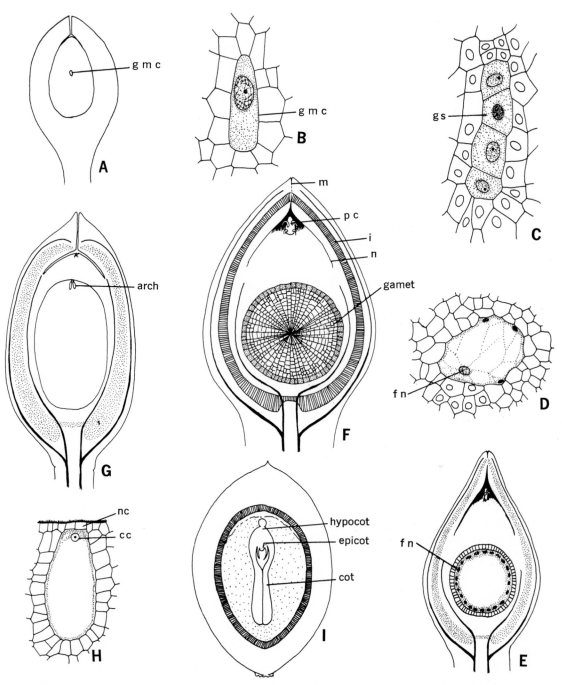

FIGURE 23–17   Development of gynogametophyte of cycads. A, gynospore mother cell in nucellus, ×150; B, enlarged gynospore mother cell, ×250; C, tetrad of gynospores, ×900; D, four nuclei of free-nucleate stage, ×600; E, free nuclei around periphery of gametophyte, ×4; F, gynogametophyte after all nuclei have become walled, ×6; G, two archegonia at micropylar end of gametophyte, ×6; H, single archegonium showing large central cell, two small neck cells, and surrounding gametophytic tissue, ×50; I, simple embryo showing two cotyledons, two leaf primordia, epicotyl, and hypocotyl, ×4. *arch,* archegonia; *c c,* central cell; *cot,* cotyledon; *epicot,* epicotyl; *f n,* free nuclei; *g m c,* gynospore mother cell; *gamet,* gynogametophyte; *gs,* gynospore; *hypocot,* hypocotyl; *i,* integument; *m,* micropyle; *n,* nucellus; *n c,* neck cell; *p c,* pollen chamber. (B–D, after Smith with permission of *Botanical Gazette;* E–I, from *The Living Cycads* by C. J. Chamberlain by permission of The University of Chicago Press, copyright 1919.)

Following the completion of free-nuclear division, cell walls begin to form around the nuclei (Fig. 23–17F). Wall formation starts at the periphery and continues centripetally until all the nuclei are involved. The resulting tissue is the **gynogametophyte,** which produces archegonia toward the micropylar end and later acts as a nutritive tissue for the developing embryo (Fig. 23–16).

In most genera, archegonia develop from superficial archegonial initials at the micropylar end of the gametophyte (Fig. 23–17G); from one to four large archegonia mature. The archegonia are oriented with their short necks extending into an archegonial chamber that forms between the gametophyte tissue and the nucellus. At maturity, each archegonium has two neck cells (a characteristic of all cycads), a ventral canal nucleus, and an egg nucleus (Fig. 23–17H). In most instances, no wall forms between the ventral canal and egg nuclei. The layer of gametophytic cells enclosing the egg forms a jacket and functions in transferring nutrients from the gametophyte to the egg. This is facilitated by haustorial threads that extend from the egg cytoplasm through plasmodesmata into the cells of the jacket. When fully expanded, the egg measures up to 3 mm long and is extremely turgid.

The ventral canal nucleus is short-lived and begins to disintegrate soon after formation. The egg nucleus then moves to a central position and expands to 0.5 mm in some instances. The cytoplasm of the egg becomes very dense and loses its vacuolated appearance. At the same time, the nucellar tissue between the pollen chamber and archegonial chamber breaks down, forming a continuous passage. At this stage, the egg is mature and ready for fertilization (Fig. 23–18). As mentioned previously, the swollen pollen tube bursts, discharging the two androgametes and their fluid cytoplasm into the archegonial chamber. At the same time, the contents of the turgid egg swell out into the chamber, and the gametes move into the neck of the archegonium. This process is sometimes sufficiently violent to tear the band of flagella from the androgamete, leaving it behind at the neck. The androgamete nucleus then moves through the cytoplasm of the egg

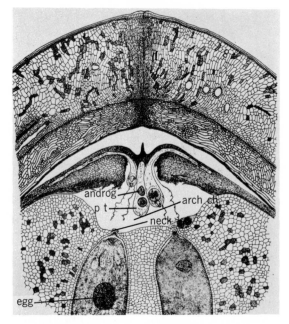

FIGURE 23–18   Vertical section of ovule of cycad just prior to fertilization, showing several pollen tubes and two archegonia ready to receive androgametes. *androg,* androgamete; *arch ch,* archegonial chamber; *neck,* neck; *p t,* pollen tube. (From *The Living Cycads* by C. J. Chamberlain by permission of The University of Chicago Press, copyright 1919.)

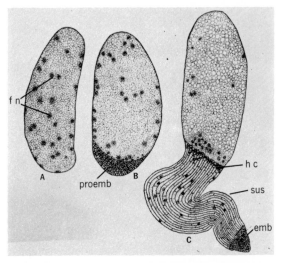

FIGURE 23–19   Early embryogeny of cycad. A, free-nuclear stage, ×16; B, cells at chalazal end forming proembryo, ×16; C, embryonic cells at tip, suspensor cells in middle, and haustorial cells next to free nuclei, ×16. *emb,* embryonic cells; *f n,* free nuclei; *h c,* haustorial cells; *proemb,* proembryo; *sus,* suspensor. (From Haupt with permission of McGraw-Hill Book Co.)

and fuses with the egg nucleus, forming the zygote.

After fertilization, the zygote nucleus undergoes a series of free-nuclear divisions. A series of as many as six to ten simultaneous divisions occurs, resulting in over 1,000 nuclei in some species (Fig. 23–19A). In several genera, for example *Cycas,* all nuclei become enclosed by walls; in others, such as *Dioon,* walls form around all nuclei but soon disintegrate, except for those at the **chalazal** end of the developing embryo; in still others, for example *Zamia,* walls form around only the **chalazal** nuclei. In all instances, the cells of the chalazal end form the proembryo, whereas those at the micropylar end provide a nutrient reserve (Fig. 23–19B).

The proembryo continues to proliferate, eventually differentiating into three zones (Fig. 23–19C): the cells at the chalazal end form a cap that develops into the embryo proper; the cells of the central zone remain meristematic and elongate markedly to form the suspensor; and a few cells toward the micropylar end function as haustoria, deriving nutrients from the upper regions of the gynogametophyte.

The cells continue to elongate, and suspensors have been reported to reach a length of 7 cm in *Ceratozamia.* As elongation progresses, the suspensor becomes coiled and the embryo is pushed deeper into the tissue of the gametophyte. While the embryo continues to enlarge, the bordering cells of the gametophyte break down and provide food materials. Although most cycads are polyembryonic, usually only one embryo will mature; the others are cannibalistically digested at various stages of their development.

In most genera, the embryo consists of two large **cotyledons;** these encompass a short axis comprising **hypocotyl** and **epicotyl** (Fig. 23–17I). At germination, the bases of the cotyledons elongate, forming a "new" hypocotyl and pushing the **radicle** out through the micropyle. The cotyledons remain for several weeks or longer in contact with the gynogametophyte, absorbing food for the developing shoot. Eventually, the young sporophyte becomes anchored in the soil and becomes independent of the food supply in the seed.

Phylogeny of Cycadales. The cycads, with a fossil record from the early Triassic, appear to have evolved from the pteridosperms. The two groups have similar pinnately compound leaves, the same stomatal pattern, and closely comparable seeds. Furthermore, in *Cycas* and to a lesser extent in *Dioon* the seeds are borne on gynosporophylls that obviously represent reduced leaves. It is likely that this has resulted from a reduction from the condition in pteridosperms, where seeds are borne on the terminal segments of fronds. Among the extant cycads, a noteworthy reduction series includes several species of *Cycas* through to *Dioon* to *Zamia* and others with much-reduced gynosporophylls. However, the cycads show less relationship to the pteridosperms in the anatomy of the stem, the girdling of leaf traces, and the nonsynangiate arrangement of androsporangia in the androstrobili.

During the late Paleozoic, it seems likely that the Cycadales and Bennettitales were both derived from the seed-fern complex, but along completely different pathways. This divergence must have occurred fairly early, since both orders are quite distinct from their first appearance in the early Mesozoic. The reasons why the cycads have persisted to the present, whereas the bennettites became extinct during the late Cretaceous, are still obscure.

REFERENCES

Andrews, H. N., Jr., *Studies in Paleobotany.* New York: John Wiley & Sons, Inc. (1961). Pp. 289–313.

Arnold, C. A., *An Introduction to Paleobotany.* New York: McGraw-Hill Book Co., Inc. (1947). Pp. 248–279.

Arnold, C. A., "Origin and Relationships of the Cycads." *Phytomorphology,* 3: 51–65 (1953).

Chamberlain, C. J., *The Living Cycads*. Chicago: University of Chicago Press (1919).

Chamberlain, C. J., *Gymnosperms: Structure and Evolution*. Chicago: University of Chicago Press (1935). Pp. 1–164.

Delevoryas, T., "Investigations of North American Cycadeoids: *Monanthesia*." *Am. J. Bot.*, 46: 657–666 (1959).

Delevoryas, T., *Morphology and Evolution of Fossil Plants*. New York: Holt, Rinehart and Winston, Inc. (1962). Pp. 128–148.

Delevoryas, T., "Investigations of North American Cycadeoids: Cones of *Cycadeoidea*." *Am. J. Bot.*, 50: 45–58 (1963).

Florin, R., "Studien über die Cycadales des Mesozoikums Nebst Erötungen über die Spaltoffnungsapparate der Bennettitales." *K. Svensk. Vetensk. Akad. Handl.,* Ser. 3, 12(5): 1–134 (1933).

Foster, A. S., and Gifford, E. M., Jr., *Comparative Morphology of Vascular Plants*. San Francisco: W. H. Freeman and Co. (1959). Pp. 337–370.

Harris, T. M., "Cones of Extinct Cycadales from the Jurassic Rocks of Yorkshire." *Phil. Trans. Roy. Soc. Lond.,* 231B: 75–98 (1941).

Thomas, H. H., and Bancroft, N., "On the Cuticle of Some Recent and Fossil Cycadean Fronds." *Trans. Linn. Soc. Lond.,* Ser. B, Botany, 8: 155–204 (1913).

Wieland, G. R., "Distribution and Relationships of the Cycadeoids." *Am. J. Bot.*, 7: 125–145 (1920).

24/DIVISION

GINKGOPHYTA

This division of vascular plants is represented in the extant flora by a single species, *Ginkgo biloba*. It is the sole survivor of a group of plants that probably originated in the late Paleozoic, and became very widespread and moderately abundant during mid-Mesozoic times. In company with the other groups that flourished during the Mesozoic, the *ginkgophytes* diminished in both numbers of taxa and individuals during the Tertiary.

Although the ancestors of the ginkgophytes are not known, the plants appear to share characteristics with both the cycadophytes and the conifers. However, the general structure is quite distinctive, and it is very possible that the ginkgophytes evolved from seed-bearing ancestors different from those that evolved into either cycads or the conifers.

The earliest plant to be assigned with confidence to the Ginkgophyta is *Trichopitys* from the early Permian of France (Fig. 24–1A). As reconstructed, *Trichopitys* has a small axis that bears leaves with narrow blades and several dichotomies. In the axils of some leaves, fertile shoots emerge and form several branches that terminate in ovules. The usual number of ovules per shoot is four to six, but as many as 20 have been recorded.

Practically the only remains of ginkgophytes in rocks of the mid-Mesozoic are leaf compressions. Some 16 genera have been recognized, but the two most common are *Baiera* and *Ginkgoites*. Leaves of *Baiera* have narrow sessile blades that branch dichotomously (Fig. 24–1B). The *Ginkgoites* leaf has a petiole, and the

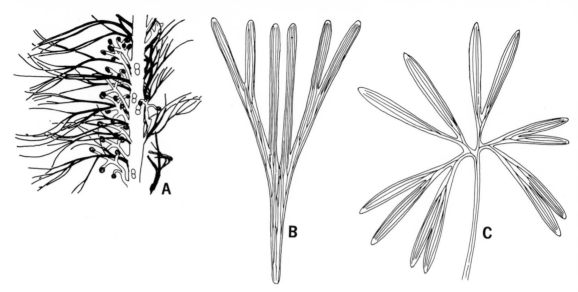

FIGURE 24–1   Leaves of fossil ginkgophytes. A, *Trichopitys* from the Permian, with sporangia-bearing axes in axils of finely dissected leaves, ×0.3; B, *Baiera,* with long dichotomous leaf segments, ×0.5; C, *Ginkgoites,* with primary, secondary, and tertiary dichotomies of blade from petiole, ×0.5. (A, after Florin with permission of *Acti Horti Bergiani;* B, C, after Heer.)

blade is either dissected or entire with lobes, depending on the species (Fig. 24–1C). In general, deeply dissected leaves are more common in the early and mid-Mesozoic, and entire forms in the later Mesozoic and Tertiary. However, both forms occur together in many early and mid-Mesozoic deposits.

Although other ginkgophyte organs are rarely found, the abundance of different leaf forms indicates much diversity in the group during the Mesozoic. It is generally assumed that most if not all ginkgophytes were trees, but there is little evidence of the stems that bore the different leaf forms.

GINKGO BILOBA.   This species, popularly called the "maidenhair tree," is often referred to as a "living fossil" and is the sole surviving member of an ancient lineage. Originally known only from gardens in eastern Asia, particularly China and Japan, it has been found in recent times in what appear to be wild stands in a small mountainous area of southeastern China. It is questionable whether these are truly indigenous populations or whether they have escaped from gardens.

Ginkgo trees have been cultivated in various countries of the world since the nineteenth century, and are becoming increasingly popular as shade trees and ornamentals. The species is dioecious, and staminate trees are preferred in cultivation because the outer fleshy layer of the seeds decays, producing butyric acid which pollutes the air with the smell of rancid butter! It was formerly impossible to tell whether a seedling was staminate or ovulate, and horticulturists had to wait for a plant to mature before segregating the staminate trees. However, investigations suggest that cytological studies of chromosomes will enable planters to determine the sex in the very early stages of growth.

Morphology and Anatomy.   Younger trees of *Ginkgo* have monopodial growth, giving them a marked pyramidal shape (Fig. 24–2A). However, as they mature, the main trunk loses its prominence, and the side branches grow relatively larger and longer to give a rounded crown (Fig. 24–2B). Some trees reach a height approaching 30 meters and a trunk diameter of over 1 meter. The tree is deciduous, and the leaves appear very late in the spring and persist well into the autumn in mid-latitudes.

As in many of the conifers, *Ginkgo* has two kinds of branches, the **long shoot** and the **spur** (or **short**) **shoot.** Long shoots have indeter-

FIGURE 24–2   *Ginkgo biloba*. A, young tree showing characteristic pyramidal branching; B, mature tree with rounded crown.

minate growth with scattered leaves and form the main branches of the tree (Fig. 24–3). However, spur shoots have limited growth, increasing only a few millimeters in length each year; they form on the long branches during the second year of growth and bear a cluster of leaves at the tip. Scars of former petioles form a prominent spiral around them. Although spurs usually remain short and leaf-bearing, in some instances a spur suddenly develops into a long shoot with scattered leaves, often as the result of injury to a neighboring long shoot. Similarly, long shoots can become retarded, changing to spur shoots. There is a marked difference in the relative amounts of tissues produced by long and spur shoots of the same age. Long shoots have a narrow pith, wide

vascular cylinder, and thin cortex. In contrast, spur shoots have a wide pith, very narrow xylem cylinder, and wide cortex (Fig. 24–4A, B).

The primary vascular tissue is dictyostelic, with the bundles surrounding a narrow pith and yielding branch and leaf traces (Fig. 24–4). Around the primary xylem, secondary xylem forms a thick cylinder of irregular radial rows of tracheids, rays, and weakly defined growth rings. The tracheids of primary xylem have helical thickenings, whereas those of secondary xylem have one to two rows of bordered pits with **crassulae** between them. As viewed in cross section, the secondary tracheids differ noticeably from those of conifer woods in their very uneven, transverse dimensions and lengths. Wood rays are characteristically short vertically

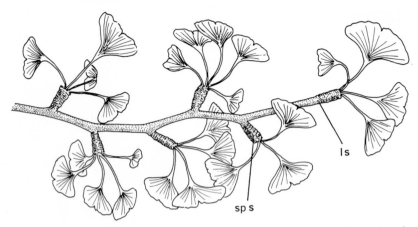

FIGURE 24–3   *Ginkgo biloba*. Section of long shoot with spur shoots bearing spirally arranged leaves, ×0.3. *l s,* long shoot; *sp s,* spur shoot.

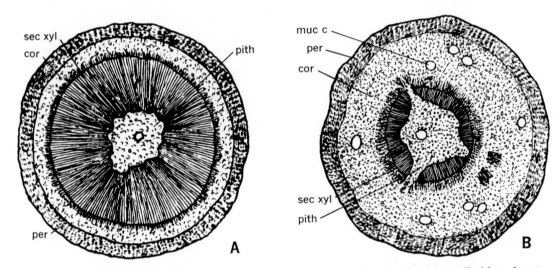

FIGURE 24–4   Transverse sections of stem of *Ginkgo biloba*. A, long shoot, with small pith and cortex, large amount of secondary xylem, and few mucilage cavities, ×14; B, spur shoot, with relatively large pith and cortex and numerous mucilage cavities, ×10. *cor,* cortex; *muc c,* mucilage cavities; *per,* periderm; *sec xyl,* secondary xylem. (From *Gymnosperms* by C. J. Chamberlain by permission of The University of Chicago Press, copyright 1935.)

and narrow in width; many are only one cell high and one cell wide. There is no xylem parenchyma in the wood. The pith and cortex are studded with mucilage cavities and cells containing calcium oxalate crystals and tannins. A periderm originates in the outer cortical layers and later, with secondary phloem, forms the bark.

The distinctive leaves of *Ginkgo biloba* have a long petiole that fans out into a broad blade (Fig. 24–5A). In leaves of long shoots, the blades are usually notched in the middle; hence, the specific epithet *"biloba."* In contrast,

leaves of spur shoots are mainly entire. The petiole contains two leaf traces that divide dichotomously in the base of the blade. Additional dichotomies occur in the blade as far as the margin, giving a fan-like appearance to the leaf. Although most vein branchings are open and dichotomous, some veins have anastomoses. The name "maidenhair tree" is derived from the resemblance to the leaf of *Adiantum,* the maidenhair fern.

Mucilage cavities are common in the leaves, occurring as elongated tubes midway between veins. Cells with tannins and oxalate

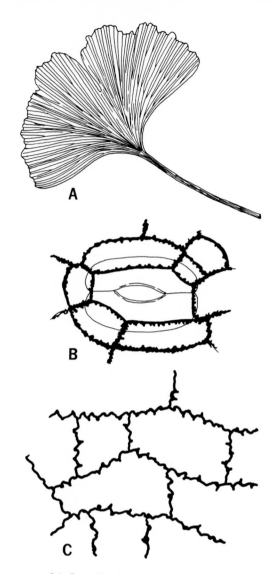

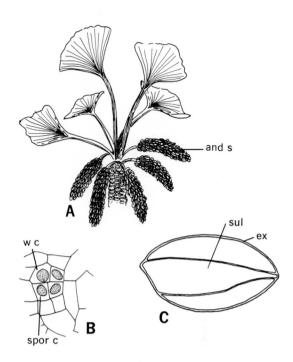

FIGURE 24–6   Reproductive organs of *Ginkgo*. A, catkin-like androstrobili (*and s*) emerging from tip of spur shoot, ×1; B, four sporogenous cells (*spor c*) surrounded by wall cells (*w c*) of androsporangium, ×800; C, single pollen grain of *Ginkgo biloba*, showing single sulcus (*sul*) extending length of grain, ×1,000. *ex*, exine. (B, after Starr with permission of *Botanical Gazette*.)

FIGURE 24–5   Leaf structure of *Ginkgo biloba*. A, simple leaf showing petiole, dichotomous venation, and central notch in blade, ×1; B, single stoma in plan view showing two guard cells flanked and overarched by six subsidiary cells, ×400; C, several epidermal cells, showing wavy outline of walls, ×400.

crystals are also numerous. Stomata are mostly on the lower surface and have four to seven subsidiary cells flanking the slightly sunken guard cells (Fig. 24–5B). The walls of the epidermal cells are somewhat wavy. The cells between veins are polygonal in outline, whereas those below the veins are rectangular—a characteristic pattern different from that of both cycadophytes and conifers (Fig. 24–5C).

Reproduction. Like the cycads, *Ginkgo biloba* is consistently dioecious. Interspersed with leaves at the tips of spur shoots, androsporangia are borne on loose strobili; ovules are borne singly at the ends of forked peduncles.

An androstrobilus of *Ginkgo* is a lax catkin-like structure bearing sporophylls spirally arranged around the axis (Fig. 24–6A). Each androsporophyll is a curved stalk bearing two androsporangia at the tip. An androsporangium has four to seven wall layers, a tapetum, and a number of central sporogenous cells (Fig. 24–6B) that function as androspore mother cells and undergo meiosis to form tetrads of spores. Before they are shed, spores begin to develop into pollen grains containing the immature androgametophytes.

Pollen grains of *Ginkgo biloba* are very similar to those of the extant Cycadales. They are generally circular to elliptical in outline, with a single longitudinal sulcus along one surface; they vary in length from 23 to 30 microns (Fig. 24–6C). Dispersal is chiefly by wind. *Ginkgo* pollen grains are often found disseminated in sedimentary rocks, particularly those of mid-Mesozoic age.

The development of the androgametophyte is similar to that of the cycads. The androsporal cell divides to form two cells, one of which is the primary prothallial cell. A second division produces a secondary prothallial cell and an antheridial initial. The antheridial initial then divides into an outer tube cell and a generative cell next to the prothallial cells. At this stage the pollen grain is shed during April–May in mid-northern latitudes.

Further development of the androgametophyte does not take place until the pollen has entered the micropyle of the ovule. The pollen tube then begins to digest its way through the nucellus. During this process, the generative cell in the pollen grain divides to form a sterile cell and an androgenous cell. These remain at the base of the tube until just prior to fertilization. However, the tube nucleus migrates into the pollen tube, and stays close to the end until discharge takes place. Just before fertilization, the androgenous cell divides to form two androgametes. As in the cycads, particles formed from the blepharoplasts become aligned helically around the gametes to form the flagella. Gametes about 80 microns long swim through the archegonial chamber to the neck of the archegonia and fuse directly with the large eggs in the venters.

Two ovules are borne on each peduncle—one at the tip of each dichotomous branch (Fig. 24–7A, B). Subtending each ovule is the gynosporophyll, a collar that develops into a leaf-like appendage. As in cycads, each ovule has a single integument with three distinct tissue regions. Following pollination, the three layers mature into an inner fleshy layer that dries out to a papery skin, a central stony layer, and an outer fleshy layer. The outer layer contains the butyric acid that causes the foul odor of the seeds in autumn.

The development of the gynogametophyte in the ovule is similar to that in cycads. The gynogametophyte begins forming in May, and

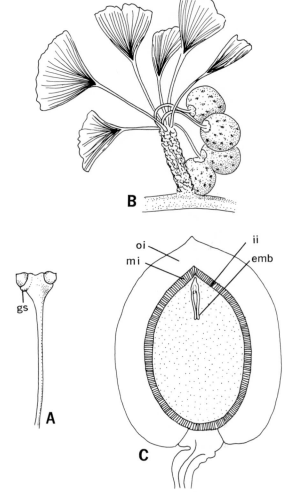

FIGURE 24–7   Reproductive organs of *Ginkgo biloba*. A, single peduncle supporting two young ovules that are subtended by collar representing gynosporophyll, ×1; B, several mature seeds borne at tip of spur shoot, ×1; C, longitudinal median section of seed with young embryo, ×2. *emb,* embryo; *gs,* gynosporophyll; *ii,* inner layer of integument; *mi,* middle layer of integument; *oi,* outer layer of integument. (C, from *Morphology of Gymnosperms* by J. M. Coulter and C. J. Chamberlain by permission of The University of Chicago Press, copyright 1910 and 1917.)

closely parallels the development in cycads. The four gynospores form as a linear tetrad following meiosis, but usually only the one at the chalazal end develops. The gynospore wall expands, and the nucleus undergoes many free-nuclear divisions. At maximum expansion, numerous nuclei are packed within the periphery of the gynospore wall. Cell wall formation pro-

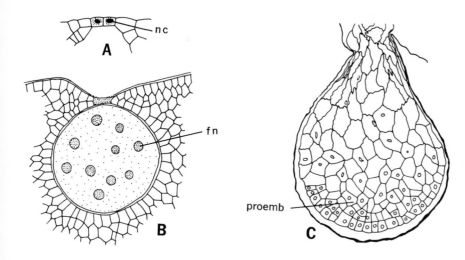

FIGURE 24–8   Reproduction in *Ginkgo biloba*. A, tip of archegonium showing two neck cells (*n c*), ×160; B, embryo in free-nuclear stage (*f n*), ×160; C, later stage of embryo showing proembryonic (*proemb*) cells at bottom which will eventually form embryo, ×80. (A, B, after Strasburger; C, after Lyon.)

ceeds centripetally, so that eventually all nuclei become walled to form the gynogametophyte. A noteworthy feature is the pale green color resulting from the development of chlorophyll in the cells of the gametophyte—a condition that occurs in some of the non-seed-producing plants.

In most instances, two or three archegonia form from outer cells at the micropylar end of the gynogametophyte. Each archegonium has two neck cells, a ventral canal cell, and a large egg (Fig. 24–8A). As in cycads, a jacket layer one cell thick forms on the outside.

Following union of the androgamete and the egg, the zygote nucleus undergoes a series of free-nuclear divisions (Fig. 24–8B). When about 256 nuclei have formed, cell walls develop almost simultaneously, producing the proembryonic tissue. This shows a gradation from small compact cells at the chalazal end to large elongated cells at the micropylar end (Fig. 24–8C). Although the micropylar cells are elongated, they do not form a definite suspensor as in cycads and conifers. Cells at the chalazal end continue to divide, forming the primordia of the cotyledons, epicotyl, and hypocotyl (Fig. 24–7C). These primordia enlarge and resorb the cell contents of the gynogameto-

phyte. Eventually, the young radicle grows through the micropyle and makes contact with the soil. The cotyledons remain attached to the seed and continue to absorb nutrient material from it.

PHYLOGENY OF GINKGOPHYTA

The ancestors of the ginkgos are unknown. Ginkgo is similar to cycads in many respects, especially in the sex organs and gametophyte development. However, the leaves are distinctive and generally unlike the pinnate leaves of cycads and pteridosperms. In addition, the stem, with extensive wood, small pith and cortex, and bordered pitting, is similar to that of the coniferophytes (see Chapter 25); the ginkgos are usually aligned with this group. The most reasonable hypotheses are that the ginkgophytes evolved either from the same stock as the Cordaitales, most likely the progymnosperms, or that they evolved from unknown ancestors, presumably pterophytes, into a separate line of seed plants. Future research on Devonian and Carboniferous plants offers the main hope for determining the phylogeny of the ginkgophytes.

REFERENCES

Andrews, H. N., Jr., *Studies in Paleobotany.* New York: John Wiley & Sons, Inc. (1961). pp. 335–347.

Arnott, H. J., "Anastomoses in the Venation of *Ginkgo biloba." Am. J. Bot.,* 46: 405–411 (1959).

Ball, E., "Growth of the Embryo of *Ginkgo biloba* under Experimental Conditions, II: Effects of a Longitudinal Split in the Tip of the Hypocotyl." *Am. J. Bot.,* 43: 802–810 (1956).

Chamberlain, C. J., *Gymnosperms: Structure and Evolution.* Chicago: University of Chicago Press (1935). Pp. 184–216.

Dorf, E., "The Geological Distribution of the *Ginkgo* Family." *Bull. Wagner Free Inst. Sci.,* Philadelphia, 33(1): 1–10 (1958).

Florin, R., "Die Fossilen Ginkgophyten von Franz Joseph Land. I, Spezieller Teil.; II, Allgemeiner Teil." *Palaeontographica,* 81B: 71–173 (1936); 82B: 1–72 (1937).

Gunckel, J. E., and Wetmore, R. H., "Studies of Development in Long Shoots and Short Shoots of *Ginkgo biloba* L., II: Phyllotaxis and the Organization of the Primary Vascular Tissue: Primary Phloem and Primary Xylem." *Am. J. Bot.,* 33: 532–543 (1946).

Li, H-L., "A Horticultural and Botanical History of *Gingko." Morris Arbor. Bull.,* 7: 3–12 (1956).

Pollock, E. G., "The Sex Chromosomes of the Maidenhair Tree." *J. Heredity,* 48: 290–294 (1957).

Seward, A. C., "The Story of the Maidenhair Tree." *Sci. Progress,* 32: 420–440 (1938).

25/DIVISION

CONIFEROPHYTA

The *coniferophytes* encompass two main orders of plants, the fossil Cordaitales and the Coniferales, which are represented by both fossil and extant families and genera. Also included is a group of Upper Devonian plants referred to as *progymnosperms*. Beck has suggested that the progymnosperms were ancestral to both the pteridosperm and coniferophyte lines. They are considered here for convenience, rather than because they show closer relationship to the coniferophytes.

If we accept the derivation of coniferophytes from progymnosperms, the most likely evolutionary link is between the progymnosperms of the Upper Devonian and the Cordaitales of the Carboniferous. The Cordaitales are most abundant in the later Carboniferous Period, where they overlap with the early conifers. The Coniferales extend from the late Carboniferous to the present. Although they appear to have reached a maximum in the mid-Mesozoic, the conifers are still major elements of the world's floras.

In spite of gaps to be filled, there is good evidence for believing that the Coniferales evolved from the Cordaitales through intermediate stages represented by the Lebachiaceae, an early Mesozoic family of conifers. The evolutionary progression is best documented from investigations of ovule-bearing appendages, as stressed in the descriptions and discussion in the succeeding pages. The Swedish botanist Rudolf Florin largely accomplished the outstanding research that led to the unfolding of the relation-

491

ships between the fossil and the modern conifers.

PROGYMNOSPERMS

Three separate orders containing eight genera have been described for this group; undoubtedly the best known is the genus *Archaeopteris*. Originally, this plant was known from leaf compressions found rather widely in Upper Devonian rocks. On the basis of leaf form and sporangia, *Archaeopteris* was usually considered an early fern, and classified with the Protopteridiales. However, in 1960 a leaf of *Archaeopteris* was found attached to a stem called *Callixylon*, a genus that had previously been allied with the Cordaitales. This discovery initiated the concept of progymnosperms, and prompted the hypothesis that *Archaeopteris* and related forms were ancestral to both the coniferophytes and pteridosperms.

As reconstructed, *Archaeopteris* is clearly an arborescent plant that reached a height of at least 20 meters (Fig. 25–1A). The largest trunk known is over 1.5 meters in diameter, and most trunks taper up to a crown of branches. The main branches appear to be horizontal or only slightly angled upward. The leaves range from less than 60 cm to over 1.5 meters in length, and are frond-like (Fig. 25–1B). In most species, some of the leaf pinnae contain both sterile and fertile pinnules, whereas others appear completely sterile. The sporangia are aligned on the leading edges of fertile pinnules, and have yielded spores that are round to deltoid, trilete, and unornamented. Although several species are reported to be heterosporous, others have only one size of spore and are presumably homosporous.

The stem contains a narrow pith, mesarch primary xylem strands, and secondary xylem. The tracheids of the secondary xylem have a unique pattern of round bordered pits that occur in patches on the radial walls in groups of six to 20, and in two to three vertical rows (Fig. 25–2). The rays are mostly uniseriate, from six to 15 cells high, and contain prominent ray tracheids.

ORDER CORDAITALES

Three families are generally assigned to the Cordaitales. Two of these comprise mainly genera of petrified wood, and their relationships are somewhat obscure. The best-known genus is *Cordaites*, in which both leaves and compound strobili have been found attached to stems.

Cordaites is a large arborescent plant that was probably the tallest of the Carboniferous trees (Fig. 25–3). Petrified stems measuring over 20 meters long have been found; some probably reached a height of at least 30 meters. Upper reaches support branches that bear long strap-shaped leaves (Fig. 25–4). Loose strobili are borne in the axils of some of the leaves.

The anatomy of the stem is well known and characteristic. The pith has a diameter up to 1.5 cm, and consists of lens-shaped cavities within the parenchyma tissue (Fig. 25–5A). Primary xylem lies immediately outside the pith, and is endarch (Fig. 25–5B). The tracheids show progression outward from helical to scalariform to bordered. The primary xylem grades into secondary xylem, which has tracheids with one to three rows of alternating and hexagonal bordered pits. Rays of the secondary wood are variable in height and usually one cell in width. The secondary xylem forms a thick cylinder of wood which, in most Carboniferous specimens, shows no growth rings. This has been cited as evidence suggesting absence of any well-defined seasonal or climatic changes during formation of the coal swamps of the Carboniferous.

The secondary phloem forms a thin, mainly parenchymatous layer on the inside of the cortex. Leaf traces, either single or double, angle through the cortex to the leaf bases. They divide in the cortex, so that several strands enter the leaf.

The leaves are thin, strap-shaped, and sometimes over a meter long and 15 cm wide (Fig. 25–4). Many length-wise veins that appear to be parallel are actually acutely dichotomous. Stomata are arranged in bands on the under surface of the leaf. Stomatal development is haplocheilic, with from four to six subsidiary

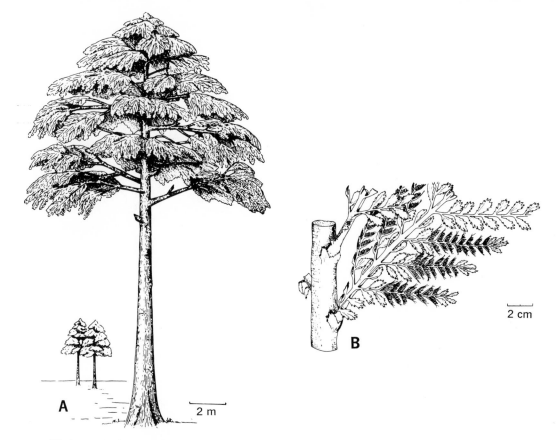

FIGURE 25–1   *Archaeopteris.* A, reconstruction of complete plant; B, branch bearing two fronds, with both sterile and fertile pinnules on lower frond. (After Beck with permission of *American Journal of Botany*.)

cells surrounding the guard cells. The leaves apparently derived much of their support from bands of sclerenchyma which extend longitudinally as I-beams between veins.

The reproductive organs of *Cordaites* consist of loose compound strobili in the axils of some leaves on outer branches. Both pollen-bearing and seed-bearing strobili are placed in the same genus *Cordaianthus* (Fig. 25–6A). The compound strobilus consists of two rows of awl-shaped bracts—one on either side of a central axis. In the axil of each bract is a short shoot bearing spirally arranged appendages, or scales. The outer scales bear pollen sacs at their tips (Fig. 25–6B). Some have yielded pollen grains that show a central body, or **corpus**, presumably of gametophytic tissue, and surrounded by a single bladder, or **saccus** (Fig. 25–6C).

As mentioned previously, the ovule-bearing strobilus forms the first stage in an evolutionary series of such organs in the Coniferophyta. The ovule-bearing strobili are similar to those bearing pollen but are known in more detail (Fig. 25–7). A long axis supports two lateral rows of bracts, each with a dwarf shoot in the axil. The dwarf shoot has spirally arranged scales—some fertile, others sterile. The fertile scales are somewhat elongate, and bear one or more terminal ovules. Ovules in some species extend well beyond the end of the dwarf shoot, but are virtually hidden in other species.

The seeds of the Cordaitales are small and heart-shaped, with the integument expanded into a wing. The integument is free from the nucellus except at the base, and the nucellus often projects into a nucellar beak. In general

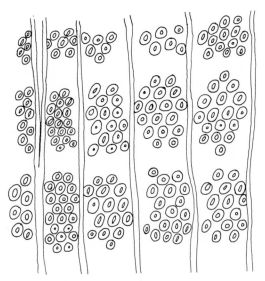

FIGURE 25–2   Section of secondary xylem of *Archaeopteris*, showing circular bordered pits occurring in patches on radial walls of tracheids, ×250.

morphology, the seeds of the Cordaitales are very similar to those of the pteridosperms. It is often difficult to decide to which group seeds belong, unless they are found attached to vegetative parts.

The work of Florin and others has suggested that the seed cone of the Coniferales was probably derived by reduction and elaboration of an inflorescence such as *Cordaianthus*. This will be considered in some detail under the extant conifers; probable intermediate stages can be noted in the ovule-bearing shoots of the family Lebachiaceae.

ORDER CONIFERALES

This is a large order with eight families, seven of which have extant genera, and one of which, the Lebachiaceae, is represented only by fossil members. The family Lebachiaceae, ranging from the late Carboniferous to the Jurassic, comprises plants that appear to be the immediate ancestors of all the families of extant conifers except the Taxaceae.

Family Lebachiaceae. This family consists of a few genera found on several continents of the Northern Hemisphere; the best-known genus is *Lebachia* from the late Carboniferous and early Permian (Fig. 25–8).

FIGURE 25–3   Reconstruction of *Cordaites*. Note compound strobili interspersed among leaves of side branches, ×0.003. (From D. H. Scott, *Studies in Fossil Botany*, Adam & Charles Black, Ltd., London.)

It was a tree of uncertain size, consisting of a main axis with pinnately arranged side branches. Two types of leaves are known. Those on the main axis and larger branches are longer, broader, and more flattened than those of smaller shoots. They are often forked at the ends—in which case the single vascular bundle also forks. Leaves on the small ultimate twigs are needle- or scale-like, entire, smaller than the first-order leaves, and have a single unbranched vein. Both leaf types have four bands of irregularly arranged stomata—two long bands on the abaxial surface and two shorter bands on the adaxial surface. The stomata are of the haplocheilic type. *Lebachia* has single-celled epidermal hairs on both sides of the leaf—a characteristic shared with many extant conifers.

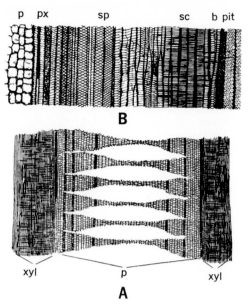

FIGURE 25–5   Stem of *Cordaites*. A, longitudinal section showing lenticular cavities in pith (*p*), and primary and secondary xylem (*xyl*), ×5; B, section of stem ranging from pith through protoxylem (*px*), metaxylem with helical (*sp*) and scalariform (*sc*) tracheids, to secondary xylem with bordered pits (*b pit*), ×72. (After D. H. Scott, *Studies in Fossil Botany,* Adam & Charles Black, Ltd., London.)

FIGURE 25–4   Twig of *Cordaites,* showing strapshaped leaves and compound strobili, ×10. (From D. H. Scott, *Studies in Fossil Botany,* Adam & Charles Black, Ltd., London.)

Internally, well-developed secondary xylem has araucarian tracheids—i.e., with one to three rows of alternate bordered pits. There are no resin canals and only a trace of xylem parenchyma. The xylem rays are uniseriate—another araucarian characteristic. Growth rings are weakly delimited.

Both seed-bearing and pollen-bearing cones are attached terminally on some of the side branches of *Lebachia* (Fig. 25–8B, C). The pollen-bearing cones consist of an axis with spirally arranged and scale-like androsporophylls. On the abaxial surface of each androsporophyll, two sporangia are partly covered by an outgrowth of the sporophyll itself. Pollen grains of *Lebachia* have a single saccus surrounding a central corpus (Fig. 25–9A). The bladder is interrupted on the distal surface by the germinal furrow. In several related genera, two sacci are attached to a corpus—a disaccate condition usual in modern conifer families, particularly Pinaceae and Podocarpaceae.

As in other genera with spiral sporophylls and two abaxial sporangia, the pollen-bearing cones of *Lebachia* are essentially simple cones or strobili and almost identical in structure to their counterparts in extant conifers. But the cones of *Lebachia* differ markedly from the pollen-bearing organs of *Cordaites,* which are compound strobili. Furthermore, androsporangia in *Cordaites* are terminal rather than abaxial on sporophylls. Thus, the marked difference in structure between *Cordaites* and the Lebachiaceae so far has not been bridged by fossil discoveries.

The seed-bearing organ of *Lebachia* is elliptical to circular in outline, with many compact bracts spirally arranged on the central axis (Fig. 25–9C). Each bract is two-forked, with a single vein that divides to provide one vein for each of the two lobes. In the axil each bract contains a dwarf shoot with spirally arranged appendages or decurrent and upright scales. Usually, only one scale is fertile and bears a single ovule at the tip (Fig. 25–9B). The seed-

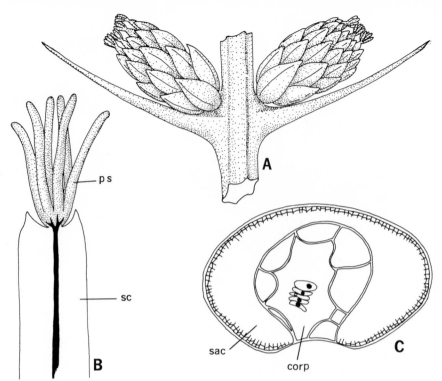

FIGURE 25–6   Reproductive organs of *Cordaites*. A, androstrobili in axils of bracts on primary strobilar axis, ×6; B, single scale (*sc*) of androstrobilus, showing attachment of pollen sacs (*p s*) at tip, ×25; C, pollen grain of *Cordaites* with several gametophytic cells in corpus (*corp*), surrounded by single saccus (*sac*), ×800. (A, after Delevoryas with permission of *American Journal of Botany;* B, C, from Florin with permission of *Palaeontographica* and *Svensk Botanisk Tidskrift.*)

bearing scale occurs next to the main axis of the cone, in the same spiral sequence as the sterile scales. The micropyle of the ovule is directed outward. The integument appears to be a continuation of the tissue of the seed scale that overarches the nucellus, forming a relatively deep micropyle.

In a closely related genus of seed organs, *Ernestiodendron,* the dwarf shoot also arises in the axil of a bract. The somewhat flattened dwarf shoots have only a few, or sometimes no, sterile scales. From three to seven spirally arranged gynosporophylls occur in central or terminal regions of the dwarf shoot. Each bears a single ovule, with the sporophyll grading into the integument as in *Lebachia*. Some of the ovules are erect, whereas others are inverted with the micropyles directed toward the axis.

The over-all structure of the compound gynostrobili in genera of the Lebachiaceae is

FIGURE 25–7   Part of compound gynostrobilus of *Cordaites* showing dwarf shoots in axils of bracts, and both sterile and fertile scales emanating from dwarf shoot. Seeds are heart-shaped, with wing-like integument (*int*) surrounding nucellus (*nuc*), ×2. (After Carruthers.)

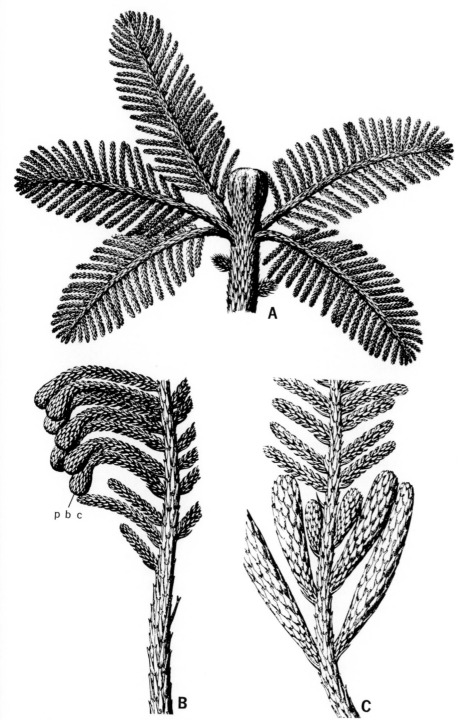

FIGURE 25–8   *Lebachia*. A, sterile branch with five twigs, showing pinnate arrangement of ultimate branches, ×0.33; B, single branch supporting both foliage twigs and pollen-bearing cones (*p b c*), ×0.33 (note forked leaves on main branch and unforked falcate leaves on ultimate branches); C, branch with seed-bearing cones and leaf-bearing twigs, ×0.33. (After Florin with permission of *Palaeontographica*.)

similar to that of *Cordaites*. In the Lebachiaceae, there is a general reduction in the length of the dwarf shoot, and in the numbers of sterile scales and ovules. This may represent an early stage in the evolution of Mesozoic and Cenozoic conifers which resulted in further reduction of parts in several directions. The final arrangements of seed-cone structures are found in the seven extant families.

Extant Conifers. During early and middle Mesozoic times, the conifers underwent marked and apparently rapid evolution. As a result, they became a predominant part of the floras of the Jurassic and early Cretaceous. During this time, most of the modern families were differentiated. However, in rocks older than the Upper Cretaceous, the conifers appear in several generalized forms that cannot be distinguished in terms of extant genera. These earlier indistinct forms, referred to as the **transition conifers,** have been given a series of form- or organ-genus names, based largely on morphology, which sometimes suggest natural affiliation—for example, *Prepinus* and *Araucarioxylon*.

During the Upper Cretaceous and Tertiary, almost all of the extant genera became differentiated, but apparently at different times. During this interval, many of the genera also began to appear in regions of present distribution, which in some instances entailed a retreat from a more widespread distribution. Such restrictions are almost certainly an indication of senescence or even of impending extinction. Some of the most dramatic examples are found in the family Taxodiaceae, where genera such as *Metasequoia* (dawn redwood), *Sequoia* (California redwood), and *Taxodium* (bald cypress) were widespread across the Northern Hemisphere during the earlier Tertiary. Today, the same genera are restricted to very narrow geographical and ecological ranges, and are almost certainly facing extinction. The main factors leading to extinction appear to be competition, particularly from angiosperms, and genetic senescence that prevents speciation in diverse ecological niches.

General Distribution of Families. The seven extant families are distributed in both

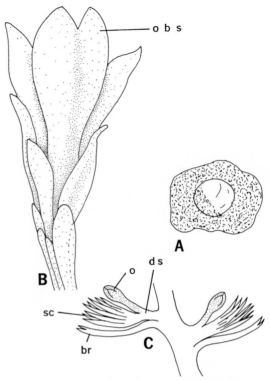

FIGURE 25–9   *Lebachia.* A, single pollen grain showing central corpus and surrounding saccus, ×185; B, dwarf shoot of seed-bearing cone showing spirally arranged scales and single ovule-bearing scale (*o b s*) at top, ×10; C, longitudinal section of seed-bearing cone showing bracts (*br*), sterile scales (*sc*), and single ovule (*o*) attached to dwarf shoot (*d s*), ×4. (After Florin with permission of *Palaeontographica.*)

hemispheres. Several, such as the Pinaceae, are more characteristic of the Northern Hemisphere, whereas others, such as the Araucariaceae, are more widespread in the Southern Hemisphere (Table 25–1).

Although some genera are declining, others appear to have evolved fairly recently—for example, *Pseudotsuga.* In terms of absolute number of extant species, there are only about one-twentieth as many conifers as ferns, and only about one-sixtieth as many conifers as monocotyledons. Thus, although the number of genera and species is relatively low, some conifers, such as *Pinus,* are conspicuous because of the large numbers of individuals which occur in certain regions. As a group, therefore, the conifers are still among the domi-

TABLE 25–1

MAIN MORPHOLOGICAL CHARACTERISTICS
AND DISTRIBUTION OF CONIFERALES

FAMILY (number of genera in parentheses)	RANGE	GENERAL CHARACTERISTICS
Pinaceae (10)	Almost entirely Northern Hemisphere	Leaves needle-like; leaves and cone scales spirally arranged; bract and ovuliferous scale distinct; pollen grains mostly saccate
Taxodiaceae (10)	China, Japan, Formosa, Tasmania, California, southern United States, and Mexico	Leaves and cone scales spirally arranged; bract and ovuliferous scale almost completely fused; pollen small with a papilla
Cupressaceae (16)	Widespread in both hemispheres	Leaves and cone scales cyclic; bract and ovuliferous scale strongly fused; pollen small with a small pore
Araucariaceae (2)	Almost completely Southern Hemisphere	Leaves and cone scales spirally arranged; bract and ovuliferous scale completely fused; ovules solitary; pollen large and nonsaccate
Podocarpaceae (7)	Mostly Southern Hemisphere, Central America and West Indies	Leaves flat and broad with either a single vein or many veins; ovules terminal and single; pollen saccate
Taxaceae (5)	Mostly Northern Hemisphere	Leaves flat and pointed; spiral; ovules terminal and solitary, with fleshy aril; pollen round and nonsaccate
Cephalotaxaceae (1)	China, Japan, tropical Himalayas	Leaves flat and narrow; spiral; cone scales decussate; 2 ovules on ovuliferous scale; pollen circular and nonsaccate

nant forest trees of the world, particularly in the boreal forests of the Northern Hemisphere. They are adapted for mesic or xeric conditions and occupy most ecological niches, except areas such as extreme deserts and the tundra. They provide our main source of lumber and wood products, including pulp and paper.

Morphology. In habit, the conifers are nearly all trees, some reaching gigantic proportions. The largest is *Sequoiadendron giganteum,* the "big tree" of California, with some specimens over 10 meters in diameter, 90 meters in height, and possibly 4,000 years old! A few genera, such as *Juniperus,* are characteristically shrubby. None is herbaceous.

Most of the conifers are monopodial, with **excurrent** and whorled or spiral branching (Fig. 25–10, 11). Some conifers, such as the Pinaceae, lose the leaves on older branch regions, whereas others, such as the Araucariaceae, retain the leaves on all but the oldest branches. Several genera such as *Pinus, Larix,* and *Cedrus* have both long and spur shoots as in *Ginkgo.* In *Pinus,* one to eight leaves are arranged spirally at the tip of the spur, which occurs in the axil of a nonphotosynthetic scale leaf of the long shoot (Fig. 25–12A). The spurs fall off after several years, leaving a scaly long shoot. In *Larix* and *Cedrus,* the leaves vary in number and are spirally arranged on the spur shoot (Fig. 25–12B).

The leaves of conifers are widely variable in shape, texture, and size. In general, four main morphological groups can be recognized (Fig. 25–13). (1) The first group includes needle leaves that are distinctly tetragonal in cross section and have a single vein; examples are found in *Picea, Cedrus, Cryptomeria,* and some species of *Araucaria, Dacrydium,* and *Podocarpus.* (2) Leaves of the second group are linear to lanceolate in outline, and usually distinctly flattened; examples are *Sequoia, Taxodium,* and *Metasequoia* in the Taxodiaceae; *Tsuga, Abies,* and *Pseudotsuga* in the Pinaceae; and some species of *Araucaria, Dacrydium,* and *Podocarpus.* The linear to lanceolate leaf form is the commonest in living conifers. (3) Leaves of the third group are much reduced, scale-like, and usually closely

FIGURE 25–10   Habit views of extant conifers.
A, *Cedrus deodara* (note hanging branches with
clusters of evergreen leaves on dwarf shoots),
×0.025; B, *Araucaria araucana* (leaves are persistent and very sharp on regularly whorled
branches), ×0.03.

FIGURE 25–11   Habit views of extant conifers.
A, *Larix laricina* with deciduous leaves on dwarf
shoots, ×0.025; B, *Abies* sp., showing pyramidal
form characteristic of genus, ×0.025.

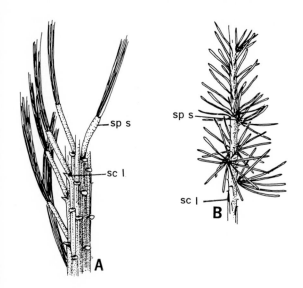

FIGURE 25-12   Leaf arrangement in conifers. A, twig of *Pinus* with spur shoots (*sp s*) emanating from axils of scale leaves (*sc l*), and bearing needles at tips, ×4; B, *Cedrus* showing both spur shoots (*sp s*) and green leaves arising from axils of scale leaves (*sc l*), ×1.

appressed to the stem; they are found most often in genera of the Cupressaceae, and in *Sequoiadendron, Taxodium,* and some species of *Podocarpus.* (4) The fourth leaf type is the least common in the conifers; leaves are flat, broad, usually ovate in outline, and many-veined. Venation appears to be parallel, but is actually acutely dichotomous. This fourth type is found almost exclusively in conifers of the Southern Hemisphere, especially in *Agathis* and some species of *Araucaria* and *Podo-carpus.*

Most of the conifers are evergreen, but several genera are deciduous (*Larix, Taxo-dium,* and *Metasequoia*). In *Larix,* the needles fall from spur shoots; in *Taxodium* and *Metasequoia,* complete leafy twigs fall each autumn. Almost all conifer leaves are adapted for xeric conditions. Typically, there is a heavy cuticle on a thick epidermis with sunken stomata (Fig. 25-14). The stomata show haplocheilic development with prominent subsidiary cells that sometimes overarch the stomatal opening, thereby providing a constricted aperture. The stomata occur in longitudinal bands on the leaves of many conifers.

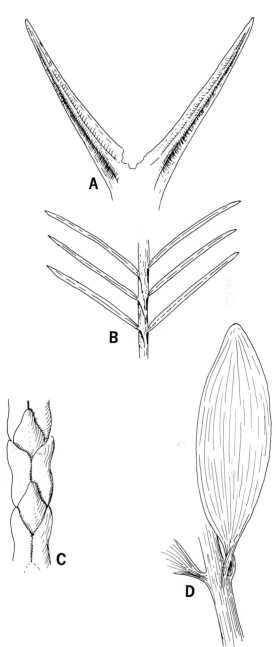

FIGURE 25-13   Leaf types of conifers. A, two leaves of *Picea* showing single vein and tetragonal shape in cross section, ×4; B, leaves of *Metasequoia* showing flattened blade and opposite arrangement on twig, ×2; C, reduced leaves of *Cupressus* in two rows on twig, ×4; D, leaf of *Agathis* showing expanded blade and steeply dichotomizing veins, ×0.75.

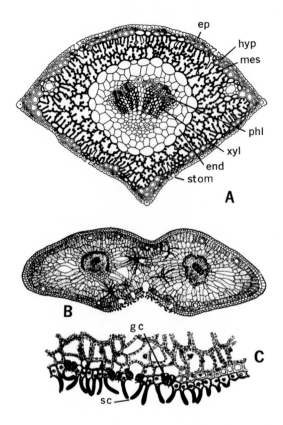

extend from the vascular bundles to the endodermis, presumably functioning in conduction between the mesophyll and vascular bundle; hence, this is referred to as transfusion tissue.

Stem Anatomy. The stems of all conifers have a narrow pith, primary vascular cylinder, and cortex (Fig. 25–15). In contrast, many have a very wide cylinder of secondary xylem. The bark may be as thick as 10 cm and in *Sequoiadendron* has been reported to reach 100 cm! The bark includes both secondary phloem and periderm, with large resin ducts in many genera. Growth rings in the secondary xylem are prominent, and vary in thickness depending on the ecological conditions of the particular year. Reconstructions of climatic fluctuations and dates of certain past events can be made from growth-ring analyses of coniferous stems. Rings are extremely narrow in areas where periods of growth are restricted by climate or soil factors, such as the muskeg regions of the subarctic. In these areas, over 200 rings within a diameter of 10 cm are not uncommon.

In some genera the secondary xylem consists of tracheids, ray parenchyma, and xylem parenchyma (Fig. 25–16). The tracheids have bordered pitting, with a single row of pits in most conifers except the araucarians, which have two or three alternate rows (Fig. 25–16B). As in *Ginkgo*, the tracheids contain crassulae between the bordered pits. These are common in all families except the Araucariaceae, where they appear sporadically. No function or significance is attached to the crassulae. In *Taxus* and *Pseudotsuga* a tertiary thickening is arranged spirally on the inside of the secondary wall. This has been credited with providing the elasticity that has made the wood of yew popular for archery bows.

The xylem rays vary in length, width, and depth; they are only a single cell wide in many genera (Fig. 25–16A). In addition to having ray parenchyma cells with simple pits, xylem rays of most genera of the Pinaceae have one to three rows of cells called ray tracheids, with bordered pits and without protoplasts at the bottom and top of the ray. In cases of wounded tissue, gradational series have been noted between ordinary and ray tracheids, suggesting an

FIGURE 25–14   Anatomy of conifer leaves. A, transverse section of *Pinus* leaf, ×60. B, transverse section of leaf of *Sciadopitys,* ×25; C, enlarged view of B, with subsidiary cells overarching stomata, ×250. *end,* endodermis; *ep,* epidermis; *g c,* guard cell; *hyp,* hypodermis; *mes,* mesophyll; *phl,* phloem; *s c,* subsidiary cell; *stom,* stoma; *xyl,* xylem. (A, after Brown with permission of Blaisdell Publishing Company; B, C, from *Gymnosperms* by C. J. Chamberlain by permission of The University of Chicago Press, copyright 1935.)

Immediately inside the epidermis occurs a **hypodermis** of one to three layers of thick-walled cells. This surrounds the mesophyll tissue, which consists of convoluted cells in the needle and scale leaves, but is differentiated into palisade and spongy layers in many of the broad flat leaves. The vascular bundles vary from one to many—usually one or two in the needle and scale leaves, and many in the broad leaf forms. In most leaves the bundle, or bundles, are surrounded by a well-defined endodermis. Often, cells with secondary walls and bordered pits

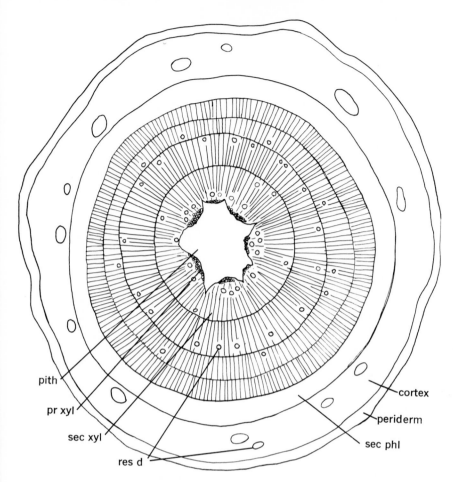

pith

pr xyl

sec xyl

res d

cortex

periderm

sec phl

FIGURE 25–15   Transverse section of four-year-old twig of *Pinus*, ×30. *pr xyl*, primary xylem; *res d*, resin ducts; *sec phl*, secondary phloem; *sec xyl*, secondary xylem.

origin of the latter from regular tracheids. Ray parenchyma cells stay alive for varying periods and apparently function in both conduction and food storage. Some rays are several cells wide and contain resin ducts. These develop from the separation of resin-producing cells, forming a central duct (Fig. 25–16C). The resin-producing cells are called **epithelial cells;** they often enlarge to close the duct, and are then termed **tylosoids.**

Resin ducts form also in the vertical plane among the tracheids. In conifers such as *Pinus*, resin ducts appear to be an integral feature of the wood. However, in many other conifers, resin ducts are apparently produced in the wood largely in response to injury. Resin ducts, or resin canals, are also common features in the

leaves and bark of many conifers. Resin is highly antiseptic and prevents invasion by certain microorganisms. It is very effective in sealing wounds in the tree. The presence of abundant resin is also credited with helping to preserve coniferous wood in different sediments.

Each year all of the secondary phloem is incorporated as an inner layer of the bark (Fig. 25–17). The secondary phloem contains sieve cells, parenchyma, and phloem fibers. The elongated sieve cells form sieve areas on the radial walls and particularly on the overlapping end walls. Certain of the phloem parenchyma cells are often filled with dense, deeply stained cytoplasm. These are called **albuminous cells** (Fig. 25–17A). Although the phloem of coni-

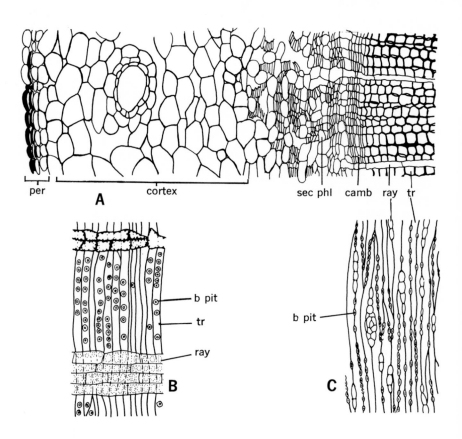

per   A   cortex   sec phl camb ray tr

b pit

tr

ray

B

b pit

C

FIGURE 25–16   Anatomy of *Pinus* stem. A, transverse section through secondary xylem to outside of bark, ×110; B, radial section of secondary xylem, ×100; C, tangential section of secondary xylem, ×100. *b pit,* bordered pit; *camb,* cambium; *per,* periderm; *sec phl,* secondary phloem; *tr,* tracheid.

fers contains no companion cells, the albuminous cells appear to function like companion cells when they are associated with sieve cells.

In addition to secondary phloem, the bark of conifers contains small amounts of crushed primary phloem and extensive periderm (Fig. 25–17B). The periderm and tissues outside of it are usually referred to as outer bark or **rhytidome.** In many conifers, the periderm forms as lenticular or conchoidal plates in successively deeper layers, and the older and outer layers split off and fall away (Fig. 25–18). The inner bark consists of phloem containing distorted and crushed fibers.

Reproduction.   Pollen sacs and ovules are borne in strobili, or cones, in all families except the Podocarpaceae, Cephalotaxaceae, and Taxaceae, which have terminal ovules and no

strobili. Most genera are monoecious, but several are reported to be dioecious. Some families, such as the Cupressaceae, have both monoecious and dioecious genera. Although there is no direct evidence, it is generally believed that the dioecious condition was derived from the monoecious—mainly because in most plant groups from the algae to the angiosperms, evolution has apparently tended toward the separation of the sexes.

In all families, the pollen-bearing organs are androstrobili clustered on smaller branches, often in lower reaches of the tree (Fig. 25–19). The androstrobili vary in length from 2 mm in *Juniperus communis* to over 12 cm in some species of *Araucaria*. In all families except the Cupressaceae, the androsporophylls are arranged spirally on the axis; in the Cupres-

504 / *VASCULAR PLANTS*

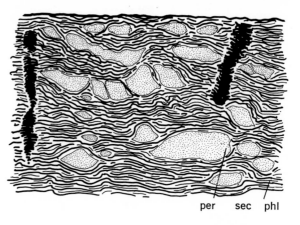

per   sec phl

FIGURE 25–18 Transverse section of bark of *Pseudotsuga,* showing lenses of periderm (*per*) embedded in secondary phloem (*sec phl*), ×1.

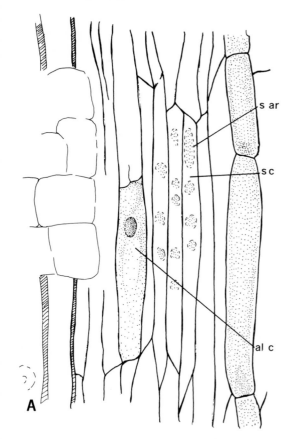

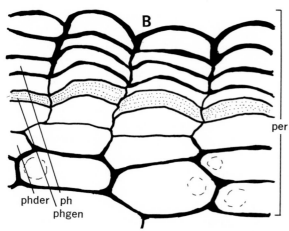

FIGURE 25–17 Anatomy of *Pinus* stem. A, longitudinal section through cambium and secondary phloem, showing sieve cells (*s c*), with sieve areas (*s ar*), and single albuminous cell (*al c*), × 1,000; B, transverse section of periderm (*per*) showing cork cambium or phellogen (*phgen*), cork cells or phellem (*ph*), and inner phelloderm cells (*phder*), ×800.

saceae, they are cyclic. The sporophylls are so regularly disposed that they appear to be aligned in vertical rows (Fig. 25–19C, D). The androsporophylls are quite variable in size and shape. In some species, such as *Araucaria cunninghamii,* the sporophyll is virtually indistinguishable from a leaf. However, in most the androsporophyll is reduced and modified in shape. Several different types are shown in Figure 25–20.

In most of the conifers, androsporangia are borne on the abaxial surface of the sporophyll. The number of sporangia varies from two to over 15, the largest numbers occurring in the Araucariaceae. The sporangia are terminal on short branched stalks in the Taxaceae and Cephalotaxaceae, similar to the arrangement in *Ginkgo.*

The pollen grains of the conifers are variable in morphology (Fig. 25–21). In size, they range from approximately 20 to 150 microns. All grains have a wall composed of two main layers—an inner thin layer called the **intine,** and an outer, thicker layer, the **exine.** In almost all grains, the exine itself is stratified into one or more distinct layers. The outer layer of the exine is often sculptured with pits, granules, reticulate markings, or other types of ornamentation. In general, the ornamentation is not particularly distinctive for genera or species, but in some cases it can be used in identification. As mentioned before, in most genera of

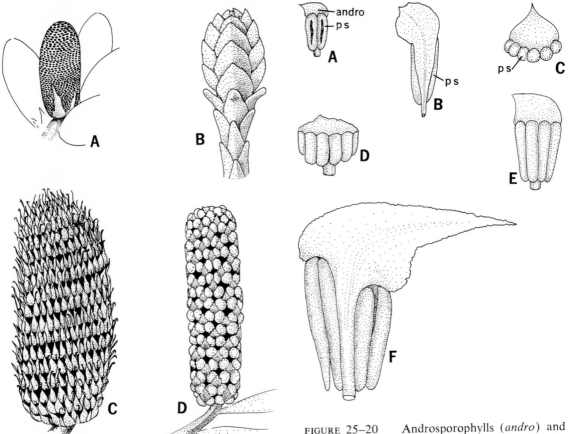

FIGURE 25–19   Habit views of androstrobili of conifers. A, *Pinus* ×3; B, *Cupressus,* ×5; C, *Araucaria,* ×2; D, *Podocarpus,* ×2.

FIGURE 25–20   Androsporophylls (*andro*) and pollen sacs (*p s*) of conifers, ×8. A, *Pinus;* B, *Picea;* C, *Cryptomeria;* D, *Cupressus;* E, *Agathis;* F, *Araucaria.* (From *Gymnosperms* by C. J. Chamberlain by permission of The University of Chicago Press, copyright 1935.)

the Pinaceae and Podocarpaceae the exine of pollen grains extends into sacci. These sacci range in number from one to several and are variable in size, ornamentation, and method of attachment to the corpus of the grain. Most of the extant genera have two sacci attached to the distal surface of the corpus.

Most conifer pollen grains have a thin specialized layer of exine that develops at the distal pole of the grain. This is called the **leptoma** (Fig. 25–21E). In saccate grains, the leptoma lies between the sacci; in bladderless grains, it variously forms a short papilla (Taxodiaceae), a small aperture (some genera of Cupressaceae), or simply a weakly defined area (*Tsuga, Athrotaxis, Callitris*). In almost all instances the pollen tube forms by an evagination of the intine at the leptoma.

All of the conifers are **anemophilous,** or wind-pollinated. The grains are shed at different times of the year, depending on latitude, altitude, and climate. Some travel over several hundred miles from the producing trees, but most appear to settle within shorter distances. Production is often prodigious, with an estimated several million grains from a single cone of *Araucaria.* In general only a few of the millions of grains shed ever reach a micropyle to effect pollination and fertilization.

The amount of gametophytic tissue developed in the pollen varies according to the genus and, to a lesser extent, the family. In the Arau-

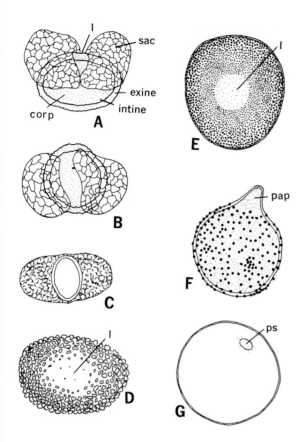

FIGURE 25–21   Pollen grains of conifers. A, B, *Pinus* (A, lateral view; B, distal view); C, *Podocarpus;* D, *Sciadopitys;* E, *Araucaria;* F, *Sequoia;* G, *Chamaecyparis.* A–E, ×500; F, G, ×1,000. *corp,* corpus; *l,* leptoma; *pap,* papilla; *ps,* pseudospore; *sac,* saccus.

cariaceae and Podocarpaceae, the first two or three prothallial cells continue to divide to form several to many cells. The Pinaceae have two prothallial cells, whereas most genera of the Taxodiaceae and Cupressaceae have none. The stages following the development of the prothallial cells and antheridial initial from the androsporal cell are almost identical to those in the cycads and *Ginkgo* (Fig. 25–22). At first the antheridial initial divides to form a generative cell and a tube cell. In many conifers, the pollen is shed at this stage. If a grain lands on a micropyle and conditions are favorable, development of the androgametophyte continues. As the tube nucleus migrates toward the tip of the pollen tube, the generative cell divides to form

a sterile cell and an androgenous cell (Fig. 25–22E). In most instances, the androgenous cell lies between the tube nucleus and the sterile cell. As the tube lengthens, the sterile cell loses its wall and, together with the androgenous cell, begins to move into the pollen tube. Just before fertilization, the androgenous cell divides to form two androgametes (Fig. 25–22F). Two types of androgametes are found in the conifers—one highly organized, with a nucleus and a definite wall; the other with no wall and a thin covering of cytoplasm. In both groups, the androgametes completely lack flagella or other appendages for locomotion.

In almost all conifers, the pollen tube grows through the nucellus until the tip of the tube reaches an archegonium. Then the tip of the pollen tube ruptures, and the androgametes are discharged into the archegonium. One gamete fuses with the egg, and the other aborts. The cytoplasm of the androgamete persists after its union with the egg, forming a dense coating on the zygote. In *Pinus,* and at least some other conifers, there is no fusion or blending of nuclei. Instead, the two sets of chromosomes remain side by side until they are incorporated into a group on a single spindle during the first mitosis of the fertilized egg.

Ovules are borne in cones in all but the Podocarpaceae, Cephalotaxaceae, and Taxaceae, where they are attached singly or in pairs to the tips of short stalks. Cones of the other four families are compound structures as in the Cordaitales and Lebachiaceae. They consist of bracts with an ovuliferous scale attached to the basal part of the adaxial surface of each bract (Fig. 25–23). The bracts are whorled in the Cupressaceae, but are spirally arranged in the Pinaceae, Taxodiaceae, and Araucariaceae. The bracts and ovuliferous scales are virtually free from each other in the Pinaceae, but are coalesced to greater or lesser extent in the Cupressaceae, Taxodiaceae, and Araucariaceae (Fig. 25–23C). Although the bract is usually much smaller than the ovuliferous scale, it reaches well beyond the scale in *Pseudotsuga* (Fig. 25–23B), *Larix,* and *Abies.* Both bract and scale have a variety of shapes and sizes which are distinctive for genera and even spe-

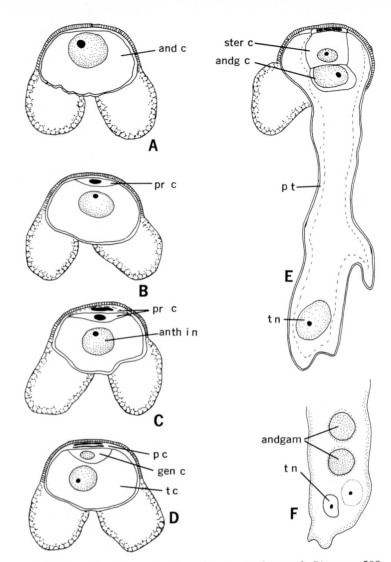

FIGURE 25–22   Development of androgametophyte of *Pinus,* ×500. A, pollen grain with androsporal cell (*and c*); B, first prothallial cell (*pr c*) and antheridial initial (*anth in*) formed from division of androsporal cell; C, second prothallial cell has formed; D, antheridial initial has produced generative cell (*gen c*) and tube cell (*t c*); E, tube nucleus (*t n*) has migrated to tip of pollen tube (*p t*); and generative cell has divided to form sterile cell (*ster c*) and androgenous cell (*andg c*); F, androgenous cell has divided to produce two androgametes (*andgam*), while tube nucleus remains at tip of pollen tube. (A–E, from *Morphology of Gymnosperms* by J. M. Coulter and C. J. Chamberlain, by permission of The University of Chicago Press, copyright 1910 and 1917; F, after Coulter.)

cies in all families. The differences are often valuable in identification of species.

Much controversy has centered around the origin and structure of the bract and scale of coniferous gynostrobili. Initially, the bract was most likely derived from a leaf. However, the ovuliferous scale has been equated to many structures, including a flattened branch in the axil of a leaf (the bract), a ligule, an open carpel, a placenta, the blended integuments of two ovules, a leaf of an axillary shoot, and the first two leaves of an axillary shoot fused along

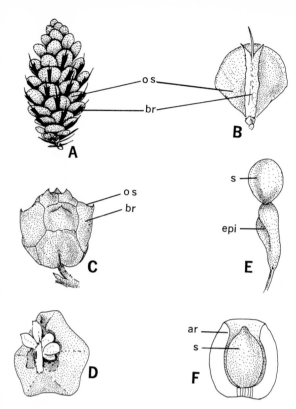

FIGURE 25–23   Gynostrobili of conifers. A, B, *Pseudotsuga;* note elongated bracts (*br*) protruding beyond ovuliferous scales (*o s*); A, ×0.5; B, ×1; C, D, *Cupressus* (bract and ovuliferous scales are almost completely fused, and several ovules are borne on each scale), C, ×0.5; D, ×1; E, *Podocarpus,* with epimatium (*epi*) subtending single seed (*s*), ×0.5; F, *Taxus,* with fleshy aril (*ar*) surrounding single seed, ×2.

one margin. A clue to the probable origin and evolution of the ovuliferous scale can be found in the opposite orientation of the xylem and phloem in the bract and ovuliferous scale of extant conifers (Fig. 25–24C). In the bract, the phloem of the vascular bundles is on the lower (abaxial) side of the xylem in the normal arrangement for a leaf on a stem. By contrast, in the ovuliferous scale the phloem is on the upper (adaxial) side of the xylem. The most likely explanation for this opposite orientation is that the ovuliferous scale represents a sporophyll originally attached to the upper (adaxial) surface of the dwarf shoot as in *Cordaianthus* or *Lebachia* (Fig. 25–24A, B). In fact, as illustrated in Figure 25–24B, this is exactly the orientation of the flattened ovule-bearing spo-

rophyll in the genus *Lebachia.* This orientation of the sporophyll would account for the phloem being on top of the xylem. As shown by Florin, reduction of the dwarf shoot appears to have occurred in the evolutionary series from *Cordaites* with several sporophylls, to *Lebachia* with one sporophyll on the adaxial surface, to the extant conifers in which the ovuliferous scale is all that remains of the fertile dwarf axis (Fig. 25–24C).

The ovules are attached to the adaxial surface of the ovuliferous scale, varying in number from one to seven. They are oriented in two main ways. In the Pinaceae, Araucariaceae, and many of the Podocarpaceae, the micropyle is directed toward the cone axis. In the Cupressaceae, Taxaceae, and most genera of the Taxodiaceae, the micropyle is directed away from the axis.

All ovules have only one integument, free or partly fused to the nucellus (Fig. 25–25A). Unlike the cycads or *Ginkgo,* there is no pollen chamber or nucellar beak. The integument is divided into an outer fleshy, a middle stony, and an inner fleshy layer. The outer layer is thin and usually sloughs off. The ovules of most conifers lack vascular tissue, but some have bundles at the base. Only *Podocarpus* has vascular bundles extending to the tip of the integument.

In some species of conifers, the seed has an attached wing. In *Pinus,* it is long and flat, and assists in wind dispersal of the seed. The wing is not actually a part of the seed, but is the upper surface of the ovuliferous scale that abscises at the time of seed maturation.

Ovules of the Taxaceae, Cephalotaxaceae, and Podocarpaceae are covered by a fleshy outgrowth of the stalk called an **aril** in plants of the first two families, and an **epimatium** in the Podocarpaceae (Fig. 25–23E, F). The origin of this extra covering is debatable. Some investigators suggest it is a second integument, and others claim it represents a modified ovuliferous scale; the latter explanation appears more reasonable.

The development of the gynogametophyte is very similar to that in the cycads and *Ginkgo.* The spore mother cell develops hypodermally, sometimes deeply within the nucellus (Fig. 25–25A). Four gynospores are formed at mei-

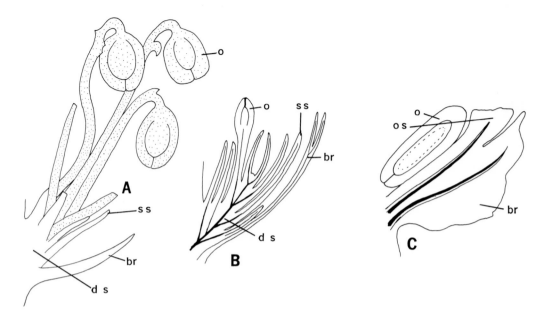

FIGURE 25–24   Probable evolution of gynostrobilus in coniferophytes. A, *Cordaites,* with several ovules (*o*) and sterile scales (*s s*) attached to dwarf shoot in axil of bract (*br*), ×2; B, *Lebachia,* in which ovules are reduced to one on dwarf shoot (*d s*) with sterile scales, again in axil of bract, ×4; C, *Pinus,* with two ovules attached to ovuliferous scale (*o s*) which almost certainly is homologue of ovule-bearing scale in *Lebachia,* ×5. (A, B, after Florin with permission of *Palaeontographica.*)

osis, nearly always in a linear tetrad (Fig. 25–25B). As a rule only one develops, but several are known to function up to the free-nuclear stage in *Taxus.* The gynospore expands greatly, undergoing free-nuclear division (Fig. 25–25C). Walls then form centripetally, producing a central mass of gametophytic cells, with the cells toward the chalazal end charged with nutrient materials.

In all conifers, the archegonia arise from the differentiation of superficial cells at the micropylar end or along the flanks of the nucellus (Fig. 25–25D). The number of archegonia that develop is variable, ranging from one to 200. There are two main types of archegonial arrangement. In most families, each archegonium is separated from others by prothallial cells. In the Cupressaceae and Taxodiaceae, archegonia occur in groups. Some genera of these two families have the archegonial group directly behind the micropyle, whereas others have the group on the lateral wall of the gametophyte.

The archegonia usually develop two tiers of neck cells, each tier with four cells (Fig. 25–25E, F). Occasionally there are eight cells in each tier, and sometimes as few as two. Extremes are found in *Tsuga canadensis* with only one tier of two neck cells, and in *Austrotaxus* with one tier of 16 cells. There are no neck canal cells. In the Pinaceae, the ventral canal nucleus is separated by a wall from the egg. In the other conifers, no intervening wall is formed. The conifers with a cell wall surrounding the ventral canal nucleus also have thick membranes around the androgametes; the converse also is true.

Following fertilization, the zygote undergoes a period of free-nuclear division in all conifers except *Sequoia* (Fig. 25–26A). In most families, four to eight nuclei are formed, but as many as 64 are reported in the Araucariaceae. Again, except in the Araucariaceae, the nuclei migrate to the basal end of the egg cell, where they form into a single plane. The nuclei undergo several additional divisions accompanied by wall formation, resulting in three tiers of four cells each in the Taxodiaceae, Cupressaceae, and Araucariaceae, and four

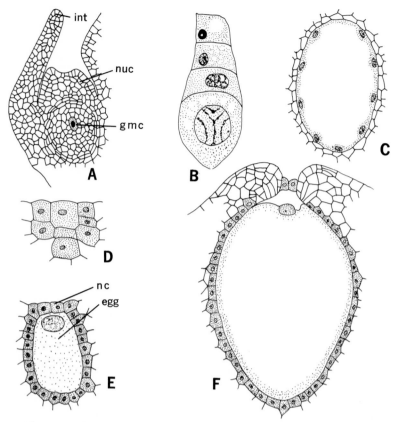

FIGURE 25–25   Development of gynogametophyte of conifers. A, longitudinal section of young ovule, showing integument (*int*) partly fused to nucellus (*nuc*) and a single gynospore mother cell (*g m c*) in central part of nucellus, ×40; B, linear tetrad of gynospores, with lowest enlarging and other three beginning to abort, ×485; C, free-nuclear stage with nuclei arranged around periphery of gynospore; D, archegonial initials at micropylar edge of gametophyte; E, immature archegonium showing two neck cells (*n c*) and large egg; F, mature archegonium with fully expanded egg and egg nucleus sitting just below neck; C–F, ×55. (A–C, after Ferguson; D–F, from *Morphology of Gymnosperms* by J. M. Coulter and C. J. Chamberlain by permission of The University of Chicago Press, copyright 1910 and 1917.)

tiers of four cells in the Pinaceae (Fig. 25–26B–E). In at least one section of *Podocarpus,* the 16 early cells are in three tiers. The basal tier has a single binucleate cell, the second contains from seven to nine cells, and the third comprises the remaining nuclei without complete walls. The proembryo includes the early stages of development before a mature embryo is formed.

In all the conifers, a greatly elongated suspensor develops. In *Pinus* and most of the Pinaceae, the suspensors originate from cells of the second tier which were formed by division of cells of the basal tier (Fig. 25–26C, D). These cells, called **primary suspensors,** elongate rather quickly to shove the basal tier down into the gametophyte. At the same time, the basal tier divides to produce one, two, or three additional tiers of cells called **secondary suspensor cells** or, alternatively, **embryonal tubes.** These cells elongate to variable extents, and function in pushing the embryonic cells deeper into the gametophyte (Fig. 25–26E).

In other genera such as *Podocarpus, Sciadopitys,* and *Dacrydium,* the original second tier of cells which developed from the free-

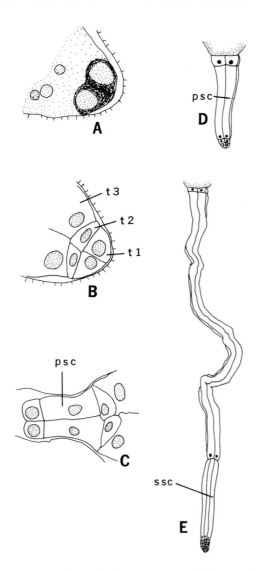

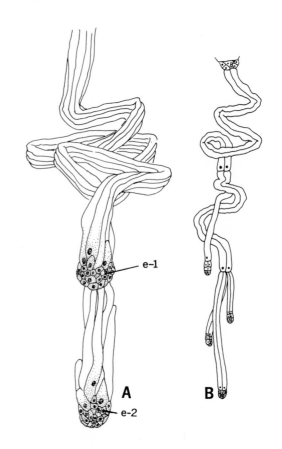

FIGURE 25–27 Two types of embryony in conifers. A, simple polyembryony in *Dacrydium*, showing two embryos (*e* − 1 and *e* − 2) formed from separate fertilized eggs, ×75; B, cleavage embryony in *Tsuga* with four embryos differentiated from one original embryo, ×50. (After Buchholz with permission of *Botanical Gazette*.)

FIGURE 25–26 Embryonic development in conifers. A, free-nuclear stage with two proembryonic nuclei at chalazal end, ×100; B, longitudinal section of proembryo showing three tiers of cells (*t* 1, *t* 2, *t* 3), each with four cells, ×100; C, cells of central tier elongated to form primary suspensor cells (*p s c*), ×100; D, primary suspensor cells further elongated, and cells of first tier divided to form several tiers of embryonic initials, ×40; E, primary suspensors greatly elongated, and secondary suspensor cells (*s s c*) have formed to push embryonic cap even deeper into gametophytic tissue, ×50. (A–C, adapted from Donald Alexander Johansen, *Plant Embryology—Embryogeny of the Spermatophyta*, copyright 1950, The Ronald Press Company, New York; D, E, after Buchholz with permission Illinois State Academy of Science.)

nucleate condition functions very early as a suspensor. The term **prosuspensor** is usually applied to such cells that elongate markedly in early stages. After the embryonic tier at the tip of the proembryo has undergone several divisions, some of the more distal cells elongate, forming secondary suspensor cells (embryonal tubes) that develop into a rather massive secondary suspensor. In both types of proembryo, the suspensor becomes twisted and coiled, and pushes the developing embryo deeper into the gametophytic tissue. When the embryo has finished its development, the suspensor in most instances forms a cap of tissue over the tip of the radicle.

In all conifers, more than one embryo is likely to begin development in the ovule; normally, only one matures. In some instances, embryos develop from more than one fertilized egg—a process called **simple polyembryony** (Fig. 25–27A). In others, the cells of the basal tier of the proembryo split, each cell then developing into a separate embryo; this is termed **cleavage polyembryony** (Fig. 25–27B). Both types occur in each family of conifers, but one type only is characteristic for each genus.

Later stages of embryo development are relatively poorly known. Some appear to have an apical cell, whereas others appear to have a **tunica-corpus** or **histogen** arrangement of meristems. As maturation proceeds, the lobes of the two to 18 cotyledons at the chalazal end and the radicle at the micropylar end become recognizable; some of the central cells begin to elongate, suggesting the initials of pith and possibly vascular tissue. The cells of the outer layer or **dermatogen** assume the brick-shaped outline characteristic of epidermal cells.

BRIEF DESCRIPTIONS OF FAMILIES OF CONIFERALES. In the following paragraphs, brief descriptions of the main morphological and anatomical features of the genera of each family are presented. This is intended as an introduction to the families, not as an exhaustive coverage. For more detailed treatment, the reader can refer to several excellent references given in the bibliography.

Family Pinaceae. This is a family represented by ten genera and some 250 species of trees almost entirely of the Northern Hemisphere. The plants are characterized by needle-like leaves, arranged either spirally on the stem or grouped into fascicles on spur shoots (Fig. 25–28). Most genera are evergreen, but *Larix* and *Pseudolarix* are deciduous. The androstrobili are relatively large, elliptical, and compact. They have spirally arranged sporophylls bearing two androsporangia on the abaxial surface. Pollen grains of all except *Larix* and *Pseudotsuga* are saccate, ranging in length from 40 to 150 microns. Gynostrobili have spirally arranged bracts and ovuliferous scales that are more or less separate. Typically, there are two

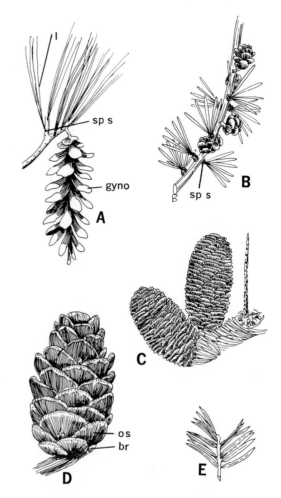

FIGURE 25–28   Foliage and cones of Pinaceae. A, *Pinus,* showing fascicles of needles (*l*) on spur shoots (*sp s*) and one pendulous gynostrobilus (*gyno*), ×0.5; B, *Larix,* with spurs, needles, and gynostrobili, ×0.5; C, *Abies,* with erect gynostrobili, ×0.5; D, *Keteleeria,* showing bracts (*br*) and ovuliferous scales (*o s*), ×0.5; E, foliage shoot of *Keteleeria* showing flattened and pointed needle leaves, ×0.3.

inverted ovules on the adaxial surface of the scale. The woody gynostrobili are pendulous in all but *Cedrus, Abies, Larix,* and *Keteleeria.*

The main genera are *Pinus* (90 species), *Abies* and *Picea* (40 species each), and *Larix* (10 species). Together they extend over North America and Eurasia, mostly on poorer soils and in cooler climates. *Tsuga* and *Pseudotsuga* occur in both North America and southeastern Asia. *Tsuga* thrives in wet cool climates such as the Himalaya Mountains and the west coast of North America. *Pseudotsuga,* on the other hand, grows well on the west coast of North America and also on drier sites such as the interior plateau region of western North America. *Keteleeria* and *Pseudolarix* are native only to China; the latter has only one species. *Cedrus* occurs in the Mediterranean region and the western Himalayas, but grows well as an ornamental on the Pacific coast of North America.

Trees of the Pinaceae are important economically as sources of timber, pulpwood, and naval stores (particularly turpentine and pitch). They are also sources of Canada balsam (*Abies balsamea*), Venetian turpentine (*Larix* species), and edible seeds (*Pinus* species). The Christmas tree industry consumes large numbers of pinaceous trees each year, particularly those of *Pinus, Abies,* and *Pseudotsuga.* There is also an increasing trend to use exotic varieties in landscaping—particularly blue varieties of *Picea,* dwarf specimens of *Pinus,* and *Cedrus.*

The family has a fossil history from at least the Jurassic to the present, but most extant genera have not been recognized with certainty until later periods. *Pinus* is known from the Lower Cretaceous, but most other genera are not recorded until the Upper Cretaceous or at later times in the Tertiary. Some genera, such as *Tsuga* and *Pseudotsuga,* still appear to be actively evolving, whereas others, such as *Pseudolarix,* are almost certainly static and may be heading toward extinction.

Family Cupressaceae. This is a large family with 16 genera scattered over both hemispheres, but more abundant in the Northern. The genera and their distribution are listed in Table 25–2. The largest are given first, and seven monotypic and endemic genera are listed at the end. Representative foliage, cones, pollen, and seeds are shown in Figure 25–29.

The most distinguishing characteristics of the Cupressaceae are the reduced scale-like leaves and the relatively small gynostrobili. In both, the arrangement of parts is either spiral or opposite. The ovuliferous scales and bracts are usually completely fused, resulting in a single unit often called the cone scale. In most genera

TABLE 25–2

DISTRIBUTION OF GENERA OF CUPRESSACEAE

GENUS (NUMBER OF SPECIES IN PARENTHESES)	DISTRIBUTION
Juniperus (70)	Temperate North America; widespread
Callitris (20)	Australia and Tasmania; New Caledonia
Cupressus (15)	Western regions of North and Central America; Asia eastward to North Africa
Libocedrus (9)	Pacific coast in North and South America; New Zealand; China and Formosa; New Guinea and New Caledonia
Chamaecyparis (6)	Pacific coast and eastern North America; Japan and Formosa
Thuja (5)	Northern North America; China and Japan
Widdringtonia (5)	Southern tropical Africa
Folsenia (3)	China
Actinostrobus (2)	Western Australia
Fitzroya (1)	Southern Chile
Pilgerodendron (1)	Chile
Tetraclinis (1)	Southern Spain and North Africa
Thujopsis (1)	Japan
Callitropsis (1)	New Caledonia
Diselma (1)	Western Tasmania
Arceuthos (1)	Southeastern Europe

the androstrobili are very small, terminal on the twig, and with tiny peltate sporophylls. The pollen grains are characteristically small, circular, and with a small aperture called a **pseudopore.**

Species of this family grow in a wide variety of habitats. They are generally well-adapted for xeric conditions resulting either from dry climate or from physiologic drought, but some

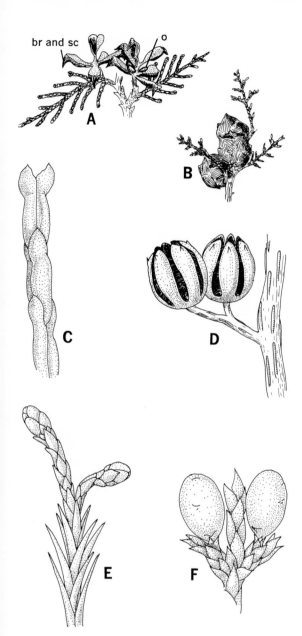

br and sc

o

A

B

C

D

E

F

FIGURE 25–29   Foliage and cones of Cupressaceae. A, *Biota*, showing fused bracts (*br*) and scales (*sc*) that are opened, with several ovules (*o*) still attached, ×0.5; B, *Cupressus*, showing very small and closely appressed scale leaves, and relatively large gynostrobili, ×0.25; C, *Callitris*, with perfectly decussate scale leaves, ×2; D, *Callitris*, with partly opened bract-scale segments, and very small scale leaves; E, *Juniperus*, showing the relatively large leaves on the branches and scale leaves of cone-bearing twigs, ×2; F, *Juniperus* with gynostrobili with almost completely coalesced bracts and scales, ×2.

species require fairly moist conditions for their best growth.

Many genera contain important trees for timber, especially *Thuja* and *Callitris*. Others such as *Juniperus*, *Cupressus*, and *Libocedrus*, have wood with various shades of red and cream, and are used for rustic furniture, cabinet making, and lead pencils. Various oils and aromatic compounds are derived from certain species—for example, the oil from *Juniperus* ovules for flavoring gin, the sandaraque oil of *Tetraclinis* from Morocco used in varnish, and the oil of cedar from *Thuja occidentalis* used for microscope immersion oil.

The family has a fossil record from the early Mesozoic, but like the Pinaceae, most of the extant genera did not become distinct until the later Cretaceous and Tertiary. Many of the modern genera have limited ranges and few species, suggesting that they may be heading toward extinction. However, with most genera the former distributions are poorly known, and the modern trends in distribution cannot be accurately assessed.

Family Taxodiaceae.   The ten genera of this family have very restricted ranges (see Table 25–3). Only one genus, *Athrotaxis*, occurs in the Southern Hemisphere.

The family is a heterogeneous group with a wide range of structural characteristics. The leaves are either scale-like, flat-bladed, or needle-like (Fig. 25–30). They are deciduous only in *Taxodium* and *Metasequoia*, in which whole leaf-bearing twigs break off in the autumn. The genera are all strictly monoecious, with androstrobili generally small and compact, and with two to nine androsporangia on the abaxial surface of each sporophyll. The pollen grains are small, spherical, and with a distinct papilla in all but *Sciadopitys*. Together with other distinguishing characteristics, this has suggested to some botanists that *Sciadopitys* may belong in a distinct family.

The gynostrobili are generally small, with fused spiral bracts and ovuliferous scales. They are flattened and somewhat peltate. The seeds number from two to nine, and are virtually wingless. In all characteristics, the Taxodiaceae appear to be more closely related to the

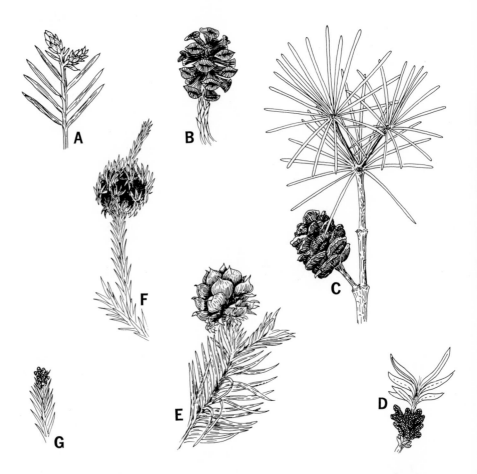

FIGURE 25–30   Foliage and cones of Taxodiaceae. A, *Sequoia,* showing two androstrobili at tip of twig, and several flattened and two-ranked leaves, ×0.5; B, *Sequoia,* showing scale leaves on twig and flattened scale-bract units that have opened and shed seeds, ×0.5; C, *Sciadopitys,* with spiral clusters of relatively large leaves at branch tips and one gynostrobilus, ×0.5; D, *Cunninghamia,* showing cluster of androstrobili subtending several falcate needle leaves, ×0.5; E, *Cunninghamia,* showing lanceolate, and sharp-pointed needle leaves and one gynostrobilus, ×0.5; F, *Cryptomeria,* with sharp-pointed needle leaves, and one gynostrobilus with branched bract-scale structures, and main branch growing beyond axis of strobilus, ×0.5; G, *Cryptomeria,* showing cluster of androstrobili at branch tip, ×0.5.

Cupressaceae than to any other family.

Some genera are important timber trees—for example, *Sequoia,* the redwood in California, and *Cunninghamia,* the "sha-mu" from China. The commercial value of most species is enhanced by their resistance to disease caused by microorganisms, or to infestations from insects and other invertebrates.

The fossil record of the family goes well back into the Mesozoic, with early representa-

tives showing relations to *Sciadopitys.* Many of the extant genera became distinct in the Cretaceous and Tertiary, and they present one of the most interesting records of rise and fall in the plant kingdom. During the early Tertiary in the Northern Hemisphere, the fossil evidence shows that *Sequoia, Taxodium, Metasequoia,* and *Glyptostrobus* were important and widespread tree elements in the flora. The record indicates that all of these occurred in Siberia,

TABLE 25–3

DISTRIBUTION OF GENERA OF TAXODIACEAE

GENUS (NUMBER OF SPECIES IN PARENTHESES)	DISTRIBUTION
Sequoia (1)	Southern Oregon and northern California
Sequoiadendron (1)	California—very restricted
Taxodium (3)	Southern United States and Mexico
Metasequoia (1)	Western China—very restricted
Glyptostrobus (1)	Southeastern China
Cunninghamia (2)	Southeastern China and Formosa
Cryptomeria (1)	Japan
Sciadopitys (1)	Japan
Taiwania (1)	Formosa
Athrotaxis (3)	Tasmania

Spitzbergen, Greenland, the Arctic Islands, and the higher latitudes in North America. During the later Tertiary, these genera were gradually eliminated in the high northern latitudes. By the middle Pliocene, *Metasequoia* and *Glyptostrobus* were gone from North America, but survived to the present on the eastern rim of the Pacific. Likewise, *Sequoia* and *Taxodium* disappeared from Europe and Asia during the Tertiary, surviving at latitudes up to 60° N. on the North American side of the Pacific.

From the record of the Pliocene and Pleistocene, and from the modern distribution, it is quite apparent that the four genera were progressively restricted during the later Tertiary. Today, *Sequoia* and *Metasequoia* are so narrowly limited that they are almost certainly facing extinction. The gradual cooling of the climate during the Tertiary, coupled with the rigorous competition from the rapidly evolving angiosperms, appear to have spelled the doom of the once widespread and abundant genera of the Taxodiaceae.

Family Podocarpaceae. Six of the seven genera of this family are restricted to relatively small regions of the Southern Hemisphere. Only the genus *Podocarpus* is widespread and ranges north of the equator in Central America, Africa, and from Malaya to Japan (Table 25–4).

The leaves are quite variable, ranging from broad and strap-shaped in *Podocarpus* to small and scale-like in *Dacrydium* (Fig. 25–31). The genus *Phyllocladus* has expanded, flattened, and leaf-like lobes of branches called **phylloclads.** The much-reduced leaves occur as spiny teeth on the rim of the phylloclad.

The androstrobili consist of compact sporophylls bearing two sporangia. In most, the androstrobili are cylindrical and elongate. The pollen grains are saccate, except in *Saxegothaea,* which has papillated pollen similar to the Taxodiaceae. As many as seven prothallial cells have been noted in the pollen grains of *Podocarpus.*

The ovules are borne singly on the tips of stalks (Fig. 25–31B). In some species, such as *Podocarpus spicatus,* the ovules are arranged in two rows along an axis, each in the axil of a bract, thus simulating a strobilus. In all except *Microstrobus,* the ovules are covered by the epimatium, which has been variously equated to an ovuliferous scale (most likely), an aril, and a second integument.

Both the androstrobili and the ovule-bearing shoots of the podocarps are subtended by bracts. This has suggested to some that they are perfectly homologous with the dwarf shoots of the strobili of the Cordaitales and the Lebachiaceae. In the podocarps, the dwarf shoot bearing the single ovule would represent a reduction of several fertile and sterile appendages of the cordaites and lebachias.

Podocarpus and to a lesser extent *Dacrydium* are important sources of timber in New Zealand and Indochina. Four of the genera are cultivated as ornamentals: *Podocarpus, Phyllocladus, Saxegothaea,* and *Dacrydium.*

The history of the Podocarpaceae goes back at least to the Jurassic. Recent investigations of fossil pollen have indicated that the family was formerly widespread in Asia, Europe, and North America, as well as the Southern Hemisphere. Withdrawal to the present lim-

TABLE 25-4
DISTRIBUTION OF GENERA OF THE PODOCARPACEAE

GENUS (NUMBER OF SPECIES IN PARENTHESES)	DISTRIBUTION
Podocarpus (100)	Australia; New Zealand; Indonesia and India; East Africa; Central and South America
Dacrydium (20)	New Zealand; New Caledonia; Indochina; Australia; New Guinea; Malaya; Philippines
Phyllocladus (6)	New Zealand; Tasmania; New Guinea; Borneo
Saxegothaea (1)	Southern Chile
Microcachrys (1)	Tasmania
Acmopyle (1)	New Caledonia
Microstrobus (2)	Tasmania

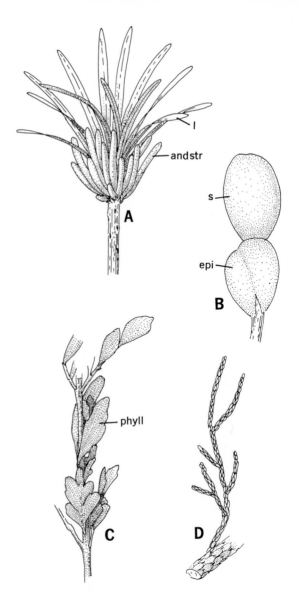

FIGURE 25–31 Foliage and cones of Podocarpaceae, ×0.5. A, *Podocarpus* showing androstrobili (*andstr*) clustered below leaves (*l*) at branch tip; B, *Podocarpus*, single seed (*s*) subtended by epimatium (*epi*) that probably represents ovuliferous scale; C, *Phyllocladus*, in which leaflike appendages or phylloclads (*phyll*) are modified branches; D, *Dacrydium*, with small scale leaves closely appressed to twig.

its appears to have occurred during later Tertiary times. This has raised the question of whether the family actually had its origin in the Southern Hemisphere as has generally been accepted.

Family Araucariaceae. There are only two genera, *Araucaria* and *Agathis*—both predominantly of the Southern Hemisphere. *Araucaria* has about 16 species and ranges from New Guinea to Australia; in South America it also occurs in Chile, Argentina, and Brazil. *Agathis,* with 20 species, is found in Malaya, Indonesia, the Philippines, New Caledonia, Fiji, Australia, and New Zealand.

Both genera consist of trees over 30 meters in height, and are characterized by more or less symmetrical and whorled branches. Leaves are persistent, often two-ranked, and are dimorphic in some species. They have from one to many parallel veins, and vary from small scale and needle leaves in *Araucaria* to broad lanceolate forms in *Agathis* (Fig. 25–32). Androstrobili are long and cylindrical with many spiral sporophylls (Fig. 25–32B).

The sporophylls are similar to the sporangiophores of *Equisetum,* with a peltate shape, and bear five to 20 androsporangia on the abaxial surface. Typically, the androsporangia are directed toward the cone axis. Pollen grains in

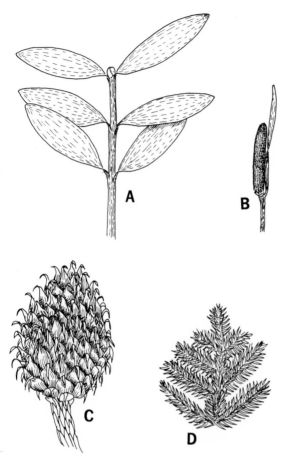

FIGURE 25–32 Foliages and cones of Araucariaceae, ×0.5. A, leaves of *Agathis*; B, androstrobilus of *Agathis*; C, androstrobilus of *Araucaria araucana*; D, twigs and falcate leaves of *Araucaria excelsa*.

both genera are nonsaccate, with a weak leptoma in a thick wall. The pollen of the araucarias has the largest number of prothallial cells in the coniferalean order. The pollen grains are also characterized by numerous large starch grains surrounding the prothallial and androgenous cells.

The gynostrobili are relatively large, and are borne at the ends of the branches, usually at the tree top (Fig. 25–32C). They consist of many spirally arranged appendages that comprise bract and partly fused ovuliferous scale in *Araucaria*. However, in *Agathis*, only a single structure is generally credited with being a bract; it has a completely reduced and fused ovuliferous scale. In general, the number of

ovules is usually one, rarely two. The ovule is large, and a second layer around the integument has been referred to as a specialized leaf or as a second integument. The nucellus, very prominent at the micropyle, functions like a stigma in holding the pollen grains.

Certain species of both *Araucaria* and *Agathis* are used for lumber, especially for general construction, cabinet making, and veneer wood. In South America, two species of *Araucaria* are utilized. One of these, *Araucaria araucana*, the Chilean pine, is relatively inaccessible in the Andes of Chile and Argentina, and hence is not widely exploited. The other is *A. angustifolia*, the Paraná pine of southern Brazil, Paraguay, and northern Argentina—one of the most exploited trees in South America. It is used largely locally, but some is exported to the United States and Europe.

Agathis is exploited largely for a resinous material called copal used in the manufacture of high-grade varnish, patent leather, sealing wax, and other resinous products. The legendary Kauri pine of New Zealand, *Agathis australis*, is highly valuable for timber; but it is no longer economically important because of widespread decimation from fires and native gum-diggers in earlier times, and because of the introduction of exotic softwood species, especially *Pinus* species.

The Araucariaceae is one of the earliest recognized families of conifers, and wood from the Triassic has been called *Araucarioxylon* because of its similarity to living araucarian wood. Foliage compressions related to both *Araucaria* and *Agathis* are known from the Jurassic to the present. Pollen of *Araucaria* has been reported from several Tertiary localities in Europe, suggesting that the family became restricted to more southerly latitudes fairly late in geological time.

Family Taxaceae. This family has five extant genera (Table 25–5) and three that are known only from the fossil record. Good evidence has been presented to show that the Taxaceae and Cephalotaxaceae have been distinct from the other families of conifers at least from the Carboniferous. Accordingly, the two families are often treated as a separate

TABLE 25–5

DISTRIBUTION OF GENERA OF TAXACEAE

GENUS (NUMBER OF SPECIES IN PARENTHESES)	DISTRIBUTION
Taxus (7)	Widely scattered—North America; Mexico; Europe; India; China; Japan; Indonesia
Torreya (5)	China; Japan; California; Florida
Amentotaxus (1)	Western China
Austrotaxus (1)	New Caledonia
Nothotaxus (1)	Southern China

order, the Taxales. In many features of morphology and anatomy, the Taxaceae resemble the conifer families, especially the Podocarpaceae. The main distinguishing feature is the possession of a single terminal ovule instead of ovules in cones.

Most of the plants are small trees or shrubs. The leaves are spirally arranged but mostly two-ranked, with linear to lanceolate blades (Fig. 25–33). The pollen-bearing organs are androstrobili that consist of spirally arranged sporophylls. Each sporophyll is characteristically peltate, with a thickened apex, and three to nine androsporangia that hang from the outward rim. The pollen grains are circular and moderately thick-walled, with a coarsely granular exine and a weakly defined leptoma. They resemble grains of the Cupressaceae rather closely.

Ovules are solitary, terminal, and not in cones or strobili. The ovule is surrounded by a fleshy aril that has been variously interpreted. Some relatively recent work by André has shown that the aril develops from a modification of one of the last leaves of the branch tip, and can thus be equated to a sporophyll.

The wood of *Taxus* has long been prized for archery bows and in cabinet making. Both *Taxus* and *Torreya* are planted as ornamentals.

Fossils of this group are known with certainty from the Jurassic to the present. The Taxaceae appear to be quite distinct from the other conifers, and may have had their origin from other ancestral forms.

Family Cephalotaxaceae. This family comprises a single genus, *Cephalotaxus*, with five species ranging from the tropical Himalayas through southern and central China to Japan.

The habit is similar to that of the Taxaceae. The plants are either trees or shrubs, with opposite branching and spirally arranged two-ranked leaves (Fig. 25–34). Each androstrobilus consists of a dwarf shoot in the axil of a leaf, which supports secondary sporangia-bearing shoots in the axils of bracts (Fig. 25–34A). The lobed androsporangia hang pendently from the secondary dwarf shoots. The pollen grains are spherical, moderately thick-walled, granulate, and with a slightly evaginated leptoma.

The ovules are solitary and terminal on short stalks located in the axils of scale appendages. These scale appendages are in turn located on longer stalks in the axils of foliage leaves. The latter stalks (primary) are either naked or clothed at the base with spirally arranged scales. Thus, the ovule-bearing organ is either a simple or compound strobilus, both of which occur in the same species. The ovule is subtended by a rudimentary aril (Fig. 25–34C). At maturity, the integument becomes differentiated into three distinct layers—an outer fleshy, a middle stony, and an inner fleshy layer.

Fossils related to *Cephalotaxus* have been found in the Cretaceous of North America and the Tertiary of Europe. They appear to be related to the Lebachiaceae and Cordaitales, and to have undergone little reduction from these ancestors.

PHYLOGENY OF CONIFERALES. There is good evidence from investigations of both fossil and modern representatives that evolution has proceeded from the progymnosperms to the Cordaitales, and through the Lebachiaceae to modern families. This is based mainly on researches of the ovule-bearing organs, which provide a series suggesting that reduction in the size and number of parts has occurred. Thus, a

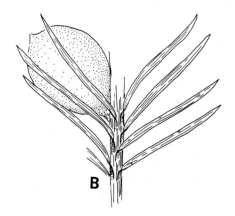

FIGURE 25–33   Foliage and seeds of the Taxaceae, ×0.5. A, *Taxus* showing two ranked leaves and seed (*s*) surrounded by aril (*ar*); B, *Torreya* with several needle leaves and single seed.

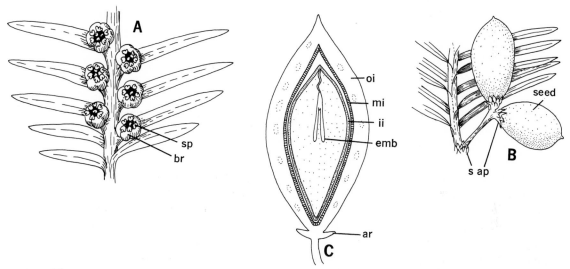

FIGURE 25–34   Foliage and seeds of *Cephalotaxus*. A, androstrobili in axils of flattened needle leaves, showing sporangia (*sp*) and bracts (*br*), ×1; B, two seeds at tip of fertile shoot, showing scale appendages (*s ap*), ×1; C, longitudinal median section through seed showing the inner (*ii*), middle (*mi*), and outer (*oi*) integuments, the rudimentary aril (*ar*), and a single dicotyledonous embryo (*emb*), ×2.

series from *Cordaites–Lebachia*–extant conifers shows a reduction from a short shoot bearing many sterile and fertile appendages to a single ovuliferous scale in the extant genera.

In some vegetative structures, especially the leaves, major gaps occur between the progymnosperms and the Cordaitales, and again between the Cordaitales and the Lebachiaceae. However, at the same time anatomical similarities exist among the three groups, especially in the bordered pitting on the tracheids of the secondary xylem.

Figure 25–35 depicts the general and probable evolution of the conifers. From the Lebachiaceae of the late Carboniferous and Permian, the conifers evolved rapidly during the early Mesozoic. In this interval, all of the extant families became differentiated. The earliest families are the Araucariaceae and the Pinaceae, and there has been a long-standing controversy as to which of these has the most primitive characteristics. The controversy centers mainly around the nature of the pitting of the tracheids, the relationship of bract and

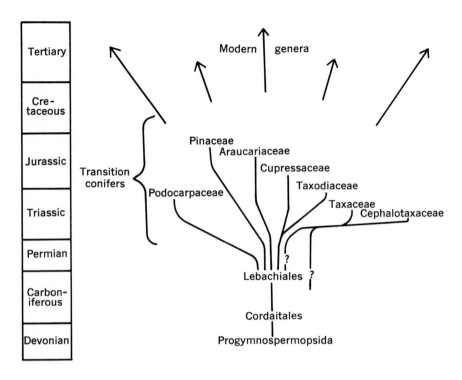

Tertiary	
Cre-taceous	
Jurassic	
Triassic	
Permian	
Carbon-iferous	
Devonian	

FIGURE 25–35   Flow chart depicting probable evolutionary pattern of conifers. Note questionable origins of the Taxaceae and Cephalotaxaceae and long period during which transition conifers were evolving.

ovuliferous scale, and the type of development of the gynogametophyte. It is generally held that the Araucariaceae are more advanced in sporophytic characteristics, whereas the Pinaceae show advanced characteristics in the gametophyte and early embryogeny. The controversy is far from being resolved and, like many other similar problems, will require additional fossil evidence for solution.

Florin has suggested that the Taxaceae and Cephalotaxaceae represent an evolutionary line independent from the Coniferales and should be considered as a separate order, the Taxales. In the fossil record, the Taxales apparently did not become a distinct group until the Mesozoic. At least one other student has derived the Taxales from the Lebachiaceae. In

foliage and pollen characteristics, the Taxales resemble the Cupressaceae and Taxodiaceae more than any other groups. However, whether these characteristics are more indicative of relationship than those of the ovule-bearing structures is questionable—hence, the question marks in the chart in Figure 25–35 at the points of derivation of the Taxaceae—Cephalotaxaceae and the Taxodiaceae–Cupressaceae.

In the later Mesozoic, many of the modern conifer genera became distinct. While these have persisted down to the present, many have become reduced in number and areal distribution. Some genera seem to be heading toward extinction, whereas others appear to be still evolving.

REFERENCES

André, D., "Contribution à l'Étude Morphologique du Cône Femelle de Quelques Gymnospermes (Cephalotaxaceae, Juniperoidées, Taxaceae)." *Natur. Monspel.,* 8 (1956).

Andrews, H. N., Jr., *Studies in Paleobotany.* New York: John Wiley & Sons, Inc. (1961). Pp. 314–347.

Arnold, C. A., *An Introduction to Paleobotany.* New York: McGraw-Hill Book Co., Inc. (1947). Pp. 280–332.

Arnold, C. A., "Classification of Gymnosperms from the Viewpoint of Paleobotany." *Bot. Gaz.,* 110: 1–12 (1948).

Beck, C. B., "Connection between *Archaeopteris* and *Callixylon.*" *Science,* 131: 1524–1525 (1960).

Beck, C. B., "The Identity of *Archaeopteris* and *Callixylon.*" *Brittonia,* 12: 351–368 (1960).

Beck, C. B., "Reconstructions of *Archaeopteris* and Further Consideration of Its Phylogenetic Position." *Am. J. Bot.,* 49: 373–382 (1962).

Brown, W. H., *The Plant Kingdom.* Boston: Ginn and Co. (1935). Pp. 787–811.

Chamberlain, C. J., *Gymnosperms: Structure and Evolution.* Chicago: University of Chicago Press (1935). Pp. 165–360.

Delevoryas, T., *Morphology and Evolution of Fossil Plants.* New York: Holt, Rinehart and Winston, Inc. (1962). Pp. 149–167.

Emberger, L. In Chadefaud, M., and Emberger, L., *Traité de Botanique (Systématique).* Vol. II: *Les Végétaux Vasculaires.* Paris: Masson et Cie (1960). Pp. 383–459.

Florin, R., "Die Koniferen des Oberkarbons und des Unteren Perms." *Palaeontographica,* 85B: Pts. 1–8 (1938–1945).

Florin, R., "Evolution in Cordaites and Conifers." *Act. Hort. Berg.,* 15: 285–388 (1951).

Florin, R., "The Systematics of the Gymnosperms." In *A Century of Progress in the Natural Sciences.* San Francisco: California Academy of Sciences (1955). Pp. 323–403.

Foster, A. S., and Gifford, E. M., *Comparative Morphology of Vascular Plants.* San Francisco: W. H. Freeman and Co. (1959). Pp. 371–416.

Gaussen, H., "Les Gymnospermes, Actuelles et Fossiles." *Trav. Lab. Forest. Toulouse,* Fasc. 1–2 (1944); Fasc. 3 (1946).

Johansen, D. A., *Plant Embryology.* Waltham, Mass.: Chronica Botanica. (1950). Pp. 22–78.

Laubenfels, D. J., "The External Morphology of Coniferous Leaves." *Phytomorphology,* 3: 1–12 (1953).

Martens, P., and Waterkeyn, L., "Structure du Pollen 'Ailé' chez les Conifères." *La Cellule,* 62: 171–222 (1962).

McLean, R. C., and Ivimey-Cook, W. R., *Textbook of Theoretical Botany.* Vol. I. London: Longmans, Green & Co. Ltd. (1951). Pp. 657–779.

Pilger, R., and Melchior, H, *Gymnospermae.* In Engler, A., *Syllabus der Pflanzenfamilien.* Vol. I. Berlin: Gebrüder Borntraeger (1954). Pp. 325–341.

Seward, A. C., and Ford, S. O., "The Araucarieae, Recent and Extinct." *Phil. Trans. Roy. Soc. Lond.,* 198B: 305–411 (1906).

Sterling, C., "Structure of the Male Gametophyte in Gymnosperms." *Biol. Rev.,* 38: 167–203 (1963).

Townrow, J. A., "On Some Disaccate Pollen Grains of Permian to Middle Jurassic Age." *Grana Palynologica,* 3(2): 13–44 (1962).

Van Campo-Duplan, M., "Recherches sur la Phylogenie des Abietinées d'après Leurs Grains de Pollen." *Trav. Lab. Forest. Toulouse,* 4(1): 1–182 (1950).

26 / DIVISION

GNETOPHYTA

This division comprises three orders of vascular plants: the Ephedrales, Welwitschiales, and Gnetales. Each order of *gnetophytes* has one family and one genus. The genera are *Ephedra, Welwitschia,* and *Gnetum*—the second is monotypic and the other two have several species each. Although the three orders are allied with the gymnosperms, they actually have little in common with one another or with other gymnosperm taxa. Features shared among the three genera are the following: primitive types of vessels in the secondary xylem; compound androstrobili and gynostrobili; a second structure surrounding the integument of the ovule, variously referred to as sporophyll, second integument, or small bracts; opposite or whorled leaves; and absence of resin canals.

The history of the Ephedrales and Welwitschiales goes back to the Permian where fossil pollen grains have been found. Confirmed fossils of *Gnetum* have not been discovered to date. Although generally classified as gymnosperms, the origin and ancestry of the three orders is completely unknown, and they stand apart from all other living and fossil taxa.

ORDER EPHEDRALES. The genus *Ephedra* has about 40 species. It is distributed sporadically around warm–temperate latitudes, occurring in the Mediterranean region, east to Persia, India, and China; in the southwestern United States; and in the mountainous regions of western South America. *Ephedra,* truly xerophytic, grows best on sandy or rocky sites such as deserts and

525

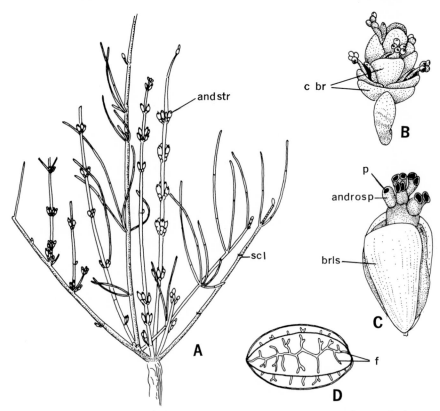

FIGURE 26–1   *Ephedra*. A, several branches bearing very tiny scale leaves (*sc l*) and whorls of androstrobili (*andstr*) at nodes, ×1; B, single androstrobilus showing whorls of cone bracts (*c br*) and protruding clusters of androsporangia, ×5; C, single secondary strobilar axis with two bracteoles (*brls*) subtending androsporangia (*androsp*) with pores (*p*), ×5; D, pollen grain in lateral view showing sinuous branched furrows, ×500. (A–C, after Métro and Sauvage with permission of Société des Sciences Naturelles et Physiques du Maroc.)

mountains. The alkaloid ephedrine obtained from one Asiatic species is widely used to contract blood vessels and to alleviate asthma.

In habit, *Ephedra* is shrubby, some species reaching a height of 2 meters. It is much-branched, and bears two to four leaves that are opposite or whorled at nodes (Fig. 26–1A). The leaves are deciduous, much reduced, and seldom reach a length over 1 cm. *Ephedra* is the only gnetophyte with haplocheilic stomata. Photosynthesis takes place chiefly in the main stem and branches.

Ephedra is usually dioecious, or rarely monoecious. The androstrobili are borne on stalks that arise at the nodes. Each androstrobilus bears two to eight opposite pairs of cone bracts on a central axis (Fig. 26–1B). Except for the basal pair, each cone bract subtends a short secondary shoot that arises from the axis and extends beyond the bract pair. At its base, the secondary shoot bears two membranous scales, the bracteoles (Fig. 26–1C); at the tip of the shoot, from one to eight androsporangia are grouped—each of which dehisces by a terminal pore. The pollen grains are fusiform, with several longitudinal furrows extending from pole to pole (Fig. 26–1D).

Gynostrobili are similar in construction to the androstrobili and are also borne on stalks at the nodes. Each gynostrobilus consists of four to seven pairs of opposite cone bracts on a central axis (Fig. 26–2A). A short secondary shoot in the axil of the upper bracts bears a single terminal ovule. The ovule is subtended by a cup-shaped disc called an **involucre**. Although this has been related to a second integument, it

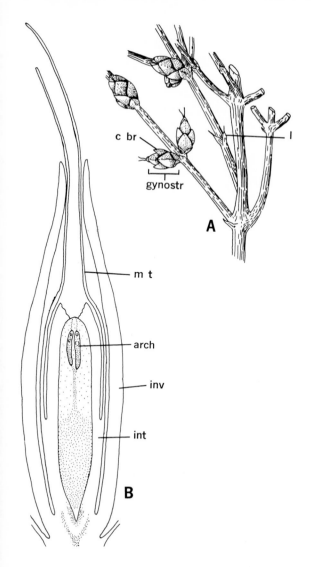

The androgametophytes and gynogametophytes develop essentially as in the coniferophytes. Inside the pollen grain are formed two prothallial cells, a tube cell, androgenous cells, and sterile cells. The tube nucleus and two androgametes migrate into the pollen tube. Wind pollination occurs about the time archegonia are formed in the ovule.

One gynospore enlarges and undergoes free-nuclear division. Prothallial cells form centripetally, and archegonia are formed on the edge of the micropylar end (Fig. 26–2B). A unique feature is the development of 40 or more neck cells in the archegonium of *Ephedra*—the highest number in all gymnosperms.

A complete breakdown of the nucellar cells at the micropyle results in a large pollen chamber with no nucellar beak. The pollen tube extends directly through the neck of the archegonium, ruptures, and discharges the two androgametes into the egg. Following fertilization, the cells of the archegonial wall generally disintegrate and fuse with the cytoplasm of the zygote.

Embryogeny is also similar to that of many coniferophytes. The zygote divides into two cells, forming a short tube. The cell nearest the micropyle develops into a suspensor, and the chalazal cell develops into the proembryo. Secondary suspensors also form from cells at the micropylar end of the proembryonic cluster, and assist in pushing the proembryo into the gametophytic tissue. Cleavage polyembryony is common, but usually only one embryo per seed matures. At maturity, the embryo is dicotyledonous and the integument has hardened into a seed coat. The usual interval of seed dormancy in *Ephedra* is five months.

ORDER WELWITSCHIALES. The single species of *Welwitschia* is the most bizarre of all gymnosperms. It is restricted to a small region near the southwestern coast of Africa, between latitudes 14° and 23° S. and from the coast to about 100 miles inland. It is an extreme xerophyte, and inhabits rocky benches or dried stream beds where the precipitation rarely exceeds 5 cm a year! Named after the botanist Welwitsch, who first collected it in 1860, the

FIGURE 26–2   *Ephedra*. A, several gynostrobili (*gynostr*) at nodes of twig with leaves (*l*) and cone bracts (*c br*), ×1; B, median longitudinal section of ovule, showing integument (*int*) that projects as micropylar tube (*m t*); involucre (*inv*) comprising fused bracteoles; and two archegonia (*arch*) at tips of nucellus, ×42. (A, from *Gymnosperms* by C. J. Chamberlain by permission of The University of Chicago Press, copyright 1935; B, after Land with permission of *Botanical Gazette*.)

appears to be homologous to the **bracteoles** of the secondary shoot in the androstrobilus. The true integument of the ovule is elongated into a micropylar tube, and is chlorophyllous at the time of pollination (Fig. 26–2B).

A

B

FIGURE 26–3 *Welwitschia.* A, habit view of
single plant showing two large spreading leaves
and bowl-like stem supporting strobili, ×0.05; B,
closeup photo showing strobili (*str*) attached to
stem (*st*), ×0.1.

plant is scarce and protected from unauthorized
collectors by law.

The plant consists of a very short yet massive, bowl-shaped stem only a few centimeters
high (Fig. 26–3A). It is elliptical in plane view,
and ranges to over 1 meter in diameter. It has
only two leaves; these are very large, strap-
shaped, and grow from the rim of the stem outward over the surface of the soil. Below the
surface, the stem tapers quickly, and merges
with a large tap root reported to extend several
meters down to the water table.

The two leaves are broad, flat, and coriaceous. They reach a width of over 20 cm and a
length of approximately 2 meters. The tips become split and tattered mainly by the action of
the wind. A basal meristem adds new growth

that compensates for terminal abrasion—a
unique feature of *Welwitschia.* Sunken stomata
with syndetocheilic development are numerous
on both surfaces of the leaf. The vascular
bundles are collateral, with adaxial xylem.
Oblique bundles are numerous and anastomose
with each other and with the main longitudinal
bundles. Transfusion tissue surrounds each
bundle and consists of shortened tracheids
with small pits. Strands of fibers cap both top
and bottom of each vascular bundle. A
palisade region of several layers is differentiated
in the outer mesophyll region.

Numerous sclereids occur in the parenchyma of both stem and mature leaves (Fig.
26–4A). These sclereids are very irregular in
outline, possess thick walls stratified with lignin
and cellulose layers, and have masses of calcium
oxalate crystals attached to the outer primary
wall. They are responsible for the coriaceous
texture of leaves and stem, and make sectioning
difficult without prior treatment with acid and
alcohol.

The reproductive organs consist of compound strobili that arise by stalks from the
cortex of the upper tip of the stem (Fig.
26–3B). The stalks are branched at nodes, and
each node bears two nodal bracts. In the androstrobili, each terminal branch bears a primary
androstrobilus that is elongate and terete in
outline, with four vertical rows of overlapping
cone bracts (Fig. 26–4B, C). Each cone bract
subtends a structure that has been called a
flower because of its superficial resemblance to
an angiosperm flower, but can more accurately
be referred to as a secondary strobilus. This
secondary strobilus consists of a short stalk
with two pairs of opposite bracteoles which
surround six androsporangia and a central
ovule (Fig. 26–4C, D). Each androsporangium
is stalked and three-lobed, thus forming a
synandrium. The central ovule is always sterile,
and the androstrobilus is therefore unisexual.

The androgametophyte in the pollen grain
is extremely reduced, approaching a typical
angiosperm in development. The first division
results in a single prothallial cell and an
antheridial initial; the latter then divides to
form a generative cell and a tube cell. The

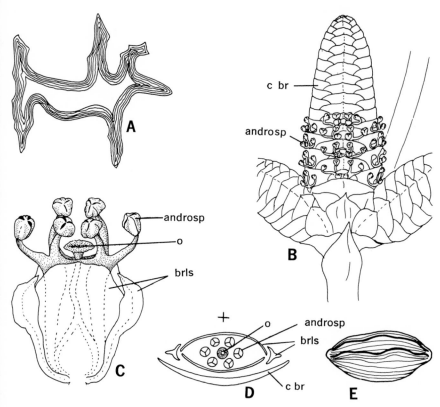

FIGURE 26–4   *Welwitschia*. A, single sclereid from androstrobilus, showing concentric layers of secondary wall, ×225; B, androstrobilus showing four rows of overlapping cone bracts (*c br*) and protruding androsporangia (*androsp*), ×5; C, single secondary strobilus showing three of four bracteoles (*brls*), central sterile ovule (*o*), and six androsporangia, ×12; D, plan view of single secondary strobilus, ×12; E, single pollen grain showing fine longitudinal ribs and furrows, and single sulcus down middle, ×500. (A, D, from *Morphology of Gymnosperms* by J. M. Coulter and C. J. Chamberlain by permission of The University of Chicago Press, copyright 1910 and 1917; B, C, after Church with permission of Royal Society of London.)

pollen is discharged at this stage (Fig. 26–4E). Upon germination, the generative cell divides directly to give two androgametes, and the prothallial cell degenerates. Thus, the androgametophyte consists at all times of only three nuclei.

The gynostrobili are borne on separate plants on similar branched stalks subtended by nodal bracts (Fig. 26–5A). The primary gynostrobilus is also terete, with four vertical rows of imbricated cone bracts. In the axil of each cone bract is an ovule, closely surrounded by a fused pair of bracteoles (Fig. 26–5B, C). The integument of the ovule is much elongated and protrudes well above the bracteoles.

The ontogeny of the gynogametophyte is very similar to that in *Ephedra* and the coniferophytes. However, a most interesting difference is found in the archegonia. Instead of forming in the usual way, the archegonium of *Welwitschia* develops as a tube that grows from the outer layer of the prothallus into the nucellus. This archegonial tube carries the egg nucleus and meets a pollen tube in the nucellus; fertilization takes place within the united tubes (Fig. 26–6A).

Embryonic development is very similar to that in *Ephedra* (Fig. 26–6B–D). The zygote divides to form two cells—a primary suspensor and an embryonic initial. Secondary suspensor

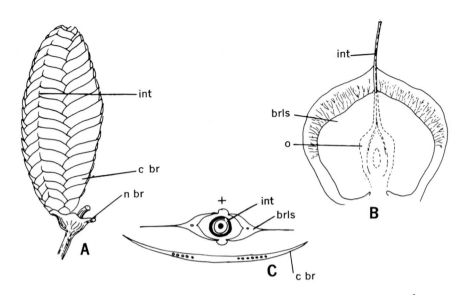

FIGURE 26–5 *Welwitschia.* A, single gynostrobilus showing rows of overlapping cone bracts (*c br*), nodal bract (*n br*), and protruding integuments (*int*), ×5; B, single ovule (*o*) surrounded by bracteoles (*brls*), and showing protruding integument (*int*), ×12; C, diagrammatic plan view of secondary gynostrobilus showing cone bract (*c br*), two fused bracteoles (*brls*), and integument (*int*), ×12. (A, B, after Church; C, after Pearson with permission of Royal Society of London.)

cells are numerous, elongating to form rings around the primary suspensor. The embryonic initials form a cap, which is later sloughed off. The embryo itself develops from a plate of four cells lying between the cap and secondary suspensors. As in *Ephedra* and *Gnetum,* there are two cotyledons on the young seedling.

ORDER GNETALES. This order is represented by the genus *Gnetum,* which has about 30 species inhabiting the more luxuriant tropics. Most of the species are native to Indonesia and tropical Asia, two occur in tropical Africa, and 12 in Central and South America. None of the species is common to both Western and Eastern Hemispheres.

Most species of *Gnetum* are lianas that climb and twine or trail on other plants. Several are shrubs, and a few are trees. They have both long and short shoots. In lianas, leaves are borne only on short shoots. The leaves are opposite, with flat blades,. pinnate secondary venation, and syndetocheilic stomata (Fig. 26–7A). Thus, the leaves resemble closely those of some dicotyledons and, without comparing reproductive organs, can easily be mistaken for members of that group of angiosperms.

The primary vascular tissue of the stem is a **eustele,** with two or more concentric rings of bundles, each containing a small amount of primary xylem with helical and scalariform tracheids. Secondary wood on the outside of the primary bundles consists of vessels, tracheids, and ray parenchyma. The perforations in the vessels resulted during evolution from the circular bordered pits in the end walls of tracheids. In this respect they differ fundamentally from vessels of angiosperms, which appear to have developed by the dissolution of elongated bordered pits to produce first a scalariform perforation plate and later a single opening in the end wall. The phloem contains sieve cells, and cells functioning as companion cells that arise directly from the cambium instead of from a common mother initial as in angiosperms. As in *Welwitschia,* the cortex consists of parenchyma, fibers, and sclereids.

The pollen-bearing organ is a compound strobilus consisting of whorls of cone bracts on

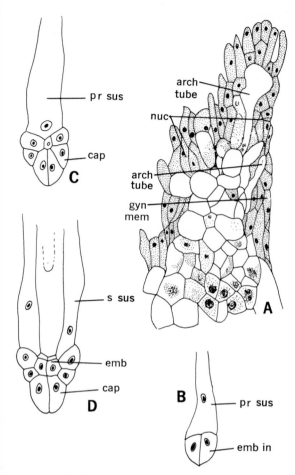

aperture, and with many fine spines on the exine (Fig. 26–7D).

As in *Welwitschia, Ephedra,* and angiosperms, the androgametophyte of *Gnetum* is much reduced, without any development of prothallial cells. The antheridial initial divides to form a generative cell and a tube cell. The generative cell then divides to give a spermatogenous cell and a sterile cell. The androgametes result from the division of the spermatogenous cell, one of which fertilizes the egg.

The ovules are borne in compound gynostrobili (Fig. 26–8A). The primary gynostrobili are arranged in whorls on small tertiary branches. Each primary strobilus occurs in the axil of a bract that is joined to the others of the whorl. The secondary strobilus is similar to that of *Welwitschia,* having a pair of outer bracteoles and a pair of inner bracteoles that are often called an outer integument (Fig. 26–8B). The actual integument (inner integument) is prolonged into a beak that protrudes beyond the bracteoles.

The gynogametophyte of *Gnetum* differs from that of other gymnosperms in remaining free-nucleate at its micropylar end until after fertilization (Fig. 26–8C). *Gnetum* also is unique among gymnosperms in not forming archegonia. Instead, one (or more) of the free nuclei acts directly as an egg, uniting with an androgamete nucleus to form a zygote (Fig. 26–8D). In this respect, *Gnetum* is somewhat closer to the condition in some angiosperms, in which no gametophytic tissue is formed and free nuclei combine directly with androgamete nuclei to form the zygote and endosperm.

The early embryo consists of a branching system of primary suspensors from which, in some species, secondary suspensors arise by the division of apical cells. Proembryos are formed from the apical cells, and range in number from one to several, depending mainly on the number of branches of the primary suspensor.

PHYLOGENY OF GNETOPHYTA

The origin and relationships of these three very distinct genera are obscure. Pollen grains similar to *Ephedra* and *Welwitschia* have been

FIGURE 26–6   *Welwitschia.* A, upper part of nucellus in which archegonial tubes (*arch tube*) are expanding upward to meet pollen tubes that will grow downward (*nuc,* nucellus; *gyn mem,* gynospore membrane), ×70; B, early stages of embryonic development, showing two embryonic initials (*emb in*) and single primary suspensor (*pr sus*), ×300; C, later stage of embryonic development showing cells at tip forming cap, and single primary suspensor cell, ×300; D, later stage still with embryonic cells forming behind cap, and two secondary suspensors flanking primary suspensor, ×300. (After Pearson with permission of Royal Society of London.)

a central axis (Fig. 26–7B). In its axil each cone bract contains a structure referred to as a secondary androstrobilus. It consists of a collar of almost completely fused bracteoles surrounding a central androsporangium (Fig. 26–7C). The androsporangium is a synandrium with two to four locules. The pollen grains are small and circular, with no apparent germinal

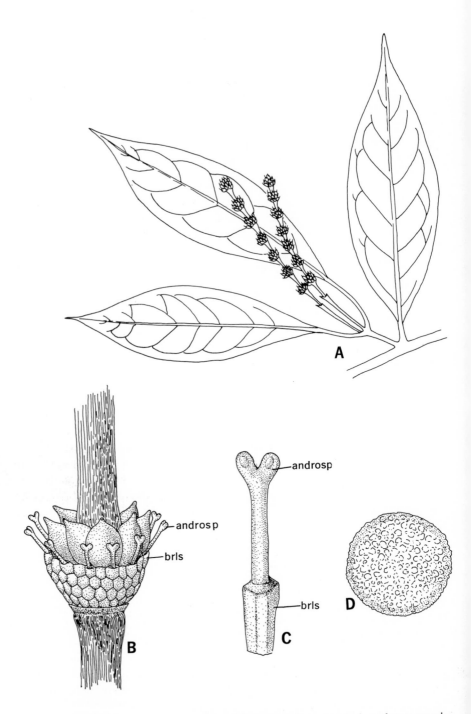

FIGURE 26–7   *Gnetum*. A, several leaves and compound androsporangia, ×0.5; B, single whorl of androsporangia (*androsp*) and attendant bracteoles (*brls*) at node of fertile stalk, ×15; C, two androsporangia (*androsp*) with bracteoles cloaking base, ×15; D, single pollen grain showing low coarse spines on wall, ×500. (A–C, after Brown with permission of Blaisdell Publishing Company.)

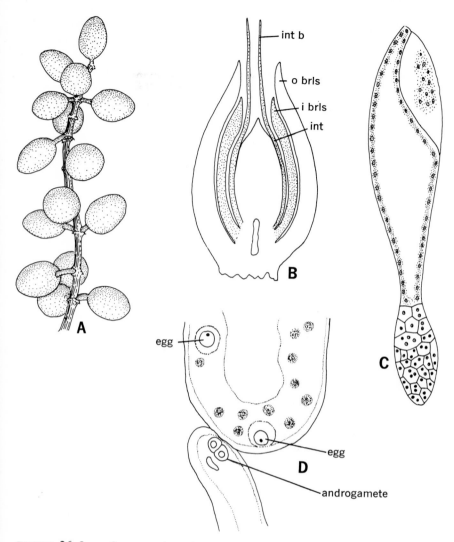

FIGURE 26–8   *Gnetum*. A, twig with seeds, ×0.4; B, median longitudinal section of single ovule, showing integument (*int*) extended into integumentary beak (*int b*), inner bracteoles (*i brls*), and outer bracteoles (*o brls*), ×40; C, gynogametophyte with free nuclei in upper part and cells below, ×50; D, part of gynogametophyte with free nuclei and two eggs (above), and pollen tube with two androgametes (below) just prior to fertilization, ×600. (A, after Brown, with permission of Blaisdell Publishing Company; B, C, after Lotsy; D, after Thompson with permission of *American Journal of Botany*.)

found as early as the Permian, whereas pollen assigned to *Gnetum* has only been reported from the Tertiary. On the basis of fossil pollen, *Ephedra* and *Welwitschia* appear to have had more species in former times than they do now, suggesting that they have declined in numbers of species since the early Mesozoic. Also, some pollen grains in Mesozoic and Tertiary rocks are associated with mesophytic plants, suggesting that *Ephedra* and *Welwitschia* may not always have been restricted to xeric environments.

The gnetophytes have been cited as a transitional group between gymnosperms and angiosperms, and some have considered them to be the immediate forerunners of angiosperms.

The angiosperm characteristics include vessels in the xylem, compound strobili that resemble flowers, bracteoles that are often compared with a second integument, and the type of fertilization in *Gnetum*. However, the free-nucleate gametophyte is a typically gymnospermous characteristic, as is the absence of carpels; and the gnetophytes are almost certainly more closely allied to gymnosperm ancestors than to any angiosperm stock.

The evidence from fossil and modern pollen grains suggests that *Ephedra* and *Welwitschia* are more closely related to one another than either is to *Gnetum*. In addition, evidence from other pollen associated with the Permian pollen of *Ephedra* and *Welwitschia* suggests that these two genera were probably derived from the early coniferophyte line. But the pollen of *Gnetum,* with numerous small spines, suggests it might be a much-reduced angiosperm. This view is supported by the general morphology of the *Gnetum* leaf, lack of archegonia, and the typically angiospermous embryogeny. However, for all three genera the fossil ancestry and lines of descent are completely obscure, and we must await further discoveries to clarify relationships with other groups.

REFERENCES

Chamberlain, C. J., *Gymnosperms: Structure and Evolution.* Chicago: University of Chicago Press (1935). Pp. 361–426.

Eames, A. J., "Relationships of the Ephedrales." *Phytomorphology,* 2: 79–100 (1952).

Emberger, L. In Chadefaud, M., and Emberger, L., *Traité de Botanique (Systématique).* Vol. II: *Les Végétaux Vasculaires.* Paris: Masson et Cie (1960). Pp. 460–472.

Foster, A. S., and Gifford, E. M., *Comparative Morphology of Vascular Plants.* San Francisco: W. H. Freeman and Co. (1959). Pp. 417–442.

Martens, P., "Études sur les Gnetales, III: Structure et Ontogenèse du Cône et de la Fleur Femelles de *Welwitschia mirabilis.*" *La Cellule,* 60: 169–286 (1959).

Martens, P., "Sur l'Ontogenèse de la Fleur Mâle de *Welwitschia mirabilis* Hooker." *Phytomorphology,* 11: 37–40 (1961).

Martens, P., "Études sur les Gnetales, VI: Recherches sur *Welwitschia mirabilis;* III: L'Ovule et le Sac Embryonnaire—Les Sacs Embryonnaire Extra-floraux." *La Cellule,* 63: 307–330 (1963).

Negi, V., and Lata, M., "Male Gametophyte and Megasporogenesis in *Gnetum." Phytomorphology,* 7: 230–236 (1957).

Pearson, H. H. W., *Gnetales.* London: Cambridge University Press (1929).

Rodin, R. J., "Leaf Anatomy of *Welwitschia,* I: Early Development of the Leaf." *Am. J. Bot.,* 45: 90–95 (1958).

Rodin, R. J., "Leaf Anatomy of *Welwitschia,* II: A Study of Mature Leaves." *Am. J. Bot.* 45: 96–103 (1958).

Rodin, R. J., "Anatomy of the Reproductive Bracts in *Welwitschia." Am. J. Bot.,* 50: 641–648 (1963).

Thompson, W. P., "Independent Evolution of Vessels in Gnetales and Angiosperms." *Bot. Gaz.,* 65: 83–90 (1918).

Vasil, V., "Morphology and Embryology of *Gnetum ula." Phytomorphology,* 9: 167–215 (1959).

Waterkeyn, L., "Études sur les Gnetales, II: Le Strobile Mâle, la Microsporogenesis, et le Gametophyte Mâle de *Gnetum africanum* Welw." *La Cellule,* 60: 5–78 (1959).

Waterkeyn, L., "Études sur les Gnetales, IV: Le Tube Micropylaire et la Chambre Pollinique de *Gnetum africanum* Welw." *La Cellule,* 61: 79–96 (1960).

Wilson, L. R., "Geological History of the Gnetales." *Oklahoma Geol. Notes,* (129): 35–40 (1959).

27/DIVISION

ANTHOPHYTA

In the more recent schemes of classification of the plant kingdom, the subdivision Angiospermae of the old division Spermatophyta is raised to the rank of division and composed of two classes: the Dicotyledonae and the Monocotyledonae. As has already been noted, the other group of seed plants which used to be included in the subdivision Gymnospermae is now distributed among several divisions.

The Anthophyta includes all that are commonly known as *flowering plants,* and as such it is the largest and most conspicuous group in the modern flora. About 300 families are recognized, including about 275,000 species. Some believe that man could not have evolved without the angiosperms. Certainly we could not exist without them, since ultimately we are completely dependent on them for food. If for no other reason, we should be interested in learning something about Anthophyta because our economy is largely based upon them. From various species we get wood (for construction, cabinet work, and flooring), fibers, condiments, spices, essential oils, and the raw material for certain medicines.

Characterizing the Anthophyta is difficult. As Lam very properly points out, the only single characteristic that distinguishes this division is **double fertilization** and the consequent development of **endosperm.** In the great majority of instances, the possession of a closed **carpel,** and the **fruit** arising from it, are distinctive. Other features held to be characteristic of the flowering plants are

536

to be found to a greater or lesser extent in other divisions of vascular plants. Nevertheless, anthophytes in general have the following: vessels in the xylem; companion cells in the phloem; flowers with some of the floral parts sterile and others functioning as reproductive structures; and carpels enclosing one or more ovules that may mature into seeds and, together with the carpel wall, form a fruit. The Anthophyta can only be separated by a combination of characteristics and, since the most significant of these are apparently hidden in the ovule, the chance of detecting their initial evolutionary stages in fossils is most improbable.

Unfortunately, the fossil record of the anthophytes gives us few clues to their origin. It has been suggested that *Sanmiguelia* and *Furcula* from the Triassic have certain angiospermous foliage characteristics. Russian reports of angiospermous pollen from the Carboniferous are of great interest, as are the conclusions that certain *Glossopteris* structures from the Permian show anthophyte affinities. We know that by the mid-Cretaceous the anthophytes were very highly developed morphologically, that many modern families were clearly differentiated, and that a number of modern genera are recognizable.

A very interesting and phylogenetically important question is: How can this sudden appearance of the anthophytes be explained? One possibility is that they evolved faster than other groups, such as the gymnosperms. Another is that they had a long pre-Cretaceous history of development for which we have no record. Again, we may fail to recognize at the present some records of pre-angiosperms in groups like the Mesozoic pteridosperms.

The evidence for and against both points of view has been reviewed by Axelrod, and by Scott, Barghoorn, and Leopold. Axelrod concluded that the evidence favors an origin for anthophytes long before the Cretaceous, back even into Triassic and Permian times. According to this view, a fossil record may be lacking because the early flowering plants evolved and existed on upland sites in situations where fossilization was unlikely. Scott, Barghoorn, and Leopold believe that angiosperms evolved rapidly during the early part of the Cretaceous from pre-angiosperm stock, and flourished in response to their newly acquired characteristics; according to these investigators, the lack of any *bona fide* anthophyte pollen grains and other fossils from rocks earlier than Cretaceous strongly indicates that anthophytes had not evolved up to that time. Engler derived anthophytes from hypothetical Mesozoic groups that he called protoangiosperms. Others derived them from a group of gymnosperms known as the hemiangiosperms. Still others consider that they were derived from the Bennettitales of the division Cycadophyta. Probably the most widely held view is that anthophytes were derived from seed ferns of the Pteridospermophyta. Lam has supplied a very comprehensive and critical review of the various theories of phylogenetic relationships of the Anthophyta. He feels that the phylogenetic connections of the flowering plants are entirely speculative, and this view is gaining favor among systematists. According to Constance, there is general agreement that sufficient evidence to formulate a satisfactory phylogenetic arrangement of flowering plants is not yet available.

The modern anthophyte flora is primarily terrestrial, and representatives are found in practically all such habitats. Some are hydrophytes, immersed as *Elodea,* or floating as *Lemna;* at the other extreme, they can be found growing under most xeric conditions. They are found in the tropics, as well as in the Arctic and Antarctic to the highest latitudes at which vegetation exists. Some lacking chlorophyll are obligate saprophytes, others are parasites. Among the latter are the mistletoes and dodders. Morphologically anthophytes are tremendously varied, ranging in size from the little aquatic *Wolffia,* which is like a green pinhead floating on the surface of small ponds, to a giant species of *Eucalyptus* (*E. regnans*) that has been recorded at a height of over 100 meters and a diameter of almost 3 meters.

A few general characteristics are ordinarily used to separate the two classes of Anthophyta. In the Dicotyledonae, two **cotyledons** (seed leaves) are present in the seed, and the stem is dictyostelic with a functioning cambium in most species; in the Monocotyledonae, a single cotyledon is generally present, and the stem is polystelic without a functional cambium. **Dicotyledonous** leaves ordinarily have a special type of venation described as net-veined; leaves of **monocotyledons** are parallel-veined. Finally, in dicotyledons the floral parts are generally in fours, fives, or multiples of these; floral parts of monocotyledons are typically in threes or multiples of three.

However, the boundary between these two classes is actually rather blurred. Exceptions to the above generalizations emphasize that the systematic position of a plant must be determined from all characteristics. Simple "key" characteristics have their place as aids to identification, but other characteristics may be more important morphologically and phylogenetically. For example, *Maianthemum,* with floral parts in fours, may appear out of place in the monocotyledons, but it is actually closely linked to them in all other features.

Leaves are conspicuous on most flowering plants. Because these organs usually persist for some time and are subjected to continued environmental stresses, they must be well adapted to their surroundings. In most instances it is not difficult to see the adaptive value of a particular leaf morphology as the outcome of continued selection operating over long periods of time. Therefore, it is not surprising to find leaves of all sizes and shapes: some are thin, some thick, some scale-like, others many meters long, some with petioles, others sessile, some hairy, and others smooth. Despite these differences, all generally have the common function of facilitating photosynthesis. In particular instances leaves may be highly modified for other functions, such as storage in many desert species; for vegetative reproduction, as in the development of plantlets from adventitious buds in *Kalanchoe;* as brightly colored floral bracts in poinsettia (*Euphorbia pulcherrima*) and the flowering dogwood (*Cornus nuttallii*); as tendrils in many Leguminosae; and as specialized insect traps in *Drosera, Dionaea, Sarracenia,* and several other genera. Another general type of leaf, the small scale-like **cataphyll,** is found on certain rhizomes and as protective scales enclosing buds.

In many dicotyledonous genera a pair of appendages, called **stipules,** develop at the base of the petiole. These occur in a variety of forms (Fig. 27–1, 2), some of which at least are obviously adaptive. They may be free or adnate to the petiole, evanescent or persistent, relatively large or small. In some cases (*Pisum, Lathyrus, Galium, Viola*) the stipules are foliaceous and undoubtedly make a significant photosynthetic contribution; in *Smilax* they develop as tendrils; in *Robinia, Acacia,* and many other legumes the stipules become thorns; in instances such as the tulip tree (*Liriodendron*) they have the role of bud scales. The morphological nature of stipules is still an open question, and their ontogeny varies with the way in which they are related to the leaf base.

FLORAL MORPHOLOGY

It seems proper to limit the use of the term *flower* to the sexually reproductive organs of the Anthophyta, although this is not always done (see p. 468). In the past botanists have referred to flowers in some gymnosperms; others have drawn attention to the fact that the strobili in the Gnetales are somewhat like **inflorescences** that bear flowers and have a vestigial perianth. There is much speculation and debate about how flowers evolved; particularly controversial are the origins of **stamens** and **carpels.** Unfortunately, there is little paleobotanical evidence to give much help in interpreting early stages in flower evolution; however, a number of genera in the Ranales that are considered primitive on other grounds, probably offer valid clues to the general nature of the ancestral flower.

The literature dealing with floral morphology and its interpretations is very extensive. Space does not permit a presentation of the current points of view, but these can be found in Esau and Lam. Along with bibliographic references, Esau gives a critical summary and points out that in the oldest and still most popular concept, the flower is a shortened determinate shoot and the parts are modified leaves. Opposing this classical view are a number of modern botanical philosophers whose

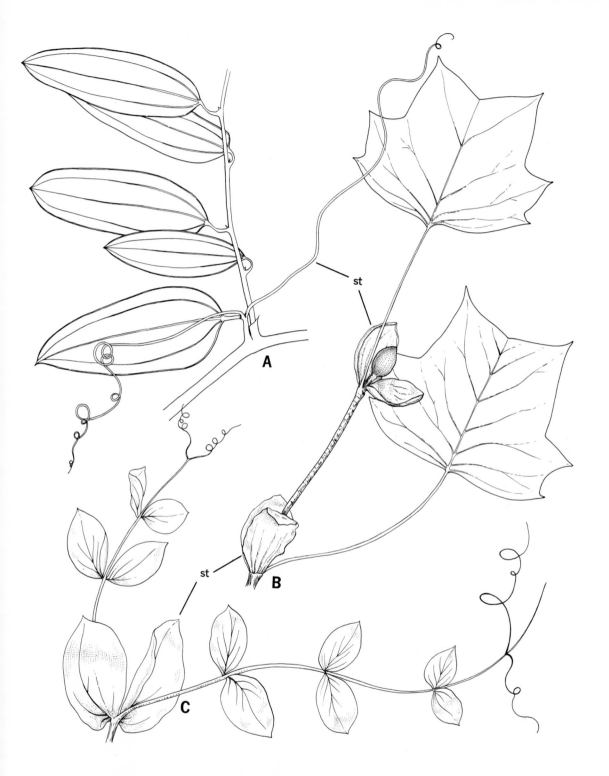

FIGURE 27–1   Stipules. A, *Smilax laurifolia* with stipular tendrils, ×0.5; B, *Liriodendron tulipifera* with stipules functioning as bud scales, ×0.5; C, *Pisum sativum* with foliaceous stipules, ×1. *st,* stipule.

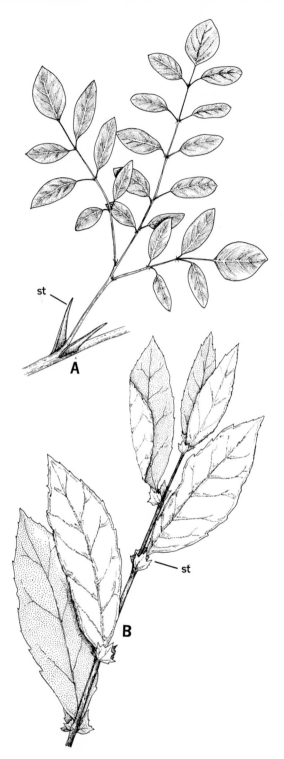

arguments are summarized by Lam. However, Foster and Gifford state that ". . . marked resemblances can be demonstrated between vegetative leaves and floral appendages with respect to their initiation, early ontogeny, and basic plan of vasculation." The degree of resemblance to foliage leaves varies considerably with both the genus and the organ—for example, **sepals** and **petals** are basically more leaf-like than are some extremely specialized stamens and carpels.

FLOWERS

Perianths range in size from 1 mm or even less in diameter in the case of some tiny annuals to nearly 1 meter across in species of *Rafflesia*. The primary function of the perianth is to attract pollinating insects, and secondarily to protect the pollen and attractant nectar from rain and from depredation by nonpollinating insects. The extent to which floral morphology is related to pollinating mechanisms and agencies will be dealt with later.

The conventional flower is made up of both sterile and fertile parts. The sterile parts comprise the **calyx,** made up of sepals, and the **corolla,** made up of petals. In certain instances it is convenient to combine calyx and corolla under the term **perianth,** particularly if, through lack of differentiation or through de-differentiation, it is difficult to distinguish between the calyx and the corolla. The fertile organs of the flower are the **androecium,** made up of stamens, and the **gynoecium,** made up of carpels.

PERIANTH

If the parts of the perianth resemble one another closely, as in the tulip (*Tulipa*), the units are referred to as **tepals.** If the undifferentiated perianth contains only one whorl, by convention the whorl is regarded as the calyx—unless there is good evidence to the contrary as in the Valerianaceae and the Compositae, where the calyx is much reduced and in some instances fails to develop at all. If there is no corolla, or if the petals are inconspicuous,

FIGURE 27–2   Stipules. A, *Robinia pseudo-acacia* with stipular thorns, ×1; B, *Salix scouleriana,* vigorous shoot with persistent foliaceous stipules, ×0.5. *st,* stipule.

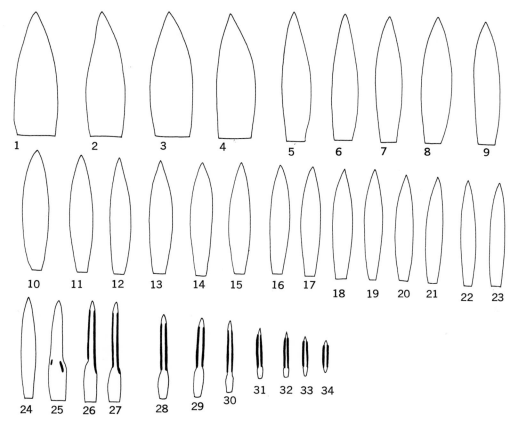

FIGURE 27–3   Floral parts showing transitions. 1–4, sepaloid; 5–24, petaloid; 25–34, stamens. (After Gibbs.)

the calyx may be petaloid, as in such genera as *Anemone, Clematis,* and *Helleborus.* Ordinarily, sepals are quite leaf-like in appearance and have three major vascular bundles, which is the general case for leaves. As a rule sepals are green and photosynthetic, but not differentiated to the extent of having a palisade layer.

Petals are much more varied in shape and size than sepals, and can usually be distinguished from them by color. Color is due to chromoplasts or dissolved pigments in the cells. Despite certain superficial resemblances to sepals, petals are anatomically—and in some instances even morphologically—more like sterile stamens. As in the stamen, a single trace usually enters the base of the petal. In certain instances, the close relationship is shown by "double" flowers in such genera as *Paeonia, Rosa, Pelargonium,* and *Dianthus,* in which the extra petals are clearly transformed stamens. However, genera like *Trillium* often show par-

tial or complete reversion of the petals to green sepal-like structures. In certain members of the Magnoliaceae, Calycanthacea, and Nymphaeaceae there is a continuous transition from sepals through petals to stamens (Fig. 27–3). As Eames points out: "The corolla has undoubtedly arisen in two ways. It represents modified stamens in most families; in some families it represents the distal part of a primitive unspecialized perianth." This probably means that through convergent evolution the corolla in some instances is derived secondarily from stamens, whereas in other instances it is derived directly from modification of leaves.

ANDROECIUM

The androecium is the aggregation of stamens in a flower. The stamens range from many to one depending on the species, and are indefinite or definite in number depending on the species. The stamens develop on the **receptacle** above (inside) the corolla. In arrangement they may be spiral, whorled, or fasciculate—the fascicles usually occurring in whorls. Studies in dicotyledonous families such as the Winteraceae, Dilleniaceae, Magnoliaceae, Nymphaeaceae, and even some genera of the Ranunculaceae, show the primitive androecium to consist of many, spirally arranged stamens.

In its commonest form the stamen is composed of a thread-like **filament** supporting on its upper end an **anther** that contains two pairs of **androsporangia.** It is a fair assumption that a stamen of this type is in a relatively advanced stage of evolution. In the past, several theories have been advanced to explain its origin and phylogenetic development. According to Goethe's theory, stamens are the homologues of leaves. Until fairly recently morphological resemblances between stamens and leaves were not recognized. Furthermore, most flowering plants have stamens with a single vascular bundle—not three as in leaves. However, we now know that some reduced leaves have only a single bundle, and that stamens of primitive genera may have three. A number of investigators studying primitive members of ranalian stock have shown that here at least the stamen is undoubtedly a sporophyll. In *Degeneria,* which Canright considers to be the closest of all *known* types to a primitive angiosperm stamen, the stamen is a broad leaf-like organ with very little distinction between the fertile and sterile parts and with three vascular bundles. In his survery of the Magnoliaceae, Canright has arranged the various stamen types in what he believes to be an evolutionary phenetic series starting with a broad, foliar, three-veined androsporophyll, and ending with an androsporophyll with marginal sporangia and a distinct filament and anther (Fig. 27–4).

The **connective,** the tissue lying between the pairs of sporangia, is a strip not distinguishable histologically from the tissues of the wall of the anther. In *Degeneria,* for example, there is no distinction between the filament, the connective, and the anther; and the sporangia are borne close to the center of the sporophyll, with

the lamina of the sporophyll extending beyond them (Fig. 27–5C). In the course of evolution the lamina has apparently become progressively narrower, with the basal part becoming the filament. The contracted upper part has become the anther, with the connective at first extending beyond the sporangia as an appendage. In some families the connective is reduced to a slender median axis, and in others it is reduced only to a point of attachment for the anther lobes. However, in some relatively specialized families, such as the Violaceae, the connective may be prominent; this is generally regarded as a secondary development related to pollination. The connective forms a nectary in *Viola* (Fig. 27–6).

The evolutionary history of the stamen is clearly summarized by Eames. "The primitive stamen was laminar, with two pairs of sporangia borne on either the adaxial or the abaxial side. From this simple stamen has been developed the slender, complex organ with marginal pairs of sporangia. Dorsiventral form has largely been lost; the specialized anther of the higher families is more or less four-angled and the filament terete. The marginal position of the pairs of sporangia—one member of each pair apparently adaxial, the other abaxial—suggests that the sporangia belong two to one side and two on the other, but, in the primitive stamen, all four are on one side" (Fig. 27–5).

Departures from the conventional stamen morphology can nearly always be related to some special pollinating mechanism. The same is mostly true of the method of dehiscence of the anthers. Dehiscence is **introrse** when the opening is toward the center of the flower, **extrorse** when outward. In most genera, anthers will shed their pollen through narrow, lengthwise slits (longitudinal dehiscence). Transverse dehiscence (through transverse slits) occurs very infrequently, while porose dehiscence (through small, rounded openings) is characteristic of a few families such as the Ericaceae. In some instances the slit is shaped to free a valve-like flap of tissue (valvular dehiscence), characteristic of the Berberidaceae and Lauraceae in particular.

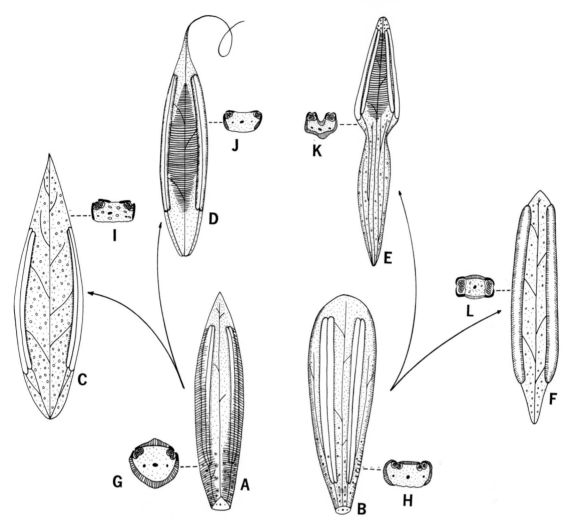

FIGURE 27-4   Main trends of specialization in stamens of Magnoliaceae. A–F, individual stamens shown in adaxial view; G–L, cross-sectional diagrams of individual stamens. (After Canright with permission of *American Journal of Botany*.)

GYNOECIUM

The gynoecium is made up of the ovule-bearing organs, the carpels or gynosporophylls. As with stamens, the carpels range in number from many in primitive flowers, to one in more advanced cases; in arrangement they vary from spiraled to whorled. Numerous spirally arranged carpels are found in such families as the Magnoliaceae, and many of the genera of the Ranunculaceae and Rosaceae.

Like the stamen, the carpel is an elongate organ, primitively flattened laterally. Also similar to the stamen, the carpel is leaf-like in all its relationships to the stem; however, the carpel differs by developing **gynosporangia** only on the adaxial side, whereas the androsporangia develop on either the adaxial or the abaxial side. In the course of evolution the margins of the carpel blade have apparently been folded adaxially toward the midrib, thereby enclosing the gynosporangia in a cavity known as the **locule** (Fig. 27–7).

Evolutionary developments have apparently resulted in the complete closure of the carpel, a reduction in the number of ovules, and a restriction of ovules to the lower part of the carpel **(ovary);** the sterile upper part became the

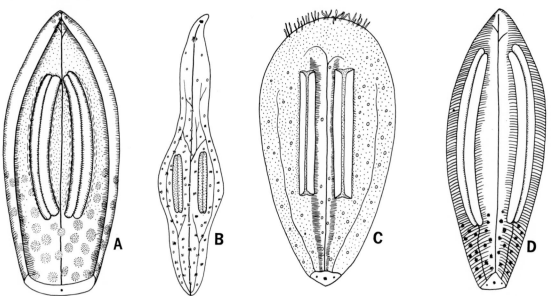

FIGURE 27–5   Diagram comparing androsporophylls of representative ranalean genera. A, *Austrobaileya*; B, *Himantandra*; C, *Degeneria*; D, *Magnolia*. A, D, adaxial views; B, C, abaxial. (After Canright with permission of *American Journal of Botany*.)

style, with the **stigma** localized at its apex. Bailey and Swamy point out that, in more primitive flowers, the style is clearly conduplicate and is commonly vascularized by both the dorsal and the two ventral veins.

According to Bailey and Swamy, the least modified form of contemporary carpel appears to be that of *Drimys piperita*. At **anthesis,** this carpel is stipitate with a relatively thin, conduplicately folded blade that encloses a number of ovules attached to its adaxial surface. These ovules are in a more or less linear series between the dorsal and the lateral veins. The **placentation** is clearly laminal and somewhat medial, rather than marginal. The margins of this carpel are not coherent (Bailey and Swamy refer to them as being "unsealed"), and there is no localized stigmatic surface. Instead, stigmatic hairs are extensively developed on the inner surfaces, and on the free margins of the carpel the hairs form a pair of stigmatic crests extending from top to bottom on the open ventral side. The space between the closely opposed ventral surfaces of the carpel becomes filled with a felt-like development of these hairs. Pollen grains are held by the external glandular hairs, and the pollen tubes grow inward among

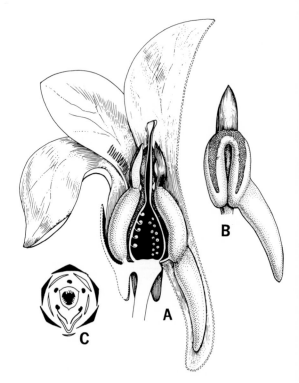

FIGURE 27–6   *Viola* flower, ×5. A, median section showing lateral view of stamen with basal part of connective extending into spur as nectary; B, stamen in adaxial view; C, floral diagram. (After Jones with permission of Blackie and Son, Ltd.)

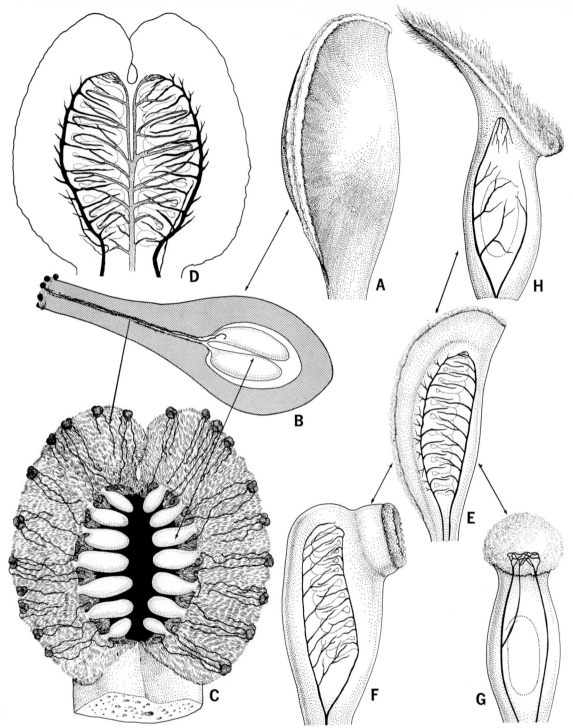

FIGURE 27–7   A–D, primitive carpels. A, side view, showing paired stigmatic crests; B, transverse section, showing pollen grains and penetration of pollen tube; C, unfolded lamina, showing placentation, distribution of glandular hairs, and course of pollen tubes; D, cleared unfolded lamina, showing vasculature. E–H, trends of modification of primitive carpels. E, primitive form of conduplicate carpel; F, lateral and terminal closure, with stigmatic crests restricted to projecting unsealed part; G, laterally sealed carpel with capitate stigma; H, laterally sealed carpel, with expanded, terminal, stigmatic crests. (After Bailey and Swamy with permission of *American Journal of Botany;* and adapted from Irving W. Bailey and B. G. L. Swamy, "The Conduplicate Carpel of Dicotyledons and Its Initial Trends of Specialization," in *Contributions to Plant Anatomy,* by Irving W. Bailey, 1954, The Ronald Press Company, New York.)

the hairs to the ovules. In another section of the genus *Drimys,* the opposed ventral surfaces of the carpel are partly, or even completely, grown together except toward the top of the carpel. The much-reduced, paired stigmatic crests are limited to this unsealed part. In a related genus *Zygogynum* the dorsal side remains short and the ventral portion overgrows the dorsal, carrying the stigmatic crest over to the dorsal side. However, the ventral condition is probably the primitive one.

Gynoecia may be made up of one or more free carpels **(apocarpy);** or two or more fused carpels **(syncarpy).** As pointed out above, the ovules are borne on the adaxial surface of the carpel. Their arrangement is referred to as the placentation; the tissue from which the ovules are developed, often somewhat enlarged or swollen, is the **placenta.** The primitive condition of the placenta is probably shown in the genera *Degeneria* and *Drimys,* which have only slight placental ridges. In advanced genera, the placenta may be large and complex in structure and form. Free carpels mainly show two types of placentation: most commonly the ovules occur in rows near margins of the carpels (submarginal placentation), but in a few instances the ovules occur irregularly over the surface of the lamina (laminar placentation). There is good evidence that the laminar type is primitive and is probably only found in families generally accepted as primitive—e.g., Nymphaeaceae, Cabombaceae, Butomaceae, and Lardizabalaceae. Certain families show a phenetic progression in which the number of ovules is reduced in the more advanced genera.

Syncarpy is a common feature associated with the specialization of the gynoecium. There is general agreement that syncarpy has arisen independently in many unrelated taxa, and variation in the extent of fusion may be found even within a single genus. Commonly carpels become connate by the fusion of the dorsal surface of folded or inrolled laminae, and much less commonly by the ventral margins (Fig. 27–8). Where the fusion occurs along the whole length of the carpels, the ovaries, styles, and stigmas will be involved; if fusion is only in the basal part of the carpel, the styles and stigmas will be free. When closed, or nearly closed, carpels are laterally connate and the ovules are submarginal. The placentae will lie close together around the vertical center of the gynoecium. This is **axile placentation,** considered a primitive type of syncarpous gynoecium and one from which free-central and some kinds of **basal placentation** have been derived. **Parietal placentation** in all probability had a different origin. In a syncarpous, unilocular gynoecium with parietal placentation, the ovules are developed in longitudinal rows on the wall of the cavity (Fig. 27–9).

Free-central placentation exists when the ovules are borne on a central column in a unilocular, syncarpous ovary free from the carpel walls. Ontogenetic studies of certain genera of the Portulacaceae and Caryophyllaceae show that during the development of the flower, axile placentation is transformed into free-central placentation by the breaking down of the lateral walls of the carpel. A more advanced condition is found in certain of the Primulaceae, in which there is congenital free-central placentation.

The last type of placentation to be discussed is basal, when the ovules develop at the base of the locule. It is derived most commonly from free-central placentation through reduction of the size of the fused placentae and a decrease in the number of ovules. It may also be derived from axile placentation, as in the Fagaceae. The Droseraceae series *Drosera–Drosophyllum–Dionaea* begins with parietal placentation and ends with basal, *Drosophyllum* being intermediate. The foregoing types of placentation and their presumed evolutionary development are shown in Figure 27–9.

In the past century morphologists have probably given more attention to the morphology of the **inferior ovary** than to any other problem. Douglas summarizes the many theories advanced, and Eames considers in detail the two theories with the greatest number of supporters—the **appendicular** and the *axial* theories. Under the appendicular theory, the outer whorls of the flower are considered to be concrescent around the ovary and adnate to it. The axial theory supposes that the whole of the

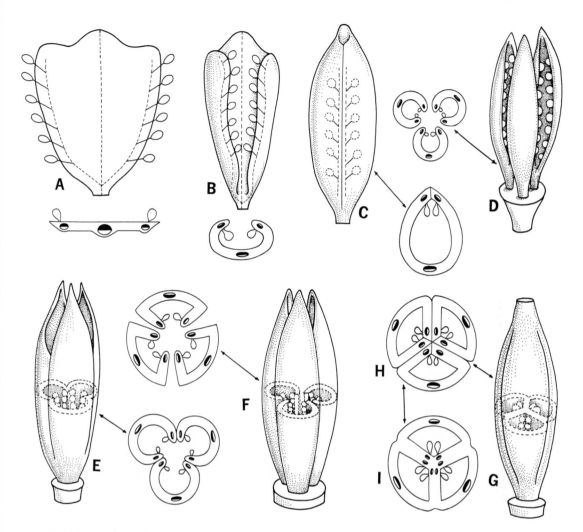

FIGURE 27–8.   Hypothetical evolution of simple and compound ovary (vascular strands shown with xylem elements blackened). A, three-lobed carpel with submarginal ovules; B, same, somewhat involute; C, simple ovary derived from B by infolding of ovules and fusing of ventral margins; D, axis bearing three involute, open carpels; E, compound ovary derived from D by fusion of edges of adjoining carpels; F, axis with three open carpels, adjoining sides more or less parallel; G, compound ovary derived from F by fusion of adjoining sides and margins; H, cross section of G (hypothetical); I, transverse section of G (actual). (After Lawrence, *Taxonomy of Vascular Plants,* used with permission of publisher, copyright 1951 by The Macmillan Company.)

inferior ovary consists of receptacular tissue bearing ovules, and that the walls of the carpels are reduced to a sterile covering including little more than the styles and stigmas. The appendicular theory seems to find favor with the majority of North American botanists as offering the best interpretation of most inferior ovaries, although the axial theory has a great many supporters in other parts of the world.

In support of the appendicular theory it should be pointed out that there is a general ontogenetic tendency for fusion between floral parts that are close together, both horizontally and vertically. This results in the cohesion and adhesion so frequently present in flowers where the parts develop in close whorls. Flowers with their parts in spiral arrangements show little fusion. In many instances where coherence

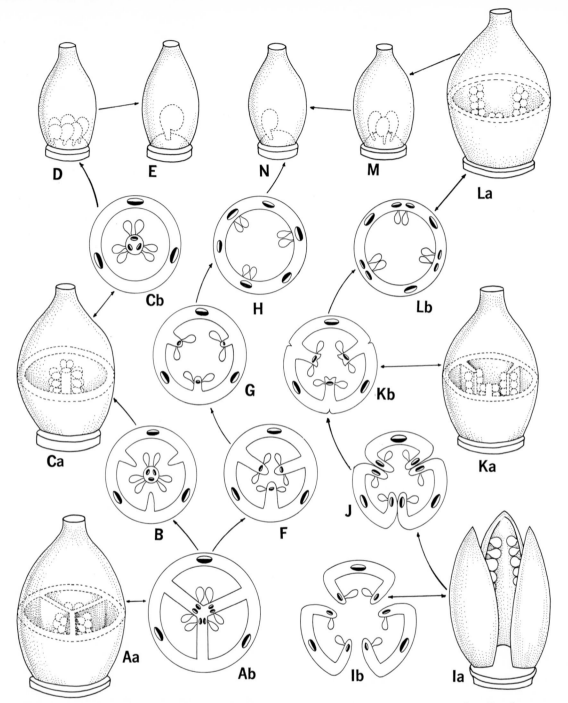

FIGURE 27–9   Presumed evolutionary development of ovary and placentation types. A, trilocular ovary with axile placentation, derived as shown in Figure 27–8; Aa, schematic view of ovary; Ab, transverse section of ovary, showing carpellary vascularization (xylem elements blackened); B, intermediary stage between Ab and C; C, unilocular ovary with free-central placentation, derived from Aa; Ca, schematic view of ovary; Cb, transverse section of ovary, differing from B only in complete loss of septation; D, compound ovary with basal placentation, derived from Ca by reduction of central placentae; E, compound ovary with single basal ovule, derived from D by ovule reduction; F, transverse section of unilocular tricarpellate ovary with parietal placentation, derived from Ab; G, same as F but with septa reduced; H, advanced stage of G (no placental intrusion); I, hypothetical, primitive situation of axis with three open carpels; Ia, schematic view; Ib, transverse section of same; J, compound ovary (unilocular, tricarpellate) with parietal placentation, derived by fusion of adjoining carpel margins; K, compound ovary with parie-

and adherence are not superficially obvious, they are often revealed by careful anatomical study. For example, in the genus *Rosa* the lower part of the "hip" is an invaginated receptacle with the carpels borne on the surface toward the bottom. The upper part consists of the fused bases of the sepals, petals, and stamens and so is appendicular. The exact location of the boundary between these two parts is clearly shown by the sharp downward bending of the stelar bundles. The tribe Pomoideae of the Rosaceae is often cited as an example of inferior ovaries in which the receptacle plays a conspicuous part; the outer fleshy part of the fruit of apples and pears has been called cauline, implying a receptacular origin. However, comparative studies of floral anatomy of the Rosaceae show definitely that this part of the fruit consists of the fused bases of the outer appendages, and that it is morphologically homologous with the base of the **hypanthium** in such genera as *Fragaria* (strawberry) and *Rubus* (raspberry). Only the slender part of the "core" extending between the carpels is cauline; the rest of the flower and fruit is appendicular. One is inclined to agree with Puri that in many instances the interrelationships between cauline and appendicular are so close that there seems little to be gained by continuing the debate!

The anthophyte ovule consists of a central mass of **archesporial** cells, of which most are sterile while one or more function as gynospore mother cells. The functional gynospore is enclosed by one or, more commonly, two integuments. It is borne on a basal stalk, the **funiculus,** which arises from the placenta. The central mass of cells consists of a distal part, the nucellus, and a basal part, the chalaza (Fig. 27–10). The ovule primordium arises from the placenta as a conical protuberance with a rounded apex.

The first, and usually the only, gynospore mother cell can be recognized by its size and the density of its cytoplasm. The inner integument arises from a collar-like ring of meristematic cells slightly below the apex of the protuberance. It grows faster than the nucellus and partially encloses it, leaving a little canal-like micropyle. If the outer integument develops, it arises slightly below the inner integument and grows in the same way.

Several types of ovules are distinguished by variations in general form and in the position of the micropyle. All ovules are fundamentally much alike and are probably evolutionary modifications of a basic type, and transitional forms are common. The ovule is said to be **orthotropous** when it is straight and upright on the placenta, with the micropyle distal and the funiculus short or wanting. If the ovule is completely inverted so that the micropyle faces the placenta, it is said to be **anatropous;** in such instances the ovule is usually appressed or adnate to the funiculus. Other names are applied to intermediate conditions (Fig. 27–11).

Many morphological interpretations have been given to the angiosperm ovule. It was long considered a bud because it seemed to resemble an axis with a growing point and leaves. It has more commonly and recently been interpreted as a modified leaf or portion of a leaf. The exclusive application of either of these theories resulted in such inconsistencies and strained interpretations that many morphologists were led to the conclusion that ovules might have had both origins. The fact that this state of affairs might imply different origins in even closely related anthophyte taxa has apparently not been seriously considered. According to a third interpretation, it is an independent structure borne on either axial or foliar organs, the integuments being new structures.

Increasing knowledge of the gymnosperms, and particularly of the pteridosperms, has led twentieth-century morphologists away from stressing the carpel altogether and has directed their attention to much earlier stages of

tal placentation, derived from J; Ka, schematic view of ovary; Lb, transverse section of ovary (compare normal xylem orientation of ventral strands with reversed positions in H (the retention of strands in Lb is a less advanced situation than fusion shown in H); M, compound ovary with basal placentation, derived by placental reduction of H or of La; N, compound ovary with single basal ovule, derived from M by ovule reduction. (After Lawrence, *Taxonomy of Vascular Plants,* used with permission of publisher, copyright 1951 by The Macmillan Company.)

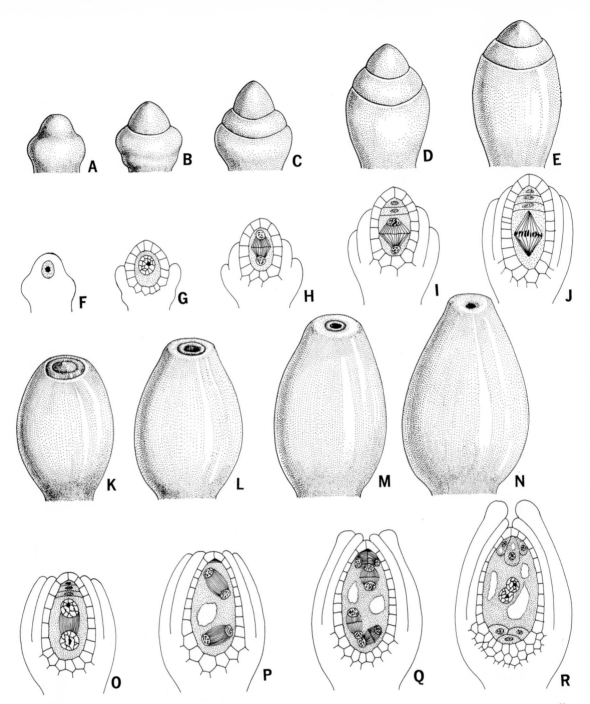

FIGURE 27–10   Development of ovule. A–E, K–N, growth of integuments; F, G, gynospore mother cell; H, I, meiosis; J, O, three gynospores degenerating, nucleus of remaining one dividing; P–R, development of female gametophyte (at micropylar end, two synergids and egg nucleus; at chalazal end, three antipodal cells; at center, two polar nuclei fusing to form primary endosperm nucleus). (After Brown.)

evolution. This has given added strength and significance to the fourth, or *sui generis,* theory in which the ovule is primarily a gynosporangium—the nucellus being the wall of the sporangium and the integuments protective structures. Although fossil evidence supports this theory, some investigators are critical of this comparatively simple and perhaps too facile

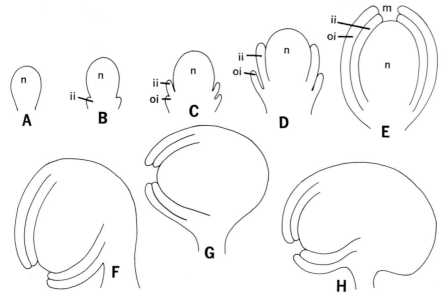

FIGURE 27–11   A–E, development of orthotropous ovule (*n,* nucellus; *ii,* inner integument; *oi,* outer integument; *m,* micropyle). F–H, anatropous, amphitropous, and campylotropous ovules, respectively. (After Gibbs.)

explanation and suggest that the stage is now set for new avenues of search for ancestral forms.

GYNOGAMETOPHYTE

In the majority of anthophytes only a single gynospore mother cell is differentiated. As in the gymnosperms, this mother cell undergoes a meiotic division to produce a linear tetrad of gynospores oriented parallel to the long axis of the ovule. In most instances only the gynospore toward the chalaza functions to produce the gynogametophyte **(embryo sac)** whereas the other three degenerate. The development of the gynogametophyte begins with the endosporal germination of the gynospore. Mitotic division of the gynospore nucleus is followed by two simultaneous divisions of the daughter nuclei, producing eight free nuclei within the now somewhat distended wall of the gynospore. Of these eight nuclei, three are at the micropylar end, three at the chalazal end, and the remaining two (termed the **polar nuclei**) migrate to the center of the gametophyte. The three micropylar nuclei enclosed by delicate walls constitute the **egg apparatus,** which includes the egg (the female gamete) and two **synergids.** The three nuclei (termed the **antipodals**) at the cha-

lazal end usually become walled also, but the polar nuclei remain unwalled (Fig. 27–10O–R).

An eight-nucleate female gametophyte with this ontogeny and arrangement of nuclei is characteristic of the great majority of flowering plants that have been examined critically. Many deviations from this so-called "normal" pattern are now known and are discussed in detail by Maheshwari and summarized by Eames. The female gametophytes of the Anthophyta fall into three classes according to whether they originate from cells that consist morphologically of one, two, or four gynospores. In the development of the bisporic and tetrasporic gametophytes, the protoplasts of the spores unite to form the gametophyte. The origin of a single gametophyte by the united growth of two or four spores is an extremely interesting evolutionary event and one that is probably unique to the anthophytes. As Eames points out: "It implies the existence, in some taxa, of gametophytes basically consisting of two or four individuals, a specialization in the gametophyte as great as any in the sporophyte, . . ." This means that in these cases the gametophyte is actually a highly integrated colony of as many as four individuals and two genotypes.

Maheshwari recognizes ten types of gametophyte based on the number of nuclear divisions intervening between the gynospore mother cell and the mature gametophyte, and on the number and arrangement of the gametophyte nuclei. The distinguishing features of these types are best shown in the accompanying diagrammatic chart reproduced from Maheshwari (Fig. 27–12). Each type has been given the name of the genus in which it was first clearly described. The number of antipodals ranges from zero in the *Oenothera* type to 11 in the *Drusa* type; the central nucleus ranges from haploid in the *Oenothera* type to octoploid in *Peperomia;* and the egg apparatus has only a single nucleus in *Plumbagella* in contrast to the normal three. In the *Plumbagella, Plumbago,* and *Adoxa* types the female gamete (egg) nucleus is produced by a single division of a meiospore—the ontogenetic extent of the gametophyte generation in each case. To find a parallel situation in the plant kingdom one has to go to the Fucales (Phaeophyta, see Chapter 11), where it is duplicated in *Fucus* with eight eggs. At an extremely early evolutionary stage in animals this type of life history must have become established as a relatively unvarying feature of all phyla. In plants an extreme reduction of the gametophyte culminates in the phaeophyte line. Then, and apparently quite independently, this reduction emerges in the anthophytes after a very long phylogenetic history that includes the intermediate morphological stages shown by the bryophytes and all the other vascular groups.

ANDROGAMETOPHYTE

In anthophytes, androspores are typically produced in large numbers in the four androsporangia (pollen sacs) of the anther. In most instances, meiosis of the androspore mother cells takes place at an early stage in the development of the flower, even when the flower bud is quite small. Meiosis is followed by endosporal germination of the androspore to the extent of one or two divisions, following which the immature androgametophyte becomes dormant until shed as a pollen grain. As in other seed plants, a pollen grain is an immature androgametophyte consisting of the androspore wall containing one, two, or three cells—or nuclei if the cell walls fail to develop. Pollination, the transfer of pollen from the anther to a stigma, will be considered later.

The tetrads of pollen grains show various grouping arrangements, resulting in differences in shape and certain surface features of the individual grains. Some of this variety in size, shape, and sculpturing of the outer wall (the exine) is shown in Figure 27–13. In shape pollen grains are usually globose, ellipsoid, or fusiform. There are two basic types: **porate** and **colpate.** Porate grains have from one to many pores in the exine, whereas colpate grains have from one to several **colpae** or furrows in the exine running from one pole toward the other. Many angiosperm pollen grains have both colpae and pores, and are called **colporate.**

The monocolpate type of pollen grain appears to be primitive, with its single colpus on the distal side—i.e., the side away from the point of contact of the grain in the tetrad. Monocolpate grains are characteristic of the monocotyledons, most of the Ranales (such as Winteraceae, Magnoliaceae, Calycanthaceae, Lauraceae), and a few other families in other orders. Essentially the same type is also found in the cycads, bennettites, and pteridosperms (see Fig. 23–13E, p. 477).

The distinguishing characteristics of pollen grains are the number and position of the furrows and the nature and pattern of sculpturing. These features also provide important diagnostic criteria for the identification of pollen grains. Fortunately, because it contains a cutin-like substance very resistant to decay, the exine persists in peat, in sedimentary rocks, and especially in coal and oil shales of all ages. The study of such microfossils and modern spores and pollen is now included in the comparatively new science of **palynology.** Results of palynological studies are shedding much light on phylogenetic relationships and also on climatological conditions in the past.

When pollen grains arrive on a compatible stigma, they germinate by developing a pollen tube. This tube begins as an extension of the

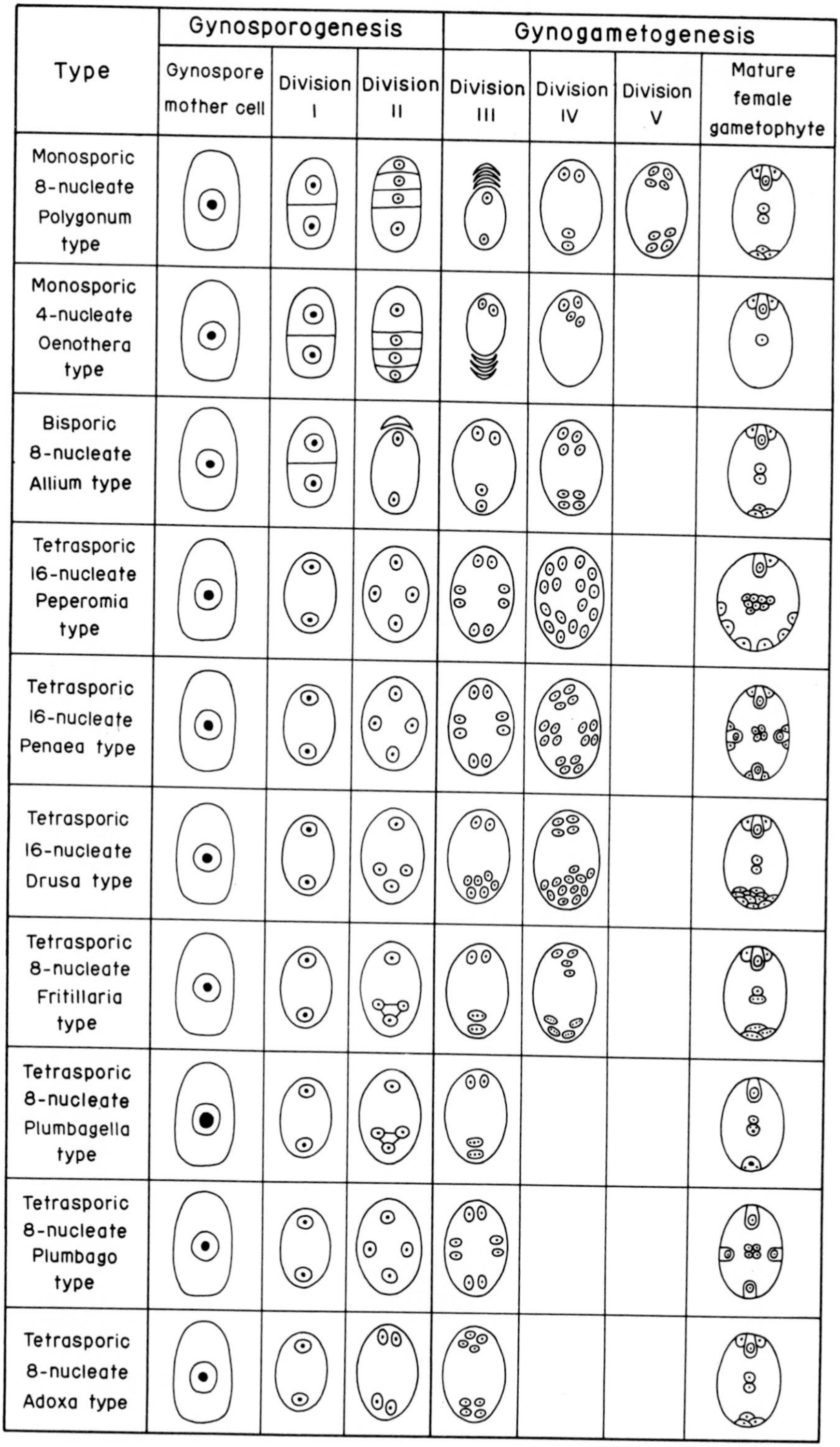

FIGURE 27–12   Important types of female gametophytes in angiosperms. (After Maheshwari.)

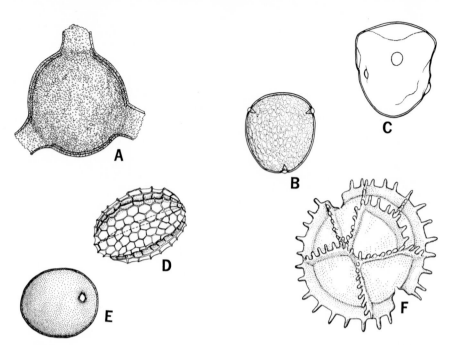

FIGURE 27–13   Angiosperm pollen grains. A, *Epilobium angustifolium* (Onagraceae), with three large pores as extensions of ectexine (note endexine forming layer inside ectexine but ending short of pores), ×400; B, *Fagus sylvatica* (Fagaceae), three colporate with scabrate exine about 2.5 microns thick, ×600; C, *Carex* sp. (Cyperaceae), having smooth wall with one large central pore and two faint lateral pores, ×800; D, *Salix sitchensis* (Salicaceae), tricolpate with fine but distinct reticulum, pollen tube forming by evagination of intine from colpae, ×1,600; E, *Bromus inermis* (Graminae), single pore is characteristic of grass pollen and is covered by operculum, which is usually lost in grains processed for microscopic examination, ×500; F, *Taraxacum* sp. (Compositae), tricolpate having elaborate branching ridges with echinate projections on crests (ridges enclose lacunae with very thin exine forming floor; surrounding ridges restrict opening of pore-like colpae, ×1,200).

inner wall (intine) of the grain, swelling out through a germinal aperture. However, the tube soon acquires growth of its own. The contents of the grain, including the nuclei, move out into the tube, and the vegetative nucleus, now known as the tube nucleus, takes the apical position. The tube frequently contains oil globules or starch grains that presumably supply some of the nutritional needs of the developing pollen tube. The starch grains are gradually digested and go into solution.

In most instances investigated, germination of the pollen grain takes place with very little delay. The tube penetrates the tissue of the stigma, follows the course of the style, and then passes through a placenta into the cavity of the ovary. Here it may take a short aerial course to the micropyle of an ovule; in other instances, it grows on the surface of the placenta, along the funiculus and integuments, and to the micropyle. What directs the course of the pollen tube is not now known. Generally the tube is regarded as chemotactic, with the attracting substance known as a pollen tube factor. According to one postulate, growth may be governed by rather specific inhibitors.

Sometimes when the pollen grain is shed—although usually before this stage—the meiospore nucleus divides into a generative nucleus and a vegetative nucleus (later known as the tube nucleus). In other instances, the generative nucleus divides again before shedding to form two male gamete nuclei, and so the pollen grain is shed in a three-nucleate stage. In either case, two gamete nuclei are present in the tip of the pollen tube when it reaches the vicinity of the egg apparatus. The fertilization that follows is unique to the Anthophyta. One male nucleus fuses with the egg nucleus, resulting in a **zygote** from which the embryo plant will develop. The other male nucleus fuses with the centrally situated fusion nucleus (made up of the two polar nuclei), producing the primary endosperm nucleus from which will develop the cellular food reserve known as the **endosperm.** This special type of fertilization in which both male gamete nuclei take part is called **double fertilization.**

Plant embryology for a long time was eclipsed by other botanical studies that seemed likely to throw more light on problems of evolution and phylogeny. There seemed to be little prospect that embryology could contribute to the history of plant evolution as it has so notably in the vertebrates. However, in the last half-century, plant embryology has begun to come into its own. Numerous investigations have shown that it is not possible to speak of a "typical" dicotyledonous or monocotyledonous embryo. There is too much diversity in ontogeny and even in the basic pattern of development. Maheshwari and Johansen summarize the immense amount of detailed comparative information now available, and their writings should be consulted for details that cannot be included here. Johansen recognizes six types of embryonic development and has further divided each main type into a number of variations. However, in practically all instances the differences are found to be in the earliest ontogenetic stages—i.e., in the proembryo. Moreover, the various embryological types show very little taxonomic affiliation, and so in themselves are of limited value as phylogenetic criteria.

In the flowering plants, as in many of the lower plants (particularly the ferns), embryos are sometimes produced without fertilization, despite the presence of a mechanism for sexual reproduction. The term **apomixis** is applied to all types of asexual reproduction which tend to replace or act as substitutes for sexual methods. Those interested in learning the extent and numerous methods of apomictic development

known in the plant kingdom should consult the monographic reviews and analysis of Gustafsson. The generally accepted classification of apomixis is based on two principle types: vegetative reproduction and **agamospermy.** The former is only considered as apomixis where it assumes the role of sexual reproduction, in whole or in considerable part. In agamospermy, embryos and seeds are formed asexually. This involves a change in the usual complementary relationship between syngamy and meiosis, since these two processes are usually circumvented. As a result, the embryo is genetically identical to its maternal parent. The simplest method of agamospermy is known as adventive embryony. For example, in various species of *Citrus,* embryos may arise directly from diploid sporophytic tissue of the nucellus or integument—the gametophyte stage failing to develop. A small group of cells usually divides actively and pushes its way into the embryo sac, eventually forming a true embryo.

Diploid gametophytes may produce embryos either **parthenogenetically** (directly from an unfertilized egg) or **apogamously** from some other cell. The former method is more common in seed plants, whereas the latter is frequent in ferns. In Chapter 1 we referred to the special type of nuclear cycle in which syndiploidy occurs following apogamy in ferns. Apomixis may be due to any one of several causes, and may be facultative or obligate in different groups. In genera such as *Antennaria,* where it is obligate, some species have both pollen-producing and ovule-producing plants, although the former are functionless; and in others, only ovule-producing plants are known. Many of the larger families of Anthophyta have genera and species that reproduce by apomixis. In the Compositae—in addition to *Antennaria—Taraxacum* and *Hieracium* are classical examples; in the Rosaceae, *Prunus, Sorbus, Rubus,* and *Crataegus;* and in the Gramineae, *Poa* and *Calamagrostis.*

The causes of sexual sterility in the Anthophyta are so numerous and varied that no simple theory can account for the origin of apomixis. It has been well established that a high correlation exists between polyploidy and apomixis, and between apomixis and the perennial habit to which vegetative reproduction is also correlated. However, all apomicts are not polyploids and *vice versa,* nor are all polyploids perennials.

SEEDS AND FRUITS

The term **seed,** like so many other morphological terms of wide application, is difficult to define. However, certain characteristics are associated with seeds, whether they are gymnospermous, monocotyledonous, or dicotyledonous in origin. A seed is a mature ovule containing an embryo plant whose development is generally arrested for a period, and which may or may not have an accompanying food reserve. While this definition covers the great majority of cases, there are exceptions that differ in degree. In the cycadophytes and *Ginkgo* no embryo may have formed at the time the seeds are "ripe" and shed—in fact fertilization frequently takes place when the ovule is on the ground. At the other end of the evolutionary scale, the Orchidaceae have seeds that consistently lack a differentiated embryo at the time they are shed. While in general a period of dormancy occurs before germination, there is great variation in the duration of the dormant period. The seeds of the poplar (*Populus*) germinate immediately after they are shed and certain tropical genera (*Myristica, Durio*) are also reported to have no dormant period; true vivipary is shown by the mangrove plants *Rhizophora, Bruguiera,* and *Avicennia.*

Seeds with endosperm are said to be **albuminous,** while those lacking it are **exalbuminous.** In albuminous seeds the embryo frequently is small and undifferentiated, as in many ranalian families; this is perhaps the primitive condition among the anthophytes. Monocotyledons commonly have albuminous seeds with the endosperm bulking quite large compared to the embryo. Exalbuminous seeds occur in many families, such as Aceraceae, Cruciferae, Geraniaceae, Cucurbitaceae, and Compositae; other families have genera with endosperm and others without, such as Ara-

ceae, Rosaceae, Papilionaceae, and Betulaceae. A variety of substances are stored in endosperm, including proteins, fats, oil, and starch (the principal carbohydrate). In the absence of endosperm, the cotyledons usually assume the storage and nutritive roles; but sometimes, as in the Brazil nut (*Bertholletia excelsa*), these roles are assumed by the hypocotyl.

Seeds vary greatly in size and weight—from the minute, dust-like seeds of orchids and some Ericaceae which weigh about 0.001 mg, to the massive seed of the *Coco-de-mer* (*Lodoicea*), the double coconut of the Seychelles, which may weigh as much as 20 kg. Seeds also vary in details of structure, although as a rule the seed coat, or **testa,** is formed from the integuments; the micropyle can be seen as a small opening in the testa close to the tip of the radicle. Especially in anatropous ovules the place of abscission of the funiculus is evident as a scar, the **hilum.** Some seeds have fleshy coats or appendages of various origins commonly referred to as arils—a loose morphological term referring to any fleshy external part of the seed. The term is applied to outgrowths of the chalaza or integuments which more or less envelop the ovule, also to the fleshy funiculus as in *Magnolia* and species of *Acacia.* In general, arils are associated with tropical seeds and are rare in plants of temperate regions. While arillate developments are particularly common among primitive angiosperms, they cannot be regarded as indications of primitiveness because fleshy outgrowths occur in such a variety of families, including gymnosperms, that they must have arisen independently during evolution. In fact, fleshy outgrowths offer good examples of so-called "parallel evolution"—a widespread phenomenon that results in similar structures in unrelated groups of plants. It seems likely that arils are an ecological modification related to dissemination.

The longevity of seeds is another topic of both biological and practical interest. The time that seeds remain viable varies from a very brief period in such genera as *Quercus, Acer, Populus, Salix, Citrus,* and some grasses to hundreds of years in other cases. It is reported that seeds of *Nelumbo* and *Albizzia*

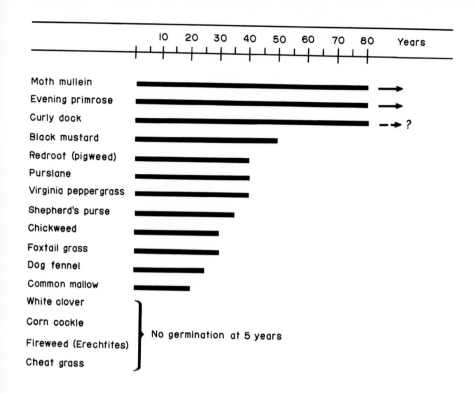

FIGURE 27–14   Longevity of seeds in Beal's experiment. (After Cronquist.)

julibrissen that had been in the British Museum for 150 years germinated after becoming wet during the "Battle of Britain." The record is apparently held by the lotus, *Nelumbo nucifera.* Seeds of this species were found by a Japanese botanist in a peat deposit in an old lake bed in Manchuria. Radiocarbon dating showed the seeds to be about 1,000 years old, although other evidence suggests an even greater age. When the seed coats were filed to permit water to enter, 100 per cent germination followed. An investigation to determine the differential viability of a number of common Michigan weed seeds was started in 1879 by Professor Beal of what was then Michigan State College. The seeds of 20 species were mixed with sand and buried in the ground in inverted open-mouthed bottles. At first samples were removed at five-year intervals to test viability; later this was increased to ten-year intervals. After 80 years three species still had viable seeds. The results are shown graphically in Figure 27–14. The experiment is planned to continue for 160 years.

In addition to functioning as reproductive structures, seeds show very considerable adaptation to the environment. For example, Went discusses in some detail the adaptation of seeds of certain species to desert conditions. He describes three groups of annuals: winter annuals, summer annuals, and an intermediate group. Germination in each group requires some rainfall but is actually triggered by temperature; summer annuals will only germinate at 26–30° C, whereas winter annuals remain dormant at these temperatures but do germinate at 10° C. Furthermore, observations in nature show that the germination of seeds of certain desert plants is not related to moisture as such, but to a sufficient amount and duration of rain. Went describes a number of different mechanisms that have been evolved to permit germination only under very favorable conditions. The first group of seeds mentioned by Went (from *Euphorbia* spp. and *Pectis papposa*) contain water-soluble germination inhibitors. Germination will only take place after these inhibitors have been completely leached from

TABLE 27–1
SUMMARY OF AVERAGE SEED WEIGHT (IN GRAMS)
OF SPECIES OF VARIOUS HABITAT CONDITIONS*

OPEN HABITAT SPECIES	SPECIES OF SEMI-CLOSED OR CLOSED NON-SHADY HABITATS	MEADOW SPECIES	HERBS OF SCRUB AND WOOD MARGIN	SHADE SPECIES	SHRUBS	TREES
Seeds 70 species 0.00119	22 species 0.002214	8 species 0.0049	32 species 0.004438	27 species 0.013686	21 species 0.0937	— —
Fruits 30 species 0.001629	16 species 0.00224	— —	15 species 0.003385	6 species 0.00505	3 species 0.0107	20 species 0.6534
Gramineae 7 species 0.00246	13 species 0.000814	— —	3 species 0.002892	3 species 0.002602	— —	— —
All propagules 98 species 0.001315	51 species 0.001862	— —	50 species 0.004029	36 species 0.011323	24 species 0.085435	20 species 0.6534

Ratios of averages (open habitat species as unity)
Seeds   1: 1.86 : 4.1 : 3.7 : 11.5 : 80 : —
All propagules 1: 1.41 : — : 3.06 : 8.6 : 64.9 : 496

*After Salisbury with permission of G. Bell and Sons, Ltd.

the seeds. In the second group, germination is inhibited by salt concentrations in the soil somewhat higher than those tolerated by the growing plants of the same species. A heavy rainfall will leach the salts out of the upper layers of soil and so permit germination. In the third group, delay in germination is probably due to the presence of encasing structures, such as husks in certain grasses. Heavy precipitation causes sand and gravel to **scarify** these structures, making germination possible. Went discusses other mechanisms, but the foregoing are sufficient to indicate one aspect of evolution where the origin of certain structures is related closely to the environment.

Another line of evolutionary development is discussed by Salisbury, who has made a number of searching quantitative studies into the reproductive capacity of 240 species of British seed plants. He defines the *average reproductive capacity* of a species as the product of the average seed output and the fraction representing the average percentage germination. It is generally assumed that the process of natural selection has brought about a state of equilibrium between seed output and mortality. If this is

true, the *potential reproductive capacity* of a species would be a measure of its susceptibility to natural mortality. However, Salisbury suggests that a pronounced fluctuation in numbers of offspring may have a definite survival value. He theorizes that, owing to the general lag in increase of predators and parasites, an intermittent high reproductive capacity might well lead to an increase in abundance of a species. In contrast, a reproductive capacity maintained at a continuing high level would not have the same effect, since the plants' enemies would be maintained at the same high level.

Studies of 300 species from different habitats indicate that seed and fruit weights tend to increase as the amount of shade given to the seedlings increases. Salisbury states that the capacity to colonize in the face of competition appears to be associated with the amount of food reserve which the seeds contain. However, this rule does not apply to parasites and saprobes that have their own special modes of nutrition. It is also suggested that the mycorrhizal habit (as in Ericaceae and Orchidaceae) confers a similar immunity. Table 27–1 presents a summary of Salisbury's findings on the

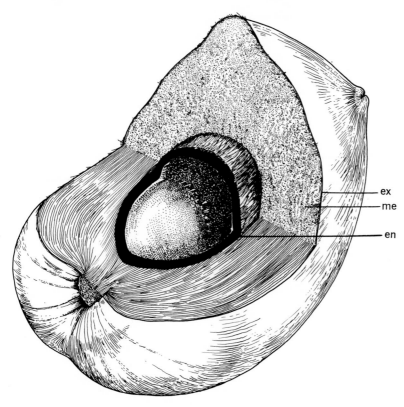

FIGURE 27–15   Coconut fruit (*Cocos nucifera*) cut to show three layers of pericarp, ×0.5. *ex,* thin hard exocarp; *me,* fibrous mesocarp; *en,* stony endocarp.

relation between weights of propagules and habitat.

The adaptation of seeds to various methods of dissemination and distribution will be discussed later in this chapter (p. 561) when the topic is treated in connection with fruits.

The term **fruit** is often very loosely used and is difficult to define precisely. It has been called a "mature flower," which is a good definition if all the implications are appreciated. However, in all cases a flower (or flowers) precedes the development of a fruit; and flowers at anthesis have immature parts, at least in the gynoecium. In general, a fruit consists of a matured gynoecium and may include accessory parts of the flower—even the axis of the inflorescence, pedicel, or peduncle in particular cases. Pollination followed by fertilization is the usual prelude to fruit development; but in many instances, **parthenocarpy** occurs—that is, a complete fruit is formed without fertilization.

Such parthenocarpic fruits do not contain seeds. A well-known example is the banana (*Musa*); others with fleshy fruits are seedless varieties of oranges (*Citrus*), cucumber (*Cucumis*), and grapes (*Vitis*); with dry fruits are maples (*Acer*), peas (*Pisum*), tobacco (*Nicotiana*), and poppies (*Papaver*). It should be noted that the development of parthenocarpic fruits can be induced by the plant hormone indoleacetic acid.

The ripened ovary wall in a fruit is the **pericarp,** which may be dry or fleshy, fibrous or stony. Three distinct layers can often be recognized in the pericarp: the outer **(exocarp),** the middle **(mesocarp),** and the inner layer **(endocarp)** (Fig. 27–15). Pericarp features are used considerably in classifying fruits—a process often artificial but very useful for taxonomic purposes.

In classifying fruits, three main types are recognized (see Table 27–2). The first group is

TABLE 27-2

(For illustrations of fruits see Figures 27–15, 16, 17, 18)

I. Fruits dry, pericarp dry when fruit is mature.

    A. Indehiscent fruits in which the pericarp remains closed at maturity.

        a. *Achene*—a small single-seeded fruit with a relatively thin pericarp; except for its attachment by the funiculus, the seed lies free in the cavity of the ovary: buttercup (*Ranunculus*), crowfoot (*Potentilla*), water plantain (*Alisma*), buckwheat (*Fagopyrum*).

        b. *Caryopsis*—achene-like except that it is derived from a compound ovary and the seed coat is firmly united to the pericarp: characteristic fruit of the Gramineae.

        c. *Cypsela*—achene-like but derived from an inferior, compound ovary: characteristic fruit of the Compositae.

        d. *Nut*—like an achene but derived from two or more carpels, and with a hard or stony pericarp: hazel nut (*Corylus*), basswood (*Tilia*), acorn (*Quercus*).

        e. *Samara*—a winged achene: elm (*Ulmus*), ash (*Fraxinus*), tree-of-heaven (*Ailanthus*), hop tree (*Ptelea*).

        f. *Schizocarp*—the product of a compound ovary that splits apart at maturity into a number of one-seeded portions termed mericarps: maple (*Acer*), many Umbelliferae, Labiatae, Malvaceae, Geraniaceae.

    B. Dehiscent fruits in which the fruit splits, or opens in some manner to release the seeds.

        a. *Follicle*—derived from a single carpel that splits at maturity down one side, usually along the ventral suture: columbine (*Aquilegia*), peony (*Paeonia*), *Delphinium*, milkweed (*Asclepias*).

        b. *Legume*—also from a single carpel, but dehiscing down both the dorsal and ventral sutures to form two valves: characteristic fruit of Papilionaceae.

        c. *Silique*—the product of a superior compound ovary of two carpels, the pericarp separating as two halves leaving a persistent central portion with the seed or seeds attached to it: characteristic fruit of Cruciferae.

        d. *Capsule*—from a compound ovary; various types of dehiscence are found—e.g., longitudinal, porous, or circumscissile; in general the dehiscence is from top downward and the separated portions (valves or teeth) remain attached: characteristic of numerous families.

II. Fruits fleshy, pericarp partly or wholly fleshy or fibrous.

        a. *Drupe*—carpels one or more but usually single-seeded; mesocarp fleshy but the endocarp hard and stony: cherry, peach, plum (*Prunus*), coconut (*Cocos*), olive (*Olea*).

        b. *Berry*—one to several carpels, usually many-seeded; both mesocarp and endocarp are fleshy: one-seeded, nutmeg (*Myristica*), date (*Phoenix*); single carpel and several seeds, baneberry (*Actaea*), barberry (*Berberis*), *Mahonia;* others with more than one carpel, grape (*Vitis*), tomato and potato (*Solanum*), *Asparagus*.

        c. *Pome*—derived from a compound inferior ovary; much of the fleshy portion is the enlarged base of the perianth tube with only the central part composing the pericarp; both the exocarp and mesocarp are fleshy while the endocarp (the core) is stony or cartilaginous: characteristic fruit of the Pomoideae, apple (*Malus*), pear (*Pyrus*), quince (*Cydonia*), mountain ash (*Sorbus*).

comprised of **simple fruits** formed from a single simple or compound ovary. The second type includes **aggregate fruits** formed from a single flower but with separate unfused carpels, each actually forming a fruit but the whole aggregating as a unit—e.g., raspberry (*Rubus*), strawberry (*Fragaria*), and *Magnolia*. In the third type, **multiple fruits,** several flowers are involved—as in the flowering dogwood (*Cornus nuttallii*), plane tree (*Platanus*), mulberry (*Morus*), and pineapple (*Ananas*).

As fruits mature, they become either dry or fleshy. Dry fruits may remain closed (indehiscent) when ripe or they may open in one of several ways (dehiscent). Fleshy fruits as a rule are indehiscent. When applying names to different kinds of fruits, botanists differ considerably in usage. Some emphasize the nature of the pericarp, without concern for the number of carpels or whether the ovary is superior or inferior. Other botanists are more precise, and feel that the names should carry ontogenetic implications. The former botanists are akin to the "lumpers" of taxonomy, whereas the latter are the "splitters."

In both aggregate and multiple fruits, the individual elements are described in the same terms as for simple fruits—e.g., in the strawberry the actual fruits are achenes borne on a fleshy receptacle, whereas in the raspberry the

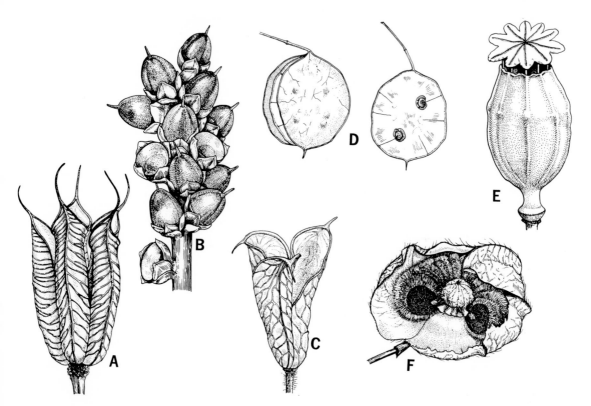

FIGURE 27–16   Dry dehiscent fruits. A, follicles (*Aquilegia*), ×3; B, pyxis (*Plantago major*), capsular fruit with circumscissile dehiscence, ×7; C, follicles (*Delphinium*), ×2; D, silicle (*Lunaria annua*), short silique, showing replum, ×1; E, capsule (*Papaver somniferum*) with porous dehiscence, ×1.5; F, schizocarp (*Malva moschatus*) showing numerous, coarsely hairy mericarps, ×3.5.

fruits are druplets. The pineapple (*Ananas*) is a special type of multiple fruit in which the axis of the inflorescence enlarges to become part of the fruit. In the syconium of the fig we find a multiple fruit; the actual fruits are achene-like inside the hollow urn-shaped structure, which is the expanded, deeply concave axis of the inflorescence.

In the array of fruit types, the plant biologist is likely to see adaptations that protect the embryo plant from desiccation or, what is more general, a series of devices to assist and promote the spread of species into new areas. Fruits may be agents in the dissemination of seeds, or may themselves act as **disseminules.**

Of prime importance to world-wide occurrence is the dispersal of plants—i.e., their transportation from place to place—whether as fruits, seeds, or specialized vegetative structures. It may be argued that dispersal is a more important factor in the evolution of flowering plants than their many and ingenious adaptations for pollination. Apparently few species suffer from lack of pollination due to the absence of an essential pollinator; on the other hand, the migration of plants to new areas very closely depends on modifications for dispersal. In view of the undoubted biological importance of dispersal and of the variety of related adaptations that have evolved in the flowering plants, it is surprising that this study has not caught the attention of more investigators. The encyclopedic work of Ridley, which provides the basis for the following account, should be consulted by any who wish to pursue this topic further.

DISSEMINATION BY WIND

Tumble-weeds.   The whole plant, or the fruiting portion, breaks off and is blown by wind across open country, scattering seeds as it goes. Such plants are always herbaceous and usually annuals. They include Russian thistle (*Salsola kali*), pigweeds (*Amaranthus*), certain Gramineae, and tumbling mustard (*Sisymbrium*).

Light Fruits and Seeds. These are blown about by the wind and owe dispersal to their lightness—e.g., Orchidaceae and many Ericaceae.

Winged Fruits. Wings are usually formed by persistent bracts or perianth parts, or the whole pericarp may develop as a wing. Winged fruits, commonest in trees and shrubs, include dipterocarps (*Dipterocarpus*), maple (*Acer*), ash (*Fraxinus*), elm (*Ulmus*), dock (*Rumex*), and Betulaceae (Fig. 27–18).

Winged Seeds. The fruit is usually a capsule that dehisces to release seeds in which the testa has developed into a thin wing. This is common in trees and shrubs, and particularly climbers—e.g., jacaranda (*Jacaranda*), trumpet vine (*Tecoma*), catalpa (*Catalpa*), and many other genera of Bignoniaceae, butter-and-eggs (*Linaria*), and yam (*Dioscorea*). (See Fig. 27–19E, G, H.)

Plumed Fruits. Plumes develop from the **pappus** in some Compositae, from the perianth in various Cyperaceae, from the persistent style (*Geum, Anemone, Clematis*), or from the pedicels of spikelets in certain Gramineae (Fig. 27–19A–D).

Plumed Seeds. Tufts of light silky hairs may develop at one (rarely both) end of the seed, as in fireweed (*Epilobium*), milkweed (*Asclepias*), dogbane (*Apocynum*), and epiphytes such as some Bromeliaceae (Fig. 27–19F).

Woolly Fruits or Seeds. The pericarp or the seed coat may be covered with woolly hairs, as in willows and poplars (*Salicaceae*), cotton (*Gossypium*), kapok (*Bombax*), and *Anemone*.

DISPERSAL BY WATER

Rain. Rainwash in the plains, both in temperate and tropical regions, is of very great importance in the dispersal of seeds. The action of rain is accentuated in the mountain forests of

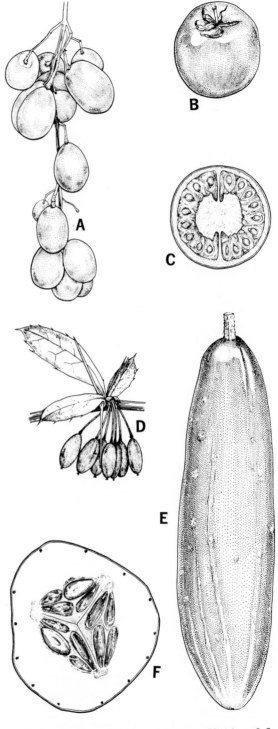

FIGURE 27–17 Berries. A, grape (*Vitis*), ×0.5; B, C, tomato (*Lycopersicum esculentum*), ×0.5; D, barberry (*Berberis*), ×0.5; E, F, cucumber (*Cucumis sativus*), a special type of berry known as pepo, ×1.

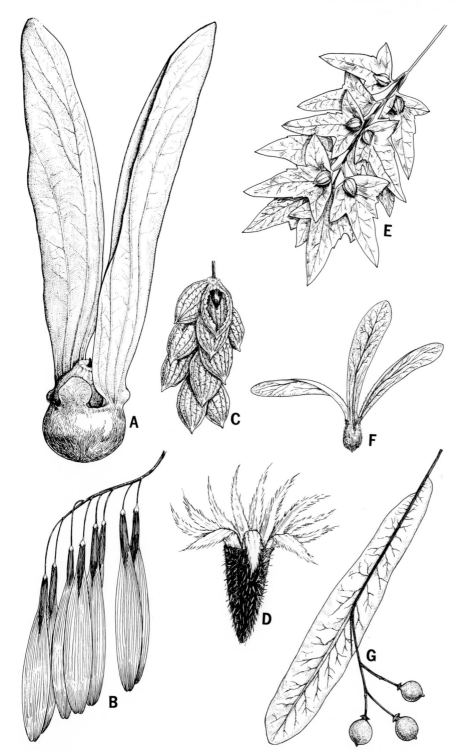

FIGURE 27–18   Winged fruits. A, *Dipterocarpus retusus* (the two wings are part of persistent calyx), ×0.5; B, *Fraxinus,* samara, ×1; C, *Ostrya virginiana,* with each fruit contained in inflated, involucral sac, ×1; D, *Galinsoga,* with cypsela fruit and wings of pappus scales, ×50; E, *Carpinus caroliniana,* with nutlike fruit subtended by single involucral bract, ×1; F, *Triplaris,* with wings of elongated perianth lobes, ×1; G, *Tilia,* with petiole adnate to a large, strap-shaped bract, ×2.

563

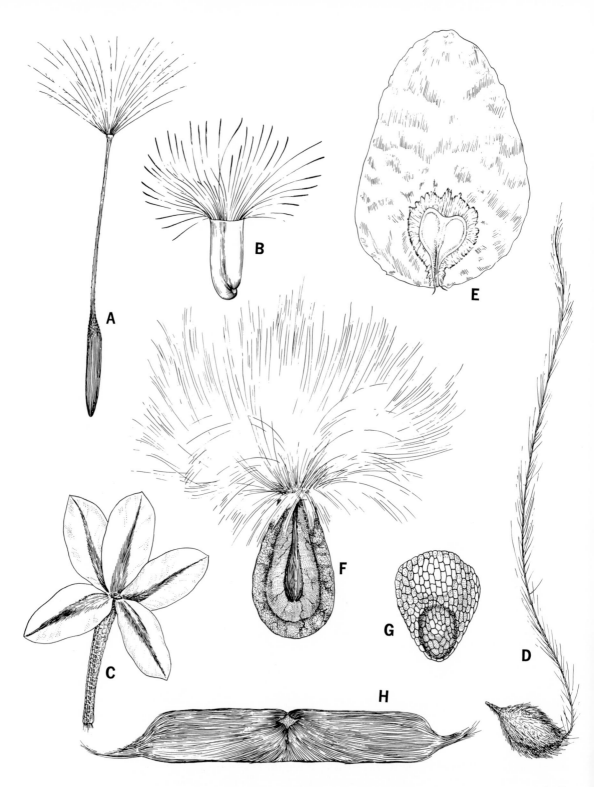

FIGURE 27–19   Airborne fruits and seeds. A–D, fruits. A, *Hypochaeris*, ×5; B, *Centaurea*, ×5; C, *Ursinia*, ×5; D, *Clematis*, ×5. E–H, seeds. E, *Spathodea*, ×5; F, *Asclepias*, ×5; G, *Castilleja*, ×20; H, *Catalpa*, ×2.

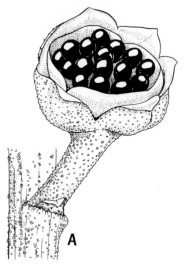

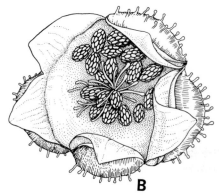

FIGURE 27–20   "Splash-cups." A, mitrewort (*Mitella*), ×5; B, pearlwort (*Sagina*), ×5. Under damp conditions, seeds are splashed out of capsules by rain. (B, after Gibbs.)

the tropical rain zone. Periodically the rush of water from mountains is tremendous. At such times vast numbers of seeds are brought down and strewn in suitable places for growing in the plains below. In general these occurrences are fortuitous, and the seeds show no special adaptation. In a few cases—e.g., pearlwort (*Sagina*) and mitrewort (*Mitella*)—the opened capsule with seeds lying in it strongly suggests a "splash-cup" mechanism so common in the fungi (Fig. 27–20).

Streams.   The fruits and seeds of many streamside and aquatic plants are adapted for floating for short periods of time, usually by reason of air trapped in some part of the disseminule—e.g., marsh marigold (*Caltha*) and several aquatic Umbelliferae with corky

mericarps. In some cases, seedlings are buoyant and are carried by water—e.g., loosestrife (*Lythrum*), monkey flower (*Mimulus*). Immersed and floating aquatics are also dispersed by streams through the transport of winter buds or fragments of the plants themselves.

Sudd.   This is the name given to dense masses of vegetation growing out from the banks of rivers and often blocking the channel. The whole mass, or a portion of it, may be torn away by a sudden flood and carried down the stream, often ending up in adjacent lakes or pools. Sudd usually occurs in slow-moving rivers in flat open country, such as the Nile or Ganges. Good examples of sudd plants are papyrus (*Cyperus papyrus*), water hyacinth (*Eichornia*), water chestnut (*Trapa*), and water lettuce (*Pistia*).

Oceans.   Ocean currents disperse plants over very long distances, certainly over 1,000 miles. For two reasons the number of species that can travel effectively in this manner is limited. First, the seed or fruit must be able to float for a long period without becoming waterlogged or germinating too soon. Second, the seeds must be ecologically adapted to establishment on the littoral conditions of a sand or mud bank. Species in many genera are so adapted—e.g., *Erythrina* (Papilionaceae), *Cakile* (Cruciferae), *Arenaria peploides* (Caryophyllaceae), *Calophyllum* (Guttiferae), *Hibiscus tileaceus* (Malvaceae), *Carapa* (Meliaceae), all species of Rhizophoraceae, *Ipomoea* (Convolvulaceae), and *Cocos nucifera* (Palmae).

DISPERSAL BY ANIMALS

Transport by animals may be either internal or external.

Ingestion of Fruits and Seeds.   Birds and mammals eat fleshy fruits of many kinds and pass the seeds through the alimentary tract unharmed, and even with germinability increased. It appears that the majority of fruits with a fleshy pericarp are specially adapted for this mode of dissemination; common examples are cherry (*Prunus*), raspberry (*Rubus*), currants and gooseberries (*Ribes*), Oregon grape (*Mahonia*), and flowering dogwood (*Cornus nut-*

tallii). Herbivorous animals may ingest small seeds with foliage and not harm them by chewing; good examples include seeds of some of the Papilionaceae, and the small dry fruits of Gramineae.

Ants. One investigator has reported that the fruits and seeds of species from more than 60 genera are disseminated locally by various kinds of ants—sometimes over 30 meters. The majority of these fruits or seeds are provided with special oil bodies (elaiosomes) which may be of very diverse morphology and origin. About a dozen types of such disseminules can be distinguished depending on the part of the flower, fruit, or seed which bears the elaiosomes.

Adhesion to Fur and Feathers. The adaptations in these cases are generally well known and consist of the development of prickles, hooks, spines, hairs, and sticky or viscid fruits and seeds. The whole inflorescence may be involved as in the burdock (*Arctium*) with its hooked involucral bracts; in *Agrimonia* there is a crown of incurved prickles on the outside of the receptacle; in many Compositae (e.g., *Bidens*) the pappus may develop **awns** that are often barbed; many species of Boraginaceae and *Galium* have various forms of hooks on the exocarp; the style too may become hooked as in some species of *Geum;* many grass fruits are provided with awns or stiff hairs on the florets; in some plants, such as the twinflower (*Linnaea borealis*), the bracts bear adhesive viscid glands, with the abscission of the fruit taking place below the bract; viscid, glandular involucral bracts are not uncommon in Compositae (e.g., *Adenocaulon*); viscid hairs on the calyx are found in *Plumbago;* and in certain species of Gramineae, *Juncus* and *Plantago,* a very adhesive, mucilaginous secretion is evident on wetting the fruits or seeds (Fig. 27–21).

The fruits of one family, the Pedaliaceae, are characterized by highly specialized and most formidable hooks in almost all genera. In the mule-grab (*Proboscidea*) the woody fusiform capsules are about 8 cm long, ending in two curved sharp claws 15 cm long. The fruit lies on the ground with the claws upward; if an animal steps on it, the fruit tips up and the claws clasp the fetlock. The seeds are shed from the capsule as the animal moves about. In the South African genus *Harpagophytum* (grapple plant) the woody fruit has four wings, each cut into a number of very stout linear arms with many strong hooks chiefly on the tips of the arms. The fruits become attached, almost irremovably, to the feet or tail of any large animal unfortunate enough to come in contact with them. Again the seeds are dislodged from the capsule as the animal moves about (Fig. 27–22).

The tropical and subtropical genus *Pisonia* (Nyctaginaceae) has one-seeded fruits covered by an extremely sticky perianth tube. So viscid and glutinous are the fruits that they sometimes trap small birds that cannot disentangle themselves. It is said that the ancient Hawaiians actually used gum from a species of *Pisonia* for catching birds. There can be no question that this exudate causes the fruits to adhere firmly to the feathers of birds with consequent dispersal. The missel thrush has long been associated with the European mistletoe (*Viscum album*) because the birds feed on the berries. The flesh of the berries contains an abundance of a glutinous material which is only partially digested by passage through the alimentary tract. The excreted seeds and skins of the fruit are stuck together by the gluten, and the mass frequently becomes securely fastened to the branches of trees. Also, seeds may become attached to the bills of missel thrushes after berries are eaten. Such seeds may be removed when rubbed against the bark of a branch and so placed in position for germination.

Adhesion of Small Disseminules. A large number of plants probably owe their distribution to the adherence of disseminules to the fur, feathers, or feet of passing mammals and birds. These disseminules are mostly picked up in mud and show no particular adaptations except their small size. This form of dispersal is especially likely for the seeds and fruits of water and marsh plants. In the *Origin of Species,* Darwin reports an examination and study he made of about half a pound of dried mud. He wet it and

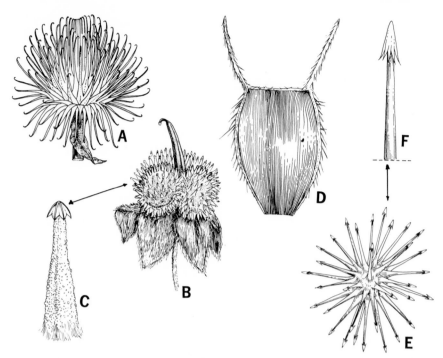

FIGURE 27–21   Animal-dispersed fruits. A, *Arctium minus*, involucral bracts with stiff hooked tips, ×2; B, *Cynoglossum officinale*, nutlets covered with short barbed spines, ×2; C, single spine of *Cynoglossum*, ×20; D, *Bidens*, pappus represented by two stiff barbed awns, ×10; E, *Acaena*, with sepals sharp and spiny, ×7.5; F, showing grapnel-like tips of sepaline spines in *Acaena*, ×25.

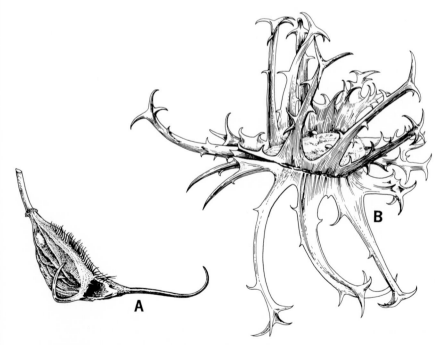

FIGURE 27–22   Fruits highly specialized for animal dispersal. A, *Proboscidea*, ×0.5; B, *Harpagophytum*, ×0.5. Both are capsular fruits.

kept it covered under conditions suitable for germination. In the course of six months no less than 537 seedlings of various species appeared. In another case he took a ball of mud from the leg of a partridge, and from this raised 84 plants of three species. Man himself has been an active agent in dispersal through the attachment of mud to his boots and his vehicles.

MECHANICAL DISPERSAL

In some species—mostly herbaceous—the mature fruit explodes and throws its seeds a considerable distance from the parent plant. Such fruits are found in many families, but even within a genus the species may differ in discharge of seeds. Best known is perhaps the touch-me-not (*Impatiens*—Fig. 27–23D). Its fleshy capsules are often somewhat dilated at the upper end where the seeds are borne. The pericarp develops a high turgor pressure and elastic cell walls. As the fruit ripens, it separates from the ovary, and the valves become only very slightly coherent. When ripe, the valves separate suddenly, either spontaneously or when touched. Each valve curls inward with considerable force and throws the seeds for some distance. Certain species of *Oxalis* have developed a similar mechanism.

Species of *Geranium* have evolved a very ingenious sort of sling mechanism that is remarkably efficient (Fig. 27–23B). The fruit is a schizocarp consisting of five carpels, each containing a single seed. In effect, the seeds are each in a pouch at the base of a somewhat elongated beak-like stylar column. As the fruit ripens, the outer tissues of this column split suddenly into five springs that curve up and out, slinging out the seeds for a distance of a meter or more. In the witch hazel (*Hamamelis*) the fruit is a woody capsule with two valves that split apart at the top when dry, exposing two black seeds in each valve. As the fruit dries further, the endocarp contracts, discharging the seeds with great force as far as 14 meters (Fig. 27–23E).

The dehiscence of the fruits of many legumes is related to a hygroscopic mechanism. The different layers of the pericarp contract to different extents as they dry out, so that considerable tensions are set up between them. When these tensions overcome the cohesion of the cell walls, the walls suddenly separate. In many instances the valves of the legume flick into a spiral and forcibly eject the seeds (Fig. 27–23A). It is usual for the separation to be both violent and rapid, so that the seeds are discharged for a distance of a meter or more.

Quite a different kind of dehiscing mechanism is found in the squirting cucumber (*Ecballium elaterium*), a trailing herb of dry Mediterranean regions (Fig. 27–23C). The fruit is an oblong berry about 5 cm in length borne on a stout pedicel. The apex of the pedicel projects into the base of the fruit like a stopper. When the fruit is ripe, the tissues around the stopper break down and its connection with the fruit becomes loosened. The seeds by this time are surrounded by a mass of semi-liquid mucilage. A considerable turgor pressure builds up inside the fruit, distending the outer layers and putting them in a state of tension. Finally, the tissue at the base of the pedicel breaks, and it is blown out like a cork; the wall of the fruit contracts, discharging the whole juicy contents, including the seeds which travel some distance.

POLLINATION

Another interesting evolutionary study in the anthophytes is the relationship between floral morphology and pollination. Pollination in the flowering plants can be defined as the transfer of pollen from an anther to a stigma. This is brought about in a great variety of ways, many of which are remarkably ingenious and show a high degree of adaptation and specialization. There is a vast literature on the subject, and only some of the highlights can be sketched here. For further details and a selected bibliography, consult Meeuse's recent book, *The Story of Pollination*.

A mystical relationship between pollen and the formation of fruit was apparently known to the ancient Mesopotamians in the ninth century B.C. Bas-reliefs of this period

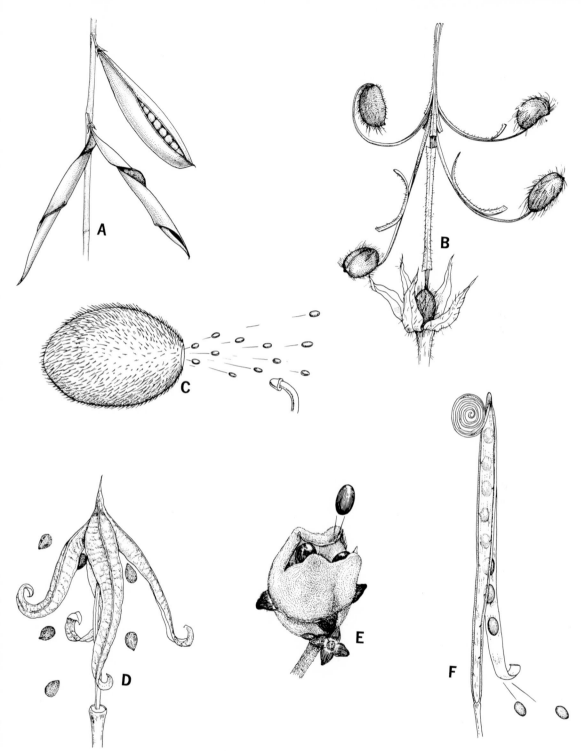

FIGURE 27–23   Examples of mechanically dispersed seeds. A, *Vicia gigantea* (Leguminosae), ×1; B, *Geranium bicknellii* (Geraniaceae), ×4; C, *Ecballium elaterium* (Cucurbitaceae), ×0.5; D, *Impatiens aurella* (Balsaminaceae), ×6; E, *Hamamelis virginiana* (Hamamelidaceae), ×3; F, *Cardamine hirsuta* (Cruciferae), ×4. (C, after Kerner v. Marilaun and Oliver.)

illustrate a ceremonial dusting of the fruit-bearing date palms with the inflorescences from pollen-producing plants. However, this practical folk lore was without any scientific basis until toward the end of the seventeenth century A.D. when Nehemiah Grew wrote that the grains within the stamens represented male parts, and the seed-producing parts were female. The first recorded experiments on sex in plants are those of Camerarius in 1694. He discovered that unless pollen came in contact with a stigma, fruit would not develop.

Now we have very precise information on pollination in many instances. Pollination can be carried out by a number of agencies. The most important are wind **(anemophily)**, insects **(entomophily)**, and birds **(ornithophily)**; pollination by bats **(chiropterophily)** and water **(hydrophily)** occur, but are relatively uncommon.

ANEMOPHILY

The earliest seed plants probably were wind-pollinated, as in most modern gymnosperms. However, in many angiosperms there is good evidence that wind pollination has been acquired and that the flowers probably have been derived from entomophilous ancestors. A case in point is the meadow rue (*Thalictrum*). This genus belongs to a family (Ranunculaceae) noted for brilliant flowers and considerable specialization for insect visits, yet it lacks a corolla and is wind-pollinated. In other families, such as the Ulmaceae and Fagaceae, it is quite possible that primitive anemophily persists.

In general, anemophilous flowers are marked by negative characteristics. They have no nectar, scent, or brilliantly colored perianth parts. On the positive side, we find special features of the stamens, stigmas, and pollen grains. The anthers are often suspended from long filaments hanging free from the flower. In catkin inflorescences whole flowers are swayed by the wind, and the pollen is dislodged and caught up in air currents (Fig. 27–24). The stigmas, like the stamens, are freely exposed; they are often branched, feathery, or provided with brush-like outgrowths suitable for inter-cepting air-borne pollen (Fig. 27–25). The pollen grains are generally small, smooth, and produced in very large quantities.

ENTOMOPHILY

Although the first seed plants probably were wind-pollinated, irregular insect visits to flowers may have occurred even in the seed ferns. The insects of the Carboniferous had biting jaws, rather than mouth parts adapted for sucking nectar. Part of their food may have been fleshy sporophylls and possibly even spores. It was not until the Tertiary, when flowering plants predominated and most modern families became differentiated, that most contemporary orders of insects also appeared. It is almost certain that the intimate association between particular flowers and their insect visitors began during several epochs of the Tertiary.

An insect visits a flower to obtain food, either in the form of nectar or sometimes of pollen. Nectar is a watery fluid, about 25 per cent glucose, secreted by special glands known as nectaries. In different genera and species nectaries differ in their nature and position; they may be extrafloral or floral. Floral nectaries can be associated with a variety of organs and may occupy a number of positions. In fact, almost any part of the flower may secrete nectar (Fig. 27–26).

Insects are attracted to flowers chiefly by color and scent, and the appeal of the two attractants varies with the type of insect visitor. Much experimental work has been done on the color perception of different kinds of insects. We know that bees, for example, can see yellows, blues, and purples—which explains why bee flowers characteristically have these colors. However, bees do not necessarily prefer these colors because they are attracted by them. Rather, bees distinguish these colors and associate them with nectar. In different species of flowers, different means of guiding the way to the nectar have evolved (Fig. 27–27, 28D). Sometimes it is a vivid patch of color in sharp contrast to the background color of the corolla, as in forget-me-not (*Myosotis*), certain irises (*Iris*), and toadflax (*Linaria*); some flowers

FIGURE 27–24   Anemophilous flowers. *Garrya elliptica,* ×1. Male catkin is shown; female flowers are in similarly pendant catkins.

have a set of darker stripes or streaks of dots—e.g., nasturtium (*Tropaeolum*), broom (*Sarcothamnus*), violet (*Viola*), foxglove (*Digitalis*), and monkey flower (*Mimulus*).

Many details of floral structure can be related to the morphology, size, and habits of particular insects, and the way they visit a flower. Entomophilous flowers have been divided into a number of classes, partly on the basis of their structure and partly according to their insect visitors. Only some of these types of flowers will be discussed briefly below.

Pollen Flowers. These lack nectar but have an abundance of pollen which is gathered

FIGURE 27–25   Anemophilous flowers. *Corylus
avellana,* ×2. Male flowers are in pendant catkins,
female in short budlike spike with conspicuous
stigmas.

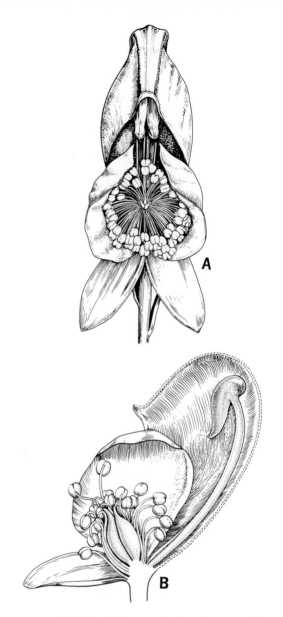

FIGURE 27–26   Flower of *Aconitum napellus,*
×2. A, front elevation; B, median section showing
in hood one of two posterior petals modified to
nectary.

for food, especially by bees and certain beetles.
Pollen flowers include poppy (*Papaver*), rose
(*Rosa*), and rockrose (*Cistus*). In *Cassia,* spe-
cial sterile stamens produce "food pollen."

Hymenoptera Flowers.   These are visited
almost exclusively by bees. The specialized
morphology of the flowers permits the visit of
only one particular insect or of a limited group
of about the same size. In some of these flowers
the nectar is so deeply located in a tube that
only an insect with a very long tongue or proboscis can reach it. A good example is red
clover (*Trifolium*) (Fig. 27–28H, I), where

the nectar is situated about 9 mm from the
mouth of the flower and is available only to
bumble bees. In others, the parts of the corolla
are so firm that only a heavy insect can open the
flower—e.g., snapdragon (*Antirrhinum*) and
broom (*Sarcothamnus*) (Fig. 27–28A–C). In
markedly zygomorphic flowers a landing stage
for the insect is combined with nectar at the

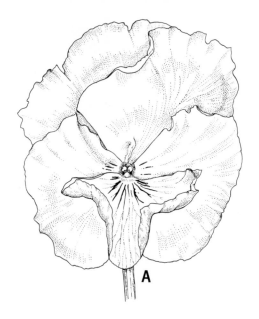

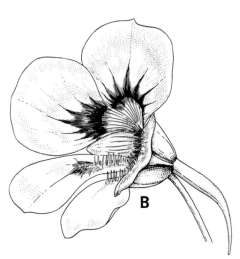

FIGURE 27–27   Honey guides. A, *Viola,* ×1;
B, *Tropolaeum,* ×1.

base of a long corolla tube, or at the base of
spurs. Examples include sage (*Salvia*—Fig.
27–28E–G), monkshood (*Aconitum*—Fig.
27–26), violet (*Viola*), and many Orchidaceae. In many such flowers, small flies and
beetles may be prevented from entering by hairs
or scales at the throat of the corolla.

Lepidoptera Flowers. Most of these flowers are actinomorphic, and their insect visitors
hover while feeding. A rather usual characteristic is a somewhat pungent but aromatic scent.

In flowers such as tobacco (*Nicotiana*), night-
scented stock (*Matthiola*), and night-blooming
cacti—which are pollinated by night-flying
moths—the scent is much stronger in the evening. This type of flower is usually relatively large
and pale, and presumably can be distinguished
better by insects as a result.

Many lepidopterous flowers have nectar
concealed in spurs. A classical case is a Madagascar orchid (*Anagraecum sesquipedale*),
which carries its nectar at the bottom of a
slender spur nearly 30 cm long (Fig. 27–29).
Alfred Wallace predicted that an insect would
some day be discovered with a tongue long
enough to reach the nectar. Thirty years passed
before a moth with such a tongue was found
and Wallace's prediction justified.

Diptera Flowers. These are visited
largely by flies and are generally less specialized
than the last two types. Floral morphology in
itself is probably only important in such cases
as the speedwell (*Veronica*), pollinated by
hover flies (Fig. 27–30C–E). The corolla is
slightly zygomorphic, with the somewhat larger
posterior petal formed by the cohesion of two
petals. There are only two stamens with long,
widely divergent filaments. A long slender style
with a small capitate stigma is positioned over
the anterior petal. A nectary located at the base
of the corolla tube is protected by hairs. In
pollination the lower (posterior) petal acts as a
landing platform on which a fly alights and
comes in contact with the style. If the fly is
carrying pollen on its ventral surface, pollination is effected. In trying to reach the nectar,
the fly grasps the filaments of the two stamens,
draws them under its body, and is dusted with
pollen.

The starflowers (*Stapelia*) of South African deserts may be taken as an example of
another class of dipterous flowers—those that
attract flies by a somewhat nauseous odor reminiscent of rotting meat (Fig. 27–31C). In *Stapelia* the flowers not only smell but also look
like rotten meat. The female carrion flies are
attracted to the blossoms, pollinate them, and
are so completely fooled that they lay their eggs
(or deposit their larvae) on the perianth; finding no food, the larvae perish. Carrion flies are

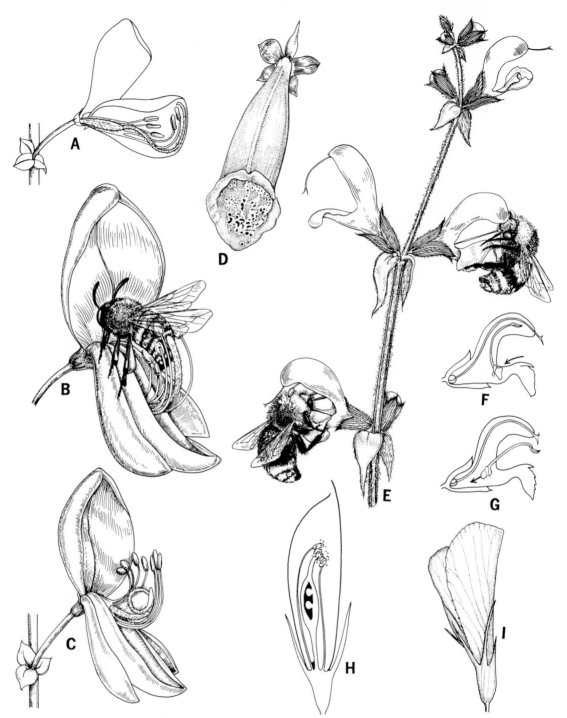

FIGURE 27–28   Hymenopterous flowers. A–C, *Sarcothamnus scoparius*. A, median section of flower showing stamens and style concealed within the keel, ×1; B, visit of heavy insect depresses keel and triggers explosive upward movement of stamens so they come in contact with belly and back of visitor, with stigma touching back, ×2; C, a "tripped" flower showing further coiling of style, ×1. D, *Digitalis purpurea,* ×1. E–G, *Salvia pratensis,* ×1. E, bumblebees visiting flowers; F, G, median sections of flowers, showing pivot mechanism at base of filament which brings anther down on back of bee, ×1. H, I, *Trifolium*-type flower in section and side views, nectary shown at base of carpel, ×5. (A–G, adapted from *The Story of Pollination,* by B. J. D. Meeuse, copyright © 1961, The Ronald Press Company, New York; H–I, after Hagerup and Petersson with permission of Ejnar Munksgaard.)

FIGURE 27–29   Lepidopterous flowers. A, *Anagraecum sesquipedale*, showing long slender spur, ×1; B, *Lilium martagon*, showing hawk moth taking
nectar from petal pouch, ×1; C, *Phyllanthus*, night-blooming cactus, ×1. (B,
after Ross and Morin.)

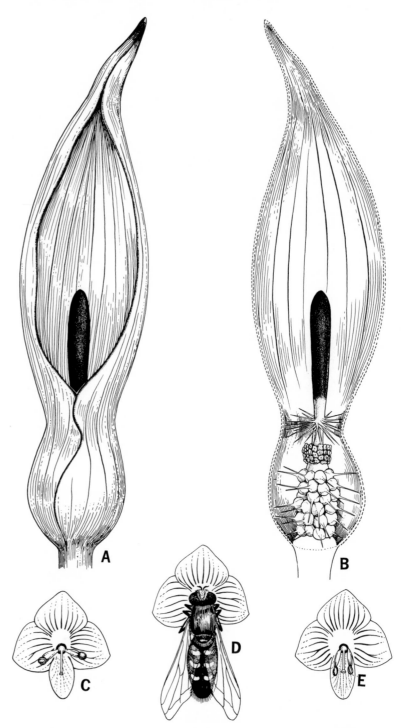

FIGURE 27–30   Dipterous flowers. A, B, *Arum maculatum.* A, inflorescence enclosed by spathe, upper part of spadix visible, ×2; B, portion of spathe removed to show sterile male flowers at constriction of spathe, functional male flowers immediately below them, and female flowers at base of spadix, ×2. C–E, *Veronica,* flowers before (C), during (D), and after (E) visit of crescent fly, ×2. (C–E, adapted from *The Story of Pollination,* by B. J. D. Meeuse, copyright © 1961, The Ronald Press Company, New York.)

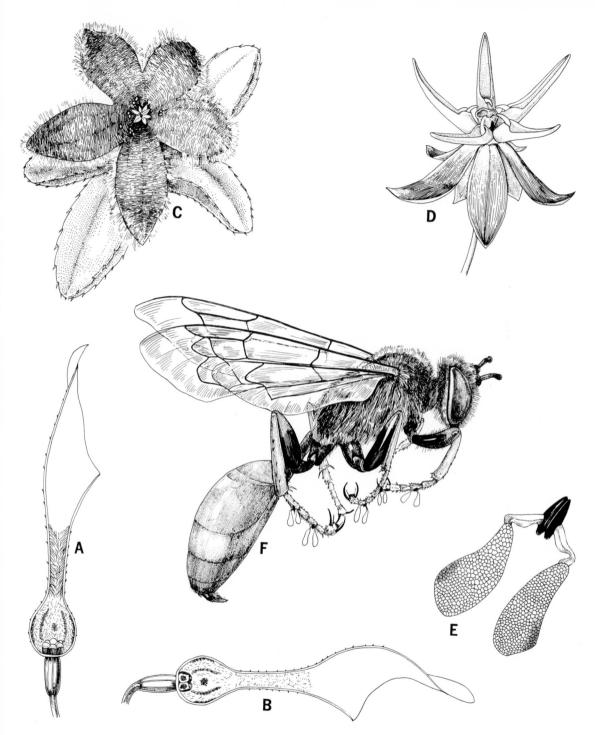

FIGURE 27–31   A, B, Dutchman's pipe (*Aristolochia sipho*). A, flower erect (stiff downward-pointing hairs on inner wall prevent escape of trapped small flies), ×2; B, flower limp and hairs wilted so that flies can escape, ×2. C, *Stapelia grandiflora,* with flower showing small masses of larvae near base of petals, ×0.5. D–F, milkweed (*Asclepias speciosa*). D, flower with five scoop-shaped nectaries and translator as dark spot between two, ×2; E, pair of pollinia suspended from translator, ×15; F, dead insect with pollinia caught on its legs, ×5. (A, B, adapted from *The Story of Pollination,* by B. J. D. Meeuse, copyright © 1961, The Ronald Press Company, New York.)

also attracted by the odor of the small European spotted arum lily (*Arum maculatum*—Fig. 27–30A, B). What is often referred to as the flower of this species is an inflorescence of a spadix, bearing numerous flowers enveloped by a large bract, the spathe. There are two sets of flowers, female at the bottom and male above; the topmost flowers are sterile and modified into a set of bristles. The upper part of the inflorescence is a naked reddish-brown **appendix,** the source of a very unpleasant smell. Small flies attracted to the appendix slide down the smooth surface of the spathe past the male flowers to the female flowers below. Their attempts to escape up the spadix are thwarted by the bristly palisade of the sterile male flowers, and they become trapped for a day. During this time they crawl over the stigmas, dusting them with any pollen adhering to their lower surfaces. On the second day the anthers of the male flowers dehisce, the bristles wilt, and the flies are freed to visit another inflorescence and continue their role of pollinators. The Dutchman's pipe (*Aristolochia*) has a somewhat similar gnat trap, although in this instance only a single flower is involved rather than an inflorescence (Fig. 27–31A, B).

ORNITHOPHILY

Birds of various kinds are important pollinating agents for a number of tropical and subtropical species. Birds active in this respect are sunbirds, honeysuckers, and humming birds—some of which are no larger than moths. Bird flowers and insect flowers are often much alike, and certainly more similar to one another than either is to wind flowers. Their colors are bright and intense, with reds predominating to the extent of more than 80 per cent in 159 species studied. Brilliant color contrasts are common, as in the bird-of-paradise flower (*Strelitzia reginae*). Most bird flowers lack scent. Meeuse states that approximately 2,000 species of birds belonging to about 50 families visit flowers more or less regularly, with about two thirds of these relying on flowers as their most important source of food. Since these bird

visitors vary so much in size and feeding habits, no one type of flower particularly adapted to bird visits has evolved. However, individually some do show special features.

Bird flowers often secrete an abundance of thin nectar. It is said that each flower of the coral tree (*Erythrina*) contains about a thimbleful. In some bird flowers the floral parts—particularly the filaments, styles, and stigmas—are quite rigid, perhaps enabling them to withstand the vigorous attentions of their visitors. Some birds, such as hummingbirds, hover while feeding on the nectar; for others a perch may be provided by a modified bract, as in *Strelitzia*. Although birds visit flowers generally for nectar, it seems likely that in some instances the purpose of the visit is actually to feed on small insects attracted by the nectar.

CHIROPTEROPHILY

There is now evidence that a surprising number of tropical trees are pollinated by bats. Two distinct types of bats are involved; the Central and South American flower bats are related to insectivores, whereas those of Africa and Asia are related to fruit-eating bats. Bat flowers open at dusk, have copious nectar, are dull in color, and frequently have a repulsive mouse-like odor that apparently is attractive to their visitors. As is to be expected, bat flowers are arranged so that bats can get at them easily. The flowers may be suspended on long stalks, as in the sausage tree (*Kigelia*—Fig. 27–32, 33); attached to the tree trunk, as in the cannonball tree (*Couroupita*); or in inflorescences standing well into the air, as in some wild bananas (*Musa*) and the southeast Asian liana *Freycinetia*.

HYDROPHILY

Certain immersed hydrophytes (e.g., *Ceratophyllum*) are monoecious; the ovulate flowers remain below the water level, and the staminate flowers shed their pollen into the water. The pollen is of the same specific gravity

FIGURE 27–32   Sausage tree (*Kigelia*), showing fruits hanging on long stalks. (Adapted from *The Story of Pollination,* by B. J. D. Meeuse, copyright © 1961, The Ronald Press Company, New York.)

as the water and so is dispersed through it; eventually some of the pollen comes into contact with the stigmas. A more ingenious arrangement has evolved in the ribbon grass (*Vallisneria*—Fig. 27–34). It is dioecious; the ovulate flower buds start out as buds well below the surface of the water. As these mature, the pedicel becomes much elongated and spiraled, eventually raising the flower to the surface of the water, where it floats. The flower then opens and lies, with its stigmas recurved, in a dimple on the water surface. The minute staminate flowers, only about 1 mm in diameter, are pro-

duced by the hundred from a single inflorescence. Each flower consists of two stamens enclosed by a perianth of two large segments and one small one. The whole flower is shed under water and gradually floats to the surface. Here it opens and the perianth recurves to form a little tripod support for the flower. The staminate flowers drift about on the surface of the water until they come close to an ovulate flower and are drawn into the dimple by surface tension. Pollination is effected when the staminate flowers are tipped over so that the anthers touch the stigmas.

DIVISION ANTHOPHYTA / 579

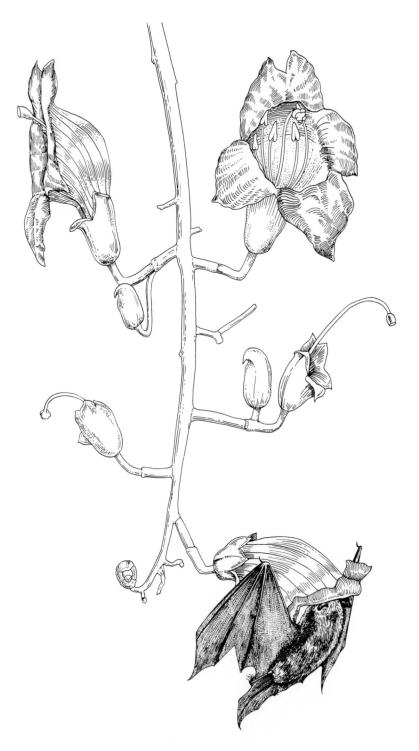

FIGURE 27–33   Bat pollinating flower of sausage tree (*Kigelia*), ×0.5. (Adapted from *The Story of Pollination*, by B. J. D. Meeuse, copyright © 1961, The Ronald Press Company, New York.)

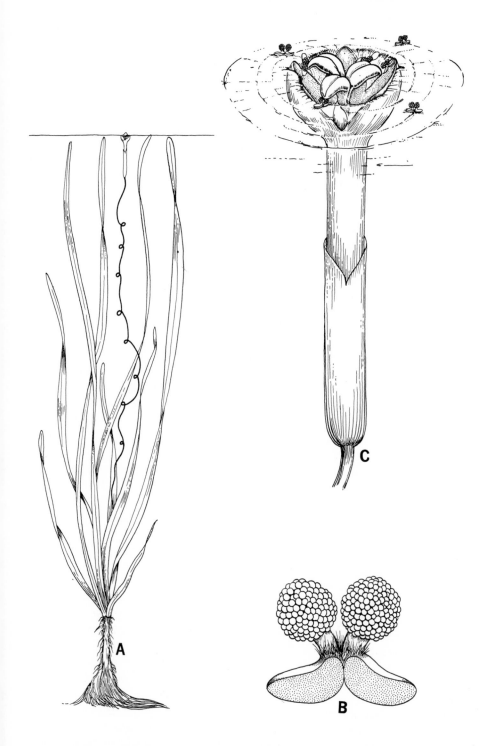

FIGURE 27–34　*Vallisneria americana.* A, female plant showing flower floating on surface of water, ×0.2; B, male flower, ×5; C, boatlike male flowers
coming in contact with stigmas, ×15. (B, after Gleason with permission of
New York Botanical Garden.)

To show the high degree of specialization for pollination achieved by some plants, four special cases will be described. All involve insects as agents, but the mechanisms are very different in each case.

Milkweeds (Asclepiadaceae). In this family (Fig. 27–31D–F) the five anthers are fused into a ring around the gynoecium of two carpels. Each anther bears a cup-like nectary in the shape of a horn. There is a narrow vertical slit between adjacent anthers, but the pollen masses **(pollinia)** of these adjacent anthers are fastened together by a little horny clip that can usually be seen quite readily as a dark dot. When an insect crawls over the flower seeking nectar, its legs are likely to slip into the slit between the anthers. As the insect tries to withdraw, bristles on its leg catch on the clip, pulling the clip and the securely attached pollinia free from the pollen sacs. The insect then departs with one or more of these little saddlebags of pollen suspended from bristles on its legs. If the insect visits another flower of the same species, a funnel-shaped cavity guides the pollinia down to the stigma, thus pollinating the flower. Sometimes the pollinia do not break away from the clip, with the result that the insect is trapped. It is not unusual to find in an inflorescence a number of dead flies and even bees caught in this way.

Spanish Bayonet (Yucca). A completely obligate relationship seems to exist between the Spanish bayonet and a small moth (*Pronuba*). Yuccas grown beyond the range of the moth will produce flowers but never set seed. The moth, on the other hand, appears to be quite dependent on the yucca as an egg-laying site. The flowers of all species of *Yucca* are borne in large panicles; the flowers are pendent, pale creamy in color, and somewhat bell-shaped. When the buds open in the evening, they are visited by *Pronuba* females that creep into the flowers and gather pollen from the small anthers. The pollen is somewhat sticky and is rolled into a tight little ball and held by the specialized mouthparts of the insect. After collecting all the pollen it can carry, the moth flies to another flower, pierces the ovary wall with its long ovipositor, and lays a batch of eggs among the young ovules. It then crawls down the style and pushes its ball of pollen into the cavity between the lobes of the stigma. The moth larvae hatch out in a few days and live on the developing seeds; when fully developed, they gnaw their way through the ovary wall, lower themselves to the ground, and pupate until the yuccas bloom again. Although about 20 per cent of the yucca seeds are destroyed in this fashion, this is a small price to pay for such efficient pollinating service.

Figs (Ficus). As far as is known, all species of the extremely large tropical and subtropical genus *Ficus* are pollinated by small chalcid wasps, and several genera are involved. Here, too, the relationship is obligatory and sometimes very complex. The cultivated fig (*Ficus carica*) of southern Europe is pollinated by a single species of wasp (*Blastophaga grossorum*) with a very complicated life history (Fig. 27–35). As mentioned previously, the fruits of *Ficus* are compound structures made up of the flattened axis of the inflorescence which becomes a hollow inverted urn with a small apical pore opening to the outside. Flowers line the inside of this urn. *Ficus carica* is monoecious and bears three generations of flowers and fruits in a year. The first is formed in February and contains staminate flowers formed chiefly around the pore, with abortive ovulate "gall flowers" lower down. The gall flower has a rudimentary ovary, a short style with an open canal, and a single rudimentary ovule incapable of forming a seed. Female wasps enter the syconium and deposit a single egg in the ovule of each gall flower. Here the larvae hatch out, feed, grow, and undergo metamorphosis. The male wasps gnaw their way out, locate the gall flowers containing females, pierce the wall of the ovary, and fertilize the females within. The male wasps then die without leaving the syconium. By this time the fruit is ripe, though tough and bitter, and the staminate flowers are shedding their pollen. The gravid female wasps leave the gall flowers and crawl out through the pore of the syconium, becoming dusted with pollen on the way.

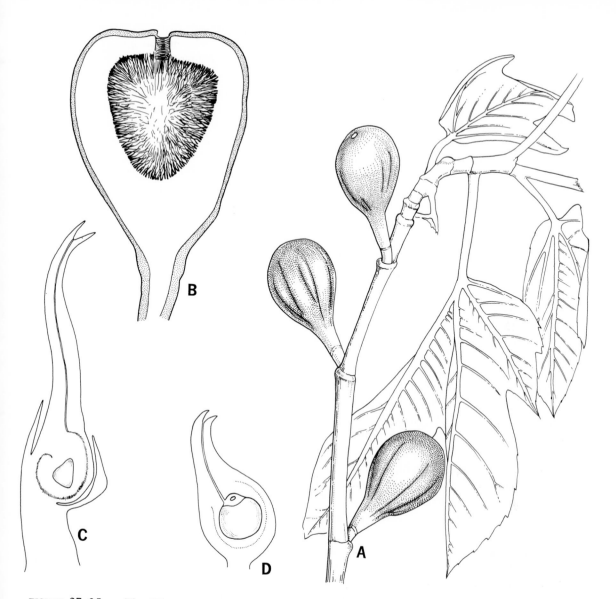

FIGURE 27–35   Fig (*Ficus carica*). A, fruiting branch with syconia, ×1; B, syconium in longitudinal section, showing apical pore (flowers line the urn-shaped interior), ×2; C, normal female flower, ×10; D, gall flower (sterile female flower), ×10. (B, after LeMaout and Decaisne; C, D, after Condit with permission of *Hilgardia*.)

This generation of wasps is very sedentary and flies very little. The wasps crawl about on the tree in search of young syconia in which to lay their eggs. These they find in the second generation of figs, which develops toward the end of May. These syconia, however, contain only normal ovulate flowers with long styles; the wasps try in vain to lay their eggs, and in so doing deposit pollen on the stigmas. These syconia ripen to become fleshy and edible. In the meantime the third generation of fruits is developing. Females finally make their way into these and lay their eggs in the gall flowers, which are the only kind present. Here the larvae pass the winter, emerging in the spring to repeat the cycle.

The cultivated fig, with its numerous varieties, is derived from the wild *Ficus carica*. It exists in two races, the fig and the caprifig, and it has been known since very early times that both races must be present in order to produce a crop of fruits. Although both races produce three generations of syconia each year, the caprifig bears staminate flowers and gall flowers; the fig only ovulate flowers. This means that the caprifig is essentially male, the fig female. We have here a very unusual instance in which a monoecious wild plant has been changed by selection into a dioecious cultivated form. When the Smyrna variety of fig was first introduced into California, it was found necessary to introduce the caprifig as well as the *Blastophaga* in order to obtain a crop. Certain varieties of fig develop edible, fleshy fruits parthenocarpically. However, these do not keep well and cannot be dried; the dried figs of commerce always contain aborted "seeds".

Orchids. The floral mechanisms of the Orchidaceae in all their variety have been given a great deal of attention ever since they attracted the interest of Charles Darwin, who published the first comprehensive monograph on the subject. Although the general principle of the pollinating mechanism is the same for the great majority of orchids, no two species agree in detail. Orchid flowers are highly specialized in relation to their insect visitors, so much so that in some instances the flowers are only attractive to and visited by the males of a single species of insect. The flowers show a bewildering number of variations on a basic morphological theme (Fig. 27–36). The special feature of the corolla is that the median petal is often much enlarged, or otherwise modified to form the lip, or labellum. The androecium is reduced to one or two functional stamens, and is united to an extension of the gynoecium to form the column. The pollen is granular and generally bound together by threads of viscin to form two pollinia, the basal portions of which are often contracted into a filamentous stalk, the caudicle. The stigma, also, is much modified. In *Cypripedium* all three stigmatic lobes are functional, but more often only the two posterior ones are receptive. The third is sterile and modified into a small beak, the rostellum, which lies below the anthers and between the

functional stigmas. In highly specialized genera the rostellum becomes an integral part of the pollinia, and is then modified into a viscid disc to which the caudicles are attached. Many orchid flowers are provided with a spur containing nectar for the attraction of insects. The visitor lands on the labellum, which is so arranged that the head of the insect comes into contact with the sticky disc. When the insect withdraws its head from the flower, the pollinia become attached to it and are carried away worn like a pair of horns. As the caudicles dry out they bend downward in position to touch the stigmas of the next flower visited.

TAXONOMY

During the 150,000,000 years or so that the Anthophyta have been evolving, they have diverged tremendously from their ancestral stock. Whether they are monophyletic or polyphyletic in origin is a very interesting and important philosophical question, but is not one that can concern us in this discussion. Contemporary flowering plants show an almost staggering diversity of form and feature. Man at different times, and for different reasons, has tried to bring some order out of this chaos by devising schemes of classification. As interest in plants has changed, and as more and more information concerning plants has been added to our common pool of knowledge, so one method of classification has replaced another. The various systems of classification that have been used or proposed give us a history of one aspect of botanical philosophy.

In the pages that follow no attempt is made to present the anthophyte flora of even one continent, such as North America, in broadest outline. Instead, a number of the more prominent orders and families have been selected for brief description to give the reader some appreciation of the systematic features of flowering plants. Many different classifications of flowering plants have been proposed. At the present time taxonomists are somewhat divided in their views on the probable relationships between certain orders and families; there are

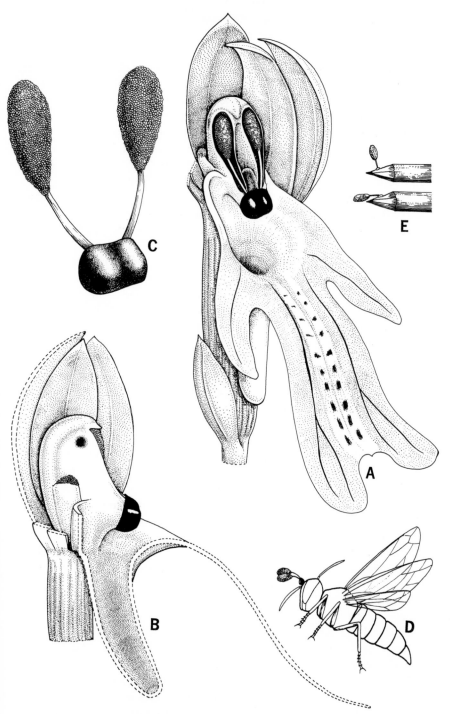

FIGURE 27–36   *Orchis militaris*. A, view of flower with one sepal and one petal removed to show central column formed of fused androecium and gynoecium (note labellum and spur), ×6. B, semidiagrammatic median section showing lateral functional stigmatic lobe, with sterile stigmatic lobe modified into beaklike rostellum (lies between two pollinia), ×6. C, pair of pollinia with their caudicles and viscidium, ×15. D, insect with two pollinia attached to its forehead by viscidium, ×2. E (top), pollinia when first attached; (bottom) pollinia depressed forward as result of unequal drying of caudicles, ×0.5. (E, after Darwin.)

even opposing schools of thought on the limits of certain higher taxa. It is a matter of debate in particular instances just where to draw a boundary. However, it is doubtful if any modern taxonomist is satisfied with the sequence of families still currently followed in most floras and texts. For the great majority of living flowering plants we have no direct knowledge of the course of evolutionary history. In general, the fossil record of anthophytes is much too fragmentary to be built upon, and so we can only theorize about their possible phylogenetic connections. In a very few instances the fossil record is sufficiently complete to give a good idea of evolution. Hutchinson, Takhtajan, Cronquist, and others have proposed considerable modifications in trying to integrate into a coherent pattern contemporary evidence drawn from many new lines of investigation (Fig. 27–37). The sequence of orders that follows is Hutchinson's; in most cases only a single family is described.

CLASS DICOTYLEDONAE

ORDER MAGNOLIALES. This order, made up entirely of woody genera, is generally considered to be the most primitive order of existing dicotyledons. The flowers are usually perfect, although they may be unisexual when the perianth is reduced. The floral parts are free, the stamens and carpels are often numerous, and the ovaries are superior. The order is mainly north temperate in distribution.

Family Magnoliaceae. The family Magnoliaceae contains only trees and shrubs. The simple alternate leaves may be deciduous or evergreen. The stipules are often large and may be folded over the young buds. The flowers are actinomorphic and showy; the perianth is not always well differentiated into calyx and corolla. There are frequently three sepals, whereas there may be six or more petals. The numerous separate stamens and carpels are spirally arranged on an elongated receptacle.

This family is largely north temperate and tropical in distribution. Many species of *Magnolia* are cultivated, and the wood of the tulip tree (*Liriodendron*) is used for cabinet making and furniture.

ORDER ROSALES. This order includes trees, shrubs, and herbs with alternate, usually stipulate leaves. The flowers are actinomorphic with separate petals. The stamens are mostly free and **perigynous** to **epigynous.** The carpels may be free, or variously united and then the ovary is often inferior. The order occurs mainly in north temperate regions.

Family Rosaceae. In this family the leaves may be of various types, either simple or compound, sometimes with gland-tipped teeth. The stipules are frequently adnate to the petiole. As a rule the flowers are perfect, mostly with five sepals and petals and numerous free stamens. The carpels range from one to many and may be free or variously united. This large family is noteworthy for the great variety of its fruits, which include achenes, follicles, drupes, and pomes.

Although mainly north temperate, the Rosaceae are cosmopolitan in distribution. The family contributes many of our most desirable fruits, such as apple (*Malus*); pear (*Pyrus*); cherry, plum, peach, apricot (species of *Prunus*); loganberry, raspberry, blackberry (species of *Rubus*); strawberry (*Fragaria*); and loquat (*Eriobotrya*). The Rosaceae also includes some of the most important ornamentals of temperate regions, such as rose (*Rosa*), *Spiraea,* firethorn (*Pyracantha*), *Cotoneaster,* pearl bush (*Exochorda*), flowering quince (*Chaenomeles*), ornamental cherries (*Prunus*), and many others.

ORDER LEGUMINALES. This is an order of trees, shrubs, and herbs with either simple or pinnately compound leaves. Stipules may be present or lacking. The flowers range from **actinomorphic** to **zygomorphic** with the petals free or somewhat united. The stamens may be numerous to few, separate or variously coherent, and frequently **diadelphous.** The single carpel is superior. The fruits are legumes but may be indehiscent. This order is of world-wide distribution and is set apart from the Rosales by a number of modern taxonomists. When placed

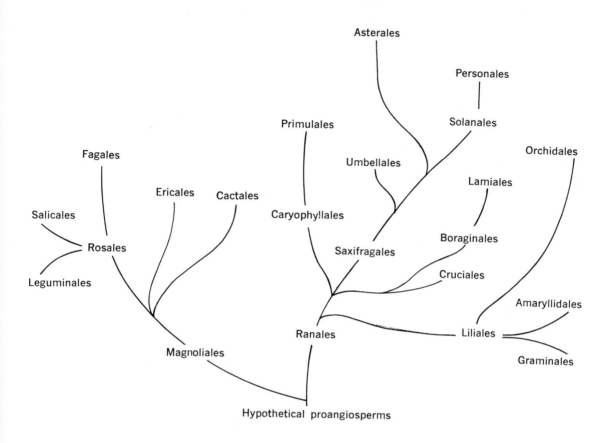

in the order Rosales its three families are usually regarded as subfamilies of the family Leguminosae. However, the members of the Leguminosae are now placed in the family Papilionaceae of the order Leguminales.

Family Papilionaceae. The flowers of this family are markedly zygomorphic, with the two anterior petals often basally connate to form the "keel." The calyx consists of five sepals fused in a tube. There are usually ten **monadelphous** or diadelphous stamens. In most genera the solitary carpel produces a typical legume, but sometimes the fruit is indehiscent, or it may be jointed (a loment), breaking up into one-seeded portions.

To this family, largest of the order, belong the majority of the legumes of the temperate regions. Economically, the Papilionaceae is one of the most valuable families. Among its impor-

tant members are peas (*Pisum*), peanuts (*Arachis*), beans (*Phaseolus*), lentils (*Lens*), soybeans (*Glycine*), clover (*Trifolium*), vetch (*Vicia*), alfalfa (*Medicago*), and sweet clover (*Melilotus*). Dyes, gums, and valuable timber are obtained from other genera.

ORDER SALICALES.   This is an order of trees or shrubs with simple stipulate leaves. The flowers are unisexual in erect or drooping catkins. Sepals are lacking or are much reduced, and petals are absent; stamens range in number from two to many.

Family Salicaceae. The leaves of this family are alternate and deciduous. The stipules are rather varied, sometimes small, and shed early; in other instances they become leaf-like and are persistent. All species are dioecious. The flowers are in dense catkins that are often produced before the leaves. Each flower is in the axil of a membranous bract. The calyx is lacking or may be represented by a small cup-like disc. The stamens are free; the gynoecium is composed of two to four coherent carpels with a superior ovary. The capsular fruit opens by valves to release numerous, very small seeds, with many fine hairs arising from the funiculus. The family includes only two genera (*Salix* and *Populus*). This family is world-wide in distribution except in Australasia and the Malay Archipelago.

ORDER FAGALES. This order contains shrubs and trees with simple stipulate leaves. The species are monoecious. The flowers are borne in either erect or drooping catkins, or the female inflorescence is sometimes reduced to cone-like spikes. The calyx is absent or much reduced, although the ovulate flowers are often surrounded by an involucre of bracts. The stamens vary from two to many, and the ovary is inferior or naked.

Family Betulaceae. This family comprises trees or shrubs with conspicuously pinnately veined leaves with serrate margins. The staminate flowers are borne in drooping catkins that are frequently developed in the previous autumn. These flowers have a four-part membranous calyx and two or four stamens with short filaments. The ovulate flowers are in cylindrical catkin-like inflorescences of various types. The ovulate flowers lack a perianth entirely, the ovary being naked. The gynoecium has two styles. The characteristic fruit is a small nut or samara. This is mainly a small north temperate zone family of two genera (*Betula, Alnus*). Various species of *Betula* supply hardwood lumber.

Family Fagaceae. This family contains trees with evergreen or deciduous leaves. The leaves are simple, and may be entire or variously pinnately lobed or cleft. The staminate flowers are in erect or catkin-like spikes; the calyx is usually four- to six-lobed; and the stamens range from four to 40. The ovulate flowers are solitary within an involucre. The lobed calyx is adnate to the inferior ovary. The fruit is a nut; the hardened involucre may be beneath it

as a cup, or the fruit may be completely enclosed by the involucre.

The members of this family often play a conspicuous role in temperate and subtropical forests. The genus *Nothofagus* is very prominent in south temperate regions except South Africa, where the family as a whole is absent. Economically, the family is important as a source of valuable hardwoods, and cork of commerce is obtained from the bark of the cork oak (*Quercus suber*). Some north temperate genera are oak (*Quercus*), beech (*Fagus*), and chestnut (*Castanea*).

ORDER CACTALES. The order Cactales possesses succulent, woody, or often very spiny plants. Floral parts, except the carpels, are numerous and in several series. Carpels are three to many; the ovary is inferior, and the fruit is a berry.

Family Cactaceae. This family comprises shrubs and herbs of very diverse size and habit. The leaves are usually much reduced. The actinomorphic flowers are solitary and perfect. The petaloid sepals and the petals are epigynous in several series. Stamens are very numerous. The gynoecium has as many stigmas as carpels. The fruit is often spiny or bristly and many-seeded.

This is exclusively a New World family. Although the species are characteristically plants of hot deserts, some occur in forests and a few extend north into Canada beyond latitude 55° N. Many species have become naturalized in warm countries, often becoming serious pests.

ORDER ERICALES. The Ericales are mostly shrubs, but a few are trees or herbs. Some are epiphytes, some parasites, and some saprophytes. Their leaves are simple, sometimes reduced to scales. Stipules are lacking. The actinomorphic to slightly zygomorphic flowers are usually perfect, and as a rule the petals are united; the stamens are commonly double the number of the corolla lobes. Anthers often open by terminal pores. These are plants of temperate regions and mountainous regions in the tropics.

Family Ericaceae. This family is composed of shrubs in a great range of size; some are trees. The simple alternate leaves are usually evergreen. The calyx is persistent; the corolla of mostly fused petals is hypogynous and arises below a fleshy disc. The anthers often have appendages and open by pores. The ovary is superior, and the fruit may be a capsule or a berry.

The Ericaceae is a very widely distributed family, with a great concentration of species of *Erica* in South Africa and of *Rhododendron* in West China. Many members of this family are prized as ornamentals, including such well-known genera as *Erica* (heather), *Rhododendron* (including azalea), *Kalmia* (mountain laurel), *Arctostaphylos* (manzanita, bearberry), *Calluna* (ling heather), *Gaultheria* (wintergreen, salal), and *Arbutus* (madroño).

ORDER RANALES. The genera of the Ranales are essentially herbaceous or at most soft woody plants. The leaves are alternate, rarely opposite, and vary from simple to much-divided. The flowers are perfect and generally hypogynous. The arrangement of parts is largely spiral, rarely completely cyclic. The parts are likely to be numerous and free, with the perianth often not differentiated into calyx and corolla. This cosmopolitan order is rare in the tropics.

Family Ranunculaceae. This family is made up of herbs with alternate leaves arising from the roots; or shrubs or climbers with opposite, frequently compound, leaves and soft woody stems with wide medullary rays. The flowers are perfect, rarely unisexual, generally actinomorphic, and sometimes subtended by an involucre of one or more leaves. Stamens are numerous and free; carpels are usually numerous, rarely few or one, and borne on a globular or somewhat elongated receptacle. The fruits are mostly achenes, rarely berry-like.

The species occur mostly in north temperate regions, with fewer in the tropics and the Southern Hemisphere. The Ranunculaceae contributes some very beautiful garden plants, such as *Ranunculus* (buttercup), *Anemome, Hepatica,* and *Clematis.*

ORDER CRUCIALES. Most of the genera in this order are herbs, but occasionally they are somewhat woody. The sepals and petals are in fours, the stamens are usually six in number, and the carpels two. The single family placed in this order is often included in the Rhoeadales.

Family Cruciferae. A few genera are somewhat shrubby, but the great majority are annual or perennial herbs. Their herbage is frequently covered with forked or stellate hairs. The flowers are perfect, mostly radially symmetrical, and borne in a **racemose** inflorescence. Usually there is a pair of long stamens and two pairs of shorter ones. The superior ovary consists of two united carpels. In most instances the fruit is a special type of capsule that dehisces by two valves.

The Cruciferae are cosmopolitan in distribution, but they are particularly common in the north temperate regions. Many genera are characterized by a peppery odor and taste. Many important food crops are obtained from the genus *Brassica,* including such vegetables as cabbage, cauliflower, Brussels sprouts, broccoli, rutabaga, and turnip. Oils are also expressed from the seeds of species of *Brassica.* Many genera are cultivated as ornamentals, such as *Matthiola* (stock), *Iberis* (candytuft), *Cheiranthus* (wallflower), *Hesperis* (sweet rocket), and *Lobularia* (sweet alyssum).

ORDER CARYOPHYLLALES. These are mostly herbaceous plants, in some cases becoming somewhat fleshy. The leaves are mainly opposite or whorled. The flowers are perfect and range from hypogynous to perigynous, with actinomorphy the rule. Petals are not always present. The gynoecium is composed of fused carpels with axile to free-central placentation.

Family Caryophyllaceae. This is a family of annual or perennial herbs with simple, entire, and opposite leaves—and the nodes are often swollen. The flowers are solitary or in **cymes.** The calyx typically consists of five sepals that may be fused basally to form a tube. The petals are of the same number as the sepals; they may be large and conspicuous or relatively small and even lacking. The superior compound ovary is unilocular with free-central placentation. The fruit is a capsule opening by valves or apical teeth.

The Caryophyllaceae occur mainly in north temperate regions. Many genera are cultivated as ornamentals; among the better known are *Dianthus* (carnations and pinks), *Gypsophila* (baby's breath), *Silene* (catchfly campions), and *Lychnis*.

ORDER PRIMULALES. This order of herbaceous genera is characterized by flowers that have a corolla of five fused petals, often more or less umbrella-shaped. The stamens are inserted on the corolla tube and opposite the lobes. The unilocular ovary is superior with basal placentation.

Family Primulaceae. The leaves of this family may be either in rosettes or borne in various arrangements on the stem. The actinomorphic flowers are produced in the axils of bracts. Although the flowers are usually bisexual they are frequently of two kinds, differing principally in the length of style—a device that favors cross-pollination. The fruit is a capsule and variously dehiscent.

Members of the Primulaceae are found mostly in the mountains of the north temperate regions; they are rare in the tropics and Southern Hemisphere. Many of the genera are cultivated—for example, *Primula, Dodecatheon* (shooting-star), *Cyclamen,* and *Androsace.*

ORDER SAXIFRAGALES. This is an herbaceous family with various types and arrangements of leaves. The flowers are usually actinomorphic and mostly perigynous. The androecium is made up of a definite number of free stamens. The carpels may be either free or fused together in varying degrees. The placentation is axile.

Family Saxifragaceae. This family of herbs has alternate leaves and lacks stipules. The bisexual flowers typically consist of five perigynous sepals and petals, with the five to ten stamens inserted with the petals. The carpels are usually coherent below, with the styles free. The fruit is a capsule. This family, found mainly in cold and temperate regions, contains

a number of garden plants—notably *Saxifraga, Astilbe, Heuchera, Bergenia,* and *Rogersia.*

ORDER UMBELLALES. The Umbellales are largely herbs, although rarely they may be somewhat woody. The stems are often conspicuously furrowed and have a large soft pith. The leaves have a wide sheathing base. Flowers are in **umbels,** and the fruit is a two-part schizocarp.

Family Umbelliferae. Leaves of the family Umbelliferae are mostly deeply and much-divided. The base of the petiole is commonly expanded to sheathe the stem. The flowers, actinomorphic and bisexual, are borne in simple or compound umbels, rarely in heads. The calyx is fused to the ovary with only the lobes free, and these lobes may be very small or even wanting. The corolla is made up of five epigynous, free petals that are mostly inflexed in the bud. The filaments of the five stamens are also inflexed in the bud. The inferior ovary is bilocular with the two styles often swollen and spreading at their base. The dry fruit consists of two mericarps that often remain suspended from the top of the central axis of the schizocarp. The mericarps are often prominently ribbed.

Umbelliferae occur mainly in temperate regions, but in the tropics they may be found on mountains (Fig. 27–38). Many of the family are aromatic due to the presence of oils in the herbage and fruits. Some are food plants, as *Daucus* (carrot), *Apium* (celery), and *Pastinaca* (parsnip); others are used as pot-herbs for flavoring, as *Carum* (caraway), *Foeniculum* (fennel), *Pimpinella* (anise), and *Anethum* (dill); a few are very poisonous, as *Conium* (poison hemlock), *Cicuta* (water hemlock), and *Aethusa* (fool's parsley).

ORDER ASTERALES. The Asterales range from herbs to woody plants, even to trees. The leaves are quite varied in arrangement; however, stipules are lacking. The inflorescence is a **capitulum,** or head, surrounded by an involucre of bracts. Two kinds of flowers may be present in the same head. The anthers are united into a tube, whereas the filaments remain free. The ovary is inferior.

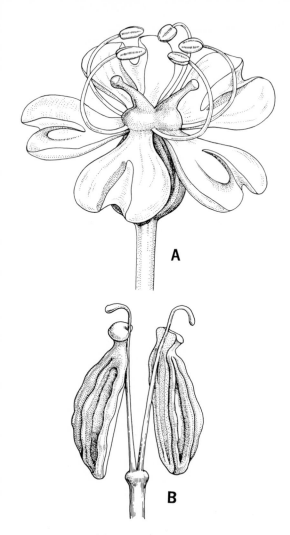

FIGURE 27–38   *Conium maculatum* (Umbelliferae), A, flower, ×15; B, fruit, ×5.

Family Compositae. This family comprises herbs and shrubs, rarely trees and climbers. The flowers may be perfect or unisexual; frequently ovulate and perfect flowers occur in the same head. The former are often zygomorphic with strap-shaped corollas, whereas the latter are actinomorphic with tubular corollas. The calyx is much-modified, and frequently it is reduced to a hair-like or bristly pappus. The characteristic fruit from the inferior ovary is a cypsela, sometimes confused with an achene.

The family Compositae is of world-wide distribution and is represented in almost all habitats. Other families are of greater economic significance, but the Compositae is usually considered to be the largest family of flowering plants. Food plants are such genera as *Lactuca* (lettuce), *Cynara* (globe artichoke), *Helianthus* (Jerusalem artichoke), *Tragopogon* (salsify), and *Cichorium* (endive). *Ambrosia* (ragweed) is an important cause of hayfever. A number of genera are noxious weeds. Ornamentals include such genera as *Chrysanthemum, Coreopsis, Dahlia, Zinnia, Aster, Callistephus* (Chinese aster), and *Senecio* (cineraria).

ORDER SOLANALES.   The members of this order are mostly herbs and climbers. The corolla is actinomorphic; the ovary is superior, often bilocular with axile placentation.

Family Solanaceae.   The family Solanaceae comprises herbaceous or woody plants. The flowers are perfect with a persistent four- to six-lobed calyx. The corolla is made up of five fused petals with five stamens inserted on the corolla tube alternately with the lobes. The ovary has two locules with very numerous axile ovules. The fruit is a capsule or a berry.

The family is generally distributed in temperate and tropical regions. There are a number of useful genera, such as *Solanum* (Irish potato and egg plant), *Lycopersicum* (tomato), *Nicotiana* (tobacco), and *Capsicum* (Chili pepper and cayenne pepper). A number of genera are grown as ornamentals, such as *Petunia, Schizanthus, Nicotiana, Salpiglossis,* and *Solanum*. A few are drug plants: *Hyoscyanus* (henbane), *Atropa* (belladonna, atropine), and *Datura* (stramonium).

ORDER PERSONALES.   This order has many features in common with the last except that the corolla is always more or less zygomorphic and the stamens fewer (often four or even two) than the corolla lobes.

Family Scrophulariaceae.   The members of the Scrophulariaceae are largely herbs but may be shrubs and even trees. The flowers are perfect and zygomorphic. The corolla is made up of fused petals and is usually four- to six-lobed, often two-lipped. The stamens are often in two pairs, or there may be only two; they are inserted on the corolla tube. The ovary is superior with two locules and numerous axile ovules. The fruit is commonly a capsule, rarely a berry.

The widely distributed Scrophulariaceae includes a number of ornamentals such as *Penstemon* (beard-tongue), *Verbascum* (mullein), *Linaria* (butter-and-eggs), *Mimulus* (monkey flower), *Antirrhinum* (snapdragon), *Veronica,* and *Calceolaria.*

ORDER BORAGINALES. This order comprises herbaceous plants with usually actinomorphic corollas and stamens adherent to the corolla tubes. The gynoecium is made up of two fused carpels. The deeply lobed ovary is superior, and the ovules are paired.

Family Boraginaceae. The foliage of members of this family is often rather harshly hairy, the leaves mostly alternate, and the stipules lacking. The flowers are perfect and borne in a special type of coiled one-sided cyme. Parts of the calyx and corolla are in fives and coherent. The five stamens are inserted on the corolla tube. The ovary is usually deeply four-lobed with the style arising from the center of the lobes. The fruit consists of four nutlets.

The widely distributed Boraginaceae are particularly common in the Mediterranean region. The family includes some beautiful garden plants—e.g., *Heliotropium* (heliotrope), *Myosotis* (forget-me-not), *Pulmonaria* (lungwort), *Anchusa* (alkanet), *Mertensia* (Virginia bluebells), and *Symphytum* (comfrey).

ORDER LAMIALES. Mostly herbaceous genera are found in this order. The leaves are usually opposite or whorled. The perfect flowers are zygomorphic and often axillary or whorled. The persistent calyx is composed of five carpels fused in varying degrees; like the corolla, the calyx is commonly two-lipped. The corolla is tubular with four to five lobes. The stamens are borne on the corolla tube. The connective is often well developed, resulting in divergent pollen sacs—or one sac may abort. The ovary is superior and is composed of two deeply lobed carpels. The fruit consists of four

achene-like nutlets. This is also a cosmopolitan order with its center in the Mediterranean region.

Family Labiatae. The Labiatae are particularly valued for their essential oils, as in *Lavandula* (lavender), *Mentha* (mint), *Rosemarinus* (rosemary), and *Salvia* (sage); among others highly regarded for flavoring in cooking are *Thymus* (thyme), *Satureja* (savory), *Origanum* (marjoram), and *Acimum* (basil).

CLASS MONOCOTYLEDONAE

ORDER LILIALES. This order consists of herbaceous plants with underground parts as rhizomes, corms, or bulbs. The leaves are various in their arrangement and size; sometimes they are reduced to scales, in which case the branchlets are leaf-like (cladodes). The flowers, also, vary in size from small and inconspicuous to large and showy; they are usually bisexual and actinomorphic. The perianth is mostly petaloid. The stamens are typically six, and the ovary is superior.

Family Liliaceae. The members of this family are mostly perennial herbs. The roots may arise from a variety of underground parts. The flowers are sometimes large and showy and are never in umbels. The parts of the perianth are mostly petaloid, but in two distinct series. The stamens are usually free, six in number, and hypogynous. The gynoecium is composed of three fused carpels, the ovary being mostly three-locular and superior. The fruit is a capsule or a berry.

The Liliaceae, world-wide in distribution, are particularly abundant in temperate and subtropical regions. The family is large and taxonomically so very complex that systematists are far from unanimous about the genera that should be included. Useful products are garden asparagus (*Asparagus officinalis*), colchicine (*Colchicum autumnale*), squill (*Urginea scilla*), and white hellebore (*Veratrum album*). Many ornamental genera are also grown, such as *Eremurus* (fox-tail lily), *Asphodelus* (asphodel), *Kniphofia* (red-hot poker), *Alöe, Convallaria* (lily-of-the-valley), *Aspidistra, Polygonatum* (solomon seal), *Maianthemum* (wild lily-of-the-valley), *Tulipa* (tulip), *Calachortus* (mariposa lily), and *Lilium* (lily).

ORDER AMARYLLIDALES. The genera of this order are all herbaceous with bulbs covered by a scaly coat; rhizomes are rarely present. The leaves are largely basal and usually narrow. The flowers are usually showy and borne in umbels. The inflorescence is subtended by an involucre of one or more bracts. Stamens are six in number and the carpels three.

Family Amaryllidaceae. The flowers of the Amaryllidaceae are mostly showy and actinomorphic. The involucre consists of two (rarely one), usually membranous bracts. The petaloid perianth may or may not be tubular; it has six lobes in two series, and a corona is often present. The ovary may be either superior or inferior. The fruit is a capsule or berry-like.

This family, found mostly in temperate and cooler subtropical regions, contains many beautiful garden plants, such as *Agapanthus* (lily-of-the-Nile), *Allium* (onion), *Galanthus* (snow-drop), *Amaryllis, Nerine* (Guernsey lily), *Hippeastrum,* and *Narcissus* (daffodil).

ORDER ORCHIDALES. This order is made up entirely of herbs that may be terrestrial, epiphytic, or saprophytic. The leaves are simple and often fleshy. The flowers are zygomorphic and mostly perfect. The perianth is frequently showy and in two whorls that often have markedly different parts. The ovary is inferior and is frequently twisted through 180°, thus reversing the position of the flower.

Family Orchidaceae. All genera of the family Orchidaceae are perennial, with rhizomes or tuberous roots. The stems are often thickened or swollen at the base to form pseudobulbs, from which aerial roots develop. The leaves are always undivided and show a great variety of shape, size, and arrangement; they nearly always have a sheathing base that encircles the stem. The variation in floral details is great and bewildering. In particular, the middle petal is likely to be highly modified and very different from the others. In many orchids it forms the landing stage for insect visitors. The stamens may be two or one and fused to the three-carpellate gynoecium. The seeds are very minute and very numerous.

The members of the Orchidaceae are widespread but are most numerous and show their greatest diversity of form in the Indo-Malayan region and in South America.

ORDER GRAMINALES. The order Graminales consists of herbaceous to sub-shrubby plants with linear leaves and sheathing at the base. The stems are mostly terete and hollow between the nodes. Inflorescences are quite varied. The perianth is reduced, and each flower is subtended by two bracts. The fruit is usually a caryopsis.

Family Gramineae. These are annual or perennial herbs, rarely shrubby or tree-like. The stems (culms) are various but usually branch only at the base. The nodes are jointed and solid, the internodes frequently hollow. The leaves are alternate and two-ranked, and a ligule develops at the junction of the blade and sheath. The ligule may be membranous or a fringe of hairs; rarely is it absent. The flowers are small and commonly bisexual, consisting of the androecium of one to six stamens and the gynoecium of three fused carpels. The perianth is represented by two or three minute remnants. The superior ovary is unilocular with a single ovule. The fruit is characteristically a caryopsis.

This is one of the largest and probably the most valuable family of flowering plants. Members may be found throughout the world wherever other flowering plants can grow. Food (generally the endosperm) of primary importance to man comes from *Oryza* (rice), *Triticum* (wheat), *Hordeum* (barley), *Avena* (oats), *Zea* (Indian corn, maize), and *Secale* (rye). Many genera provide fodder for animals.

REFERENCES

Axelrod, D. I., "A Theory of Angiosperm Evolution." *Evolution,* 6(1): 29–60 (1952).

Axelrod, D. I., "Poleward Migration of Early Angiosperm Flora." *Science,* 130: 203–207 (1959).

Axelrod, D. I., "How Old Are the Angiosperms?" *Am. J. Sci.,* 259: 447–459 (1961).

Bailey, I. V., and Swamy, B. G. L., "The Conduplicate Carpel of Dicotyledons and Its Initial Trends of Specialization." *Am. J. Bot.,* 38: 373–379 (1951).

Bailey, I. V., and Swamy, B. G. L., *Contribution to Plant Anatomy.* Waltham, Mass.: Chronica Botanica Co. (1954).

Brown, W. H., *The Plant Kingdom.* Boston: Ginn and Co. (1935). Pp. 268–325.

Canright, J. E., "The Comparative Morphology and Relationships of the Magnoliaceae, I: Trends of Specialization in the Stamens." *Am. J. Bot.,* 39: 484–497 (1952).

Condit, J. J., "Structure and Development of Flowers in *Ficus carica* L." *Hilgardia,* 6: 443–481 (1932).

Constance, L., "The Systematics of the Angiosperms." In *A Century of Progress in the Natural Sciences, 1853–1954.* San Francisco: California Academy of Sciences (1955). Pp. 408–483.

Cronquist, A., *Introductory Botany.* New York: Harper & Row, Publishers (1961). Pp. 595–645.

Darwin, C., *The Origin of Species.* London: John Murray (Publishers) Ltd. (1859).

Darwin, C., *The Various Contrivances by Which British and Foreign Orchids Are Fertilized by Insects.* London: John Murray (Publishers) Ltd. (1862).

Darwin, C., *Fertilisation of Orchids.* London: John Murray (Publishers) Ltd. (1904).

Douglas, G. E., "The Inferior Ovary, II." *Bot. Rev.,* 23: 1–46 (1957).

Eames, A. J., *Morphology of the Angiosperms.* New York: McGraw-Hill Book Co., Inc. (1961).

Esau, K., *Plant Anatomy.* New York: John Wiley & Sons, Inc. (1953).

Foster, A. S., and Gifford, E. M., Jr., *Comparative Morphology of Vascular Plants.* San Francisco: W. H. Freeman and Co. (1959). Pp. 443–539.

Gibbs, R. D., *Botany, an Evolutionary Approach.* Philadelphia: Blakiston Co. (1950). Pp. 220–454.

Gleason, H. A., *Illustrated Flora of Northeastern States.* New York: New York Botanical Garden (1952).

von Goethe, J. W., *Versuch die Metamorphose der Pflanzen zu erKlären.* Gotha (1790).

Gustafsson, A., "Apomixis in the Higher Plants, I: The Mechanism of Apomixis." *Lunds Univ. Årsskr.,* 42: 1–66 (1946).

Gustafsson, A., "Apomixis in Higher Plants, II: The Causal Aspects of Apomixis." *Lunds Univ. Årsskr.,* 43: 71–178 (1947).

Gustafsson, A., "Apomixis in Higher Plants, III: Biotype and Species Formation." *Lunds Univ. Årsskr.,* 44: 183–370 (1947).

Hagerup, O., and Petersson, V., *A Botanical Atlas.* Vol. I. Copenhagen: Ejnar Munksgaard (1956).

Hutchinson, J., *The Families of Flowering Plants,* 2nd Ed. Vols. 1 and 2. London: Oxford University Press (1959).

Johansen, A., *Plant Embryology.* Waltham, Mass.: Chronica Botanica Co. (1950).

Jones, S. G., *Introduction to Floral Mechanisms.* London: Blackie and Son Ltd. (1939).

Lam, H. J., "Taxonomy: General Principles—Angiosperms." In Turrill, W. B. (Ed.), *Vistas in Botany.* London: Pergamon Press Ltd. (1963). Pp. 3–75.

Lawrence, G. H. M., *Taxonomy of Vascular Plants.* New York: Macmillan Co. (1951).

LeMaout, E., and Decaisne, J., *Descriptive and Analytical Botany.* New York: Longmans, Green & Co. (1876).

Maheshwari, P., *An Introduction to the Embryology of the Angiosperms.* New York: McGraw-Hill Book Co., Inc. (1950).

McLean, R. C., and Ivimey-Cook, W. R., *Textbook of Theoretical Botany.* Vol. 2. London: Longmans, Green & Co. Ltd. (1956).

Meeuse, B. J. D., *The Story of Pollination.* New York: Ronald Press Co. (1961).

Melville, R., "A New Theory of the Angiosperm Flower, I: The Gynoecium." *Kew Bull.,* 16(1): 1–50 (1962).

Puri, V., "Floral Anatomy and Inferior Ovary." *Phytomorphology,* 2: 122–129 (1952).

Ridley, H. N., *The Dispersal of Plants throughout the World.* Ashford, Kent: L. Reeve and Co., Ltd. (1930).

Salisbury, E. J., *The Reproductive Capacity in Plants.* London: G. Bell & Sons, Ltd. (1942).

Scott, R. A.; Barghoorn, E. S.; and Leopold, E. B., "How Old Are the Angiosperms?" *Am. J. Sci.,* 258: 284–299 (1960).

Stebbins, G. L., Jr., "Apomixis in Angiosperms." *Bot. Rev.,* 7: 507–542 (1941).

Takhtajan, A. L., "Origins of Angiospermous Plants." *Am. Inst. Biol. Sci.* (1958). (Trans. from Russian edition of 1954.)

Thorne, R. F., "Some Guiding Principles of Angiosperm Phylogeny." *Brittonia,* 10: 72–77 (1958).

Went, F. W., *Control of Plant Growth.* Waltham, Mass.: Chronica Botanica Co. (1957).

28 / PHYLOGENY

Biologists have often said that the ultimate goal in the study of plants and animals is the establishment of natural relationships. Indeed, in the past as well as the present, much of the effort of botanists and zoologists has been in trying to relate taxa to each other at all taxonomic levels. This has led to the recognition of a separate branch of study concerned with **phylogeny** (Greek, *phylon,* "race" or "tribe"; *genes,* "born"). Because all taxa except the earliest have obviously been derived from previously existing organisms, in practice it is impossible to deal with origins without considering the relationships of taxa to others in an evolutionary series. Such relationships are termed **phylogenetic relationships.**

It is axiomatic that because evolution is the key to phylogeny, a complete picture of phylogenetic relationships above the species level can be realized only through the fossil record. The exception to this is where new species have been created experimentally, and their immediate ancestry is known. If sufficiently complete, the fossil record will reflect the actual morphological and anatomical changes that have occurred during the evolution of a particular lineage. Examples of well-documented evolutionary series include the horse in the animal kingdom, and the ovule-bearing organs of the coniferophytes in the plant kingdom. Unfortunately, good examples of evolutionary series in the plant kingdom are rare. This is mainly because plants have an **open system of growth,** and possess structural elements that are more delicate than

596

the skeletal parts of most animals. In addition, plants have always tended to fragment and decay before the opportunity for fossilization arrived, so that chiefly organs or mere fragments rather than whole plants are found.

The lack of information on evolutionary stages in plants is most apparent in the bacteria, fungi, algae, and bryophytes. Being structurally more resistant, and generally larger, the vascular plants have a much better fossil record, and there is a fairly good picture of evolution and phylogeny in most of the main groups. However, significant evolutionary gaps occur, especially concerning the origins and relationships of the divisions, and the immediate ancestors to the earliest members of the divisions. These gaps in the record are popularly referred to as "missing links."

Two main reasons are usually advanced to explain the "missing links" in the fossil record. First, no doubt many gaps occur in geological time for which we have no record of the characteristic plants or animals, particularly in terrestrial organisms. Plants and animals living and dying especially on upland regions would be lost as a result of forces of erosion and disintegration. Moreover, some evidence suggests that much of the evolution of terrestrial organisms actually occurred in more upland regions. If true, the early products of mutation, interbreeding, and natural selection would be largely and permanently lost from the record. A second explanation relates to the phenomenon that the earliest stages of evolution in any line are both rapid and of short duration. Hence, the evolutionary stages most critical for establishing phylogeny are probably more often lost. As a result, what remain are, in general, the more stable and longer-lasting stages of evolution—stages showing the least evidence of their derivation from an ancestral group.

As a result of the general lack of fossil information, botanists dealing with the fungi, algae, bryophytes, and angiosperms have leaned heavily on structural and physiological features of extant organisms for determining phylogeny. From evidence of fossils of non-angiospermous vascular plants, it has been shown that certain trends of morphological and anatomical change have occurred. Some of the more important are reduction in numbers of parts, fusion of parts, and simplification of structure. Good examples of such trends are found in the fossil history of the leaf of the ginkgophyte line, and in the ovule-bearing organs of the coniferophytes. These trends have been applied to related taxa of extant plants in order to establish phylogenetic series. Thus, even though direct evidence of ancestry is lacking, an approximation to the evolutionary series can be made.

EVOLUTIONARY RELATIONSHIPS

The distinction between phylogeny based on fossil evidence and relationships resulting from modern comparative studies has been dramatically illustrated by Sporne. As shown in Figure 28–1, Sporne's concept can best be expressed in a three-dimensional figure. The fossil representatives of two related groups, X and Y, are shown along the radii of a circle, with probable relationships indicated as branches of different lengths. The extant members are disposed on rectangular areas of the circumference, on which probable relationships are shown as plot points on concentric circles. In taxa having no fossil representation, only the surface rectangular areas would be applicable for determining relationships. Obviously, without fossil representation, it would be difficult to establish a real phylogenetic link between X and Y, and the term **phenetic relationships** is used for such a series.

A large number of systematic botanists are engaged in trying to establish phenetic and phylogenetic classifications. The basic concepts followed and methods employed are discussed thoroughly by Sokal and Sneath. They make a clear distinction between phenetic and phylogentic classifications, and point out that special care is necessary in attempting to change a phenetic into a phylogenetic classification in the absence of a fossil record.

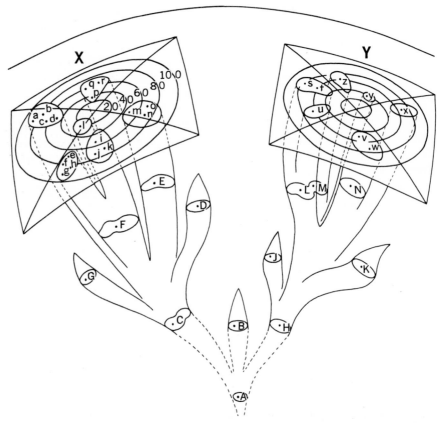

FIGURE 28–1   Two types of relationships of taxa. Finger projections along radii of circle represent evolutionary or *phylogenetical* relationships. Concentric rings along circumference represent series of criteria ranging from 0–100, and extant taxa fall within rings in groups, depending on similarity of characters— e.g., *m, n,* and *o.* Such groupings of taxa either alone or in multiples form *phenetic* series. (After Sporne with permission of *American Journal of Botany.*)

In establishing a phenetic series, it is important for the investigator to assess and use as many *different* characteristics and lines of evidence as possible to show similarities or differences between taxa. These include morphological characteristics such as number, size, shape, color, sculpturing, and appendages; anatomical characteristics such as xylem, phloem, and petiole structure; leaf anatomy, including the structure and pattern of epidermal cells, stomatal cells, and trichomes; the anatomy of floral parts; pollen and spore morphology; embryological characteristics and processes; cytological and cytogenetical characteristics; and biochemical and physiological factors.

In recent years, the study of cytogenetics has contributed much to an understanding of relationships. Of particular value are the numbers and shapes of chromosomes in both sporogenous and somatic cells. In general, the results of chromosome studies have supported conclusions previously arrived at by morphological and anatomical studies. The scope of these studies is steadily increasing, and will undoubtedly be of even greater assistance in the future.

The terms "primitive" and "advanced," used widely in both phylogenetic and phenetic studies, refer to characteristics of plants which approach the ancestral condition (primitive) or that reflect a good deal of evolutionary change (advanced). Basically, these terms refer to stages in an evolutionary series. When applied to an extant group in a phenetic series, the terms may keep the same connotation, implying that certain characteristics of the plants are either closer to or more remote from the ancestral condition. It is up to the investigator to decide which of the characteristics are most primitive, which are most advanced, and what the arrangement of species or other taxa should be in the series. The investigator bases his decisions largely on information gathered from previous studies of evolutionary trends in fossil or extant taxa. In a rather large number of instances, it is difficult to determine whether a phenetic series should be interpreted in one direction or another. In such instances, the terms "primitive" and "advanced" have little meaning, and should be abandoned.

A basic concept in phylogeny is that different parts of an organism may have evolved at different rates and to different extents. For example, the seed ferns of the Carboniferous had foliage almost identical to the ferns, but the latter are presumed by some botanists to be the ancestors of the seed ferns. Although it is often difficult to assess which characteristics of a plant are more highly evolved, careful comparative studies are often revealing and helpful.

With all characteristics, the application of statistics is of great assistance in showing correlations and in establishing the degree of similarity or dissimilarity among members of a series. This is the basis for the **doctrine of correlation.** The doctrine holds that primitive characteristics should be expected to show positive correlation, because their distribution in any taxon is not random. Thus, primitive species should have a higher number of primitive characteristics. In attempting to assess advanced characteristics, the correlation depends on how much convergence, parallelism, or divergence has occurred with evolution of a characteristic. Convergent and parallel evolution will give relatively high correlations, whereas divergence will give a low correlation. In applying the doctrine to dicotyledons, Sporne concluded on the basis of Chi Square significance tests that the following characteristics were primitive: woody habit, glandular leaves, alternate leaves, stipulate leaves, unisexual flowers, actinomorphic flowers, free petals, many stamens, many carpels, arillate seeds, seeds with two integuments, integuments with vascular

bundles, nuclear endosperm, free carpels, and axile placentation. On this basis, and assuming that all characteristics are of equal importance, Sporne attempted to assess the relative primitiveness of families of dicotyledons.

GEOLOGIC TIME AND THE EVOLUTION OF PLANT DIVISIONS

Recent estimates of the age of the earth range from 4,000,000,000 to 6,000,000,000 years. The earliest fossils we know of have been dated by **radiometric** methods at approximately 2,000,000,000 years. Although there must have been a long period of evolution of living matter before this, the record of plants (and animals) does not become prominent until the Paleozoic Era. The main record of algae and invertebrates starts approximately from the Pre-Cambrian–Cambrian boundary. In contrast, land plants do not show prominently until the late Silurian and early Devonian; but from that time on, there is a record of progressive evolution of most major groups of land plants. The general picture of distribution of the major divisions of plants in geologic time is given in Figure 28–2.

Figures for the ages of the geologic periods have been greatly refined in recent years by the application of radiometric datings. Of particular value are dates obtained by measuring the ratios of radioactive isotopes of potassium and uranium to their end products. These and other isotopes have extremely long half lives, and when the ratios are carefully calculated, they can be very useful in establishing geologic time boundaries. In general, radiometric datings have helped to refine rock ages calculated theoretically by early geologists.

The fossil record shows clearly that the algae and fungi were among the earliest plants to evolve. The blue-green algae seem to have a fairly continuous record from the Pre-Cambrian, whereas many of the other algal groups do not appear until the Cambrian and Ordovician. Several classes, such as the Bacillariophyceae, did not appear until relatively late in geologic time. The fungi do not have as

ERA	PERIOD	EPOCH	BEGINNING OF INTERVAL (MILLION YEARS)	
CENOZOIC	QUATERNARY	Pleistocene	1	0
	TERTIARY	Pliocene	13	
		Miocene	25	
		Oligocene	36	
		UPPER	45	
		MIDDLE	52	50
		LOWER	58	
		Eocene		
		Paleocene	63	
MESOZOIC	CRETACEOUS	UPPER — Maestrichtian	72	
		Campanian		
		Santonian	84	
		Coniacian	90	100
		Turonian		
		Cenomanian	110	
		LOWER — Albian	120	
		Aptian		
		Neocomian	135	
	JURASSIC	UPPER		150
		MIDDLE — Bathonian Bajocian	166	
		LOWER	181	
	TRIASSIC	UPPER		200
		MIDDLE	200	
		LOWER	(230)	
PALEOZOIC	PERMIAN	UPPER		250
		MIDDLE	260	
		LOWER	280	
	PENNSYLVANIAN (CARBONIFEROUS)			300
	MISSISSIPPIAN (CARBONIFEROUS)	Visean	320	
		Tournaisian	345	350
	DEVONIAN	UPPER	(365)	
		MIDDLE	390	
		LOWER	405	400
	SILURIAN		(425)	
	ORDOVICIAN	UPPER — Trenton	445	450
		MIDDLE		
		LOWER	500	500
	CAMBRIAN	UPPER	530	
		MIDDLE		550
		LOWER		
	? — ? — ? — ? — ? — ? — ? — ? — ? — ? — ? —			600

FIGURE 28–2   Geological time scale. Figures along right and left margins are in hundreds of millions of years—i.e., from 0 to 600 × 10⁶ years. (After Kulp, Vol. 13, p. 1111, fig. 1, with permission of *Science,* copyright 1961 by the American Association for the Advancement of Science.)

complete a record as the algae, although they occur in the Pre-Cambrian and in most later periods since the early Devonian. Presumably, bacteria were among the earliest organisms to evolve, but the fossil record gives no certain evidence of their existence.

The divisions of the fungi, bacteria, and algae listed in the table of contents, and expanded on the end papers of this book, are arranged and treated deliberately in the order shown. The lichens immediately follow the fungi, because many lichenologists consider the lichens to belong to the fungi rather than to a distinct group of plants. Also, the blue-green algae are placed close to the bacteria because of their obvious close affinities. The chlorophytan algae are placed at the end of the algal divisions to suggest that they were the most probable ancestors of the bryophytes and vascular plants. Finally, the divisions of vascular plants are arranged to reflect probable evolutionary relationships. However, in most instances it is impossible to present a true picture of phylogeny of divisions in a strictly linear sequence; and for a more plausible arrangement, refer to Figure 28–3 and to the phylogenetic discussions in each chapter.

A clear history of the bryophytes is not known before the late Devonian. Although it is generally believed that bryophytes evolved from a chlorophytan ancestor fairly early in time, botanists have been perplexed for many years that bryophytes have not been found in earlier rocks. Since bryophytes are generally scarce in rocks of all ages, the most likely explanation is that they were not preserved in terrestrial sediments because they lacked resistant tissues.

Except for questionable reports in the Cambrian and Pre-Cambrian, the first vascular plant remains are found in late Silurian rocks. From that time onward, there was a continuous progression of evolution of various groups, culminating in the angiosperms. Except for the "missing links" mentioned earlier, the evolutionary picture of the divisions of vascular plants is the most complete of all groups in the plant kingdom.

A compilation of the evidence obtained from studies of both fossil and extant plants permits a reasonable interpretation of their phylogenetic relationships. Such a scheme is presented in Figure 28–3. The flow diagram is constructed to show the likely derivation of the main taxa, but does not contain any indication of the time of their appearance in the geological record, or of the relative primitiveness or advancement of the different groups. As a result of different interpretations, such a phylogenetic chart is always open to question, and must always be revised as new evidence is accumulated. However, at the present state of knowledge, we feel that Figure 28–3 presents a reasonably accurate picture of the phylogeny of the major plant groups.

EVOLUTIONARY CONCEPTS

Since the beginning of modern botany in the nineteenth century, botanists have attempted to explain the evolution of plant groups with many theories, hypotheses, and concepts. Several of the most prominent of these are outlined briefly in the following discussion.

MONOPHYLOGENY VERSUS POLYPHYLOGENY

One of the most controversial problems is whether the main groups of plants evolved originally from a single ancestral stock (monophylogeny), or whether they evolved separately from different ancestral plants (polyphylogeny). This is a problem especially with the algae, bryophytes, and the vascular plants. As indicated in Figure 28–3, we favor the polyphyletic view: for the algae, with three main evolutionary lines; for the bryophytes with three lines; and for the vascular plants with four main lines. In the case of vascular plants, the question is whether the requisite characteristics evolved separately, and possibly at different times, from several different algal ancestors; or whether the characteristics evolved only once from one ancestor. This same question can be asked concerning the origins of the algae and bryophytes.

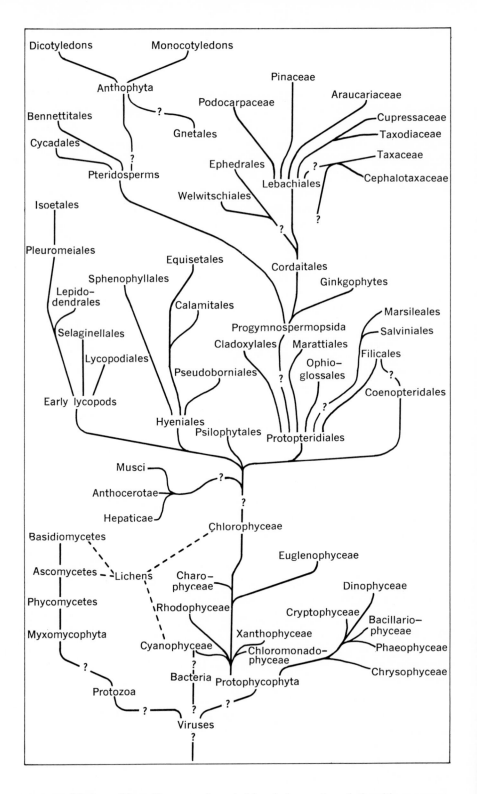

FIGURE 28–3   Flow diagram of probable phylogenetic relationships among main groups of plants.

The problem of mono- versus polyphylogeny has been brought forward and discussed in several places in the text. In most instances, the conclusions reached have suggested that a polyphyletic origin of the major groups is the most likely. However, adherence to the polyphyletic viewpoint may be a biased hypothesis, and may ultimately prove to be untenable. The apparent polyphylogeny of the major plant groups may simply reflect a lack of sufficient knowledge about the earliest fossils, and discovery of these fossils might demonstrate a monophyletic origin. At present, the two viewpoints are almost entirely theoretical, and one of them cannot be accepted in its entirety as more probable than the other.

TELOME THEORY

The Telome theory, originally proposed by Zimmermann, was based on ideas presented by earlier botanists. The theory was first formulated to explain the probable evolutionary development of all vascular plants from a psilophytalean ancestor, such as *Rhynia*. Zimmermann later elaborated and expanded the theory to explain the evolutionary development of most of the other main groups of plants. Although other theories have been presented, the Telome theory has gained the widest following in contemporary botany, particularly among paleobotanists.

To explain the evolution of the algae from primitive ancestors, Zimmermann suggests that there were three main stages of development: (1) from unicellular plants (e.g., *Chlamydomonas*) to thalloid forms with dichotomous branching and a distinct alternation of generations (e.g., marine algae such as *Dictyota*); (2) the development of earliest land plants (Rhyniaceae) from thalloid ancestors; and (3) the evolution of several types of vascular-plant habits from these early land plants.

To explain the first two stages, Zimmermann suggests that several main evolutionary developments called "elementary processes" occurred. In order, these include: (1) an interconnection of cells forming a filament (e.g.,

Ulothrix); (2) a rotation of cell axes to give branching filaments (e.g., *Stigeoclonium*); (3) the differentiation of apical and lateral meristems, and the development of permanent tissues; further evolution resulted in a bifurcation of the apical meristem to produce a dichotomous thallus (e.g., *Dictyota*); (4) a shifting in the type of alternation of generations from gametophyte-dominant through isomorphic to sporophyte-dominant (e.g., *Laminaria*); and (5) the development of central bands of sclerenchymatous tissue in the thallus. When these developments had been incorporated in the algae, the stage was set for the evolution of the earliest land plants.

The term "telome" refers to a single terminal segment of a branching axis. The portions of the axes between successive branchings are referred to as **mesomes**. According to Zimmermann, the telome first became differentiated when early thalli split dichotomously into two terminal branches (elementary process three above).

The evolutionary development of the earliest vascular plants, as illustrated by the Rhyniaceae, took place through the formation of vascular tissue, stomata, and terminal sporangia on an undifferentiated axis. Although nothing is known of the gametophytes of the Rhyniaceae, it is presumed they were small and delicate. The bryophytes developed from similar thalloid ancestors, but did not attain vascularization; and the gametophyte retained complete dominance. In the bryophytes, the sporophyte has remained dependent on the gametophyte, and represents a single fertile telome.

The evolution of the major divisions of vascular plants was accomplished by another series of elementary processes that modified the telomes of the early vascular plants (Rhyniaceae) into the different structural patterns of the major taxa. These processes, shown in Figure 28–4, include: (1) **overtopping,** in which alternate branches assumed dominance, thereby giving a main axis with lateral branches; (2) **planation,** in which dichotomies in two or more planes evolved into dichotomies in a single plane; (3) **syngenesis** of both leaf and

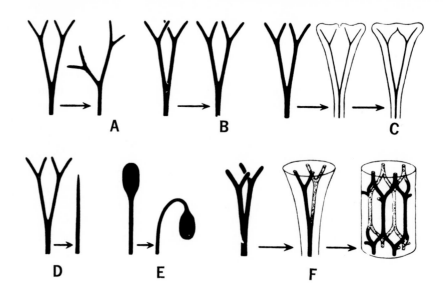

FIGURE 28–4   Main processes of the Telome theory: A, overtopping; B, planation; C, syngenesis in leaf; D, reduction; E, incurvation; F, syngenesis in axis. (After Zimmermann with permission of Birbal Sahni Institute of Paleobotany.)

axis by a fusion of adjacent telomes and mesomes; (4) **reduction** of telomes and mesomes; and (5) **incurvation** of fertile telomes to give a structure such as the sporangiophore of *Equisetum*.

The main hypothesis is that all the forms found in the several divisions of vascular plants have resulted from various combinations of these elementary processes. Thus, in the lycopods, reduction is presumed to have been the chief factor; in the articulates, planation and reduction in the leaves, and incurvation of the sporangiophores; and in the ferns, planation, overtopping, and syngenesis of the leaf have been most prominent. As a result of intricate elaborations, Zimmermann and others have explained the evolutionary development of almost all structural patterns in plants. It should be emphasized that the Telome concept is theoretical, and while it can explain some evolutionary developments, it is by no means universal in application. Many of the steps or stages of the theory are not documented by the fossil record, and may not represent what actually took place.

ENATION THEORY

The Enation theory was formally proposed by Bower, and is mainly applicable to vascular plants. According to this theory, the microphyllous leaf (as in lycopods) evolved from a leafless axis, such as *Rhynia,* by a budding or enation of the stem. As evolution progressed, the outgrowth enlarged and the vascular trace kept pace by extending farther out into the leaf. Eventually, the larger **megaphyllous** appendages such as the fern frond were evolved. In many respects, the Enation and Telome theories are alike, with the major differences occurring in the concepts of overtopping, planation, and syngenesis of the Telome theory.

REFERENCES

Andrews, H. N., "Evolutionary Trends in Early Vascular Plants." *Cold Spring Harbor Symp.,* 24: 217–234 (1959).

Bower, F. O., *The Origin of a Land Flora.* London: Macmillan & Co. Ltd. (1908).

Corner, E. J. H., "Evolution." In MacLeod, A. M., and Cobley, L. S., *Contemporary Botanical Thought.* Edinburgh: Oliver and Boyd Ltd. (1961). Pp. 95–197.

Davis, P. H., and Heywood, V. H., *Principles of Angiosperm Taxonomy.* Edinburgh: Oliver and Boyd Ltd. (1963).

Kulp, J. L., "Geological Time Scale." *Science,* 133: 1105–1114 (1961).

Simpson, G. G., *The Major Features of Evolution.* New York: Columbia University Press (1953).

Simpson, G. G., *Principles of Animal Taxonomy.* New York: Columbia University Press (1961).

Sokal, R. R., and Sneath, P. H. A., *Principles of Numerical Taxonomy.* San Francisco: W. H. Freeman and Co. (1963).

Sporne, K. R., "Statistics and the Evolution of Dicotyledons." *Ecology,* 8: 55–64 (1954).

Sporne, K. R., "The Phylogenetic Classification of the Angiosperms." *Biol. Rev.,* 31: 1–29 (1956).

Sporne, K. R., "On the Phylogenetic Classification of Plants." *Am. J. Bot.,* 46: 385–394 (1959).

Stebbins, G. L., *Variation and Evolution in Plants.* New York: Columbia University Press (1950).

Stebbins, G. L., "Cytogenetics and Evolution of the Grass Family." *Am. J. Bot.,* 43: 890–905 (1956).

Stewart, W. N., "More about the Origin of Vascular Plants." *Plant Sci. Bull.,* 6: 1–5 (1960).

Zimmermann, W., "Main Results of the Telome Theory." *Palaeobotanist,* 1: 456–470 (1952).

Zimmermann, W., *Die Phylogenie der Pflanzen,* 2nd Ed. Stuttgart: G. Fischer (1959).

GLOSSARY

abaxial   Situated facing away from the axis of the plant.

abscission layer   Cell layer that breaks down or forms cork so that one part of a plant separates from remainder of plant (usually refers to leaves or fertile organs).

abstrict   To separate and discharge part of a plant (applied to release of basidiomycete spores).

acervulus (plural, **acervuli**)   Discoid or pillow-shaped fungal structure in which conidia and conidiophores are formed.

achene   Dry, indehiscent, single-seeded fruit.

acrocarpous   In Bryidae, a growth form in which the gametophyte is erect and the sporophyte terminates the main axis.

acrogynous   In Jungermanniales, a condition in which the apical cell produces the gametangia, thus bearing the sporophyte terminally.

actinomorphic   In flowers, radially symmetrical—i.e., symmetrical about more than one plane.

actinostele   Protostele with vascular tissue arranged in radiating arms interspersed with parenchyma.

adaxial   Situated toward the axis of the plant.

adnate   Condition in which unlike parts are fused.

adventitious   Applied to a structure not arising in its usual place (such as adventitious roots emanating from a stem rather than a root).

aeciospore   Dikaryotic spore produced in an aecium of the Uredinales (Heterobasidiomycetes).

aecium (plural, **aecia**)   Structure (often cup-shaped) in which aeciospores are formed.

aerenchyma   Cortical tissue containing air spaces within the parenchyma.

aerola (plural, **aerolae**)   Wall markings in the Bacillariophyceae consisting of thin areas bounded by ridges of siliceous material and having an aggregation of many fine pores.

aethalium   A sessile, rounded, or pillow-shaped fructification formed by a massing of all or part of the plasmodium in the Myxomycetes.

agamospermy   Asexual formation of embryo and subsequent development of a seed.

agar   Complex phycocolloid substance occurring in cell wall of some Rhodophyta; also prepared as a commercial product and used to solidify culture media.

aggregate fruit   A fruit formed by the fusion of many separate carpels from a single flower.

aggregation   Movement of amoebae in Acrasiomycetes toward one point prior to pseudoplasmodium formation.

akinete   Thick-walled resting spore in the algae, generally incorporating original vegetative cell wall.

alar region   Cells in the basal corner of a moss leaf.

607

albuminous Applies to seeds containing endosperm at maturity.

albuminous cells Parenchyma cells in gymnosperm phloem morphologically and physiologically associated with sieve cells, but not derived from the same initials.

algin Phycocolloid substance occurring in cell walls and intercellular spaces of Phaeophyta (commercially marketed).

alleles Unlike genes that occur at the same locus on homologous chromosomes.

alloploid Polyploid resulting from an interspecific cross, thus containing two different genomes.

allotetraploid Tetraploid derived by doubling of the two different genomes from an interspecific cross.

alternation of generations Alternation of a sexual gamete-producing phase with a meiospore-producing stage; usually the alternation of a haploid with a diploid generation.

amitotic Division of nuclear material by cleavage or splitting without visible chromosome formation.

amoeboid Resembling an amoeba.

amphicribral Type of vascular arrangement with the phloem surrounding the xylem.

amphigastria Ventrally located row of generally smaller leaves in some Hepaticae, especially Jungermanniales.

amphigenous Growing all around, or over entire surface.

amphiphloic Arrangement of phloem on both sides of xylem.

amphipolyploid An alloploid.

amphithecium Outer layer of cells in the early embryonic capsule of the Bryophyta.

amphitrichous Having flagella at both poles of a bacterial cell.

amphitropous Used with reference to an ovule attached at the middle, and hence with its long axis parallel to the placental surface.

amyloid Appearing blue-black after addition of iodine solution, giving a starch-like reaction.

amylopectin Storage polysaccharide composed of α, 1–6, 1–4 glucoside linkages; also known as "branching factor" of starch.

amylose Portion of the storage polysaccharide starch, composed of α, 1–4 glucoside linkages.

anacrogynous Condition in some Hepaticae in which the gametangia are lateral in position, having been formed from subapical cells—thus, the sporophyte is borne laterally.

anaerobe Organism able to grow without free oxygen.

anastomose To join or come together, as in the veins of certain leaves.

anatropous Ovule position in carpel, with micropyle facing the placenta (Anthophyta).

androecium Collective term for the stamens of a flower.

androgametophyte In seed plants, gametophyte within the wall of the pollen grain which produces the androgametes.

androgenous cell Cell in pollen grain that gives rise directly to male gametes.

androsporangium In seed plants, meiosporangium that produces androspores.

androspore In seed plants, a meiospore that produces the male gametophyte (androgametophyte); in the Oedogoniales (Chlorophyta), a haploid mitospore that produces a dwarf male filament.

androsporophyll In seed plants, an appendage that bears the androsporangium.

androstrobilus A strobilus bearing microsporangia or pollen sacs.

anemophily Pollination by wind.

aneuploid Differing from the usual diploid chromosome number by the loss of a chromosome or the addition or loss of an extra one.

angiosperm Any vascular plant with seeds covered and protected by a carpel; also termed an anthophyte or a flowering plant.

anisogamy Fusion of gametes of similar form but differing in size; generally the larger gamete is considered the female and the smaller the male.

annular thickening Rings of secondary wall thickening of vessel elements and tracheids.

annulus A ring; in the Basidiomycetes, remnants of the partial veil on the stipe; in the Bryophyta and Pterophyta, a specialized ring of cells on the sporangium indirectly involved in spore release.

anther Terminal portion of stamen bearing the androsporangia or pollen sacs.

antheridial initial A cell in a pollen grain resulting from the division of the androsporal cell; the antheridial initial then divides to form a generative cell and a tube cell.

antheridiophore Specialized branch bearing antheridia in members of the Marchantiales (Hepaticae).

antheridium (plural, **antheridia**) Gametangium producing male gametes; in fungi and algae, a single cell; in bryophytes and vascular plants, many cells including sterile jacket cells.

anthesis Time of flowering.

anticlinal Perpendicular to the circumference or surface.

antipodal Vegetative cell in mature gynogametophyte of Anthophyta, usually located away from micropyle.

aplanogamete Nonmotile gamete.

aplanospore Nonmotile spore.

apocarpy Condition in which carpels are separate or unfused.

apogamy Condition in which embryo develops without fusion of gametes.

apomixis Type of asexual reproduction replacing or acting as a substitute for sexual reproduction.

apophysis Swollen basal area of capsule in some Musci.

apothecium (plural, **apothecia**) Ascocarp (often cupulate or discoid) in which the hymenium is exposed on maturity of the ascospores.

appendix Specialized upper part of inflorescence axis not bearing flowers; characteristic of the Araceae (Anthophyta).

archegoniophore Specialized branch bearing archegonia in members of the Marchantiales (Hepaticae).

archegonium (plural, **archegonia**) Multicellular gametangium producing female gamete; generally flask-shaped with elongate neck and swollen portion containing single egg.

archesporium Mass of cells from which sporogenous cells originate.

aril Fleshy covering around seeds; in Coniferophyta, formed as a fleshy outgrowth of the stalk; in Anthophyta, of diverse origin and generally associated with tropical plants.

armored Possessing articulated plates covering the cell surface, as in some Dinophyceae.

arthrospore Spore in the Eumycota resulting from hyphal fragmentation.

articulated Jointed or segmented.

ascocarp Ascus-bearing structure, or "fruiting body" of Euascomycetes.

ascogenous hypha Hypha that develops from the ascogonial surface after plasmogamy and gives rise to asci.

ascogonium (plural, **ascogonia**) In Euascomycetes, female cell that receives nuclei from the antheridium.

ascospore Spore formed within an ascus, typically the result of a meiotic and mitotic division.

ascostroma (plural, **ascostromata**) A stroma within which locules and asci develop.

ascus (plural, **asci**) A sac-like cell in which ascospores are produced; in most ascomycetes, the cell in which both karyogamy and meiosis occur.

asexual reproduction Production of more individuals identical to the parent without syngamy and meiosis.

assimilative Growing and absorbing food; vegetative or nonreproductive.

autoecious Applied to rust fungi that require a single host to complete its life cycle.

autoploid Polyploid resulting from the duplication of a single genome.

autotroph Plant that requires only inorganic substances and light as an energy source for growth.

auxiliary cell In some Rhodophyta, a cell to which the diploid zygote nucleus is transferred and where growth of the carposporophyte is initiated.

auxospore Cell in the Bacillariophyceae generally resulting from syngamy.

auxotroph Photosynthetic alga that needs an external supply of some organic substances.

awn A bristle-like appendage.

axil Angle formed between stem axis and attached leaf or other appendage.

axile Central in position; as in some algae, where the chloroplast is centrally located in the cell.

axile placentation Attachment of ovules in central area of gynoecium in Anthophyta.

bacillus (plural, **bacilli**) Straight rod-shaped bacteria.

bacteriochlorophyll Photosynthetic pigment occurring in purple photosynthetic bacteria (Thiorhodaceae and Athiorhodaceae).

bacteriophages Viruses occurring in bacteria.

bacula Rod-shaped appendage on the walls of spores and pollen grains.

bark In vascular plants, tissues external to vascular cambium.

basal placentation Attachment of ovules at base of the locule in Anthophyta.

basidiocarp Basidium-bearing structure or "fruiting body" of Basidiomycetes.

basidiospore Spore formed exogenously on a basidium, generally following karyogamy and meiosis.

basidium (plural, **basidia**) Cell in which karyogamy and meiosis occur and upon which basidiospores are borne.

basipetal Development from the apex toward the base.

benthonic (benthic) Living on and generally attached to the bottom of aquatic habitats.

berry A simple, fleshy, usually indehiscent fruit with one or more seeds—e.g., tomato.

binary fission Reproduction occurring when a single cell divides into two theoretically equal parts.

bipolar Condition referring to sexual compatibility of some Eumycota in which only two factors are involved (such as *A* and *a*).

bisexual Having both sexual reproductive structures (male and female) produced by any one individual.

bitunicate ascus Ascus with a wall consisting of two layers.

blanc mange Dessert made from milk and gelatinous or starchy substances.

blepharoplast Cell organelle associated with flagellum; may be at base of flagellum as in some fungi and algae, or associated with the nucleus as in the Cycadophyta.

bloom Dense growth of planktonic algae giving a distinct color to the water body.

bordered pit Pit in which secondary wall overarches the pit membrane (typical of gymnosperm tracheids).

brackish   With salinity less than that in the marine environment (generally less than 2 per cent).

bract   Leaf-like structure subtending one or more flowers or other reproductive organs.

bracteole   A small bract.

budding   Type of asexual reproduction in which a small protuberance develops and is separated from the parent cell.

bulb   Modified bud with thickened leaf bases.

bulbil   Special bud, often with thickened leaves, which serves as a means of vegetative propagation.

caducous   Deciduous; not persistent.

callose   Cell wall constituent in Laminariales (Phaeophyceae).

calyptra   The enlarged archegonium that surrounds and protects the developing sporophyte in Bryophyta, forming a sheathing cap over the capsule in most mosses.

calyx   Sterile outer whorl of flower parts composed of sepals.

cambium   Lateral meristem in vascular plants which produces secondary xylem, secondary phloem, and parenchyma, usually in radial rows.

campanulate   Bell-shaped.

campylotropous   Term used with reference to an ovule in which one side has grown faster than the other, bringing the micropyle near the hilum.

capillitium   In some fungi and myxomycetes, thread-like strands (often forming a network) interspersed with spores.

capitate   Having a head.

capitulum   Small head; in Sphagnidae (Musci), dense tuft of branches at apex of gametophyte; in Anthophyta, an inflorescence composed of a dense aggregation of sessile flowers.

capsule   A case; in the Schizomycophyta, an encasing layer of slime material outside the cell wall; in the Bryophyta, the spore case containing meiospores and sterile tissue; in the Anthophyta, a type of dry dehiscent fruit formed from more than one carpel.

carinal canal   Long narrow channel in stem of some Arthrophyta apparently resulting from breakdown of protoxylem cells.

carotene   General name for group of orange hydrocarbon carotenoid pigments.

carotenoid   Class of yellow or orange fat-soluble pigments; includes carotene and xanthophyll pigments.

carpel   An ovule-bearing locule of the ovary, characteristic of the Anthophyta.

carpocephalum (plural, **carpocephala**)   Specialized erect sporangium-bearing branch in Marchantiales (Hepaticae).

carpogonium   Female gametangium in the Rhodophyta.

carposporangium   Sporangium produced directly or indirectly as a result of division of the zygote nucleus in the Rhodophyta.

carpospore   Spore (may be haploid or diploid) produced by a carposporangium in the Rhodophyta.

carposporophyte   Collection of carposporangia occurring in chains (on the gonimoblast filaments) in the Rhodophyta; also referred to as the gonimoblast.

carrageenin   Complex phycocolloid occurring in the cell wall of some Rhodophyta (commercially marketed).

Casparian strip   A thickening of suberin occurring as a band on the primary cell wall of some vascular plant cells, especially typical of endodermal cells.

cataphyll   Small scale-like leaf often serving for protection.

catkin   Spike-like inflorescence, usually containing scaly bracts and frequently pendent.

caudicle   Filamentous stalk binding the pollinia of orchids.

caulid   Main shoot or "stem" of the Bryophyta gametophyte, which supports the photosynthetic and reproductive organs.

cauline Belonging to or arising from a stem.

cellulose Main polysaccharide cell wall material of plants; composed of β, 1–4, 1–6 glucoside linkages.

central canal The central cavity in aerial stems of Arthrophyta formed by breakdown of the pith.

centriole Cell organelle lying adjacent to the nucleus and possibly concerned with the flagella; generally characteristic of animal cells.

centripetal Developing from the outside toward the center.

centroplasm Inner, often colorless, part of the protoplast in the Cyanophyta.

cephalodium Epiphytic lichen growing as wart-like protuberance on upper surface of host lichen.

chalaza Basal part of ovule, adjacent to the stalk and opposite the micropylar end.

chemoautotroph Autotrophic plant that derives energy from chemical reactions such as oxidation-reduction reactions of inorganic compounds.

chemotroph Organism deriving energy from chemical reactions; *see* Chemoautotroph.

chiropterophily Pollination by bats.

chitin Polysaccharide cell wall material composed of glucoside units and nitrogen.

chlamydospore Thick-walled, nondeciduous spore produced by rounding up of hyphal cells.

chlorobium chlorophyll Photosynthetic pigment occurring in the green sulfur bacteria (Chlorobacteriaceae).

chlorophyll General name for green fat-soluble photosynthetic pigments.

chloroplast Cell organelle with lamellar structure containing chlorophyll and possibly other pigments.

chromatid One of two identical longitudinal halves of a chromosome.

chromatophore Nonlamellar pigment-bearing cell organelles occurring in photosynthetic Schizomycophyta and in animals.

chromoplasm Outer, generally pigmented part of protoplast in Cyanophyta.

chromosome Nuclear rod-shaped body containing genes in a linear order.

chrysolaminarin Storage polysaccharide composed of β, 1–3, 1–6 glucoside linkages occurring in the Chrysophyta and Xanthophyceae; also known as leucosin.

cilium (plural, **cilia**) Marginal filamentous hair; in the lichens, hairy extensions on the thallus; in the Bryophyta, may occur on the leaves or among the inner peristome teeth; also used for motile organelle almost identical to a short flagellum.

circinate vernation Characteristic coiling of young leaves (fronds) of the Filicales (Pterophyta).

circumscissile Dehiscing by being cut around circumference, as in capsular fruit.

cladode Leaf-like small branch.

clamp connection Outgrowth of one hyphal cell to an adjacent one at time of cell division in dikaryotic hyphae of the Basidiomycetes.

cleavage polyembryony Formation of several embryos resulting from splitting of basal tier cells in the proembryo.

cleistothecium Asocarp in which the hymenium is completely enclosed at maturity of ascospores.

coal ball Concretion of calcium carbonate or silicon occurring in certain coal seam layers; often containing abundant, well-preserved plant remains.

coccoid Round, spherical cell type and growth form or morphological type.

coccus (plural, **cocci**) Spherical bacterial cell.

coenobium (plural, **coenobia**) Colony of algal cells of a definite cell arrangement and number not increasing at maturity.

coenocyte Multinucleate cell or thallus lacking cross walls; generally thread-like.

coenozygote Multinucleate zygote in some Zygomycetidae (Phycomycetes).

coherent Condition in which like parts are fused (*see* Connate).

colpa (plural, **colpae**) In the exine of pollen grain, a furrow running from one pole to another.

colpate Pollen grains with one to several furrows (colpae) in the exine.

colporate Pollen grains with both furrows (colpae) and pores.

columella Small column; in Myxomycetes, often a continuation of stipe into sporangium and may be capillitial in nature; in Phycomycetes, bulbous septum of sporangiophore; in Anthocerotae and Musci, central column of sterile cells in the sporangium surrounded by the sporogenous layer.

column Structure formed by union of androecium and gynoecium in orchids.

commissure Narrow slit-like opening in the tetrad scar of spores of most land plants.

companion cell Specialized phloem parenchyma cell in the Anthophyta derived from same initial cell as sieve tube element.

compound leaf Leaf with a blade divided into leaflets.

compression Fossil plant remains (usually leaves or stems) which have been compressed on the surface of a rock layer.

conceptacle In some Phaeophyta, a cavity in thallus in which gametangia are formed.

concrescent Growing together of parts originally separate.

conduplicate Folded together lengthwise.

cone A compact strobilus containing sporophylls, and sometimes thickened bracts.

conidiophore Specialized hypha bearing conidia.

conidium (plural, **conidia**) Type of asexual spore not produced in a sporangium; actually a separable portion of a hypha.

conjugate division Simultaneous division of the paired nuclei in dikaryotic cells.

conjugation Copulation, especially of isogametes or isogametangia; in the Schizomycophyta, transfer of genetic material from a donor to a recipient; in Phycomycetes and some Chlorophyceae, fusion of gametangial protoplasts; in yeasts and others, fusion of cell protoplasts following development of a conjugation tube.

connate Fusion of like parts.

connective tissue Sterile tissue lying between pairs of androsporangia in stamen of Anthophyta.

context Sterile inner part of the cap or pileus in most Basidiomycetes.

coriaceous Leathery.

corm Shortened underground stem, vertical in position.

corolla Sterile whorl of flower parts composed of petals (interior to calyx).

corona Cells cut off from sheath cells surrounding oogonium of the Charophyceae and forming outer layer of nucule.

corpus (plural, **corpi**) The body of a bladdered pollen grain—e.g., in Coniferophyta.

cortex Tissue located internal to the epidermis but not in a central position.

corticate Having a cortex; parenchymatous.

costa (plural, **costae**) Ridge; in the Bacillariophyceae, wall marking formed by two well-defined ridges, and containing fine pores (striae); in the Bryophyta, midrib area of leaf or thallus.

cotyledon First leaf produced by embryo of seed plants; also termed seed leaf.

crassula (plural, **crassulae**) Thickening of intercellular material and primary wall occurring along margin of a pit pair in some tracheids.

crenulate Scalloped.

crossing-over Exchange of genetic material by breakage and rejoining of sister chromatids.

crozier formation   In ascogenous hyphae, formation of a hook in which conjugate nuclear division occurs and is followed by cytokinesis; crozier formation may or may not immediately precede ascus formation.

cruciate   Cross-shaped.

crustose   Lichen growth form in which the thallus adheres tightly to the substrate.

cupulate   Cup-shaped.

cupule   Sporophyte tissue that partially or completely encloses ovules; it occurs most commonly in some Pteridospermophyta and in the earliest seeds of the Carboniferous.

cutin   Waxy material covering external cell surfaces of vascular plants and some Bryophyta (the layer is referred to as cuticle).

cyanophycin   Protein storage product occurring in the Cyanophyta.

cyanophyte starch   Storage polysaccharide composed of α, 1–4, 1–6 glucoside linkages; considered to be amylopectin.

cyme   A branched, flat-topped or convex inflorescence in which the terminal flower on each axis blooms first.

cyphella (plural, **cyphellae**)   Cup-shaped depression forming regular opening through the lower cortex of some foliose lichens.

cyst   Resistant spore-like body (often thick-walled), developing by the rounding up of reproductive cells (Eumycota and Myxomycota) or vegetative cells (Schizomycophyta and some algae).

cystidium   Sterile structure produced in the hymenium of some Basidiomycetes.

cystocarp   In Florideophycidae (Rhodophyta) the structure comprising the gonimoblast (carposporophyte) and surrounding pericarp (gametophyte tissue).

cytokinesis   Cytoplasmic division, usually following nuclear division.

deciduous   Falling off; not persistent.

decurrent   Extending downward.

decussate   Pairs of appendages occurring alternately at right angles to one another (usually used with leaves, sporophylls, or branches).

dehiscence   Method of opening at maturity.

deliquesce   To become liquified.

dermatogen   Meristematic layer producing the epidermis.

detritus   Particulate organic matter.

diadelphous   Stamens in two bundles or clusters.

diarch   Having two protoxylem poles.

diatomaceous earth   Deposits of the silicified walls of fossil Bacillariophyceae.

dichotomous   Branching in which the two arms are more or less equal.

dicotyledon   Group of anthophytes characterized by having two seed leaves, dictyostelic stem with cambium, floral parts in fours or fives or multiples of these.

dictyosome (Golgi apparatus)   A series of cytoplasmic vesicles.

dictyostele   Stele with cylindrical arrangement of xylem and phloem in separate vascular bundles; a modified siphonostele.

digitate   Finger-like.

dikaryon   Nuclear pair—i.e., conjugate nuclei—found in ascogenous hyphae and in secondary hyphae of basidiomycetes.

dioecious   Refers to seed plants in which separate pollen-bearing and ovule-bearing strobili, or flowers, are borne on two separate plants.

diploid   Having a single set of paired chromosomes (twice the number of chromosomes as in the gametes); $2n$.

diploidization   Process in some Florideophycidae (Rhodophyceae) in which a specialized haploid cell (auxiliary cell) receives a diploid xygote nucleus or a derivative of it.

discoid   Round and/or flattened with rounded margins.

disseminule   Plant part that gives rise to new plant.

distal   Remote from place of attachment.

distromatic   Having thallus two cells thick.

DNA (deoxyribonucleic acid)   Main (genetic) component of chromosomes; involved in transmission of heredity.

double fertilization   Phenomenon characteristic of the Anthophyta in which one sperm nucleus fuses with the egg nucleus to form the zygote, while the second sperm nucleus fuses with the fusion nucleus to form the primary endosperm nucleus.

drupe   Type of fleshy fruit generally containing one seed in a stony endocarp—e.g., cherry.

druplet   Small drupe-like fruit.

dulse   Edible preparation of *Rhodymenia* (Rhodophyta); commercially marketed.

echinate   Spiny.

ectexine   Outer layer of exine of pollen grains or spores of vascular plants and bryophytes.

ectophloic   Arrangement of phloem external to the xylem.

ectoplasm   Outer cytoplasm of bacterial cell, generally staining more intensely than inner zone.

effused   Referring to type of basidiocarp that is spread out or flattened.

effused-reflexed   Referring to basidiocarp with a resupinate portion attached to the substrate and an upper portion extending out like a shelf.

egg apparatus   Egg and two synergid nuclei located at the micropylar end of the gynogametophyte in Anthophyta.

ejectosome   In the Chloromonadophyceae, the cytoplasmic organelle ejected when the organism is disturbed; *see also* Trichocyst.

elater   Sterile hygroscopic cell among the spores in the capsule of many Hepaticae; outer part of the meiospore in *Equisetum*.

embryo sac   Gynogametophyte of Anthophyta.

embryogeny   Formation of the embryo.

embryonal tube   Tier of cells produced by basal tier of suspensor cells in the embryo of vascular plants; also termed secondary suspensor.

enation   Outgrowth from any plant surface, but usually referring to a local outgrowth from a stem.

encrusted   Adherent and completely covered with lime as in some of the prostrate coralline Rhodophyta.

endarch   A type of xylem maturation in which the oldest xylem elements (protoxylem) are closer to the center of the axis.

endexine   Inner layer of exine of pollen grains or spores of vascular plants and bryophytes.

endocarp   Innermost layer of the carpel wall, or pericarp of fruit (Anthophyta).

endodermis   Inner layer of cortex tissue in vascular plants; often contains cells with thickened walls on the periclinal surface, with or without Casparian strips, and often surrounds individual vascular bundles.

endogenous   Development from the inside; in the Jungermanniales (Hepaticae), refers to a branch produced by internal stem cells and pushing through mature cells.

endophyte   Plant growing within another plant.

endoplasmic reticulum   A cytoplasmic network.

endosperm   Cellular food reserve of Anthophyta resulting from double fertilization.

endosporal   Referring to the development of a gametophyte within the confines of the spore wall.

endospore   Spore formed within parent cell; in the Schizomycophyta, a thick-walled resistant spore; in the Cyanophyta, a thin-walled spore; the term is also used for inner layer of spore wall.

endostome   Inner peristome.

endothecium   Inner layer of cells in the early embryonic capsule of the Bryophyta.

entomophily   Pollination by insects.

enucleate   Lacking a nucleus.

epicotyl   Portion of seedling above the cotyledons which will develop into the shoot (includes stems, leaves, etc.).

epidermis   Outer cell layer(s) in plants.

epigeous   Developing above soil surface.

epigynous   Above the gynoecium in Anthophyta.

epimatium   Fleshy outgrowth covering ovule in Podocarpaceae (Coniferophyta).

epiphragm   In most Polytrichidae (Musci), a multicellular parchment-like membrane closing the mouth of the capsule after the operculum has fallen; consists of the expanded apex of the columella.

epiphyte   Plant growing upon another plant, but not making any nutritional connection.

epitheca   Outer cell half, or frustule, of Bacillariophyceae cell.

epithecium   Layer on hymenium surface of apothecium formed by closely packed tips of paraphyses, often forming a brightly colored layer.

epithelial cells   Resin-producing cells in the resin canals of some Coniferophyta.

ergosterol   *See* Sterol.

erose   Irregularly eroded, as though gnawed.

eucarpic   In fungi, a thallus with distinct assimilative and reproductive portions.

eusporangiate sporangium   Type of sporangial development in which there are several wall layers, and in which several sporogenous initials develop from the inner side of the first initial; such sporangia are generally large and produce a large number of spores.

eustele   Cylindrical stele composed of anastomosing vascular bundles.

evagination   An outgrowth; or unsheathing.

exalbuminous   Referring to seeds lacking endosperm at maturity.

exarch   A type of maturation of the primary xylem in which the oldest xylem elements (protoxylem) are located closest to the outside of the axis.

excurrent   Used with special reference to conifers having one main stem that remains dominant during the life of the tree.

exindusiate   Without an indusium.

exine   Outer thick layer of spores and pollen grains, usually divided into two main layers: an outer ectexine and an inner endexine.

exocarp   Outermost layer of carpel wall, or pericarp.

exogenous   Developing on the outside.

exosporal   The development of the gametophyte outside the confines of the spore wall.

exospore   Type of spore formed basipetally, and one at a time, in some Cyanophyta.

exostome   Outer peristome.

extant   Living; used in reference to present-day plants.

extrorse   Opening of the anther toward outside of flower.

eyespot   Red to orange carotenoid-containing organelle in motile cells of many algae.

facultative   Parasite having the ability to exist either saprobically or parasitically.

falcate   Sickle-shaped.

false branching   In some Cyanophyta, breakage of filament with one or both ends protruding from the sheath.

false vein   Specialized cells supporting the margin of the delicate lamina of some Hymenophyllaceae (Pterophyta).

fascicle   A close cluster or bundle.

fasciculate   Spiral or whorled.

fen   Low-lying, swampy marsh land, generally somewhat alkaline or neutral.

fertilization tube   Branch from male gametangium which transfers male nuclei to female gametangium in some Phycomycetes.

fibril   In *Sphagnum,* thickenings of the hyaline cell walls.

filament   Thread-like process, structure, or growth form; in the Anthophyta, the stalk of the stamen supporting the anther.

filamentous   Elongate, thread-like cellular growth form or morphological type.

filiform   Thread-shaped.

fission   Splitting in two; characteristic especially of Schizomycophyta, yeasts, and some Myxomycota and Cyanophyta; also termed binary fission.

flagellate   Referring to cells that possess organelles for motility; also a growth form or morphological type.

flagelliferous   Whiplike.

flagellum (plural, **flagella**)   Long whip-like cell organelle controlling movement of motile cell; distinguished from cilium by type of movement.

floridean starch   Polysaccharide storage product composed of α, 1–4, 1–6 plus 1–3 glucoside linkages occurring in the Rhodophyta; somewhat similar to amylopectin.

floridoside   Storage product of some Rhodophyta.

foliaceous   Having leaflike shape.

foliose   Leaf-like; in lichens, a growth form in which the flattened prostrate thallus may be easily removed from the substrate; in algae, a flattened, usually erect blade-like thallus.

follicle   Dry fruit of one carpel that splits along one suture.

foot   In Bryophyta, haustorial-like, basal sporophytic cells; in some vascular plants, the basal lobe of the embryo.

forespore   Clear area in cytoplasm of bacterial cell which becomes surrounded by a refractile wall in endospore formation.

form family   Family consisting of form genera—i.e., genera based upon sexual reproductive structures.

form genus   In fungi, genus name based on morphology of asexual structures; in fossil plants, a name for parts with the same form or morphology.

form order   In the Fungi Imperfecti, order based on the imperfect (i.e., asexual) structure.

fragmentation   Breaking apart.

free-central placentation   Attachment of ovules around central column and free from carpel wall except at base.

frond   Fern leaf, or similar leaf-like structure.

frondiform   Leaf-like; in some Musci, flap-like, unistratose, and erect.

fructification   Reproductive organ or fruiting structure.

fruit   Mature gynoecium including associated accessory floral parts.

frustule   One half of cell wall in Bacillariophyceae.

fruticose   Lichen growth form in which the thallus is shrub-like and generally erect branched.

fucoidin   Phycocolloid occurring in cell walls and intercellular spaces of Phaeophyta (commercially marketed).

fucosterol   *See* Sterol.

fucoxanthin   Xanthophyll pigment characteristic of Chrysophyta and Phaeophyta.

funiculus   Basal stalk of ovule arising from the placenta in Anthophyta.

funori   Phycocolloid of some Rhodophyta (commercially marketed).

fusiform Cigar- or spindle-shaped.

gametangial contact Sexual reproduction in which, following contact of gametangia, nuclei are transferred from the antheridium to the eggs through a fertilization tube (Phycomycetes).

gametangial copulation Sexual reproduction of some Phycomycetes in which the entire protoplasts of two gametangia fuse.

gametangium (plural, **gametangia**) Structure producing gametes; in fungi and algae, generally a single cell; in Bryophyta and vascular plants, a multicellular structure with an outer sterile protective layer.

gamete Sex cell; capable of fusion with another gamete to form a zygote.

gametophyte Gamete-producing plant; generally haploid, and producing gametes by mitosis.

gelatinous Composed of proteinaceous material; in the lichens a growth form appearing moist.

gemma (plural, **gemmae**) Specialized group of cells for vegetative reproduction; in Bryophyta, produced on the gametophyte; in Lycopodophyta, produced on the sporophyte.

gemmiferous Bearing gemmae.

gene Unit of inheritance, arranged in a linear sequence on the chromosome.

gene mutation Change in structure of a gene; also known as point mutation.

generative cell In the pollen grain, cell of androgametophyte that produces sperm nuclei.

genome The basic set of chromosomes (n) contributed by each parent via gametes.

genotypic sex determination Determination of sex by single gene difference.

girdle Encircling, or middle; in Dinophyceae, transverse groove containing flagellum; in Bacillariophyceae, region where frustules overlap.

girdle view Side view of cell in Bacillariophyceae.

gleba Spore-producing zone in basidiocarp of some Gasteromycetes.

globose Nearly spherical.

globule In Charophyceae, male reproductive structure, including sterile and fertile cells.

glutinous Nature of glue; sticky.

glycogen Complex polysaccharide similar to starch, but probably with more amylopectin; does not give blue-black color with iodine solution.

gonimoblast Collection of gonimoblast filaments and carposporangia occurring in the Rhodophyta; also referred to as the carposporophyte.

gonimoblast filaments Cells of carposporophyte (or gonimoblast) bearing carposporangia.

gradate sorus Sorus in which sporangia mature from the center toward the outside.

granular Refers to the pattern of ornamentation on the walls of spores and pollen grains resulting from numerous small protuberances.

guard cells Specialized epidermal cells forming a stoma.

gullet Longitudinal groove present in some Cryptophyceae and Euglenophyceae.

gymnosperm Vascular plant having an integumented seed not protected by carpel tissue; includes Pteridospermophyta, Cycadophyta, Ginkgophyta, Coniferophyta, and Gnetophyta.

gynoecium (plural, **gynoecia**) Collective term for the carpels of a flower.

gynogametophyte In seed plants, gametophyte within the ovule which produces archegonia and female gametes (eggs).

gynosporangium Meiosporangium within the ovule of seed plants which produces gynospores; also termed the nucellus.

gynospore Meiospore in the ovule of seed plants which produces the gynogametophyte.

gynosporophyll A leaf-like appendage bearing gynosporangia in seed plants.

gynostrobilus A strobilus bearing megasporangia, ovules, or seeds.

gyrate Convolute like a brain.

haplocheilic Development of the stomatal apparatus in which the two guard cells develop from a single initial and the subsidiary cells originate from ordinary epidermal initials.

haploid Having a single set of unpaired chromosomes; the chromosome complement present in the gametes; $1n$.

hapteron (plural, **haptera**) An attaching structure in some Phaeophyceae; usually multicellular, branched, and root-like.

haptonema Coiled cell organelle for attachment, occurring in some Chrysophyceae.

haustorium (plural, **haustoria**) An absorptive structure that derives food from host by penetrating the cells.

helical thickening Secondary walls of vessel elements and tracheids in the form of a helix or coil.

hematochrome Red pigment granules, probably xanthophyll in nature, occurring in some Chlorophyceae and Euglenophyta.

herb Vascular plant with little, if any, secondary growth.

herbaceous Having characteristics of an herb; with little, if any, secondary growth (and thus not woody).

herbage Herbaceous vegetation, especially foliage and young stems.

hermaphroditic Producing male and female gametangia on a single thallus; also termed bisexual or homothallic in some instances.

heterocyst Spore-like structure produced by some Cyanophyta; may be a spore or a degenerate cell.

heteroecious Applied to rust fungi requiring two hosts to complete its life cycle.

heterogeneous Differing or unlike; heterozygous.

heterokaryotic Refers to mycelium in which there are two or more genetically distinct types of nuclei.

heterokont Having flagella of unequal length on a motile cell.

heteromerous Lichen thallus in which algal cells are restricted to a specific layer, creating a stratified appearance.

heteromorphic Morphologically unlike.

heterosporous Producing meiospores of two different sizes, one of which develops into a female gametophyte and the other into a male gametophyte.

heterothallism In Zygomycetidae (Phycomycetes) and Basidiomycetes, having thalli separable into two or more morphologically similar sexual strains, with conjugation occurring only when compatible mating types are paireu; in Euascomycetidae (Ascomycetes), the term has been used for hermaphroditic, self-sterile species, but it is more properly applied only to fungi that lack distinguishable male and female gametangia.

heterotrichy Occurrence of erect filaments arising from prostrate portion in some algae and bryophytes.

heterotroph Plant that requires an external source of one or more organic compounds as an energy source.

heterozygous Having two different genes (or alleles) at same locus of homologous chromosomes.

hilum Scar resulting from abscission of funiculus from the seed.

histogen Meristem in root or shoot which differentiates into a definite tissue system in vascular plants.

holdfast Attaching discoid or root-like structure of some algae.

holocarpic   In some Phycomycetes, thallus in which entire protoplast becomes reproductive.

homoiomerous   Lichen thallus in which algal cells are scattered throughout, creating an unstratified appearance.

homokaryotic   Refers to a mycelium in which all nuclei have same genetic make-up.

homologous   Used with reference to structures that have a similar origin (e.g., chromosomes).

homosporous   Production of meiospores of only one size.

homothallism   In Zygomycetidae (Phycomycetes) and Basidiomycetes lacking distinguishable male and female gametangia, condition where a single thallus is able to reproduce sexually without the interaction of two differing thalli; in Ascomycetes, sometimes used inappropriately for species that are hermaphroditic and self-fertile.

homozygous   Having identical genes (not alleles) at same locus on homologous chromosomes.

hormogonium (plural, **hormogonia**)   Multicellular segment capable of gliding motion, in the filamentous Cyanophyta.

host   Living organism serving as substrate and/or energy source for another.

hydrophily   Pollination by water.

hygroscopic   Readily absorbing and retaining moisture; refers to certain cells or structures that respond to changes in humidity.

hymenium   Aggregation of asci or basidia and related sterile structures in a continuous layer; also termed fertile or fruiting layer.

hyophloedal   Thallus growing beneath the bark.

hypanthium   Receptacle tube upon which calyx, corolla, and androecium are borne in some Anthophyta.

hypha (plural, **hyphae**)   One of the tubular filaments composing mycelium.

hypnospore   Spore formed inside parental cell and secreting new wall.

hypocotyl   Part of seedling below the cotyledons (may include the root).

hypodermis   Layer of cells immediately internal to epidermis.

hypogeous   Developing below soil surface.

hypogynous   In Anthophyta, below the gynoecium; in some Rhodophyta, beneath the carpogonium.

hypophysis   Expanded apophysis.

hypothallus   Thin, shiny, membranous adherent film at base of fructification of Myxomycota.

hypotheca   Inner cell half, or frustule, of Bacillariophyceae cell.

hypothecial layer   Sterile layer below hymenium of Ascomycetes.

hypothecium   The layer or zone supporting the hymenium in an apothecium.

imperfect flower   Flower lacking either stamens or carpels.

imperfect stage   Asexual stage in the Eumycota in which spores may or may not be produced.

incubous   Leaf insertion in Jungermanniales (Hepaticae) in which the upper margin of a leaf lies on top of the lower margin of the leaf directly above it on the same side of the stem.

incurvation   Curving, or bending inward.

indusium (plural, **indusia**)   Outgrowth of leaf tissue covering sorus in Pterophyta.

inferior ovary   Ovary situated below the receptacle.

inflorescence   Collective term for the grouping of flowers on an axis.

inoperculate   Opening of a sporangium by an irregular tear or plug to discharge spores.

integument   Outer cell layer or layers of the ovule which covers the gynosporangium.

intercalary   Inserted, or between two cells or tissues.

intercalary meristem   Meristem in a position some distance from the apex.

internode   Portion of axis between two nodes.

interseminal scales   Scales located between seeds of a compound gynostrobilus or ovary.

intertidal region   Portion of sea floor exposed between the highest and lowest tide levels.

intine   Innermost, thin wall layer of spores or pollen grain.

introrse   Opening of the anther toward inside of flower.

invagination   An ingrowth; or ensheathed.

inversion   Mutation in which there is a reversal of a segment of a chromosome or sequence of genes in relation to the rest of the chromosome.

involucre   Covering; in Gnetophyta, cup-shaped disc subtending the ovule; in Anthophyta, bracts subtending an inflorescence.

involute   Having the edges rolled inward.

isidium (plural, **isidia**)   Rigid protuberance of upper part of lichen thallus which may break off and serve for vegetative reproduction.

isodiametric   Having equal diameters; used to describe cell shape where length and width are essentially equal.

isogamy   Fusion of gametes that are the same size and are morphologically alike.

isokont   Having flagella of same length.

isomorphic   Morphologically alike.

karyogamy   Fusion of two sex nuclei following fusion of protoplasts (plasmogamy).

keel   Canal or cleft; in valve of some Pennales (Bacillariophyceae).

kombu   Edible product of some Laminariales (Phaeophyta).

labellum   Tip of an orchidaceous flower formed by the modification of a petal.

lacuna (plural, **lacunae**)   Any space within a cell or tissue; usually refers to the large cavity inside the cell, or air spaces in leaf, stem, or root parenchyma.

lamella (plural, **lamellae**)   Plate, or layer; submicroscopic structure of chloroplast indicates the pigments are in lamellae; in Bryophyta, refers to thin sheets or flap-like plates of tissue on the dorsal surface of the thallus or leaves; in Basidiomycetes, the gills of a mushroom.

lamina   Leaf or blade; in Phaeophyta, expanded leaf-like part of thallus; in vascular plants, expanded part of leaf.

laminarin   Storage polysaccharide composed of β, 1–3, 1–6 glucoside linkages, characteristic of the Phaeophyta.

lanceolate   Narrow, and tapering toward each end.

laver   General name given to edible dried preparation made from algae such as *Ulva* (green laver, Chlorophyta) and *Porphyra* (purple laver, Rhodophyta).

leaf cushion   Rhomboidal to circular area where a leaf abutted on the stem in the Lepidodendrales (Lycopodophyta).

leaf gap   Region of parenchyma tissue where a leaf trace departs from the vascular tissue of the stem.

leaf trace   Vascular bundle in stem extending from the vascular system of the stem into the base of the leaf.

lenticular   Lens-shaped (a double convex).

leptoma   A thin region of exine at distal pole of a pollen grain which usually functions as the point of emergence of pollen tube.

leptosporangiate sporangium   Type of sporangial development in which a single initial cell develops into a sporangium; such sporangia are generally small, with a single wall layer, and produce a small number of spores.

leucoplast   Colorless plastid, generally for starch storage in many green plants.

leucosin   *See* Chrysolaminarin.

liana   Woody climbing plant, characteristically occurring in the tropics.

lichenic acid   Water-insoluble organic acid produced by some lichens; often accumulates as crystals.

lichenin   Storage polysaccharide in lichens; gives negative reaction with iodine solution.

lignin   Complex polysaccharide occurring in primary and secondary walls of some vascular plants.

ligule   A tongue-like outgrowth on the adaxial surface of leaves and sporophylls in heterosporous Lycopodophyta.

linkage group   Genes occurring on the same chromosome and transmitted as a group to the progeny.

lirelline   Long and narrow.

lobate   Divided into lobes.

locule   Compartment, cavity, or chamber; in Ascomycetes, stromatic chambers containing asci; in Anthophyta, cavity in ovary containing ovules.

lophotrichous   Having flagella as a tuft at one or both poles of a bacterial cell.

lorica   Surrounding case that is separate from protoplast in some algae.

lutein   Xanthophyll pigment present in vascular plants, Bryophyta, and many algae.

mamilla (plural, **mamillae**)   Large, rounded protuberance (type of sculpturing on spore walls).

mannan   Polysaccharide material occurring in cell walls of some Rhodophyta, Chlorophyceae and yeasts.

mannitol   Saccharide alcohol part of the polysaccharide laminarin.

mannoglycerate   Saccharide storage product in some Rhodophyta.

massula (plural, **massulae**)   Refers to a segment of the periplasmodium which is derived from the sporangia of *Azolla* (Pterophyta); the individual massula contains many androspores, or in the megaspore one massula surrounds the megaspore and the other three sit on top of the megaspore as a cap.

mastigoneme   Hair-like thread or process occurring along the length of some flagella; also known as "flimmer" or tinsel.

medulla   Innermost region of thallus in lichens, and in some Phaeophyta and Rhodophyta.

megaphyllous   Having large leaves with several to many veins.

megasporangium   Meiosporangium producing usually one to four megaspores.

megaspore   Large meiospore of some Lycopodophyta and Pterophyta which forms the female gametophyte.

megasporophyll   Leaf-like appendage bearing megasporangia.

meiocyte   Meiospore mother cell, or cell in which meiospores are produced.

meiosis   Reduction division in which the number of chromosomes is reduced from the diploid ($2n$) to the haploid (n) state.

meiosporangium   Structure in which spores are produced by meiosis (reduction division).

meiospore   Spore produced by meiosis, with a reduction in chromosome number from diploid to haploid (spores usually produced in fours).

mericarp   A portion of a fruit which splits away as a perfect fruit.

meristele   Individual vascular unit of a dictyostele.

meristem   Tissue concerned with formation of new cells.

meristoderm   Outer meristematic cell layer (epidermis) of some Phaeophyta.

meromixis   General term for the types of genetic exchange occurring in some Schizomycophyta; involves a unidirectional transfer of genetic material.

mesarch   A type of maturation of the primary xylem from a central point outward; that is, the oldest xylem elements (protoxylem) are surrounded by the later-formed metaxylem.

mesocarp   Middle layer of pericarp or carpel wall.

mesome   Portion of axis between successive branches of telome.

mesophyte   Plant growing in conditions of moderate moisture.

metaboly (metabolic)   Capable of changing shape, as in the cells of many Euglenophyta.

metaxylem   Primary xylem formed secondarily after the protoxylem; generally cell elongation is complete or almost so.

microfibrils   Submicroscopic units.

microfossil   Microscopic fossil particle, including spores, pollen grains, tracheids, pieces of cuticle, small algae, fungi, etc.

microphyllous   Having small leaves with one vein and leaf trace as in Psilophyta and Lycopodophyta.

micropyle   Small thread-like opening of ovule formed by incomplete fusion of the integuments.

microsporangium   Meiosporangium of heterosporous plants producing many microspores.

microspore   The smaller of the two types of meiospores of some heterosporous Lycopodophyta and Pterophyta that forms the male gametophyte.

microsporophyll   Leaf-like appendage bearing microsporangia.

midrib   Central vein of leaf.

mitochondrion (plural, **mitochondria**)   Cell organelle in which cellular respiration occurs.

mitosporangium   Structure producing spores by mitosis (equational division).

mitospore   Spore produced by mitosis and having same chromosome number as spore mother cell.

mixed sorus   Sorus in which random maturation of sporangia occurs.

mixotroph   Photo-autotroph capable of utilizing organic compounds in environment; may also be termed facultative heterotroph.

monadelphous   Having stamens united into one group.

monarch   Having one protoxylem pole.

moniliform   Bead-like; sometimes used to describe chromatin in nucleus.

monocotyledon   Group of flowering plants (Anthophyta) lacking functional cambium and having one seed leaf, a polystelic stem, and floral parts in threes or multiples thereof.

monoecious   Refers to seed plants in which separate pollen-bearing and ovule-bearing strobili (or flowers) are both borne on the same plant.

monokaryotic   Hyphal condition in which the compartments contain a single haploid nucleus—e.g., the primary mycelium of Basidiomycetes.

monolete   Refers to a single suture on a meiospore that is produced in a linear tetrad.

monophyletic   Evolving from a single ancestral stock.

monopodial   Having one main axis of growth.

monosporangium   Vegetative cell that metamorphoses to produce a single spore; characteristic of some Rhodophyta.

monospore   Single spore produced by metamorphosis of single vegetative cell, the monosporangium; characteristic of Rhodophyta.

monostromatic   Having thallus one cell thick.

monotrichous   Having a single flagellum, occurring at one pole of a bacterial cell.

mucilage canal   Elongate cells in the cortex of some Phaeophyta and cycads which may conduct mucilaginous materials.

mucopeptide   Complex proteinaceous material giving the bacterial wall its rigidity.

multiaxial   Main (central) axis composed of many parallel or almost parallel filaments.

multiple fruit   A fruit formed by the fusion of carpels of several flowers on a common receptacle.

multiseriate   Having many rows of cells.

multistratose   Having many layers.

mutation   Change in genetic composition.

mycelium (plural, **mycelia**)   Mass of hyphae; the thallus of a fungus.

mycobiont   Fungal partner, or component, of a lichen.

mycorrhiza   Symbiotic relationship of fungus and root or root-like structure.

myxamoeba   Naked amoeboid cell characteristic of some Myxomycota.

nannoplankton   Plankton with dimensions less than 70 to 75 microns.

neck   Slender part of archegonium through which male gamete travels to reach the female gamete.

neck canal cells   Inner row of cells in neck region of archegonium; at maturity these cells disintegrate.

nectary   The organ in which nectar is secreted.

nodal ring   Continuous ring of xylem and phloem at the nodes of the stem of *Equisetum* (Arthrophyta).

node   Point on an axis where one or more leaves is attached.

nodular   Knobby or wart-like.

nori   Edible dried preparation of *Porphyra* (Rhodophyta); also known as purple laver.

nucellus   Meiosporangium, or sporangial wall enclosing the gynogametophyte in the ovule of seed plants.

nuclear body   Structure in bacterial or cyanophyte cell containing nuclear material and embedded in a matrix distinct from cytoplasm.

nucule   In Charophyceae female reproductive structure including oogonium and outer protective cells.

nutlet   A small nut.

obligate   Generally used for an organism that must be a parasite.

ontogeny   Development of an organism in its various stages from initiation to maturity.

oogamy   Production of gametes in which the female is large and nonmotile with the male small, and either motile or nonmotile.

oogonium   Female gametangium consisting of a single cell (occurring in fungi and algae).

oosphere   Egg or female gamete produced in an oogonium (Phycomycetes).

oospore   Thick-walled resting spore of some Phycomycetes developing from a fertilized oosphere.

open system of growth   Manner of growth typical of plants in which new cells are formed at the apices.

operculate   Opening of a sporangium or ascus by a small lid or cover.

operculum   Lid or cover; in the fungi, part of a cell wall; in the Bryidae, a multicellular tissue in the capsule.

organ   Distinct and differentiated plant part composed of tissues.

organ-genus   A genus name used for parts of fossil plants which can be classified in a family.

organelle   Part of cell (such as a flagellum, or chloroplast).

ornithophily   Pollination by birds.

orthotropous   Upright ovule position in carpel with micropyle away from placenta and on short funiculus (Anthophyta).

ostiole   Opening or pore.

overturn   Complete mixing of a body of water from surface to bottom resulting from several ecological factors.

ovule   A sporangium surrounded by an integument and maturing into a seed following fertilization.

paleobotanist   One who studies fossil plants and their relationships to environment and age of rocks.

palmelloid   Growth form or morphological type, in which single cells are embedded in a gelatinous matrix.

palynology   Study of pollen grains and spores.

papilla (plural, **papillae**)   Blunt projection or protuberance.

papillose   With small sharp warts, descriptive of sculpturing of spores and cell walls.

pappus   Bristle or scale-like calyx.

paraflagellar body   Swelling near base of flagellum in some Euglenophyta; possibly serves as a photoreceptor.

paramylon (paramylum)   Polysaccharide storage product composed of β, 1–3 glucoside linkage, occurring in Euglenophyta.

paraphyllium (plural, **paraphyllia**)   Filamentous or leaf-like chlorophyll-containing outgrowth on stem near leaf base, occurring in some pleurocarpous Bryidae and some Hepaticae.

paraphysis (plural, **paraphyses**)   Sterile hair or thread; in the Ascomycetes, sterile hypha in the hymenium; in Phaeophyta and Bryophyta, unicellular or multicellular hair associated with the sporangia or gametangia.

parasexuality (parasexual cycle)   Mechanism of recombination of hereditary material based on the mitotic cycle rather than the sexual cycle; occurring in some Eumycota.

parasite   Organism that derives its nutrients and energy from a living host.

parenchyma   Tissue composed of living, thin-walled, randomly arranged cells.

parenchymatous   Composed of living, thin-walled, randomly arranged cells.

parichnos   Scar on leaf cushion representing parenchyma strands adjacent to leaf vein of *Lepidodendron* (Lycopodophyta).

parietal   Peripheral in position; as in some algae, the chloroplast is located near the periphery of the cell.

parietal placentation   Attachment of ovules in longitudinal rows on carpel wall.

parthenocarpy   Fruit development without fertilization.

parthenogenetic   Production of new plant from an unfertilized egg; *see* Apogamy.

partial veil   Membranous layer covering the developing hymenium in some Basidiomycetes.

pathogenic   Disease-causing.

peat   Deposits of incompletely decomposed plant material, primarily *Sphagnum* (Musci).

pectin   Polysaccharide material in cell wall and middle lamella.

pedicel   Stalk bearing reproductive structures.

peduncle   Stalk bearing a strobilus or an inflorescence.

pellicle   Thin membrane or covering around protoplast in the Euglenophyta.

peltate   Shield-shaped.

penultimate   Next to the last.

pepo   Specialized berry with a hard rind—e.g., cucumber, pumpkin.

perennate   Perennial.

perennial   Refers to a plant that continues to live from year to year for several years.

perfect flower   Flower possessing both stamens and carpels in one flower.

perfect stage   Sexual stage in the Eumycota.

perianth   Protective organs around reproductive structures; in Jungermanniales

(Hepaticae), sheath of leaves surrounding archegonia and developing sporophyte; in Anthophyta, calyx and corolla of the flower.

pericarp Around fruit; in Rhodophyta, urn-shaped gametophyte tissue surrounding the carposporophyte (sometimes collectively referred to as cystocarp); in Anthophyta, the mature ovary wall.

pericentral Around the central axis.

perichaetial leaves Leaves surrounding or subtending the archegonia of some Hepaticae and most Musci.

perichaetium Enlarged leaves surrounding archegonia of bryophytes.

periclinal Parallel to the circumference or the surface.

pericycle Stelar tissue located between endodermis and vascular tissue in many vascular plants.

periderm Outer protective and supportive secondary tissue of some vascular plants, formed by cork cambium.

peridiole Lenticular body in which basidiospores are formed in the Nidulariales (Basidiomycetes).

peridium Membranous covering, or outer sterile layer of sporangium of Myxomycota, and some Basidiomycetes.

perigonial leaves Leaves surrounding the antheridia of some Musci and Hepaticae; also known as perigonial bracts in Jungermanniales.

perigonium (plural, **perigonia**) Antheridium plus associated perigonial leaves or bracts in Hepaticae and Musci.

perigynium (plural, **perigynia**) In Hepaticae, a sleeve-like extension of stem or thallus tissue that surrounds the archegonia.

perigynous Around the gynoecium.

periphysis (plural, **periphyses**) Sterile hypha lining the ostiolar canal of perithecia in some Ascomycetes.

periplasmodium Multinucleate, mucilaginous mass derived from sporangium wall of *Azolla* (Pterophyta).

periplast Membrane surrounding the protoplast of some algae.

perispore A wrinkled outer covering of some vascular plant spores, especially ferns of the Polypodiaceae and Dennstaedtiaceae (Pterophyta).

peristome Capsule mouth of Musci.

peristome teeth Multicellular tooth-like structures ringing mouth (peristome) of capsule of Musci.

perithecium Ascocarp in which the hymenium is completely enclosed at maturity of the ascospores except for a small opening or ostiole; generally urn-shaped.

peritrichous Having flagella over all the surface of a bacterial cell.

petiole Leaf-stalk bearing lamina or blade.

petrified A condition in which any organ or tissue is partly or entirely impregnated with mineral matter.

phaeophyte tannin Tannin-like substance in refractive granules near the nucleus in some Phaeophyta; originally thought to be a polysaccharide, and termed fucosan.

phagotroph Organism that ingests solid food particles.

pharyngeal rod Rod-like structure lining the gullet in some Euglenophyta.

phellem cells Cork cells forming the outer layer of periderm.

phellogen Cambium that produces cork, also known as cork cambium.

phenetic system Classification of extant taxa arranged according to morphological, anatomical, physiological, or biochemical criteria; the arrangement does not reflect phylogeny, because the evolutionary history is unknown.

phloem Food-conducting tissue of vascular plants.

photic zone Depth of water through which light penetrates.

photo-autotroph Autotrophic plant that derives energy for metabolism from sunlight.

photoreceptor Organelle believed to be light-sensitive; appears as a swelling near base of flagellum in some Euglenophyta.

phototropism Directional growth in response to light.

phycobilin Water-soluble pigment, similar to bile pigment, occurring in Cyanophyta, Rhodophyta, and Cryptophyceae.

phycobiont Algal partner or component of a lichen.

phycocolloid Complex colloidal substance produced by algae, especially some Phaeophyta and Rhodophyta.

phycocyanin Blue phycobilin pigment occurring in Cyanophyta, Rhodophyta, and Cryptophyceae.

phycoerythrin Red phycobilin pigment occurring in Cyanophyta, Rhodophyta, and Cryptophyceae.

phyletic slide Apparent evolutionary shift of fern sporangia from terminal to marginal to abaxial position on the leaf.

phyllid Flattened-leaf-like appendage in the Bryophyta; also termed leaf, although lacking any vascular tissue.

phylloclad Expanded, flattened, leaf-like lobe of branches in *Phyllocladus* (Coniferophyta) and some Anthophyta.

phylogeny Relationships of groups of organisms as reflected by their evolutionary history.

phylum (plural, **phyla**) One of the main categories used in classification of organisms (often restricted to the animal kingdom).

phytoplankton Free-floating, or weakly swimming, aquatic plant life.

pileate Having a pileus.

pileus Cap or structure bearing hymenium on lower surface in some Ascomycetes and Basidiomycetes.

pinna (plural, **pinnae**) Subdivision of compound leaf or frond.

pinnate Branching at right angles from a central axis, and all in one plane (as in a feather).

pinnule The ultimate subdivision of a pinna of a compound leaf or frond.

pit Thin area or place in cell wall.

pit connection Protoplasmic connection between cells.

pit membrane Middle lamella and primary cell wall that forms the bottom of the pit cavity.

pith Parenchyma tissue in center of roots and/or stems.

placenta Carpel tissue to which ovules are attached in the Anthophyta.

placentation Arrangement of ovules in an ovary.

planation Dichotomies in two or more planes evolving into one plane.

plankton Aquatic organisms that are microscopic, and free-floating or weakly swimming.

planogamete Motile gamete, generally by means of one or more flagella.

planospore Motile spore with one or more flagella; also termed zoospore.

planozygote A zygote motile by means of flagella.

plasmodesma (plural, **plasmodesmata**) Cytoplasmic strand connecting protoplasm of adjoining cells.

plasmodiocarp Sessile sporangium developing from main plasmodial branches in Myxomycetes.

plasmodium Naked, acellular, assimilative stage in Myxomycetes.

plasmogamy Fusion of protoplasts of two haploid cells, without fusion of nuclei (characteristic of Ascomycetes and Basidiomycetes).

plectostele   A protostele split into many plate-like units.

pleomorphism   Having more than one form or shape.

pleurocarpous   Growth form in Bryidae in which gametophyte is much branched and creeping (sporophyte is borne on short lateral branch).

plicate   Pleated.

plurilocular   Having many chambers; used to describe gametangia and mitosporangia occurring in Phaeophyta.

pneumatocyst   Hollow area of stipe which helps keep some Phaeophyta afloat.

podetium (plural, **podetia**)   Stiff erect secondary branch of the thallus bearing the apothecia in some lichens (especially reindeer lichens).

point mutation   Change in structure of a gene; also known as gene mutation.

polar nucleus   One of two nuclei which migrates to the center of an anthophyte gynogametophyte, ultimately fusing with other nuclei to form the endosperm.

polarilocular spore   Lichen ascospore with thick median septum, appearing two-celled.

pollen (pollen grain)   Immature androgametophyte seed plants.

pollen chamber   Flask-shaped chamber at the top of the nucellus in the ovule, where pollen lands in seed-producing plants other than Anthophyta.

pollen drop   Exudate of gynosporangium in which pollen is held in seed plants other than the Anthophyta.

pollen tube   Tube formed by pollen grain that transports male gamete to vicinity of female gamete in most seed plants.

pollination   Transfer of pollen to the vicinity of the ovule.

pollinium (plural, **pollinia**)   Mass of pollen grains.

polycyclic   Series of concentric siphonosteles.

polyembryony   Production of several to many embryos; *see* Cleavage polyembryony and Simple polyembryony.

polyphylogeny (polyphyletic)   Evolution from more than one ancestral stock.

polyploid   Having multiple genomes.

polysaccharide   Organic compound composed of a large number of sugar (saccharide) units attached to one another.

polysiphonous   Composed of several filaments in tiers of parallel, vertically elongate cells.

polyspore   Type of mitospore in which more than four spores are produced from one spore mother cell (occurs in Rhodophyta).

polystelic   Having more than one stele.

porate   Having one to many pores in the exine of a pollen grain.

poroid (porose)   Having small openings or pores.

postical   Branches arising in plane of amphigastria (some Hepaticae).

preferns   Fossil fern-like plants from the Devonian and early Carboniferous periods.

primary producers (primary food producers)   Photosynthetic organisms that are able to convert light energy into chemical energy for use by other organisms.

primary suspensor   Cells derived from second tier of proembryonal cells.

primary tissue   Tissue originating from primary meristems which are responsible for growth in elongation (generally not offering much support).

primary xylem   Formed by procambium; consists of protoxylem and metaxylem.

primordium   The early cells in the differentiation of an organ.

probasidium   Young basidium where karyogamy and meiosis usually occur.

proembryo   Earliest stages of embryo before main body and suspensor (if present) are differentiated.

progametangium   (plural, **progametangia**) In Mucorales (Phycomycetes), the fertile branch top in conjugation (the gametangium develops by deposition of a wall in the progametangium).

prosenchymatous   Fungal "tissue" in which the hyphal elements are recognizable as such.

prosuspensor   Elongate cells in early stage of embryo development.

prothallial cell   Sterile cells formed during development of pollen grain of seed plants other than Anthophyta.

prothallus   (plural, **prothallia**)   Gametophyte of a vascular plant.

protonema   (plural, **protonemata)**   Filamentous gametophyte stage of Charophyceae and many Bryophyta; usually results from spore germination.

protostele   Stele having solid column of vascular tissue.

protoxylem   Primary xylem that is the first formed before elongation is completed.

proximal   The part nearest the point of attachment.

pseudoaethalium   In Myxomycetes, clusters of sporangia fused with one another and resembling an aethalium.

pseudocapillitium   Thread-like plasmodial threads in fructification of some Myxomycetes.

pseudocilia   Thin, hairlike processes.

pseudocyphella   (plural, **pseudocyphellae**) Pore in upper and lower cortex appearing as white dot in some lichens (soredia may be erupted through it).

pseudoelater   Sterile structures among meiospores in sporangium of Anthocerotae.

pseudomonopodial   Appearing monopodial; refers to branching in which the main leader or branch is not completely domi-

nant (mainly in Psilophyta and Lycopodophyta).

pseudoparenchymatous   Mass of densely packed filaments which have lost their individuality and are randomly arranged, resembling parenchyma tissue.

pseudoplasmodium   Structure formed from aggregation of myxamoebae in Acrasiomycetes.

pseudopodium   False foot; in Andreaeidae and Sphagnidae(Musci), leafless gametophytic tissue acting as a seta, raising the capsule above the main part of the gametophyte.

pseudopore   An especially thin area in the leptoma of the pollen grain of some Coniferophyta, especially Cupressaceae and Taxaceae.

pseudoraphe   Clear area on valve between rows of striae or costae in some Pennales (Bacillariophyceae).

puncta   (plural, **punctae**)   Wall marking in the Bacillariophyceae; actually containing finer pores, but not as complicated as an aerola.

putrescent   Capable of rapid decay.

pycnidium   (plural, **pycnidia**)   Flask-shaped structure in which conidia are formed in some Ascomycetes and Fungi Imperfecti.

pyrenoid   Organelle associated with chloroplasts of some algae and the Anthocerotae; often a center for starch formation, especially in Chlorophyta.

pyriform   Pear-shaped.

racemose   Having form of indeterminate inflorescence composed of primary axis bearing stalked flowers.

rachis   Axis of a compound leaf, or inflorescence.

radicle   Primary root of embryo below the hypocotyl.

radiometric   Measuring radioactivity by comparing ratio of end product with original radioactive element.

raphe   Vertical unsilicified groove or cleft in valve of some Pennales (Bacillariophyceae).

ray   Tissue initiated by cambium and extending radially in secondary xylem and phloem; consists mainly of parenchyma but may include tracheids in the xylem.

receptacle   Part of floral axis supporting floral parts.

reciprocal parasitism   Partnership between two dissimilar organisms, in which both benefit; also referred to as symbiosis.

refractile   Capable of reflecting.

reniform   Kidney-shaped.

replum   A framelike placenta from which the valves fall away.

reservoir   Enlarged posterior part of gullet in some motile cells such as Cryptophyceae.

resupinate   Flat or spread on the substrate with hymenium on outer side.

reticulate   Net-like.

reticulate thickening   In tracheids and vessels, secondary wall thickening in the form of a network.

reticulum   Network.

retort cell   Flask-shaped cell with an apical pore, occurring on the stem of some Sphagnidae (Musci).

rhizine   Bundle of hyphae which attaches the lichen thallus to the substrate.

rhizoid   Unicellular or multicellular root-like filament that attaches some nonvascular plants and gametophytes of some vascular plants to the substrate.

rhizome   Underground stem.

rhizophore   Prop-like organ produced at a node and forming roots at its tip; present in some Lycopodophyta.

rhizoplast   Thread-like organelle connecting blepharoplast to nucleus in some motile cells.

rhizopodial   Morphological type or growth form in which the cell is somewhat amoeboid.

rhomboidal   Approaching rhombic outline.

rhytidome   Outer tissues of bark.

rootstock   Short erect or horizontal stem bearing roots.

rosette   A cluster of parts in circular form.

rostellum   Sterile modified stigmatic lobe in some orchids.

rugulate   Wrinkled or wormy (type of spore wall marking).

saccate   Sac- or bag-shaped.

saccus (plural, **sacci**)   Wing-like extensions of the exine in conifer pollen giving buoyancy to the pollen grains.

samara   A winged achene, as in ash (*Fraxinus*) or elm (*Ulmus*).

saprobe   Heterotrophic organism deriving its source of energy from dead organisms; also termed saprophyte.

saprophyte   *See* Saprobe.

scabrate   Rough or scaly.

scalariform thickening   Secondary wall material deposited in a ladder-like pattern in vessel elements and tracheids.

scarify   To scratch or cut the seed coat as an aid in germination.

sclereid   A sclerenchyma cell that is not elongated, but somewhat isodiametric, and often much ramified.

sclerenchyma   Tissue composed of cells with thick lignified walls; generally dead at maturity.

sclerenchyma fiber   Elongate tapering cell with thick lignified wall; dead at maturity; important in support.

sclerotium (plural, **sclerotia**)   In Myxomycota, a hard plasmodial resting stage; in Eumycota, a resting body composed of a hardened mass of hyphae, and frequently rounded in shape.

secondary suspensor   Elongated cells derived from divisions of the basal tier of proembryonal cells, after the formation of the primary suspensor.

secondary tissue Tissue produced by lateral or secondary meristems; results in growth in diameter and generally provides support.

secondary xylem Tissue produced by vascular cambium providing conducting and supporting tissues; also referred to as wood.

seed Mature ovule containing an embryo, generally in arrested stage of development; a food reserve may or may not be included.

segmental interchange An exchange of nonhomologous segments between two chromosomes.

segregation Separation of homologous chromosomes and hence linkage groups of genes at time of meiosis.

sensu In the sense of (in reference to someone).

sepaline Relating to sepals.

separation disc Breakage area in a filament formed by death of a cell (Cyanophyta).

septum (plural, **septa**) A crosswall, generally perpendicular to length of filament.

serrate Toothed.

sessile Without a stalk.

seta Sporophyte stalk in the Bryophyta.

sheath Covering external to cell wall.

shizocarp Dry indehiscent fruit which splits into segments at maturity.

short shoot *See* Spur shoot.

shrub Perennial, low woody plant with many stems or branches.

sieve cell Type of phloem cell characteristic of nonflowering vascular plants.

sieve element One cell in a series constituting a sieve tube.

sieve plate area Area in wall of sieve tube element or sieve cell with fine pores and occupied by connecting protoplasmic strands; also termed sieve plate or sieve area.

sieve tube In Anthophyta and some Phaeophyta, a phloem-conducting structure composed of tube-like series of sieve tube elements with sieve plate areas in common end walls.

silicle A small silique.

silique A fruit with a compound ovary of two carpels—e.g., Cruciferae.

simple fruit A fruit derived from a single carpel or compound ovary of one flower.

simple leaf An undivided or incompletely divided blade; not compound.

simple polyembryony Multiple embryos in a seed, resulting from fertilization of more than one egg.

simple sorus Sorus in which sporangia mature simultaneously.

sinuate (sinuous) With a deep wavy margin.

siphonostele Stele having vascular tissue in form of hollow cylinder, surrounding a central pith.

siphonous Morphological type of growth form which is nonseptate and multinucleate, and often elongate.

siphonous line Line of evolution in the green algae (Chlorophyceae) containing organisms with multinucleate thalli.

sitosterol *See* Sterol.

solenostele An amphiphloic siphonostele.

somatogamy Fusion of somatic (assimilative) cells instead of differentiated sexual cells as in the Basidiomycetes and some Ascomycetes; does not include karyogamy.

soredia Mass of algal cells surrounded by fungus hyphae, extruded through upper or outer cortex of lichen.

sorediate Lichen growth form which is uniform in organization and lacking distinctive morphology; appears as a powdery layer on the substrate.

sorocarp The simple fruiting body of Acrasiomycetes; lacks a containing membrane and often is of irregular shape.

sorophore   Stalk holding the sorus in the Acrasiomycetes.

sorus (plural, **sori**)   Cluster of spores or spores together with sporangia; may include associated sterile elements.

spadix   Spike with a fleshy or succulent axis, supporting inflorescence of Arales (Anthophyta).

spathe   Leaf-like, often colored bract, investing the inflorescence of Arales (Anthophyta).

spatulate   Spatula-shaped; spoon-shaped.

species   Taxonomic unit in which the organisms included possess one or more distinctive characteristics and generally interbreed freely.

spermagonium   Flask-shaped structure producing the small spore-like spermatia in some Ascomycetes and in the Uredinales (Basidiomycetes).

spermatangium   Structure that produces one or more spermatia in Rhodophyta.

spermatium (plural, **spermatia**)   Nonmotile cell functioning as male gamete in some Ascomycetes, Uredinales (Basidiomycetes), and the Rhodophyta.

spikelet   Unit of inflorescence of Gramineae (Anthophyta).

spirillum (plural, **spirilla**)   Helical or coiled morphological form of bacterial cell; also termed spiril.

sporangiola   In some Mucorales (Phycomycetes), a small sporangium with one to a few spores and lacking a columella.

sporangiophore   Special branch bearing sporangia.

sporangiospore   Spore produced in sporangium.

sporangium   Structure in which spores are produced; unicellular in algae, fungi, and bacteria; in Bryophyta and vascular plants, multicellular with outer sterile layer of protective cells.

spore   General name for reproductive structure, usually unicellular, but multicellular in some Eumycota and rarely in Bryophyta.

spore mother cell   Cell that undergoes division (either mitosis or meiosis) to produce two or more spores.

sporeling   Young plant produced by germination of a spore.

sporocarp   Many-celled structure bearing spores; a fruiting body.

sporophyll   Leaf-like appendage bearing sporangia.

sporophyte   Spore-producing plant (generally diploid and producing meiospores).

squamule   Small, loosely attached lobe in squamulose lichen.

squamulose   Lichen growth form similar to foliose type but with numerous, small, loosely attached thallus lobes, or squamules.

stamen   Androsporophyll of Anthophyta, typically with two pollen sacs borne on a filament; part of the androecium.

statospore   Type of resting cell formed within a cell and often ornamented, in some Chrysophyta and Xanthophyceae.

stele   Vascular cylinder composed of pith, xylem, phloem, and pericycle.

stellate   Star-shaped.

stephanokont   Having an anterior ring of flagella.

sterigma (plural, **sterigmata**)   Minute spore-bearing process (Basidiomycetes).

sterol   Type of organic compound present in some plants, possibly as a storage product; includes ergosterol, fucosterol, and sitosterol.

stigma   Receptive surface of carpel.

stipe   Stalk lacking vascular tissue; may be unicellular or multicellular.

stipitate   Having a stipe or special stalk.

stipule   One of a pair of appendages at base of petiole.

stolon Aerial runner; in Eumycota, aerial hyphae, usually bearing rhizoids and sporangiophores at points of contact with the substrate; in vascular plants, aerial stem, usually prostrate.

stoma (plural, **stomata**) Pore in epidermis formed by two generally kidney-shaped guard cells.

stria (plural, **striae**) Linear row of punctae in some Bacillariophyceae.

striate Lined.

strobilus (plural, **strobili**) Collection or lax aggregation of sporophylls and associated bracts.

stroma (plural, **stromata**) A compact mass of fungus cells, or of mixed host and fungal cells, in or on which spores or sporocarps are formed.

suberin Waxy material impregnated in the cell wall, generally impervious to water.

submarginal Near the margin.

subsidiary cell Epidermal cell associated with guard cells of stomata, often assisting in the stomatal function.

substrate Foundation; underlying surface providing point of attachment, or host for plant.

subtend To extend under, or be opposite to.

subtidal region Portion of sea floor below the lowest low-tide level (never exposed).

succubous Leaf insertion in Jungermanniales (Hepaticae) in which the lower margin of a leaf lies on top of the upper margin of leaf directly below it on the same side of the stem.

sudd Masses of vegetation which break away, often blocking the channel of tropical rivers.

sulcus Longitudinal furrow; in pollen grains, a relatively broad longitudinal leptoma; in Dinophyceae, longitudinal posterior groove containing the trailing flagellum.

superior ovary Ovary situated above the receptacle.

supporting cell Specialized cell from which carpogonial branch arises in some Florideophycidae (Rhodophyta).

sushi A type of Japanese sandwich made with seaweed (*Porphyra*).

suspensor Multicellular filamentous structure produced by the first divisions of the embryo in seed plants.

suture Line formed by fusion of two adjacent margins; also line of dehiscence or splitting.

swarm cell Flagellated cell resulting from spore germination in Myxomycota (also called swarmer).

swarmer *See* Swarm cell.

syconium Special type of multiple fruit with superior ovaries.

symbiosis Partnership between two dissimilar organisms, in which both benefit; also referred to as reciprocal parasitism.

sympodial Axis formed of successive dichotomous branches in which one branch is shorter or suppressed.

synandrium (plural, **synandria**) United androsporangia.

synangium (plural, **synangia**) United sporangia.

syncarpy United carpels.

syndetocheilic Stomatal development in which subsidiary cells and guard cells originate from same initial.

syndiploidy Meiosis without syngamy; results from doubling of chromosome number immediately prior to meiosis.

synergids Micropylar nuclei associated with the egg in Anthophyta; part of the egg apparatus.

syngamy Fusion of gametes; fertilization.

tapetum Nutritive layer of cells within a sporangium.

taxon (plural, **taxa**)   General term that can be applied to any taxonomic grouping.

teliospore   Thick-walled resting spore that bears the basidium in some rusts and smuts (Basidiomycetes).

telium (plural, **telia**)   Structure producing teliospores in some rusts and smuts (Basidiomycetes).

telome   Single terminal segment of a branching axis; can be either sterile or fertile.

tepals   Units of an undifferentiated perianth.

terete   Cylindrical and tapering.

ternate   Arranged in threes.

testa   Seed coat.

tetraploid   Polyploid having four times the haploid chromosome number.

tetrapolar   Condition referring to sexual compatibility of some Eumycota in which two sets of factors are involved (such as *A, a,* and *B, b*).

tetrarch   Protostele with four protoxylem poles.

tetrasporangium   Meiosporangium in Florideophycidae (Rhodophyta) in which four spores are produced.

tetraspore   Meiospore produced in Florideophycidae (Rhodophyta).

tetrasporine line   Evolutionary series in the green algae (Chlorophyceae) ranging from the palmelloid type to filamentous growth form.

tetrasporophyte   Plant producing tetraspores, usually free-living diploid plant (Rhodophyta).

thallose   Having a simple plant body without differentiation into leaves or leaf-like structures; type of growth form in some Hepaticae.

tinsel flagellum   Flagellum with many fine hairs, or mastigonemes, in one or two rows along the length of the flagellum.

tissue   Group of cells organized into a structural and functional unit.

trabecula (plural, **trabeculae**)   Row of cells bridging an intercellular space.

tracheid   A xylem conducting element in vascular plants that has no perforations in end wall, although pits are abundant throughout the wall; several kinds of secondary thickenings occur, such as annular, bordered, helical, reticulate, or scalariform.

trama   Supporting portion between adjacent hymenial layers in a basidiocarp.

transduction   Transfer of genetic material from one bacterial cell to another by bacterial viruses (bacteriophages).

transformation   The incorporation of genetic material of dead cells from the medium into the genetic make-up of a living cell, as in some bacteria.

transfusion tissue   A tissue in the leaves of some gymnosperms, consisting of tracheids and parenchyma cells, and occurring between the vascular bundles and the mesophyll.

transition zone   Intercalary meristem between lamina and stipe in some Phaeophyta.

translator   The gland to which one or more pollinia are attached in orchids.

triarch   Protostele with three protoxylem poles.

tricarpellate   Having three carpels.

trichoblast   Simple or branched, often colorless, hair-like branch in some Rhodophyta.

trichocyst   Cytoplasmic organelle in some Cryptophyceae and Chloromonadophyceae; those released upon being disturbed also known as ejectosomes.

trichogyne   Receptive hair-like extension of female gametangium in Rhodophyta and Ascomycetes.

trichothallic   Intercalary growth at base of hair-like, uniseriate filament in Phaeophyta.

tricolpate   Having three colpae, as in anthophyte pollen grains.

trigone   Conspicuous corner thickening in cell walls of leaves of Hepaticae.

trilete   Spores with a three-armed tetrad scar in the shape of a "Y".

trilocular   Three-celled or three-chambered.

triploid   Polyploid having three times the haploid chromosome number.

trisomic   Presence of one or more chromosomes in triplicate while others present only in duplicate; an aneuploid with an extra chromosome.

tube cell   Cell of the androgametophyte believed to control the production of the pollen tube.

tuber   Underground storage rhizome; in the Bryophyta, swollen end of stem (caulid).

tufa   Porous calcareous rock, formed in calcium-rich water bodies, and often encrusting organisms, and thus leading to their ultimate fossilization.

tunica-corpus   Arrangement of apical meristem of stem when it is differentiated into two regions—an outer peripheral layer (tunica) and an inner area (corpus).

turbinate   Shaped like a top.

tylosoid   Resin-producing cell often closing the resin duct in some Coniferophyta.

umbel   Umbrella-shaped inflorescence, in which pedicles radiate from a common point like the ribs of an umbrella.

umbonate   Bearing a convex elevation in the center.

unarmored   Lacking specific articulated plates or armor, as in some Dinophyceae.

uniaxial   Main (central) axis consisting of a single filament of usually large cells.

unilocular   Having one chamber; usually refers to the meiosporangium in the Phaeophyta.

uniseriate   Having a single row of cells.

unisexual   Having only one type of sexual structure (either male or female) produced by any one individual.

unistratose   Having one layer.

unitunicate ascus   Ascus with wall appearing to consist of a single layer.

universal veil   Membrane covering the developing basidiocarp in the Agaricales (Basidiomycetes).

uredinium (plural, **uredinia**)   Structure producing uredospores in some rusts (Basidiomycetes).

uredospore   Dikaryotic repeating spore in some rusts (Basidiomycetes).

vacuole   A cavity in the protoplasm of a cell containing cell sap.

vallecular canals   Air-containing canals alternating with the vascular bundles in stem of some Arthrophyta.

valve   Top or bottom surface of frustule of Bacillariophyceae.

valve view   Surface view of cell in Bacillariophyceae.

vascular system   A plant conductive system composed of xylem and phloem.

vegetative reproduction   Asexual reproduction (progeny have same genetic constitution as parent).

velum   Flap-like outgrowth of the sporophyll partially shielding the sporangia in *Isoetes* (Lycopodophyta).

venter   Lower swollen, egg-containing portion of archegonium.

verruca (plural, **verrucae**)   A wart.

verrucate   Wart-like.

verticillate   Whorled.

vessel   Xylem conducting structure of some vascular plants composed of tubelike series of vessel members with perforations in common end walls; several kinds of secondary thickenings occur, such as annular, bordered, helical, reticulate, or scalariform.

vessel member (vessel element) One cell in a series constituting a vessel.

vibrio Short, curved, rod-shaped bacterial cell.

violaxanthin Xanthophyll pigment occurring in the Phaeophyta. Chlorophyceae, Bryophyta, and vascular plants.

vivipary Germination of a seed while still attached to parent plant.

volutin Stored food substance in bacteria, often appearing as granules.

volva Cup-like fragment of universal veil at base of stipe of some Agaricales (Basidiomycetes).

volvocine line Evolutionary series in the green algae (Chlorophyceae) exemplified by a series of colonial forms with cells not arranged in a filament.

whiplash flagellum Smooth-surfaced flagellum (without mastigonemes); may have distal thinner region.

xanthophyll General name for group of yellow, carotenoid pigments composed of oxygenated hydrocarbons.

xerophyte Plant living in a dry habitat.

xylan Water-soluble polysaccharide occurring in cell wall of some Rhodophyta and Chlorophyceae.

xylem Water-conducting tissue of vascular plants; constitutes the major portion of wood.

zeaxanthin Xanthophyll pigment occurring in Cyanophyta, Rhodophyta, Chlorophyceae, Bryophyta, and vascular plants.

zooplankton Free-floating, or weakly swimming, aquatic animal life.

zoospore A spore motile by means of one or more flagella; also termed planospore.

zooxanthellae Algal cells (often yellow) living symbiotically in cells of certain invertebrate animals; algae known to be members of Dinophyceae, Cryptophyceae, and Xanthophyceae.

zygomorphic Bilateral symmetry—i.e., symmetrical only about a single axis.

zygophore Special hyphal branch involved in gametangial copulation in the Mucorales (Phycomycetes).

zygospore Thick-walled resting spore resulting from the fusion of gametangia (conjugation) in Zygomycetidae (Phycomycetes).

zygote Product of syngamy; diploid cell resulting from fusion of two haploid gametes.

INDEX

secondary tissues, 356, 370; *Botrychium,* 424
secondary zoospores; encystment and germination, 38
seed, 458, 556–559
seed habit; discussion, 464–465; origin, 378
seeds, **564;** adaptation to environment, 556, 558; dissemination, wind, 561–562; longevity, **557;** viability, **557**
seed spores, 465
segregation, 3
Selaginella, 368, 378, 379; distribution, 380; embryo, 383; female gametophyte, **385;** habit, 380, **381;** leaves, 380, **381;** male gametophyte, **384;** phylogeny, 383–384; reproduction, 382–383; rhizophores, **381;** roots, 380, 382; stem, 380; strobilus, sporophylls, and spores, 383; transverse section of stem, **381, 382**
Selaginellales, 367; evolution, 378–379
Selaginellites, 378, **379,** 383
Selenomonas, 135
self-fertilization, 4, 59
semicell, 291, **293, 294, 295**
senecio, 591
separation disc, 164, **165**
septa, 38, **50,** 52, 69, 73, **77;** false, 32
Septobasidiaceae, 70
Septoria, 97, **98**
Sequoia, 498, 499, **507, 516,** 517
Sequoiadendron, 356, 499, 501, 502, 517
sereological reactions, 131
seta, **305,** 306
sewage, 272
sex differentiation, 464
sexual reproduction, 2, 3, 5, 6, 36, 40, 45, 51, 130–131
Sha-mu tree (*Cunninghamia*), 516
sheath, 135
sheathed bacteria, 134
shellfish, 141
shelving basidiocarps, 85
shooting-star, 590
sieve areas, 359
sieve cells, 375, 380, 503, **505**
sieve plate (*see* phloem)
Sigillaria, 373
Silene, 590
siliceous skeleton, 179, **180**
silicification, 187, 189, 192
silicle, **561**
silicoflagellates, 179, **180,** 183
silicon, in algae, 148–149, 184–185, 187, 261, 263
silique, 560
Silurian, 299, 355, 599, **600**
simple fruit, 560
simple ovary, **547**
Siphonales, 274, 275, 282, 299, 300

siphonein, 148–149
Siphonocladales, 274, 276, 282, 296, 300
Siphonocladus, 296, **299**
siphonostele, 380; ferns, 410, **434**
siphonous form, 153, 261, **263**
siphonous line, 276, **277,** 282, **284, 285, 286,** 299, 300
siphonoxanthin, 148–149
sirenin, 37
Sisymbrium, seed dissemination, 562
sitosterol, 148–149 (*see also* sterol)
Sium, 76
slime bacteria, 142
slime molds, 16–29, 31
Smilax; stipules, 538; *S. laurifolia,* stipules, **539**
smuts, 78, 80
snapdragon, 572, 592
snares, fungus, 100
snow-drop, 593
soil fertility, Cyanophyceae, 168
Solanaceae, 6, 591
Solanales, 591
Solanum, 560, 591
Solenia, 86, **87**
solenostele, **412,** 428
Solenostoma crenuliformis, oil bodies, **313;** *S. sphaerocarpa,* oil bodies, 313
solomon seal, 593
Solorina crocea, cephalodia, 111; *S. saccata,* habit, 107
somatogamy, 52, 68, 69, 75
Sorbus, 555, 560
Sordaria fimicola, 54, **59**
soredia, **112;** function, 111
sorediate, lichen thallus, 106, **107**
sorophore, 26
sorus, 26, 28, 70, 77, 80, 412, 448
soybeans, 587
spadix, **576,** 578
Spanish bayonet, pollination, 582
Sparassis, 86; *S. radicatus,* **87**
Spartina alterniflora, 5; *S. maritima,* 5; *S. townsendii,* 5
spathe, **576,** 578
Spathodes, seed, **564**
species, 12; binomial, 13; nomenclature, 13
specific epithet, 13
speedwell, pollination, 573
sperm, 33, 261, **278,** 287, **291, 292, 295,** 296, **305,** 377
spermagonium, 51, 69, 75, 76
spermatangium, 232, 238, **239, 242,** 248, **249, 250, 253, 255**
spermatiophores, 51, 59, 75
spermatium, 51, 52, 69, 75, 77, 232, 238, **239, 242,** 248, **249, 250, 253, 255**
spermatization, 52, 68, 69
spermatogenous cell, 377
Spermatophyta, 536

Sphacelaria, **197,** 203, **204,** 210, 218
Sphacelariales, 202, 203, **204**
Sphaerocarpales, 318, **319,** 349
Sphaerocarpos, **319;** genetic studies, 318
Sphaerophorus globosus, apothecia, **107**
Sphaeropsidales, 97–98
Sphaerotheca, 57
Sphaerotillus, 138; *S. natans,* **139**
Sphagnidae, 327, 328, **330**
Sphagnum, 341; absorption of liquid, 329; bog, 183; bog formation, 331; calyptra, 329; capsule, 329, **330;** ecological importance, 313, 331; economic importance, 332; fossil record, 349; gametophyte, 326, 328–329; liquid absorption, 303; prothallial protonema, **330;** relationships, 331–332, 333; rhizoids, 326; spore dispersal, 331; spores, 331; sporophyte, 331, 332; stomata, 327; *S. magellanicum,* **330;** *S. papillosum,* **330;** *S. squarrosum,* **330;** *S. tenellum,* **330**
Sphenolobus minutus, gemmae, **307**
Sphenophyllales, 396–399
Sphenophyllum, 398; phylogeny, 399; reconstruction, **399;** sections of cones, **400;** transverse section of root, **400;** transverse section of stem, **400**
sphenopsids, 394
spiders, 62
Spiraea, 586
spirilla, **121,** 132, 135
Spirillaceae, 135
Spirillum beyerinckii, **138;** *S. serpens,* **138**
Spirochaetaceae, 140
Spirochaetales, 126, 139–140
Spirogyra, **34,** 273, **274,** 291, 293
Spirulina, 160, **163,** 164
Splachnaceae, 327
Splachnum luteum, sporangium, **344**
"splash-cups," **565**
sporangia, 18, 33, 34, 35, 36, 37, 38, 40, 41, 43, 45, 355, 359; development, 44; gradate, 429, **430;** mixed, 429, **430;** myxomycetes, 19, 20, 21, 23; simple, 429, **430**
sporangiola 43, 45
sporangiophores; Arthrophyta, 395, 396, 399, **400, 403, 406;** fungi, 40, 41, 44; phototropism, 44
sporangiospores, 41, 45, 128, 142; development, 32, 44
spore (*see* akinete, aplanospore, arthrospore, ascospore, basidiospore, carpospore, chlamydospore, cyst, hypnospore, mono-

Vascular Plants

DIVISION	CLASS	ORDER	FAMILY
Psilophyta (*Psilophytes*)		Psilophytales Psilotales	
Lycopodophyta (*Lycopods*)		Lepidodendrales Pleuromeiales Isoetales Selaginellales Lycopodiales	
Arthrophyta (*Articulates*)		Hyeniales Pseudoborniales Sphenophyllales Calamitales Equisetales	
Pterophyta	(*Preferns*)	Protopteridiales Cladoxyales Coenopteridales	
	(*True Ferns*)	Marattiales Ophioglossales Filicales	Osmundaceae Schizaeceae Gleicheniaceae Matoniaceae Polypodiaceae Hymenophyllaceae Dicksoniaceae Cyatheaceae Dennstaedtiaceae
		Marsileales Salviniales	
Pteridospermophyta (*Seed Ferns*)		Pteridospermales	Lyginopteridaceae Medullosaceae Peltaspermaceae Corystospermaceae Caytoniaceae
Cycadophyta (*Cycads*)		Bennettitales Cycadales	Cycadeoidiaceae Williamsoniaceae
Ginkgophyta (*Ginkgos*)		Ginkgoales	
Coniferophyta (*Conifers*)		Cordaitales Coniferales	Lebachiaceae Pinaceae Cupressaceae Taxodiaceae Podocarpaceae Araucariaceae Taxaceae Cephalotaxaceae
Gnetophyta (*Gnetophytes*)		Ephedrales Welwitschiales Gnetales	
Anthophyta (*Flowering Plants*)	Dicotyledonae (*Dicots*)	Magnoliales Laurales Dilleniales Rosales Leguminales Araliales Hamamelidales Salicales Fagales	Magnoliaceae Winteraceae Lauraceae Myristicaceae Dilleniaceae Rosaceae Calycanthaceae Caesalpinaceae Mimosaceae Papilionaceae Cornaceae Araliaceae Caprifoliaceae Hamamelidaceae Platanaceae Salicaceae Betulaceae Fagaceae Corylaceae

(Gymnosperms)

(Angiosperms)